Beginning Algebra

Sixth Edition

Supplemented with:

- Multimedia Electronic Lecture Notes for Teachers.
- Multimedia Tutorial for Students
- On-line Testing and Practice Testing
- Several Technology Tools to support instructions including:
  - ✓ On-line grade book for faculty and progress reports for students
  - ✓ On-line student survey and reports
  - ✓ Student activity reports
  - ✓ Solution manuals

Man M. Sharma
Clark Atlanta University

Educo International Inc.
1-800-963-3826

ACKNOWLEDGEMENTS

Managing Editor

Aman Bhardwaj, Educo International, Inc.

Editors

Roxann King, Prince George's Community College, MD

Brenda Teal, Prince George's Community College, MD

Donna Strain, El Centro College, Dallas TX

Kamal Hajallie, LaGuardia Community College, NY

Ray Treadway, Bennett College, NC

Steve Castillo, Los Angeles Valley College, CA

Mary Bradley, Southwestern Community College, NC

Production Services

Educo International, Inc.

Desktop Publishing

Sunita Verma and Ramesh Thomas

Educo International, Inc.

Evaluators

The following persons have made significant contributions in this edition of the book. Several presentations throughout the book have been changed based on their contributions or recommendations.

Kalawati Iyer	Los Angeles Valley College, CA
Diana Moore	El Centro College, Dallas, TX
Lynda Little	Antelope Valley College, CA
Robert Mardirosian	Los Angeles City College, CA
Ray Treadway	Bennett College, NC

Special Thanks

Dr. Ravinder Kumar, Professor of Mathematics at Alcorn State University, MS for his contributions to the development of this book in its initial stages.

ISBN: 978-1-888469-92-9

Printed at: Replika Press Pvt. Ltd.,

PREFACE

This textbook is written for college students whose preparation did not include beginning algebra or who graduated from school a long time ago. It is written with students in mind, using simple language, highlighted key words, and a step-by-step approach. Each section of a chapter is divided into logically arranged objectives. Each objective has:

- **discussion** leading to the statement of rules and procedures.

- **examples** showing step-by-step procedures. Each example, in the electronic version of this book, has several randomly generated versions.

- **margin exercises** found in the margin near each example, to be used as warm up exercises.

Each **section ends** with a set of exercises for each of the objectives. Each chapter ends with the **Chapter Summary, Review Exercises,** and a **Self Test**. The chapter summary provides definitions of key words or phrases, rules and procedures, and worked-out examples in the margin for each rule or procedure.

This book is supplemented with an electronic version that can be accessed from the web by faculty as lecture notes and by students as tutorials. The electronic version of the book is 100% compatible with this printed textbook and has the advantage of dynamic graphics, pedagogically sound animations, and visually appealing screen designs with attractive color combinations. As a tutorial for students, the electronic version provides an effective tool that is highly interactive and engaging. The electronic version can also be used for online teaching.

Highlights of Contents:

The textbook contains nine chapters. The chapter topics are listed in the Table of Contents.

TECHNOLOGY SUPPORT

One of the **most useful features** of this book is the technology support to students in the form of tutorials, practice tests, instructor-created online quizzes and tests, and instant progress reports. These features are described below in more detail. **All technology components are provided through Macromedia Flash and HTML, delivered through the web and requiring no special installations**. These features are described below in more detail.

A. Multimedia Electronic Lecture Notes (ELN) for Instructors and Tutorials for Students

- Tutorials with examples are embedded with dynamic graphics, animations, and step by step solutions.

- Vivid screen designs and animations make the presentation of topics clearer, as documented by students and instructors in several pilot studies.

- The ELN for instructors are designed to enhance interactivity with students, affording instructors minimal writing and drawing and more emphasis on class discussion.

- The ELN, which can be used in class to supplement conventional teaching, are available to students as tutorials from the web for self study, from anywhere at anytime. Each example in the tutorial has several versions generated by randomized parameters. The student can see the solution to the first version, and then click the 'Next Version' to attempt similar exercises.

- The Tutorials feature has built-in diagnostics and several other learning activities to help in learning the concepts.

B. Practice tests

- These pre-created tests, one for each section of all chapters, are available to reinforce the concepts learned in the Tutorials.

- Each practice test has several sets of questions with step-by-step solutions. Students may choose one set with solutions, and another set without solutions.

- All practice tests contain only Free Response questions.

C. Homework on the Internet with Embedded Tutorial

- Different types of free response questions, with several variations for each question, are used to create online homework. Instructors can create the homework using a large question bank of free response questions, provided by the system, or just assign the pre-created homework.

- Each student gets a different set of questions, with tutorial type assistance, a solution to the first variation, and feedback for other variations, with the option to change the answer. Students can complete the assignment in multiple sessions.

- Homework is instantly graded by the system and scores are transferred automatically to the grade book.

- Students can print the graded homework report.

D. Quizzes/Tests on Internet (Free-Response, or Multiple-Choice or Mixed)

- Responses to test questions may be entered from the keyboard, or through a **small online keypad using the mouse**.

- The keypad contains mathematical symbols needed for the responses to enter the item being attempted. After every quiz, students get instant feedback on their score. They can see step-by-step solutions, go to practice mode with an embedded tutorial, or take the quiz over again, if allowed by the instructor.

- There will be no loss of work done by the students if during a test or homework sessions the power goes off, the web connection is lost, or the student closes Test/Assignment window improperly.

- The work completed at the time of disconnect will be considered work submitted and the rest of the work can be completed in a new login session.

- A large question bank of , both Multiple Choice and Free Response, is available for each objective of the content for web based testing and practice testing.

- A browser based math editor is available to instructors to add their own questions to the quizzes or tests.

- An easy-to-use online test generator, is available to instructors to create online quizzes/tests, to print multiple versions of class test with answer keys, or to generate and administer online tests.

- The test generator provides several options to instructors to deliver tests and homework to students in several test modes: with or without feedback, with or without solutions, single or multiple sessions, graded or just for practice, and several more.

- Instructors may allow students to take quizzes more than once, from anywhere at any time, and every time the quiz is different, covering similar types of items.

- For every graded test created by the instructors, the system generates online practice tests for students. Items for these practice tests are selected by the system and cover the objectives selected by the instructor for the graded test. The system provides different sets of items for every practice test session.

- Instructors may print multiple versions of quizzes or tests along with answer keys.

- Instructors may conduct proctored major tests, password-protected, in local computer labs, or print the tests and transfer the scores to the online graded book

E. Test Your Skill Activity (TYS)

- This activity, one for each section of all chapters is available to test the speed and accuracy with which a student can complete a set of questions.

- Students can set their own time limit, and select their own attempt mode (with or without feedback).

- Each TYS activity contains several sets of 10 to 30 questions. Students can attempt various sets with different time limits to increase their speed, or develop quick reflexes for completing the problems.

F. Activity Reports

- Instructors can view/print student activity reports at any time. These provide detailed information on time spent by students on each activity.

- There is an enhanced electronic grade book (online) with several unique features including; direct transfer of scores to the grade book, and **individualized progress reports for students**.

G. Internal E-mail

- Instructors can compile e-mails using the system's full function e-mail editor: bolding, underlining, bulleting, and attachment. There are multiple target audiences:

    - Students to instructor or classmates.
    - Instructor to students (of a section, a course, or all courses).
    - Campus coordinator to instructors, students, Educo.

H. Several other Communication Tools

- **Announcements**

    - Faculty to his/her students.
    - Campus coordinator to Instructors, students of a section/course or to all.
    - Educo to different groups of users.

- **Chat, threaded discussion, group discussions**

To the students:

We sincerely hope that the approaches followed in this book with several options of technology support will help you better prepare for your next course in mathematics.

To the instructors:

The authors would appreciate any suggestion for improvement in any component of this package, either for the presentation of the textbook or its support materials on the web. Suggestions can be forwarded through **Contact us** link on the login page.

Man M. Sharma

TABLE OF CONTENTS

Sample Screen

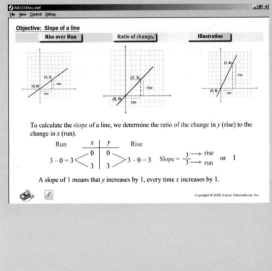

Contents

Sample Screen

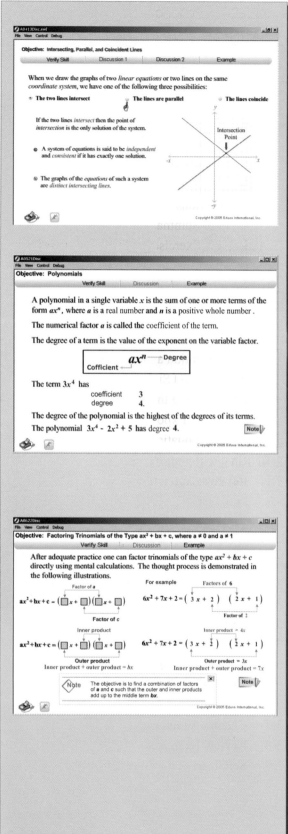

Sample Screen

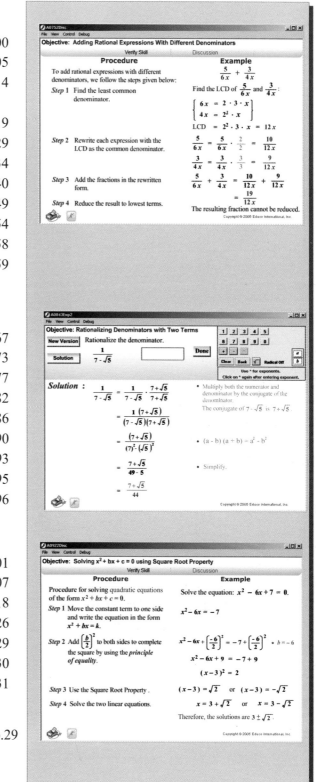

Review of Pre-Algebra

A0113Disc.swf

File View Control Debug

Objective: Review of Integers; Operation on Integers

Verify Skill | Discussion

Procedure	Example
Simplifying a numerical expression involving more than one operation.	$28 \div (4 - 8)(2) - 12 \div 3 + (-5)^2$
Step 1 Parentheses - Perform the operations within grouping symbols first (parentheses, brackets, fraction bar, etc.) in the order.	$= 28 \div (-4)(2) - 12 \div 3 + (-5)^2$
Step 2 Exponents - Do the operations indicated by the exponents.	$= 28 \div (-4)(2) - 12 \div 3 + 25$
Step 3 Multiplication and Division - Perform multiplication and division in the order of their appearance from left to right.	$= \dfrac{28}{-4} \cdot (2) - 12 \div 3 + 25$ $= -7(2) - 12 \div 3 + 25$ $= -14 - 4 + 25$
Step 4 Addition and Subtraction - Perform these operations in the order of their appearance from left to right.	$= -(14 + 4) + 25$ $= -18 + 25 = 7$

Click or Press Spacebar to Continue

Copyright @ 2005 Educo International, Inc

1 REVIEW OF PRE-ALGEBRA

This chapter is designed for a quick review of concepts considered as the pre-requisite for this course. Some concepts such as the real numbers, square roots, and order of operations are discussed in a little more detail. Presentations in the first four sections on integers, fractions, decimals, and percents have three major components **1)** definitions of key terms and symbols, **2)** demonstrations (examples) of rules and procedures, and **3)** exercises.

Because this Chapter is a review of the pre-requisites, Chapter Summary and Review Exercises are not given. However, a comprehensive Chapter Test is provided at the end.

This chapter is divided into six sections.

1.1 *Review of Integers;*

1.2 *Review of Fractions;*

1.3 *Review of Decimal Numbers and Square Roots;*

1.4 *Review of Percents;*

1.5 *Real Number System; and*

1.6 *Translations: Statements to Mathematical Expressions*

1.1 REVIEW OF INTEGERS

A. IMPORTANT VOCABULARY

1. The set of **Integers** is the set of all whole numbers and their opposites.

     Integers: …–3, –2, –1, 0, 1, 2, 3,…

2. **The positive integers** are the integers that are greater than zero: 1, 2, 3, 4, …

3. **The negative integers** are the integers that are less than zero: – 1, –2, –3, – 4,…

4. **The number line** is a line that is used to visualize numbers and relationships between numbers.

5. The **opposite** of an integer '*a*' is denoted by '*–a*' and is read as "**the opposite of *a***" or "**the additive inverse of *a***".

   The *opposite* of a positive number is a negative number, and the opposite of a negative number is a positive number.

> OBJECTIVES ■ ■ ■ ■
>
> After completion of this section, you will be able to:
>
> A. Understand the use of important terms and symbols;
>
> B. Represent integers on a number line; and
>
> C. Perform operations on integers.

The opposite (or the additive inverse) of 4 is -4;

The opposite (or the additive inverse) of -5 is 5;

The opposite (or the additive inverse) of 0 is 0 itself.

6. **Additive inverse property:** The sum of an integer and its additive inverse is 0.

$4 + (-4) = 0; (-2) + 2 = 0$

7. The **absolute value** of an integer and of its opposite is the same positive number.

$$|4| = 4, \quad |-4| = 4, \quad |0| = 0.$$

8. **Even digits:** 0, 2, 4, 6, and 8.

   Odd digits: 1, 3, 5, 7, and 9.

9. **Even integers** are the integers whose ones digit is an even digit. For example,

   $30 ; 46 ; -178 ; 4,032 ;$ and -874

10. **Odd integers** are the integers whose ones digit is an odd digit. For example,

    $13 ; 79 ; -225 ; 1,237 ;$ and -441

    Every integer is either even or odd, but it cannot be both.

B. REPRESENTATION OF INTEGERS ON A NUMBER LINE

Integers can be graphed as points on a number line. Consider the line L in Figure 1.1 with a point Z on it representing the number 0. We use 0 as a reference point for graphing all other integers.

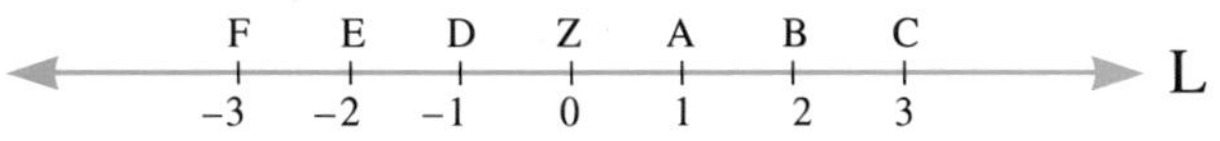

	F	E	D	Z	A	B	C	
	-3	-2	-1	0	1	2	3	L

Figure 1.1

Mark points 1, 2, 3 at distances of 1 unit, 2 units, and 3 units, from 0 on the right of 0. The unit may be an inch, a centimeter, or any arbitrary length. The numbers on the right of 0 are all positive. Similarly, we can plot points for negative integers on the left of 0. Points, $-1, -2, -3$ are the graphs of numbers at distances 1, 2, and 3 units to the left of 0. With this plan we can represent any integer, positive or negative, by points on the line. The line used to represent numbers like this is called the **number line.**

EXAMPLES

1.

Number	The opposite
-15	15
4	-4
0	0

1. To find the **opposite** of an integer, just reverse its sign. The graph of the opposite of an integer is a point on the number line on the opposite side of 0, but at the same distance from 0.

2. The **absolute value** of a number is the distance between the graph of the number and the graph of 0 on the number line.

The absolute value of an integer a is written as $|a|$ and it is equal to :

    (a) the number itself, if it is positive, or

    (b) the opposite of a number, if it is negative.

2.	*Number*	*The absolute value*
	12	$\|12\| = 12$
	–5	$\|-5\| = 5$
	0	$\|0\| = 0$

C. OPERATIONS ON INTEGERS

EXAMPLES

1. **Adding integers with like signs**

To add two or more integers with *like* signs, add their absolute values and affix the common sign.

1. a) $\quad 4 + 5 = 9$

b) $-3 + (-12) = -(|-3| + |-12|)$
$$= -(3 + 12)$$
$$= -15$$

2. **Adding integers with unlike signs**

To add two integers with *unlike* signs, subtract their absolute values (the smaller from the larger) and append the sign of the integer with larger absolute value.

2. a) $\quad 4 + (-8) = -(8 - 4)$
$$= -4$$

b) $\quad -23 + 15 = -(23 - 15)$
$$= -8$$

c) $\quad -3 + 7 = +(7 - 3)$
$$= 4$$

3. **Subtracting integers**

To subtract an integer from another integer, change the sign of the integer to be subtracted and add it to the other integer.
$$a - b = a + (-b)$$

In other words, don't subtract integers. Add the opposite of second integer instead.

3. a) $\quad -15 - 4 = -15 + (-4) = -19$

b) $\quad 7 - (-8) = 7 + (8) = 15$

4. **To multiply (divide) two integers,** multiply (divide) their absolute values. If the signs are alike, the result is positive ; if the signs are different, the result is negative.

RULE OF SIGNS

in Multiplication	*in Division*
$+ \cdot + = +$	$+ \div + = +$
$+ \cdot - = -$	$+ \div - = -$
$- \cdot + = -$	$- \div + = -$
$- \cdot - = +$	$- \div - = +$

4. a) $\quad 6\,(5) = 30$

b) $\quad 8\,(-5) = -40$

c) $\quad -3\,(4) = -12$

d) $\quad (-3)(-8) = 24$

e) $\quad 8 \div (-2) = \dfrac{8}{-2} = -4$

f) $\quad 225 \div 15 = \dfrac{225}{15} = 15$

g) $\quad (-15) \div 3 = -\dfrac{15}{3} = -5$

h) $\quad -(28) \div (-7) = \dfrac{-28}{-7} = \dfrac{28}{7} = 4$

5. a) $0 \div 3 = 0$ **b)** $\dfrac{0}{5} = 0$

c) $3 \div 0$ is undefined

d) $\dfrac{-6}{0}$ is undefined.

6. a) $(-2)(-3)(5)(-1)(-4)$
$= +(2 \cdot 3 \cdot 5 \cdot 1 \cdot 4) = 120$

b) $5(-3)(-1)(-2) = -(5 \cdot 3 \cdot 1 \cdot 2)$
$= -30$

7. To find the sum:
$-44 + 37 + (-59) + 45$
$= [-44 + (-59)] + [37 + 45]$
$= [-103] + [82]$
$= -(103 - 82)$
$= -21$

8. a) $32 = 2 \cdot 2 \cdot 2 \cdot 2 \cdot 2$
$= 2^5$

b) $36 = 2 \cdot 2 \cdot 3 \cdot 3$
$= 2^2 \cdot 3^2$

c) $225 = 5 \cdot 5 \cdot 3 \cdot 3$
$= 5^2 \cdot 3^2$

d) $1024 = 2 \cdot 2 \cdot 2 \cdot 2 \cdot 2 \cdot 2 \cdot 2$
$\cdot 2 \cdot 2 \cdot 2$
$= 2^{10}$

9. a) $(-5)^1 = -5, \ 8^1 = 8$

b) $(-3)^4 = (-3)(-3)(-3)(-3) = 81$

c) $(-5)^3 = (-5)(-5)(-5) = -125$

d) $(-5^2) = -25$

e) $(-5)^2 = +25$

---

5. $0 \div n = \dfrac{0}{n} = 0$ and $n \div 0 = \dfrac{n}{0}$ is undefined for all non-zero integers n. $0 \div 0$ is undefined.

a. $0 \div 42 = 0$ **b.** $\dfrac{0}{-3} = 0$ **c.** $42 \div 0$ is undefined.

d. $\dfrac{-3}{0}$ is undefined. **e.** $0 \div 0$ is undefined.

6. **To multiply several integers** together, multiply their absolute values. If the number of negative factors is even, the product is positive and if the number of negative factors is odd, the product is negative.

7. **Addition of a group of integers**

Step 1 Add all the positive integers and add all the negative integers separately.

Step 2 Add the two sums obtained in step 1.

8. **Writing a product using exponents**

To write a product using exponents, express repeating factors in exponential form. Consider the product

$$24 = 2 \cdot 2 \cdot 2 \cdot 3$$

- Since the factor 2 is used three times, it can be written in exponential form as 2^3, where 2 is the *base* and 3 is the *exponent* or the *power.*

$$\text{base} \leftarrow \mathbf{2}^{3 \ \rightarrow \ \text{power}}$$

- 2^3 is often read as "two cubed" or "2 to the power 3" or "2 to the third power".

- The symbol 2^3 represents 2 multiplied by itself 3 times.

- Similarly, 2^2 is read as "two squared" or "2 to the power 2" or "2 to the second power".

9. **Computing values of a numerical expression** containing exponents :

i. If the exponent is 1, the value is the base number.

ii. If the base is not zero and if the exponent is larger than 1, then use the base as a factor as many times as the exponent.

10. Evaluating a numerical expression involving more than one operation.

   Order of operations:

   Step **1**   **Parentheses** - perform the operations within grouping symbols first (parentheses, brackets, fraction bar, *etc.*) in the order given in steps 2, 3, and 4.

   Step **2**   **Exponents** - Do the operations indicated by the exponents.

   Step **3**   **Multiplication and Division** - Perform multiplication and division in the order of their appearance from left to right.

   Step **4**   **Addition and Subtraction** - Perform these operations in the order of their appearance from left to right.

10. $28 \div (4 - 8)\,(2) - 12 \div 3 + (-5)^2$

$= \mathbf{28 \div (-4)\,(2)} - 12 \div 3 + 25$

$= \dfrac{28}{-4} \cdot (2) - 12 \div 3 + 25$

$= \mathbf{-7(2)} - \mathbf{12 \div 3} + 25$

$= \mathbf{-14 - 4} + 25$

$= -(14 + 4) + 25$

$= -18 + 25 = 7$

EXERCISE   1.1

A. **In exercises 1-5, find the opposite of the given number.**

1. -5 **2.** 9 **3.** -13 **4.** $-(-5)$ **5.** $-[-(-3)]$

In exercises 6-10, find the absolute value of the given number.

6. -4 **7.** -13 **8.** 25 **9.** $-(-3)$ **10.** $-(-(-9))$

In exercises 11-15, what are the possible values of *n* for which the given statement is true.

11. $|n| = 16$ **12.** $|16| = n$ **13.** $|n| = -4$ **14.** $|n| = 0$ **15.** $|n - 1| = 7$

B. **In exercises 16-17, graph the given integers on a number line.**

16. $\{-5, -4, -2, 2, 4, 5\}$ **17.** $\{-3, -1, 0, 4, 5\}$

C. **In exercises 18-27, find the sum.**

18. $4 + 9$ **19.** $9 + (-4)$ **20.** $(-9) + 4$ **21.** $(-9) + (-4)$ **22.** $(-4) + (-2)$

23. $(-10) + 9$ **24.** $(-5) + (11)$ **25.** $(-13) + (18)$ **26.** $(-91) + (-48)$ **27.** $(-119) + (82)$

In exercises 28-37, find the difference.

28. $9 - 4$ **29.** $5 - 7$ **30.** $7 - 15$ **31.** $-4 - 8$ **32.** $-8 - 3$

33. $-\left|4 - 2\right|$ **34.** $29 - 101$ **35.** $-18 - 107$ **36.** $32 - \left|-25\right|$ **37.** $15 - \left|-92\right|$

In exercises 38-47, evaluate the given expression.

38. $15 + 9 - 4 - 11$ **39.** $12 - 9 - 7 - 4$ **40.** $10 - 9 - 7 - 2$ **41.** $-2 - 7 + 8 - 11$

42. $-5 - 7 - 8$ **43.** $-7 - 9 + 8 + 13$ **44.** $-6 - 5 - 4 - 3 - 9$ **45.** $\left|-3\right| + \left|-2\right| - \left|-9\right|$

46. $\left|-11\right| - 9$ **47.** $\left|-13\right| - \left|-15\right|$

In exercises 48-57, find the product.

48. $5(7)$ **49.** $(-5)(7)$ **50.** $(-5)(-7)$ **51.** $(-2)(3)(-4)$

52. $3 \times 4 \times (-5)$ **53.** $(-3)(-2)(-4)(4)$ **54.** $(-7)(-2)(-5)(-2)$ **55.** $-10(-6)(-4) \cdot \left|-4\right|$

56. $-2(-7)(-10)(-3)$ **57.** $-5 \cdot \left|-4\right| \cdot \left|-6\right|$

In exercises 58-67, find the quotient.

58. $\dfrac{44}{4}$ **59.** $\dfrac{-20}{4}$ **60.** $\dfrac{8}{-2}$ **61.** $\dfrac{-27}{-3}$ **62.** $\dfrac{-20}{0}$

63. $\dfrac{(-2)(-4)}{-8}$ **64.** $\dfrac{7(-3)(-2)}{(-6)}$ **65.** $\dfrac{-8(-4)}{2(-2)}$ **66.** $\dfrac{5 \cdot \left|-4\right|}{-10}$ **67.** $\dfrac{5(-3)(-4)(2)}{-10(-6)}$

In exercises 68-87, follow the rules for order of operations and evaluate the expression.

68. $-2 + 3(-4)$ **69.** $4 - 3(5)$ **70.** $15 - 2(-4) + (-8)$ **71.** $3^2 - 4(-3)$

72. $(-4)^2 - 4(-5)$ **73.** $(-2)^3 + 2(7 - 9)$ **74.** $4 - 2(7 - 9)$ **75.** $-9 + 2(-3)^2 - 12$

76. $(-5)^2 - 2(7 - 11)$ **77.** $(-2)^4 \div (-4)$ **78.** $4 + 2(3^2 - 2 \times 4)$ **79.** $15 - 24 \div (-4)$

80. $\dfrac{12 + 3(7 - 9)}{(2)^3 - 2(3)}$ **81.** $\dfrac{4 - 3 \times 2^2}{5 + 3(3^2 - 8)}$ **82.** $\dfrac{6 + 3(-2)(-4)}{(-2)^5 + 2}$ **83.** $4 + 3[2^2 - 3(7 - 9)]$

84. $17 \div [21 - (-2)^3 \div (-2)]$ **85.** $12 - 2[15 - 3(20 - 2^2 \times 3)]$

86. $21 + (-2)^3[7 - 3(19 - 17)]$ **87.** $\dfrac{14 - 3(2^3 - 4 \times 2)}{10 + 2[(-3)^2 - 3 - (-2)^2]}$

1.2 REVIEW OF FRACTIONS

In this section we will review the concept of fractions.

A. IMPORTANT VOCABULARY AND SYMBOLS

1. **Divisor** and **divisible:** In $48 \div 6 = 8$, 6 is a **divisor** of 48 and 48 is **divisible** by 6.

2. **Factor :** In $48 = 6 \cdot 8$, 6 and 8 are **factors** of 48.

3. **Even integers** are divisible by 2. Every *even* integer can be expressed as $2n$ where n represents an integer.
$$26 = 2 \cdot 13, \quad 48 = 2 \cdot 24, \quad -34 = 2 \cdot (-17)$$

4. **Odd integers** are not divisible by 2. Every *odd* integer can be expressed as $2n + 1$ where n represents an integer.
$$9 = 2 \cdot 4 + 1, \quad 13 = 2 \cdot 6 + 1, \quad 3 = 2 \cdot 1 + 1$$

5. A **prime number** is a whole number greater than 1 with **exactly two** different factors, 1 and the number itself.

   1 is not a prime number.

   2 is the smallest prime number.

   3, 5, 7, 11 and 13 are examples of prime numbers.

6. A **composite number** is a whole number with **more than two** different factors. Every positive even number other than 2 is a composite number.

   - 2 is the only number which is both *even* and *prime*. Every other even number is a composite number.

   - 0 and 1 are neither prime nor composite.

   - $15 = (3 \cdot 5)$, and $24 = (2 \cdot 3 \cdot 2 \cdot 2)$ are examples of composite numbers.

7. **Prime factorization:** Expressing a number as a product of prime numbers is called the **prime factorization** of the number.
$$24 = 2 \cdot 2 \cdot 2 \cdot 3 \quad \text{is the prime factorization of 24.}$$

8. **The Fundamental Theorem of Arithmetic** states that every composite number has exactly one prime factorization.

9. **Multiples :** The first five multiples of 6 are 6, 12, 18, 24, and 30 since :
$$6 \cdot 1 = 6, \quad 6 \cdot 2 = 12, \quad 6 \cdot 3 = 18, \quad 6 \cdot 4 = 24, \quad 6 \cdot 5 = 30.$$

10. **LCM** is the abbreviation for the **Least Common Multiple**.

11. A **fraction**, such as $\frac{3}{5}$ (read as three-fifth) is the name for a number. A fraction has two components, the **numerator**, and the **denominator**. These two components are separated by a line called the **fraction bar**.

Fraction bar ⟵ $\frac{13}{15}$ ⟶ Numerator ⟶ Denominator

12. **Proper and Improper Fractions:** A fraction whose numerator is smaller than the denominator is called a **proper** fraction. If the numerator is greater than or equal to the denominator then the fraction is called an **improper** fraction.

13. **Rational Numbers:** Numbers which can be written as fractions are called **rational numbers**.

> *Definition* : A rational number is a number that can be written in the form $\frac{a}{b}$, where a and b are integers and $\boldsymbol{b} \neq 0$.

Every integer is also a rational number : $3 = \frac{3}{1}$; $0 = \frac{0}{1}$; $-5 = \frac{-5}{1}$

14. Fractions representing the same number are called **equivalent fractions**. For example:

$$\frac{8}{12} = \frac{2}{3}; \qquad \frac{10}{15} = \frac{2}{3}$$

Therefore, $\frac{8}{12}$, $\frac{10}{15}$, and $\frac{2}{3}$ are equivalent fractions.

15. **Reducing a fraction to lowest terms** means to write an *equivalent fraction* in which the numerator and denominator have no common factors other than 1.

16. **Reciprocal numbers** are a pair of numbers whose product is 1.

$\frac{3}{5}$ and $\frac{5}{3}$ are reciprocal numbers because $\frac{3}{5} \cdot \frac{5}{3} = 1$

> The **reciprocal** of $\frac{a}{b}$ is $\frac{b}{a}$ $(a \neq 0, \ b \neq 0)$
>
> The reciprocal of $\frac{2}{5}$ is $\frac{5}{2}$; of 6 is $\frac{1}{6}$; the reciprocal
>
> of $\frac{1}{4}$ is 4, and the reciprocal of 1 is 1 itself.

The number 0 does not have a reciprocal.

17. The **multiplicative inverse** of a *non-zero* rational number is its reciprocal. The inverse of a is denoted by a^{-1}.

> The product of a number and its inverse is always 1.
> $$a^{-1} \cdot a = a \cdot a^{-1} = 1$$

0^{-1} is not defined

18. **LCD**, the abbreviation for **Least Common Denominator** of two or more fractions, is the LCM of all the denominators of the fractions.

19. Fractions having the same denominators are called **like fractions**.

$\dfrac{7}{5}, \dfrac{13}{5}, \dfrac{2}{5}$ are like fractions and the common denominator is 5.

$\dfrac{3}{5}$ and $\dfrac{4}{7}$ are **unlike fractions** since the denominators are not the same.

20. Grouping symbols:

( ) are called **parentheses** ; { } are called **braces** ; [ ] are called **brackets** ;

21. Fractions such as $\dfrac{\frac{3}{5}}{\frac{2}{7}}$ and $\dfrac{1\frac{3}{5} + \frac{1}{2}}{3 - \frac{2}{3}}$ are called **complex fractions**.

B. DIVISIBILITY TESTS

1. **Divisibility by 2 :** A number is divisible by 2, if its one's digit is even.

1. $878,50\overset{\downarrow}{6}$ is divisible by 2.

   $15,73\underset{\uparrow}{5}$ is not divisible by 2

2. **Divisibility by 3 :** A number is divisible by 3, if the sum of its digits is divisible by 3.

2. 4872 is divisible by 3.
   (The sum of digits is 21)

3. **Divisibility by 4 :** A number is divisible by 4, if the last two digits (to the right) form a number divisible by 4.

3. $75,\overset{\uparrow}{4}00$ is divisible by 4.

   $145,\overset{\uparrow}{3}72$ is divisible by 4.

   $43,9\overset{\uparrow}{3}7$ is not divisible by 4

4. **Divisibility by 5 :** A number is divisible by 5, if its one's digit is either 0 or 5.

4. $84,2\overset{\uparrow}{5}0$ is divisible by 5.

   $293,71\overset{\uparrow}{5}$ is divisible by 5.

   $4,62\overset{\uparrow}{9}$ is not divisible by 5.

5. **Divisibility by 8 :** A number is divisible by 8, if the last three digits (to the right) form a number divisible by 8.

5. 325,**000** is divisible by 8.

   29,**376** is divisible by 8.

   735,**433** is not divisible by 8.

EXAMPLES

6. 50,391 is divisible by 9;
the sum of the digits is 18.

478, 301, 956 is not divisible by 9;
the sum of the digits is 43.

7. 2570 is divisible by 10.

930,258 is not divisible by 10.

6. **Divisibility by 9 :** A number is divisible by 9, if the sum of its digits is divisible by 9.

7. **Divisibility by 10 :** A number is divisible by 10, if its ones digit is 0.

 Note | If you do not know a divisibility test for a specific number, you can always check divisibility by dividing. If there is no remainder, upon division by *"a"* then the given number is divisible by *"a"*.

C. REDUCE, MULTIPLY AND DIVIDE FRACTIONS

EXAMPLES

1. To raise $\dfrac{3}{5}$ to higher terms with a denominator of 20:

Since $20 \div 5 = 4$, we multiply and divide by 4.

$$\frac{3}{5} = \frac{3 \cdot 4}{5 \cdot 4} = \frac{12}{20}$$

2. To reduce $\dfrac{-24}{30}$ to the lowest terms :

$$\frac{-24}{30} = \frac{-4 \cdot 6}{5 \cdot 6} = \frac{-4}{5}$$

3. To multiply $\dfrac{5}{12}$, $\dfrac{7}{25}$, and $\dfrac{15}{7}$:

$$\frac{5}{12} \times \frac{7}{25} \times \frac{15}{7}$$

$$= \frac{\overset{1}{\cancel{5}} \cdot \overset{1}{\cancel{7}} \cdot \overset{3}{\cancel{15}}}{\underset{4}{\cancel{12}} \cdot \underset{5}{\cancel{25}} \cdot \underset{1}{\cancel{7}}} = \frac{1}{4}$$

1. **To raise (or build) a fraction to higher terms:** Multiply both the numerator and the denominator by the same non-zero number.

2. **To reduce a given fraction to lowest terms:**

Step 1 Write the numerator and denominator in factor form.

Step 2 Divide both the numerator and the denominator by the common factors.

Step 3 Repeat step 1 and step 2, and continue until there are no common factors in the numerator and in the denominator.

3. **To multiply two or more fractions:**

Step 1 Write the indicated products of the numerators and the denominators of the given fractions.

Step 2 Cancel out the common divisors (if any) between the numerator and denominator.

Step 3 Multiply the remaining factors of the numerator for the numerator of the product, and multiply the remaining factors of the denominator for the denominator of the product.

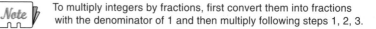 *Note* | To multiply integers by fractions, first convert them into fractions with the denominator of 1 and then multiply following steps 1, 2, 3.

4. To find reciprocal of a number:

Step 1 **(a)** If the number is a proper fraction, find the reciprocal by interchanging the numerator and denominator.

(b) If the number is a non-zero integer, first write it as an improper fraction, then find the reciprocal as above.

(c) If the number is a mixed number, convert to an improper fraction then find the reciprocal by interchanging the numerator and denominator.

Step 2 Verify that the product of a number and its reciprocal is 1.

> *Caution :* The number zero 0, does not have a reciprocal.

5. To divide a fraction by another fraction:

Step 1 Multiply the first fraction by the reciprocal of the divisor (second fraction).

Step 2 Simplify the product to lowest terms.

> *Note* If the division involves integers, first write them as fractions and then divide by the above procedure.

6. To simplify the powers of fractions:

Step 1 Reduce the fraction to lowest terms (if possible).

Step 2 Distribute the exponent over the numerator and the denominator of the fraction.

Step 3 Simplify the numerator and the denominator.

7. To find a part of a number, multiply the number by the fraction expressing that part.

4. (a) The reciprocal of $\dfrac{2}{11}$ is $\dfrac{11}{2}$;

(b) The reciprocal of 55 $\left(\text{or } \dfrac{55}{1}\right)$ is $\dfrac{1}{55}$;

(c) The reciprocal of -2 $\left(\text{or } \dfrac{-2}{1}\right)$ is $\dfrac{1}{-2}$ or $-\dfrac{1}{2}$.

5. a) $\dfrac{9}{32} \div \dfrac{3}{8} = \dfrac{9}{32} \times \dfrac{8}{3}$

$= \dfrac{\overset{3}{\cancel{9}}}{\underset{4}{\cancel{32}}} \times \dfrac{\overset{1}{\cancel{8}}}{\underset{1}{\cancel{3}}} = \dfrac{3}{4}$

b) $\dfrac{15}{14} \div 5 = \dfrac{15}{14} \div \dfrac{5}{1}$

$= \dfrac{\overset{3}{\cancel{15}}}{14} \times \dfrac{1}{\underset{1}{\cancel{5}}} = \dfrac{3}{14}$

6. To simplify $\left(\dfrac{16}{20}\right)^4$:

$\left(\dfrac{16}{20}\right)^4 = \left(\dfrac{4 \cdot 4}{4 \cdot 5}\right)^4$

$= \left(\dfrac{4}{5}\right)^4 = \dfrac{4^4}{5^4} = \dfrac{256}{625}$

7. a) Two-thirds of $45 = \dfrac{2}{\underset{1}{\cancel{3}}} \cdot \overset{15}{\cancel{45}} = 30$;

b) Three-fifths of $\dfrac{25}{9} = \dfrac{\overset{1}{\cancel{3}}}{\underset{1}{\cancel{5}}} \cdot \dfrac{\overset{5}{\cancel{25}}}{\underset{3}{\cancel{9}}} = \dfrac{5}{3}$

c) One-sixth of $-\dfrac{15}{4} = \dfrac{1}{6} \cdot \left(-\dfrac{15}{4}\right)$

$= -\dfrac{1 \cdot \overset{5}{\cancel{15}}}{\underset{2}{\cancel{6}} \cdot 4} = -\dfrac{5}{8}$

D. ADD AND SUBTRACT FRACTIONS

1. Add: $\dfrac{3}{5} + \dfrac{4}{5} - \dfrac{9}{5}$

$= \dfrac{3 + 4 - 9}{5}$

$= \dfrac{-2}{5}$

Caution: $\dfrac{1}{7} + \dfrac{4}{7} \neq \dfrac{5}{14}$

$\dfrac{1}{7} + \dfrac{4}{7} = \dfrac{5}{7}$

1. **To add like fractions,** add the numerators to obtain the numerator of the sum and use the common denominator as the denominator of the sum.

> *Caution*: Do not add denominators while adding like fractions.

2. $\dfrac{2}{3}, \dfrac{4}{5}, \dfrac{7}{10}$

LCD = LCM of 3, 5, and 10 = 30

$\dfrac{2}{3} = \dfrac{2}{3} \cdot \dfrac{\mathbf{10}}{\mathbf{10}} = \dfrac{20}{30}$

$\dfrac{4}{5} = \dfrac{4}{5} \cdot \dfrac{\mathbf{6}}{\mathbf{6}} = \dfrac{24}{30}$

$\dfrac{7}{10} = \dfrac{7}{10} \cdot \dfrac{\mathbf{3}}{\mathbf{3}} = \dfrac{21}{30}$

2. **To change a group of fractions to like fractions using the LCD for the common denominator:**

Step 1 Find the LCM of the denominator. This is the LCD.

Step 2 Change each fraction to an equivalent fraction with the LCD as the common denominator.

3. Check if $\dfrac{4}{10}$ and $\dfrac{14}{35}$ are equivalent.

Method 1: $\dfrac{\overset{2}{\cancel{4}}}{\underset{5}{\cancel{10}}} = \dfrac{\mathbf{2}}{\mathbf{5}}, \quad \dfrac{14}{35} = \dfrac{\mathbf{2}}{\mathbf{5}}$

Fractions are equivalent.

Method 2: $\dfrac{4}{10} \diagdown\!\!\!\!\diagup \dfrac{14}{35} \begin{array}{l} = 140 \\ = 140 \end{array}$

Fractions are equivalent.

3. **To check whether two fractions are equivalent:**

Method 1:

Reduce each fraction to lowest terms. If the reduced fractions are equal, then the given fractions are equivalent.

Method 2:

Step 1 Find the product of the numerator of the first fraction and the denominator of the second.

Step 2 Find the product of the denominator of the first fraction and the numerator of the second.

Step 3 If the products obtained in step 1 and step 2 are equal, then the given fractions are equivalent.

4. Identify which of the two, $\dfrac{-7}{5}$ or $\dfrac{-5}{3}$, is greater.

LCD = 15

$\dfrac{-7}{5} = \dfrac{-21}{\mathbf{15}}, \quad \dfrac{-5}{3} = \dfrac{-25}{\mathbf{15}}$

$-21 > -25$. Therefore $\dfrac{-7}{5} > \dfrac{-5}{3}$

4. **To compare two fractions:**

Step 1 Change the fractions to equivalent fractions with a common denominator.

Step 2 The fraction with the larger numerator is the larger fraction.

5. To list a group of fractions in ascending or descending order :

> **Step 1**   Build the given fractions to a common denominator.
>
> **Step 2**   Arrange the new fractions in the desired order of the numerators.
>
> **Step 3**   Replace each of them by the original fraction.

6. To add two or more fractions :

> **Step 1**   Build the fractions to a common denominator.
>
> **Step 2**   Add the numerators of the new fractions, and retain the common denominator.
>
> **Step 3**   Simplify the sum to lowest terms and simplify.

---

5. Arrange $\dfrac{7}{5}, \dfrac{2}{3}, \dfrac{4}{30}$ in ascending order .

LCD = 30

$$\dfrac{7}{5} = \dfrac{42}{30}; \quad \dfrac{2}{3} = \dfrac{20}{30}; \quad \dfrac{4}{30} = \dfrac{4}{30}.$$

Since $4 < 20 < 42$, therefore

$$\dfrac{4}{30} < \dfrac{20}{30} < \dfrac{42}{30} \Rightarrow \dfrac{4}{30} < \dfrac{2}{3} < \dfrac{7}{5}$$

The desired list is $\dfrac{4}{30}, \dfrac{2}{3}, \dfrac{7}{5}$.

6. Add: $\dfrac{2}{5} + \dfrac{3}{10} + \dfrac{7}{20}$

$$LCD = 20$$

$$\dfrac{2}{5} + \dfrac{3}{10} + \dfrac{7}{20} = \dfrac{8}{20} + \dfrac{6}{20} + \dfrac{7}{20}$$

$$= \dfrac{21}{20}$$

E. PERFORM OPERATIONS ON MIXED NUMBERS

1. To change an improper fraction to a mixed number :

> **Step 1**   Divide the numerator by the denominator.
>
> **Step 2**   (a) If the remainder is zero, the fraction is a whole number, the quotient.
>
> (b) If there is a remainder, then
>
> the mixed fraction = quotient + $\dfrac{\text{remainder}}{\text{divisor}}$.

2. To convert a mixed number into an improper fraction :

> **Step 1**   Multiply the whole number by the denominator, and obtain the product.
>
> **Step 2**   Add the numerator to the product obtained in step 1 to get the numerator of the desired fraction.
>
> **Step 3**   Write the fraction using the numerator obtained, the denominator remains unchanged.

---

1. Change to mixed numbers :

 (a) $\dfrac{45}{9}$ (b) $\dfrac{45}{7}$.

 a) $\dfrac{45}{9} = 5\,R\,0 = 5$

 b) $\dfrac{45}{7} = 6\,R\,3 = 6 + \dfrac{3}{7}$

$$7\overline{)45} = 6\dfrac{3}{7}$$
$$\underline{42}$$
$$3$$

2. Convert $-12\dfrac{5}{8}$ into an improper fraction.

$$-12\dfrac{5}{8} = -\left(12 + \dfrac{5}{8}\right)$$

$$= -\left(\dfrac{96}{8} + \dfrac{5}{8}\right)$$

$$= -\left(\dfrac{96 + 5}{8}\right) = \dfrac{-101}{8}$$

---

3. $5\dfrac{3}{4} + 2\dfrac{4}{5} + \dfrac{1}{2} = \dfrac{23}{4} + \dfrac{14}{5} + \dfrac{1}{2}$

$$= \dfrac{115}{20} + \dfrac{56}{20} + \dfrac{10}{20}$$

$$= \dfrac{181}{20} = 9\dfrac{1}{20}$$

4. To subtract $\dfrac{5}{18}$ from $3\dfrac{1}{4}$:

$3\dfrac{1}{4} - \dfrac{5}{18} = \dfrac{13}{4} - \dfrac{5}{18}$ LCD = 36

$$= \dfrac{117}{36} - \dfrac{10}{36}$$

$$= \dfrac{117 - 10}{36}$$

$$= \dfrac{107}{36} \text{ or } 2\dfrac{35}{36}$$

The difference is already in lowest terms.

5. (i) $\left(-3\dfrac{4}{7}\right)\left(6\dfrac{4}{5}\right)$

$= \dfrac{-25}{7} \cdot \dfrac{34}{5} = \dfrac{-25 \cdot 34}{7 \cdot \cancel{5}_1}{}^{5} = \dfrac{-170}{7}$

(ii) $6\dfrac{1}{4} \div 7\dfrac{1}{2}$

$= \dfrac{25}{4} \div \dfrac{15}{2} = \dfrac{25}{4} \cdot \dfrac{2}{15} = \dfrac{\cancel{25}^{5} \cdot \cancel{2}^{1}}{\cancel{4}_2 \cdot \cancel{15}_3} = \dfrac{5}{6}$

6. $3 \div \left(\dfrac{17}{8} - 1\dfrac{1}{2} \cdot \dfrac{1}{3}\right)$

$= \dfrac{3}{1} \div \left(\dfrac{17}{8} - \dfrac{\cancel{3}}{2} \cdot \dfrac{1}{\cancel{3}}\right)$

$= \dfrac{3}{1} \div \left(\dfrac{17}{8} - \dfrac{4}{8}\right)$

$= \dfrac{3}{1} \div \left(\dfrac{17 - 4}{8}\right)$

$= \dfrac{3}{1} \div \dfrac{13}{8}$

$= \dfrac{3}{1} \cdot \dfrac{8}{13}$

$= \dfrac{24}{13}$

---

3. To add mixed numbers:

Step 1   Change mixed numbers to improper fractions.

Step 2   Add the fractions.

Step 3   Change the final answer to a mixed number, if desirable.

4. To subtract mixed fractions:

Step 1   (a) If subtraction involves mixed numbers, first change them to improper fractions.

  (b) Build each fraction to a common denominator, the LCD.

Step 2   Subtract the numerators of the new fractions, and retain the common denominator.

Step 3   Simplify the difference to lowest terms.

5. To multiply (or divide) mixed numbers:

Step 1   Change each mixed numbers to improper fraction.

Step 2   Multiply (or divide) the resulting fractions.

Step 3   Reduce and change the resulting answer to a mixed number.

F. SIMPLIFY A NUMERICAL EXPRESSION

6. To simplify (or evaluate) a numerical expression involving fractions:

Step 1   **Grouping symbols:** Perform the operations within the grouping symbols in the order given in step 2, 3, and 4, starting at the innermost grouping symbol.

Step 2   **Exponents:** Simplify the exponents.

Step 3   **Multiplication and Division:** Perform all multiplications and divisions from left to right in the order in which they appear.

Step 4   **Addition and Subtraction:** Perform all additions and subtractions from left to right in the order in which they appear.

Note — If no grouping symbols are present, then evaluate the expression following steps 2, 3 and 4 in this order.

EXERCISE 1.2

B. 1. Which of the following numbers are divisible by 3.

(a) 12   **(b)** 25   **(c)** −31   **(d)** 27   **(e)** −102   **(f)** 2064

2. Which of the following numbers are divisible by 9.

(a) 81   **(b)** −92   **(c)** 1341   **(d)** −2,451,348

3. Find fractions equivalent to the given fractions with the given number as new denominator.

(a) $\dfrac{2}{3}$; 12   **(b)** $\dfrac{-3}{5}$; 15   **(c)** $\dfrac{-4}{11}$; 55   **(d)** $\dfrac{5}{12}$; 72

C. 4. Reduce the following fractions to lowest terms.

(a) $\dfrac{-4}{12}$ **(b)** $\dfrac{-27}{36}$ **(c)** $\dfrac{105}{90}$ **(d)** $\dfrac{-2235}{960}$

5. Multiply the fractions and reduce the product to lowest terms.

(a) $\dfrac{5}{12} \cdot \dfrac{24}{15}$ **(b)** $\left(\dfrac{-3}{5}\right)\left(\dfrac{20}{27}\right)$ **(c)** $\left(\dfrac{-4}{15}\right)\left(\dfrac{-25}{16}\right)$ **(d)** $\dfrac{-2}{3} \cdot \dfrac{-4}{15} \cdot \dfrac{45}{16}$ **(e)** $\dfrac{12}{35} \cdot \dfrac{21}{16} \cdot \dfrac{25}{27}$

6. Find the reciprocal of the following fractions.

(a) $\dfrac{2}{3}$ **(b)** $-\dfrac{3}{2}$ **(c)** $\dfrac{1}{9}$ **(d)** $-\dfrac{5}{1}$

7. Perform division and express your answer as a reduced fraction.

(a) $\dfrac{12}{25} \div \dfrac{16}{40}$ **(b)** $\dfrac{21}{48} \div \dfrac{35}{64}$ **(c)** $\dfrac{-24}{35} \div \dfrac{80}{98}$ **(d)** $\left(-\dfrac{12}{35}\right) \div \left(-\dfrac{30}{175}\right)$

8. Check whether the pair of fractions are equivalent (Yes/No).

(a) $\dfrac{-3}{5}, \dfrac{-9}{15}$ **(b)** $\dfrac{12}{25}, \dfrac{2}{5}$ **(c)** $\dfrac{9}{10}, \dfrac{27}{30}$ **(d)** $\dfrac{-7}{9}, \dfrac{-42}{54}$ **(e)** $\dfrac{18}{54}, \dfrac{12}{36}$

9. Identify in each of the following groups of fractions, the fraction with largest value.

(a) $\dfrac{1}{2}, \dfrac{1}{3}, \dfrac{1}{4}$ **(b)** $\dfrac{2}{3}, \dfrac{4}{3}, \dfrac{-1}{3}$ **(c)** $\dfrac{2}{3}, \dfrac{3}{4}, \dfrac{5}{8}$ **(d)** $\dfrac{2}{3}, \dfrac{4}{5}, \dfrac{6}{7}$ **(e)** $\dfrac{2}{9}, \dfrac{4}{7}, \dfrac{5}{3}$

D. 10. List each of the following groups of fractions in increasing order.

(a) $\dfrac{1}{2}, \dfrac{1}{3}, \dfrac{1}{4}$ **(b)** $\dfrac{-2}{3}, \dfrac{-4}{5}, \dfrac{-7}{8}$ **(c)** $\dfrac{-5}{12}, \dfrac{-7}{8}, \dfrac{-5}{6}$ **(d)** $\dfrac{3}{4}, \dfrac{5}{8}, \dfrac{9}{16}$

11. Perform addition:

(a) $\dfrac{-2}{5} + \dfrac{7}{5} + \dfrac{-3}{5}$ **(b)** $\dfrac{3}{4} + \dfrac{2}{5}$ **(c)** $\dfrac{-7}{8} + \dfrac{-5}{4}$ **(d)** $\dfrac{2}{3} + \dfrac{4}{5}$ **(e)** $\dfrac{3}{5} + \dfrac{-4}{3}$

E. 12. Perform addition:

(a) $1\dfrac{2}{3} + 4\dfrac{2}{5}$ **(b)** $-3\dfrac{2}{7} - 4\dfrac{3}{4}$ **(c)** $-7\dfrac{3}{5} - \left(-2\dfrac{4}{7}\right)$ **(d)** $\dfrac{2}{3} + 2\dfrac{3}{5} + 4\dfrac{3}{10}$

13. Perform the indicated operations.

(a) $-3\dfrac{1}{4} \times 11\dfrac{1}{2}$ (b) $-8 \div 4\dfrac{1}{3}$ (c) $1\dfrac{5}{6} \div (-16)$ (d) $4\dfrac{1}{2} \times \dfrac{2}{3}$

14. Perform the indicated operations:

(a) $\dfrac{-1}{2} + \dfrac{1}{4} \cdot \dfrac{-4}{5}$ (b) $\dfrac{2}{3} + \dfrac{4}{5} \cdot \dfrac{5}{12}$ (c) $\dfrac{-3}{10} \times \dfrac{15}{24} - \dfrac{3}{16}$ (d) $\dfrac{3}{4} + \dfrac{-5}{8} \div \dfrac{-3}{16}$

F. 15. Perform the indicated operations. $2\dfrac{1}{2} - \left[1\dfrac{1}{3} + \left(\dfrac{1}{6} + \dfrac{1}{2} - \dfrac{1}{3} - \dfrac{1}{4} \cdot \dfrac{2}{3}\right)\right]$

16. Find the average of the following group of fractions.

(a) $\dfrac{4}{5}, \dfrac{3}{7}, \dfrac{9}{35}$ (b) $\dfrac{2}{3}, \dfrac{3}{5}, 1\dfrac{4}{5}$ (c) $3\dfrac{3}{4}, 4\dfrac{1}{4}, 5\dfrac{1}{2}$

17. Divide the sum of $\dfrac{-1}{6}$ and $\dfrac{7}{10}$ by the sum of $\dfrac{-2}{3}$ and $\dfrac{-1}{12}$.

1.3 REVIEW OF DECIMAL NUMBERS AND SQUARE ROOTS

OBJECTIVES ■■■■

After completion of this section, you will be able to:

A. Understand important terms and symbols;

B. Use a place value chart, read decimal numbers and write decimal numbers from word description;

C. Perform basic operations with decimals; and

D. Simplify numerical expression involving decimals.

A. IMPORTANT TERMS AND SYMBOLS

1. A special way to write fractions with denominators 10, 100, 1000, ... is to use decimal points.

$$\dfrac{15}{10} = 1.5, \quad \dfrac{15}{100} = .15 \text{ or } 0.15$$

$$\dfrac{7354}{1000} = 7.354$$

The numbers obtained are called **decimal numbers**.

For example 2345.69 is a decimal number. This number has two parts, the whole number part (2345) and the decimal part (.69).

$$2345\ .69 = \overbrace{2345}^{\text{Whole number part}} + \underbrace{.69}_{\substack{\text{Decimal Part, or} \\ \text{fraction part.}}}$$

Decimal Point

2. The decimal 24.035 has three **decimal places**.

3. Decimals with same number of decimal places are called **like decimals**.

Examples :   2.015 and 31.423 are *like* decimals.

7.14 and 71.5 are *unlike* decimals.

4. $17.483 \approx 17.5$ rounded to the nearest tenth ;

   $17.483 \approx 17.48$ rounded to the nearest hundredth.

5. **Powers of 10** are : $10^1, 10^2, 10^3, 10^4 \ldots$

   or $\quad\quad\quad\quad$ 10, 100, 1000, 10000, ...

   The number 1 can also be written as a *power of 10* : $1 = 10^0$.

6. The fractions $\dfrac{1}{10}, \dfrac{1}{100}, \dfrac{1}{1000}, \ldots$ can also be written using **negative powers of 10**:

   $$\frac{1}{10} = 10^{-1}, \quad \frac{1}{100} = 10^{-2}, \quad \frac{1}{1000} = 10^{-3}, \ldots$$

7. Decimals such as 2.5, 4.52, and 7.4324 are **terminating decimals**.

8. Non-terminating Decimals, such as $23.05262626\ldots$ or $23.05\overline{26}$ are called **repeating decimals**. The bar over 26 indicates that 26 is repeated indefinitely.

9. A **perfect square** is a number which is the square of some integer.

   For example, 4, 9, 16, 25, and 36 are perfect squares because

   $$4 = 2^2 \; ; \; 9 = 3^2 \; ; \; 16 = 4^2 \; ; \; 25 = 5^2 \; ; \; 36 = 6^2.$$

10. A number a is called **square root** of another number b if $a^2 = b$.

    The square root of 16 is 4 since $4^2 = 16$;

    The square root of 25 is 5 since $5^2 = 25$.

11. The symbol $\sqrt{}$, called a **radical sign**, is used for square roots :

    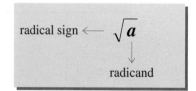

    $\sqrt{16} = 4$ $\quad$ (read : the square root of 16 is 4) ;

    $\sqrt{25} = 5$ $\quad$ (read : the square root of 25 is 5).

12. The complete expression such as $\sqrt{16}$ or $\sqrt{45}$ is called a **radical** expression, and the number under the radical sign is called the **radicand**.

    In $\sqrt{45}$, 45 is the radicand.

13. A **right triangle** is a triangle having a right angle (90°). The **hypotenuse** is the *longest* side of a right triangle and it is the side opposite the right angle. Each of the remaining two sides is called a **leg**.

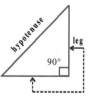

14. Terms associated with a Circle are:

 Center ; **Radius** (r) ; **Diameter** (d)

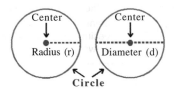

15. The **circumference** of a circle is a special name for the *perimeter* of the circle (that is, the distance around the circle).

16. The Greek letter **π** (read : pi) is used as the symbol for the ratio of the circumference of a circle to its diameter : $\pi = \dfrac{\text{circumference}}{\text{diameter}}$. Hence, the **circumference**, $C = \pi \cdot d = \pi \cdot 2r = 2\pi r$

17. π is an **irrational number** (non-terminating and non-repeating decimal). Its value, to 10 decimal places, is 3.1415926535 …, $\pi \approx 3.14$ or $\pi \approx \dfrac{22}{7}$.

Note: ≈ means approximately.

B. PLACE VALUE CHART, READING AND WRITING DECIMAL NUMBERS

PLACE VALUE CHART FOR DECIMALS

	Whole Number Part					Decimal Point	Decimal Part				
...	HUNDRED THOUSANDS	TEN THOUSANDS	THOUSANDS	HUNDREDS	TENS	ONES	TENTHS	HUNDREDTHS	THOUSANDTHS	TEN THOUSANDTHS	HUNDRED-THOUSANDTHS ...
...	100,000	10,000	1000	100	10	1	$\frac{1}{10}$	$\frac{1}{100}$	$\frac{1}{1000}$	$\frac{1}{10,000}$	$\frac{1}{100,000}$ ...
...	10^5	10^4	10^3	10^2	10^1	10^0	$\frac{1}{10^1}$	$\frac{1}{10^2}$	$\frac{1}{10^3}$	$\frac{1}{10^4}$	$\frac{1}{10^5}$ ...

Table 1

EXAMPLES

1. **a)** The word name of 123.046 is :

One hundred twenty-three **and** forty-six thousandths.

b) The word name for 0.37 is : Thirty-seven hundredths.

c) The word name for 759.0 is : Seven hundred fifty-nine.

1. To read or write a decimal number :

Step 1 Read (or write) the whole number part (that is, the whole number to the left of the decimal point).

Step 2 Read (or write) the word **and** for the decimal point

Step 3 Read (or write) the number in the fraction part (that is, the number to the right of the decimal point) as a whole number.

Step 4 Read (or write) the word name for the place value of the right most digit in the number.

If the decimal has only zero or no digit to the left of the decimal point, we omit reading or writing the whole number part. If the decimal has only zero(s) to the right of the decimal point, we read or write only the whole number part.

2. To write the decimal number from its word name:

Step 1 Write the number preceding "and" as the whole number part of the decimal.

Step 2 Replace the word "**and**" with a decimal point.

Step 3 Write the number for the word name after the word "**and**" as the fraction part.

3. To round a decimal to a given place of accuracy:

Step 1 Draw an arrow under the digit in the rounding place.

Step 2 Round up if the digit to the right of the arrow position is five or more, otherwise round down.

Step 3 Drop the unnecessary zeros (on the right of the arrow), if any.

C. OPERATIONS WITH DECIMALS

4. To add a group of decimals or to subtract two decimals:

Step 1 Rewrite the subtractions as additions.

Step 2 Write the decimals in columns so that the decimal points and the corresponding place values on either side of the decimals are lined up.

Step 3 Append zero(s) if required to make them like decimals.

Step 4 Add or subtract as integers.

Step 5 Place the decimal point in the answer directly below the other decimal points.

Step 6 Drop unnecessary zeros, if any.

5. To estimate the sum or difference of decimals:

Step 1 Round-off each of the given numbers to its largest place value (that is, the place of the left most non-zero digit in the number).

Step 2 Add or subtract the rounded numbers.

---

2. The numeral corresponding to the word name:

"One thousand three hundred twenty-five and forty-six ten thousandths" is
1325.0046

3. Round the number 246.3471 to the nearest hundredth.

$$246.3471$$
$$\uparrow$$

Round up, since the digit to the right of 4 is greater than 5.

$246.3471 \approx 246.3500$

Thus $246.3471 \approx 246.35$ to the nearest hundredth.

4. (a) Add 12.05, 3.146, and 209.6:

$$
\begin{array}{r}
12.050 \\
3.146 \\
+\ 209.600 \\
\hline
224.796
\end{array}
$$

The sum is 224.796

(b) Subtract 27.16 from -143.56:

$-143.56 - 27.16$
$= -143.56 + (-27.16)$

$$
\begin{array}{r}
-143.56 \\
+\ -27.16 \\
\hline
-170.72
\end{array}
$$

The difference is -170.72

5. (a) Estimate the sum of -293.74 and -16.095:

$$
\begin{array}{rcr}
-293.74 & \approx & -300 \\
-16.095 & \approx & -20 \\
\hline
& & -320
\end{array}
$$

(b) The estimated difference of the above numbers is

$-300 - (-20) = -300 + 20$
$= -280$

6. Multiply -2.35 and 0.012 :

$$
\begin{array}{r}
-\ 2\ .\ 3\ 5 \quad \longrightarrow 2\ \text{decimal places}\\
\times\ \ 0\ .\ 0\ 1\ 2 \quad 3\ \text{decimal places}\\
\hline
4\ 7\ 0 \quad \longrightarrow 235 \times 2\\
+\ \ \ 2\ 3\ 5\ 0 \quad \longrightarrow 235 \times 10\\
\hline
-2\ 8\ 2\ 0
\end{array}
$$

The decimal point in the product is 5 places to the left.

Hence, $-2.35 \times 0.012 = -0.0282$

---

6. To multiply two or more decimals:

***Step* 1**   Multiply the numbers as if they were integers ignoring the decimal point.

***Step* 2**   Count the number of decimal places in each of the factors and take the sum of these counts. This result is the number of decimal places in the product.

***Step* 3**   Locate the decimal point in the product by counting from the right, the number of decimal places. Insert zeros to the left of the product, if necessary, to have enough digits for decimal places.

***Step* 4**   Drop the unnecessary zeros, if any, at the right end of the number.

---

7. To compute the quotient $17.5 \div (-3)$ to the nearest tenth :

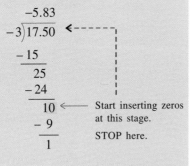

So,
$17.5 \div (-3) \approx -5.8$ to the nearest tenth.

---

7. To divide a decimal by an integer:

***Step* 1**   Use long division. Place the decimal point in the quotient just above the decimal point in the dividend.

***Step* 2**   Divide as if both numbers were integers.

***Step* 3**   Round to the given place. If no rounding place is given, divide until the remainder is zero, or continue until some digits in the quotient starts to repeat. Otherwise, choose a common place value for rounding, such as tenths or hundredths. More zeros may be appended to the decimal part of the dividend, if necessary.

---

8. To divide 3.5 by 0.03 :

$$0.03\overline{)3.5}$$

$$003.\overline{)3\ 5\ 0\ .}$$

$3.5 \div 0.03 \rightarrow 350 \div 3 = 116.\overline{6}$

So,
$$3.5 \div 0.03 = 116.\overline{6}$$
$$\approx 116.7 \text{ to the nearest tenth.}$$

---

8. To divide a decimal by a decimal:

***Step* 1**   Change the divisor to an integers by shifting the decimal point to the right of the number.

Simultaneously, move the decimal point in the dividend to the right by an equal number of decimal places. Insert zeros, if necessary, to have enough decimal places in the dividend.

***Step* 2**   Divide the resulting numbers.

9.(a) Estimate the product of -3.42 and -12.21 :

$$-3.42 \approx -3$$
$$-12.21 \approx -10$$
$$-3.42 \times (-12.21) \approx (-3) \times (-10)$$
$$\approx 30.$$

---

9. To estimate the product or quotient of two decimals:

***Step* 1**   Round each number to the left most non-zero digit.

***Step* 2**   Perform the indicated operation(s) with these rounded numbers.

(b) Estimate the quotient of $7.2 \div 0.23$:

$7.2 \approx 7$; $0.23 \approx 0.2$

So, $\dfrac{7.2}{0.23} \approx \dfrac{7.0}{0.2} = \dfrac{70}{2} = 35$

$\Rightarrow \dfrac{7.2}{0.23} \approx 35$ (estimate)

---

10. **To multiply a decimal by a power of 10,** we move the decimal point to the *right* by as many places as is the exponent of 10 (Insert zeros, if necessary).

10. -0.035×10^4

$= -0\,0\,3\,5\,0.$

$= -350$ (Drop unneccessary zeros)

11. **To divide a decimal by a power of 10,** we move the decimal point in the dividend, to the left by as many places as is the exponent of 10. (Insert zeros, if necessary).

11. $54.6 \div 10^3$

$= 0\,5\,4\,6$

$= 0.0546$

D. DECIMALS AND FRACTIONS

12. **To express fractions as decimals:**

Step **1**   Divide the numerator by the denominator.

Step **2**   Continue dividing until

    (i)   the remainder is zero, or

    (ii)   there are enough decimal places to attain the required accuracy by rounding, or

    (iii)   digits or group of digits in the quotient starts repeating.

> *Note*   If the number is a mixed number, change the fractional part to a decimal and add it to the whole number part.
> **or**
> Change the mixed number to an improper fraction first and then divide.

13. **To convert terminating decimals to fractions:**

Step **1**   Drop the decimal point and write the resulting number as the numerator of the fraction.

Step **2**   The denominator is 10, 100, or 1000 etc. if the number of decimal places are 1, 2 or 3 respectively.

Step **3**   Simplify the resulting fraction, if possible.

12. To express $\dfrac{235}{6}$ as a decimal :

$$
\begin{array}{r}
39.166 \\
6)\overline{235.000} \\
-18 \\
\hline
55 \\
-54 \\
\hline
10 \\
-6 \\
\hline
40 \\
-36 \\
\hline
40 \\
-36 \\
\hline
4
\end{array}
$$

Stop, since the digit 6 in the quotient has started repeating.

$\dfrac{235}{6} = 39.1666\ldots = 39.1\overline{6}$

13. To express -21.14 as a fraction (or a mixed number) :

$-21.14 = \dfrac{-21\overset{1057}{\cancel{14}}}{\underset{50}{\cancel{100}}}$

$= \dfrac{-1057}{50}$

$= -21\dfrac{7}{50}$

Alternatively:

$21.14 = 21\dfrac{14}{100} = 21\dfrac{7}{50}$

━━━━ **EXAMPLES** ━━━━

14. $4.8 \div (0.4 - 1.6) - (-1.5)^2$

$= 4.8 \div (-1.2) - (-1.5)^2$

$= 4.8 \div (-1.2) - 2.25$

$= -4 - 2.25 = -6.25$

14. Evaluating a numerical expression involving more than one operation.

Step **1** **Parentheses:** Perform the operations within the grouping symbols first (parentheses, brackets, fraction bar, etc.) in the order given in step 2, 3, and 4.

Step **2** **Exponents:** Do the operations indicated by the exponents.

Step **3** **Multiplication and Division:** Perform multiplication and division in the order of their appearance from left to right.

Step **4** **Addition and Subtraction:** Perform these operations in the order of their appearance from left to right.

EXERCISE 1.3

B. 1. Give the word names of the following decimal numbers.

(a) 2.4   (b) −2.04   (c) 434.134   (d) −0.004   (e) 37452.4291

2. Write the decimal numbers from the word names.

(a) Four and one tenth   (b) Negative thirty nine and four hundredths

(c) Five thousand three hundred nine and three hundred four thousandths.

3. Round the following decimals to the given place of accuracy.

(a) 4.792, tenth   (b) −79.094, hundredth   (c) 294.0799, thousandth   (d) 18.9097, tenth

C. 4. Perform the indicated operations.

(a) **Add:** −2.5, −4.3, and −12.1   (b) **Add:** 1.9, 3.4, −7.4, and 1.6   (c) **Add:** 17.92, 18.89, and 7.72

(d) **Add:** 7.45, 8.007, 9.192, and 2.3   (e) **Subtract:** −2.75 from 9.88   (f) **Subtract:** 5.89 from −12.72

5. Estimate the sum or difference as indicated, by rounding each number to its largest place (extreme left).

(a) $-79,492 + (-4,872) \approx$ (b) $0.395 + 0.587 \approx$ (c) $-49.782 - 38.47 \approx$ (d) $4,827.992 - 293.472 \approx$

6. Complete the products.

(a) $-79.4 \times (-.01)$ (b) $-4.23 \times .03$ (c) $1.02 \times (-0.05)$ (d) $.03 \times .007$ (e) -4.97×100

7. Compute the product with calculator and round the answer to two decimal places.

(a) $9.73 \times (-4.21)$ (b) 8.792×9.34 (c) -129.3×4.782 (d) $-2,953.49 \times (-9.73)$

8. Compute the quotients.

(a) $\dfrac{-2.75}{0.1}$ (b) $\dfrac{4.68}{.02}$ (c) $\dfrac{7.2}{-0.004}$ (d) $\dfrac{-7.86}{-0.003}$

9. Compute the quotients with calculator and round the answer to one decimal place.

(a) $\dfrac{-72.949}{-2.86}$ (b) $\dfrac{2,473.84}{78.92}$ (c) $\dfrac{-8.494}{.0792}$

10. Estimate the product or the quotient, as indicated, by rounding each number to its largest place (extreme left).

(a) $9.73 \times 2.15 \approx$ (b) $7.92 \times (-187.24) \approx$ (c) $-94.82 \times (-1932.49) \approx$

(d) $-7.82 \times (-12.972) \approx$ (e) $\dfrac{49.75}{-4.732} \approx$ (f) $\dfrac{2475.892}{187.72} \approx$

11. Multiply or divide a decimal by a power of 10, as indicated.

(a) -74.83×10^2 (b) 87.492×10^4 (c) $\dfrac{4.73}{10^1}$ (d) $\dfrac{-417.923}{10^3}$ (e) $\dfrac{925.434}{10^5}$

12. Simplify the following numerical expressions.

(a) $1.2 + 2.5 \times 3$ (b) $-2.4 \times .02 - 4.87$ (c) $9.87 - 1.02 \times (-0.2)$ (d) $-4.9 \div (-0.07) + (-3.1) \times 0.004$

D. 13. Express the following fractions as decimals.

(a) $\dfrac{-5}{4}$ (b) $\dfrac{3}{8}$ (c) $\dfrac{4}{5}$ (d) $\dfrac{-27}{5}$ (e) $-\dfrac{2}{3}$ (f) $\dfrac{-125}{6}$ (g) $\dfrac{925}{7}$

14. Convert the following decimals to fractions.

(a) 2.4 (b) -0.05 (c) -2.79 (d) 12.45

15. Evaluate. Round answer to the nearest hundredth.

(a) $-7.25 + 0.5 \cdot (-0.3)$ (b) $\dfrac{-11.7 + 3.82}{0.43}$ (c) $-9.5 + 8.72 \div 0.004$

(d) $0.35(9.1 - 2.86) - 2.1^2$ (e) $\dfrac{105.92}{43.1(2.2)} - 16.5$

16. Divide the sum of 8.6 and -0.4 by the product of 8.6 and -0.4.

1.4 REVIEW OF PERCENTS

After completion of this section, you will be able to:

A. Understand the meaning of important terms and symbols;

B. Identify equivalence of percents, decimals, and fractions;

C. Solve basic percent problems; and

D. Understand business related terms and concepts.

This section on percents, like the earlier sections, provides a quick review of percents. The concepts focused in this review will provide information and tools that will be very helpful in solving application problems throughout this book. The discussion is divided into four objectives.

EXAMPLES

1. $5\% = 5$ hundredths

$$= \frac{5}{100}$$

2. $8\% = 8 \cdot \frac{1}{100}$

$$= 8 \cdot (0.01)$$

$$= 0.08$$

3. 16% of $75 = \frac{16}{100}$ of 75

$$= \frac{16}{100} \overset{\downarrow}{\cdot} 75 = 12$$

A. IMPORTANT TERMS AND SYMBOLS

1. **Percent** means 'per hundred' or hundreths :
   Percent is the ratio of a number to 100.
   "*x* **percent**" means *x* hundredths, written as $x\%$.

2. The symbol %, read "percent" is used for the factor $\frac{1}{100}$ (or 0.01).

3. The word "**of**" in the expression "**percent of**" means multiply.

B. EQUIVALENCE OF PERCENTS, DECIMALS AND FRACTIONS

EXAMPLES

1. $15.2\% = .152$

2. $2.4\% = 2.4 \times \frac{1}{100}$

$$= \frac{24}{10} \times \frac{1}{100} = \frac{3}{125}$$

3. $3.45 = 345\%$

4. $\frac{13}{5} = 2.6 = 2\,6\,0.\% = 260\%$

Any of these forms of a number can be converted to the other two forms as per the following procedures :

1. **Percent to Decimal:** Shift the decimal point two digits to the left and remove the % symbol.

2. **Percent to Fractions:** Replace the % symbol with a factor $\frac{1}{100}$ and simplify the fraction.

3. **Decimal to Percent:** Shift the decimal point two digits to the right and attach the % symbol.

4. **Fraction to Percents:** Convert the fraction to a decimal, shift the decimal point two places to the right and attach the % symbol.

C. BASIC PERCENT PROBLEMS

1. Percent of profit: The ratio of the money made (*i.e.*, the amount of profit) to the money invested, when expressed as a percent is called the **percent of profit.**

1. If $38 are made by investing $200, then the **percent of profit.**

$$= \frac{\$38}{\$200} = \frac{19}{100} = 19\%$$

2. The basic percent formula is rate · base = amount or

$$R \cdot B = A$$

In this formula:

R is the **percent** (as a decimal or a fraction).

B is the **base** representing the 'whole', that is, the number on which the percentage is based.

A is the **amount** which represents the part or percentage.

2. In 16% of 75 = 12,

$R = 16\% = 0.16$

$B = 75$

$A = 12$

3. To compute percent of a number, substitute the value of *R* and *B* and solve for *A*.

3. What is 9% of 150
$\to$ 9% of 150 $= A$
$\to$ $(.09) \times 150 = A$
$\to$ $A = 13.5$
Thus, 9 % of 150 is 13.5

4. To find a number when the percent and its amount is given, substitute the value of *R* and *A* and solve for *B*.

4. 9% of **what** number is 13.5?
$\to$ $(.09) B = 13.5$
$\to$ $B = \dfrac{13.5}{.09} = 150$

5. To find the percent when the base and its amount is given, substitute the value of *B* and *A* and find *R*.

5. What percent of 150 is 13.5?
$\to$ $R \cdot 150 = 13.5$
$\to$ $R = \dfrac{13.5}{150} = 0.09 = 9\%$

D. BUSINESS RELATED TERMS AND CONCEPTS

1. Markup: *Markup* is the amount that is added to the **cost** (*C*) of an item to arrive at the original **selling price** (*S*). Thus, if *M* denotes the amount of markup, then

$$C + M = S$$

1. If the cost = $28.50,

Markup = 40% of the cost
$= (0.40)(28.50) = \$11.40$

Then, the selling price
$S = C + M = \$28.50 + \$11.40$
$= \$39.90$

2. If a store offers a 45% discount on an item that is listed for $150, then

The **rate of discount** = $45\% = 0.45$

List price = $150

Amount of discount = 45% of $150
= $(0.45)(150)$
= $67.50

Sale price = $150 − $67.50 = $82.50

2. **(a)** **Discount:** Reduction in the cost (the list price or the marked price)

$$S = C - D$$

(b) **Sale price:** Original selling price minus the discount.

(c) **Rate of discount:** Percent of original selling price to be discounted.

3. If an item is sold for $500, and the rate of sales tax is 7%, then the amount of sales tax = 7% of $500 = $35.

Thus, the buyer will pay
$500 + $35 = $535 for that item.

3. **(a)** **Sales tax:** Tax on the selling price.

(b) **Rate of sales tax:** Percent of the selling price.

4. If an item that costs a store $60 is sold for $75 then the store makes a profit of $(75 − $60) = $15.

% of profit based on cost $= \dfrac{\overset{1}{\cancel{15}}}{\underset{1}{\cancel{60}}} \times \overset{25}{\cancel{100}}$
$= 25\%$

% of profit based on selling price
$= \dfrac{\overset{1}{\cancel{15}}}{\underset{5}{\cancel{75}}} \times \overset{20}{\cancel{100}} = 20\%$

4. **(a)** **Profit:**

Gross profit = Selling price − Cost price

Net Profit = Gross Profit − overhead expenses

(b) **Percent of profit:**

% of profit **based on cost** $= \dfrac{\text{profit}}{\text{cost}}$ (expressed as percent)

% of profit **based on selling price** $= \dfrac{\text{Profit}}{\text{Selling price}}$

(expressed as percent).

5. If a person earns a commission of 25% on all sales over $600 a month and if his sales for a month are $2,170, then :

The straight commission he earns

$= 25\%$ of $($2170 − $600)$
$= 25\%$ of 1570
$= (.25)(1570)$
$= \$392.50$

5. **Commission:** A commission is the money paid to an agent, or a person engaged in selling a firm's products, for services rendered, based on a fixed percent of the sales.

Commission = rate × sale.

6. **Tip:** A tip is an amount that is paid to a provider for good service. The usual "tip" is approximately 15% of the bill.

   Special Thumb Rule for Calculating a 15% tip

   Step **1** Round off the amount of the bill to the nearest whole dollar.

   Step **2** Find 10% of the rounded-off amount by moving the decimal point 1 place to the left.

   Step **3** Divide the answer in step 2 by 2. This will represent 5% of the rounded amount.

   Step **4** Add the two amounts found in steps 2 and 3. This sum is approximately 15% of the cost and a good estimate of the tip.

6. To calculate a 15% tip (approximately) if the bill amount is $45.60 :

   Step 1 $45.60 \approx \$46.00$

   Step 2   10% tip $= \$4.60$

   Step 3   5% tip $= \dfrac{\$4.60}{2} = \$2.30$

   Step 4   15% tip $= \$4.60 + \$2.30$
   $$= \$6.90$$

7. **Simple Interest :** When the interest is calculated only on the *principal* for any length of time, it is called **simple interest.** The formula for simple interest is :

   Interest = Principal × rate × time or $I = P \cdot r \cdot t$,

   where:

P = principal = money borrowed, deposited or invested.
r = rate of interest (usually expressed as a percent per year).
t = time (usually expressed in years).
I = the amount of interest earned or paid.

7. To find the simple interest on $4,600 for 3 years at the rate of 15% :

   $P = \$4,600$
   $r = 15\% = 0.15$
   $t = 3$ years

   Therefore,
   $I = P \cdot r \cdot t$
   $= (\$4600)(0.15)(3)$
   $= \$2,070$

EXERCISE 1.4

B. **1.** Convert the following decimal numbers to percents.

   (a) 0.05   (b) 0.075   (c) 0.005   (d) 0.12   (e) 1.25

2. Convert the following percents to fractions. Reduce the fraction.

   (a) 20%   (b) 5%   (c) 32%   (d) 100%   (e) 112%

3. Convert the following percents to decimals.

   (a) 27%   (b) 7.5%   (c) 12.3%   (d) 123%   (e) 0.5%

4. Convert the following fractions to percents.

   (a) $\dfrac{1}{4}$ (b) $\dfrac{3}{4}$ (c) $\dfrac{5}{8}$ (d) $\dfrac{2}{3}$ (e) $\dfrac{8}{5}$

C. **5.** Given the money invested, and the amount of profit, find the percent of profit.

   (a) $ 4000, $ 400   (b) $ 250, $ 100   (c) $ 500, $ 95   (d) $ 1250, $ 125

6. Verify the result $R \cdot B = A$ for the following values, where R is the percent rate, B is the base number, and A is the amount of percent.

    (a) $R = 10\%$, $B = 100$, $A = 10$ **(b)** $R = 25\%$, $B = 260$, $A = 65$

    (c) $R = 60\%$, $B = 85$, $A = 51$ **(d)** $R = 5\%$, $B = 1200$, $A = 60$

7. Compute the following.

    (a) 20% of $175   **(b)** 15% of $450   **(c)** 25% of $160   **(d)** 17% of $300

D. 8. **(a)** If 10% discount on the marked price amounts to $20 savings then what is the marked price? (10% of what number is $20?).

    (b) If $250 is the actual amount of Commission then what is the total sales if the commission rate is 20%? (20% of what number = $250?)

    (c) If $375 is the actual amount of commission then what is the total sales if the commission rate is 5% (5% of what number = $375?).

9. Given the amount invested and the income, find the rate of returns.

    (a) $200, $20   **(b)** $375, $125   **(c)** $2550, $1500

10. Cost of a TV set to a store is $250 and the manager decides to make 40% gross profit. What should be the list price.

11. A store offers 40% discount on the list price of all its goods. What do you save if the list price is $ 210? How much do you pay if the sales tax charged is 4.5% on the discounted price.

12. What do you pay for an article with list price $45, if the discount is 20% and the sales tax on discounted price is 4%?

13. Robert store sells its new brand of sofa set for $1375 and it costs the store $850. What is the percent of profit on the cost price?

14. A sales representative gets 10% commission, on top of his salary, for all sales over $1500 during a month. What is his commission if his total sales during a month is $7800.

15. If the amount of your bill in a restaurant is $87.50, approximately how much tip should be paid at the rate of 15% of the bill amount.

16. Mrs. Smith invested $12,500 at 14.5% simple interest. How much interest she will earn in $3\frac{1}{2}$ years?

1.5 REAL NUMBER SYSTEM

A. NUMBER LINES

Recall that 1, 2, 3, 4... are called *natural numbers*, and **0**, 1, 2, 3, 4,... are called *whole numbers*. The set of numbers ..., −3, −2, −1, 0, 1, 2, 3... are called *integers*. The numbers ...−1, −2, −3, are called *negative integers* and 1, 2, 3,... are called *positive integers*.

We use the concept of a **number line** to further explain the relationship between positive and negative integers. Take a point O on the line.

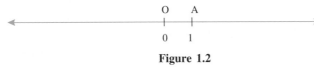

Figure 1.2

The point O will be used to represent the number 0 (zero). Choose another point A to the right of O such that the distance from 0 to A will be 1. The point A will represent the number 1. Now continue to mark points to the right of the number 1 at the same distance from each other. Label them 1, 2, 3, 4, ... *etc*. This gives a representation of whole numbers on the **number line.**

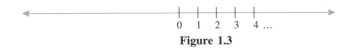

Figure 1.3

Now, starting with 0, mark points at a distance of the same unit length on the left of O. Label them −1, −2, −3, ... *etc*. This results in representation of all integers on the number line.

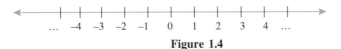

Figure 1.4

A point on the number line representing a number is called the **graph** of the number.

	Notes
1.	The number line extends indefinitely on both sides.
2.	The graphs of a number and its negative are at the same distance from O.

B. IDENTIFY DIFFERENT KINDS OF NUMBERS

Not all quantities can be measured in terms of integers. For example, when we divide two apples equally among four people, each person gets one-half of an apple. The graph of $\frac{1}{2}$ is midway between the graphs of 0 and 1 on the number line. The number $\frac{1}{2}$ is an example of a rational number.

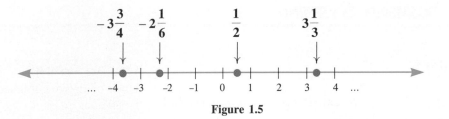

Figure 1.5

In general numbers of the type $\dfrac{p}{q}$ *, where p and q are integers and* $q \neq 0$ *are called* **rational numbers.**

Observations

(1) All integers are rational numbers: $5 = \dfrac{5}{1}, \quad 9 = \dfrac{9}{1}, \quad -4 = \dfrac{-4}{1} \ldots$

(2) Not all rational numbers are integers: $\dfrac{1}{2}$ is not an integer.

(3) All decimal fractions with a finite number of decimal places are rational numbers.

$$-0.075 = -\dfrac{75}{1000} \text{ is a rational number.}$$

(4) All decimal numbers with repeating decimals are rational numbers.

$$0.\overline{3} = 0.333\ldots = \dfrac{1}{3}$$

Note: The bar above 3 indicates that 3 repeats forever.

Not all points on the number line are rational numbers. The numbers that are not rational numbers are called **irrational numbers**.

1. The length of the hypotenuse (c) of a right triangle with its legs (a and b) each equal to 1 unit is not a rational number.

$$c^2 = a^2 + b^2$$
$$c^2 = 1^2 + 1^2 = 2$$

Therefore, length of the side AB (c) is represented by a number whose square is 2.

The symbol for such a number is $\sqrt{2}$. It can be proved that $\sqrt{2}$ cannot be expressed as a ratio of two integers. Therefore, $\sqrt{2}$ is not a rational number. The decimal representation of $\sqrt{2}$ is a non-repeating and non-terminating decimal number.

2. The ratio of the circumference of a circle to its diameter, for different circles, is the same number. This number is called pi (π). This number is an irrational number and its approximate value is 3.1416.

When all these numbers, *i.e.* integers, rationals, and irrationals, are graphed on the number line, the number line is completely filled up. This means that each point on the line represents a number, and each number can be represented by a point on the line. All these numbers put together are called **real numbers**, and the number line on which all these numbers are represented is called the **real number line**.

INTRODUCING SUBSETS OF REAL NUMBERS

Recall that

i) Set of natural numbers = {1, 2, 3,...}

ii) Set of whole numbers = {0, 1, 2, 3, ...}

iii) Set of integers = {..., –3, –2, –1, 0, 1, 2, 3,...}

iv) Set of rational numbers = Collection of all integers plus numbers of the type $\frac{1}{2}, \frac{2}{3}, -\frac{4}{5}, \ldots$
Rational numbers can be expressed as repeating or terminating decimals.

v) Set of irrational numbers = Collection of numbers of the type $\sqrt{2}, \sqrt{3}, \sqrt{7},\ldots$
Irrational numbers can be expressed as non-repeating and non-terminating decimals.

vi) Set of real numbers = Collection of all rational and irrational numbers.

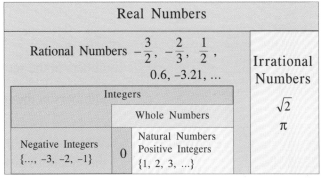

Figure 1.6

The natural numbers are contained in the whole numbers, the whole numbers are contained in the integers, and the integers are contained in the rational numbers. The real numbers contain rational numbers and irrational numbers. The following Figure 1.6 describes this hierarchy.

EXAMPLE 1 In the set $\left\{-4, 0, 1, \frac{9}{2}, -5\frac{1}{2}, 0.5, -1.\overline{3}, \sqrt{3}\right\}$ identify the numbers which can be classified as:

    a. natural numbers   **b.** whole numbers

    c. integers   **d.** rational numbers

    e. irrational numbers   **f.** real numbers

Solutions:

    a. 1 is the only **natural number** in the set.

    b. 0, 1 are the only **whole numbers** in the set.

    c. –4, 0, 1 are the only **integers** in the set.

    d. $-5\frac{1}{2}, -4, 1, 0, \frac{9}{2}, 0.5, -1.\overline{3}$ are the only **rational numbers** in the set.

WARM-UP

1. In the set $\left\{0, -5, \sqrt{6}, 3.8, \frac{2}{5}\right\}$ identify numbers which can be classified as:

    a) natural numbers

    b) whole numbers

    c) integers

    d) rational numbers

e) irrational numbers

e. $\sqrt{3}$ is the only **irrational number.**

f) real numbers

f. All members of the set are **real numbers.**

2. In the set $\left\{0, -5, 3.8, \dfrac{2}{5}\right\}$ identify those numbers which are:

a) integers, but not natural number.

b) rational numbers but not integers.

c) rational numbers, but not whole numbers.

EXAMPLE 2 In the set $\left\{-4, 0, 1, \dfrac{9}{2}, -5\dfrac{1}{2}, -3.2, 0.56, -0.\overline{16}\right\}$ identify those numbers which are:

a. integers, but not natural numbers.

b. rational numbers, but not integers.

c. rational numbers.

Solutions:

a. -4 and 0 are integers in the set which are not natural numbers.

b. $-5\dfrac{1}{2}, \dfrac{9}{2}, -3.2, 0.56,$ and $-0.\overline{16}$ are rational numbers in the set which are not integers.

c. All numbers in the set.

3. Which set of numbers are most appropriate for the situations given below.

a) height in relation to sea level.

b) global longitutes and latitudes.

c) Cost of dinner at Mc Donald's.

d) Defective items in a sample.

whole numbers, integers or rational numbers.

EXAMPLE 3 Which set of numbers are most appropriate for the situations given below.

a. distances between cities.

b. outdoor temperature in Alaska.

c. population of small towns.

d. interest rates of banks

whole numbers, integers or rational numbers.

Solutions:

a. Distances between cities on maps and in tables are usually given as **whole numbers**, such as 287 miles.

b. Temperature in Alaska are given using **integer values**, such as $-20°$ F or $2°$ F.

c. Populations are given as **whole numbers**, such as 780 persons.

d. Interest rates are given using **rational numbers**, expressed in percent form. An interest rate of 4.9% is equivalent to the rational number 0.049 or $\dfrac{49}{1000}$.

EXAMPLE 4   Graph all the numbers in the set

$$\left\{-4, 0, 1, \frac{9}{2}, -5\frac{1}{2}, -1.8\right\}$$ on number line.

Solutions:

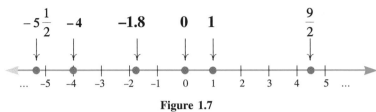

Figure 1.7

Draw a number line with tick marks representing the integers.

The graph of -4 is the fourth mark to the left of zero.

The graph of 1 is the first mark to the right of zero.

The graph of $\frac{9}{2}$ or $4\frac{1}{2}$ lies midway between 4 and 5.

The graph of $-5\frac{1}{2}$ lies midway between -6 and -5.

The graph of -1.8 lies between -2 and -1, closer to -2.

 We can determine whether or not the number is rational or not by using a calculator. See example 1, (section 1.4) in Appendix B.

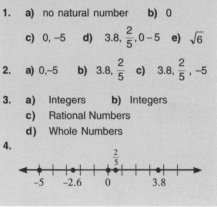

C. COMPARE REAL NUMBERS

We use inequalities to compare two real numbers.

For any two real numbers a and b, we say that a is **less than** b, if a is to the left of b on the number line.

"a is **less than** b" is written as $a < b$ in mathematical symbols.

"x is **greater than** y" is written as $x > y$ in mathematical symbols.

Notes

1. Since all positive numbers are graphed to the right of 0 on the number line, we have $a > 0$ for all positive real numbers a.   ($a > 0$ means "a is positive").

2. Since all negative numbers are graphed to the left of 0 on the number line, we have $a < 0$ for all negative real numbers a.   ($a < 0$ means "a is negative")

To determine if $a < b$ or $b < a$, locate the two numbers on the number line. The number on the left is smaller than the number on the right or the number on the right is larger than the number on the left.

EXAMPLE 5   Which of the following are true?

a. $-5 < -7$ **b.** $-1.2 < -1$ **c.** $-6 < -4$

d. $\dfrac{1}{4} < \dfrac{1}{5}$ **e.** $-\dfrac{7}{2} > -\dfrac{1}{2}$

b) $7 < 3$

c) $4 > -5$

d) $\dfrac{1}{3} > \dfrac{1}{6}$

e) $-\dfrac{1}{5} < -\dfrac{1}{4}$

Answers:

5. **a)** True   **b)** False   **c)** True

    d) True   **e)** False

Solutions:

Locate all the numbers on the number line.

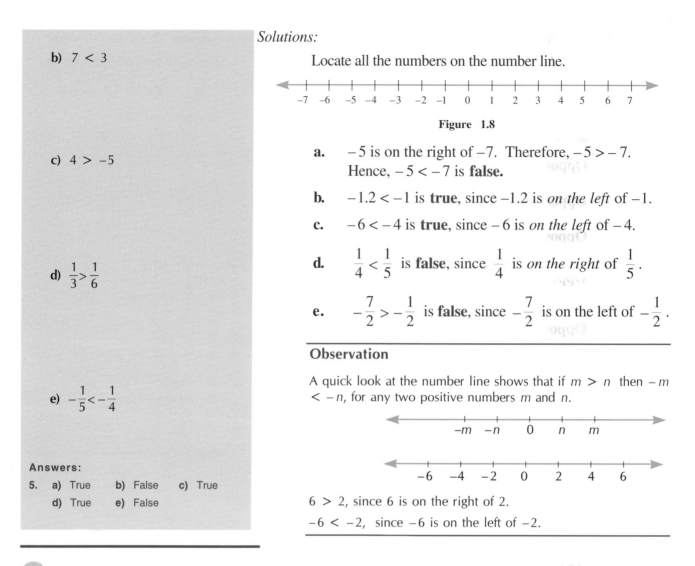

Figure 1.8

a. -5 is on the right of -7. Therefore, $-5 > -7$. Hence, $-5 < -7$ is **false**.

b. $-1.2 < -1$ is **true**, since -1.2 is *on the left* of -1.

c. $-6 < -4$ is **true**, since -6 is *on the left* of -4.

d. $\dfrac{1}{4} < \dfrac{1}{5}$ is **false**, since $\dfrac{1}{4}$ is *on the right* of $\dfrac{1}{5}$.

e. $-\dfrac{7}{2} > -\dfrac{1}{2}$ is **false**, since $-\dfrac{7}{2}$ is on the left of $-\dfrac{1}{2}$.

Observation

A quick look at the number line shows that if $m > n$ then $-m < -n$, for any two positive numbers m and n.

$6 > 2$, since 6 is on the right of 2.

$-6 < -2$, since -6 is on the left of -2.

D. **FIND THE ADDITIVE INVERSE OR OPPOSITE OF A REAL NUMBER**

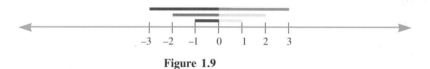

Figure 1.9

Examine the number line in Figure 1.9. The numbers **1** and **−1** are located at the same distance from 0 on opposite sides. The same is true of **2** and **−2**, and also of **3** and **−3**. We say that 1 and −1 are **additive inverses** or **opposites** of each other. Similarly, 2 and −2 are **additive inverses** or **opposites** of each other, and 3 and −3 are opposites of each other. The additive inverse of 0 is 0 itself.

For each non-zero real number x, there is exactly one other real number which is at the same distance from 0 as x but on the opposite side of zero. These numbers are called **additive inverses** or **opposites** of each other. The opposite of a number x is written as $-x$.

Observe that the opposite of 2 is –2 and the opposite of –2 is 2. The opposite of –2 is written as $-(-2)$. Therefore, $-(-2) = 2$.

In general, for any real number x, $-(-x) = x.$

EXAMPLE 6   Write down the opposites of the following numbers.

$$0, \ 3, \ -5, \ \frac{7}{3}, \ \frac{-8}{9}, \ -3.5$$

Solution: Recall that the **opposite** of a real number x is written as $-x$.

Opposite of 0 is $-(0) = 0$,

Opposite of 3 is $-(3) = -3$,

Opposite of -5 is $-(-5) = 5$,

Opposite of $\frac{7}{3}$ is $-\left(\frac{7}{3}\right) = -\frac{7}{3}$,

Opposite of $\frac{-8}{9}$ is $-\left(\frac{-8}{9}\right) = \frac{8}{9}$,

Opposite of -3.5 is $-(-3.5) = 3.5$.

E.   PROPERTIES OF REAL NUMBERS

The operations of addition and multiplication have several properties which we often use without mentioning. For example, we may add 8, 10, and 15 by using any of the following combinations.

   $8 + 10 + 15 = \mathbf{18} + 15 = 33$ or $10 + 15 + 8 = \mathbf{25} + 8 = 33$

   $10 + 8 + 15 = \mathbf{18} + 15 = 33$ or $8 + 15 + 10 = \mathbf{23} + 10 = 33$

We notice that **adding** 8, 10, and 15 in different orders yields the same result 33. Multiplying 8, 10, and 15 in different orders also yields the same result,

   $8 \times 10 \times 15 = 80 \times 15 = 1200$ or $10 \times 15 \times 8 = 150 \times 8 = 1200$

   $10 \times 8 \times 15 = 80 \times 15 = 1200$ or $8 \times 15 \times 10 = 120 \times 10 = 1200$

However, subtraction and division do not share this behavior.

For example $5 - 3 \neq 3 - 5$ and $6 \div 2 \neq 2 \div 6$.

1.   Commutative Properties:

We know that addition and multiplication are performed on two numbers at a time. The order in which the two numbers are written is not important. This is usually described as a property known as "Commutative Property".

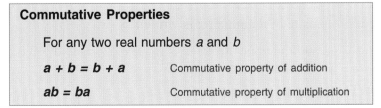

Commutative Properties

For any two real numbers a and b

$a + b = b + a$ Commutative property of addition

$ab = ba$ Commutative property of multiplication

EXAMPLE 7 Demonstrate the commutative property by completing the following statements.

a. $4 + 7 =$ _____   b. $-6 + 5 =$ _____

c. $3 \cdot 7 =$ _____   d. $(-4)(-2) =$ _____

Solutions:

a. $4 + 7 = 7 + \mathbf{4}$ Commutative property of addition

b. $-6 + 5 = \mathbf{5} + (-6)$ Commutative property of addition

c. $3 \cdot 7 = \mathbf{7} \cdot 3$ Commutative property of multiplication

d. $(-4)(-2) = (-2)(\mathbf{-4})$ Commutative property of multiplication

Subtraction and division are not Commutative.

For example:

$$6 - 2 \neq 2 - 6 \text{ and } 6 \div 2 \neq 2 \div 6$$

2.   Associative Properties:

We know that addition and multiplication are performed on two numbers at a time. For addition and multiplication of three or more numbers, any pair can be added or multiplied first. The order is not important. This is usually described as a property known as the "Associative Property".

> **Associative Properties**
>
> For any three real numbers a, b, and c
>
> $a + b + c = (a + b) + c = a + (b + c)$ Associative property of addition.
>
> $a \times b \times c = (ab)\, c = a(bc)$ Associative property of multiplication.

EXAMPLE 8 Demonstrate the associative property by completing the following statements.

a. $3 + (5 + 7) =$ _____

b. $4[5(-6)] =$ _____

c. $3[(-4) \cdot 2] =$ _____

Solutions:

a. $3 + [5 + 7] = (3 + \mathbf{5}) + 7$ Associative property.

b. $4[5(-6)] = (4 \cdot 5) \cdot (\mathbf{-6})$ Associative property.

c. $3[(-4) \cdot 2] = [\mathbf{3} \cdot (-4)] \cdot 2$ Associative property.

3.   Identity Properties:

> **Identity Properties**
>
> For any real number a
>
> $a + \mathbf{0} = a$ and $\mathbf{0} + a = a$ Identity property of addition.
>
> $a \times \mathbf{1} = a$ and $\mathbf{1} \times a = a$ Identity property of multiplication.

The number 0 is called **the additive identity** or **the identity element for addition.** The number 1 is called the **multiplicative identity** or the **identity element for multiplication.**

EXAMPLE 9   Demonstrate the identity property by completing the following statements.

a. $4 + \underline{\quad} = \underline{\quad}$ b. $-5 + (\underline{\quad}) = \underline{\quad}$

c. $1 \cdot \underline{\quad} = \underline{\quad}$ d. $6 \cdot \underline{\quad} = \underline{\quad}$

Solutions:

a. $4 + \mathbf{0} = 4$ Identity property of addition.

b. $0 + (\mathbf{-5}) = -5$ Identity property of addition.

c. $1 \cdot (\mathbf{-7}) = -7$ Identity property of multiplication.

d. $6 \cdot \mathbf{1} = 6$ Identity property of multiplication.

4.   Inverse Properties:

Inverse Properties

i)   For each real number a, its **opposite** $-a$ satisfies $a + (-a) = 0$ and $(-a) + a = 0$.

   a and $-a$ are called **additive inverses** of each other.

ii)   For each real number $a(\neq 0)$, its **reciprocal** $\dfrac{1}{a}$ satisfies $a \cdot \dfrac{1}{a} = 1$ and $\dfrac{1}{a} \cdot a = 1$.

   a and $\dfrac{1}{a}$ are called **multiplicative inverses** of each other.

EXAMPLE 10   Demonstrate the inverse property by completing the following statements.

a. $-3 + \underline{\quad} = \underline{\quad}$ b. $-\dfrac{3}{5} \cdot \underline{\quad} = \underline{\quad}$

Solutions:

a. $-3 + 3 = 0$ Additive inverse property.

b. $\left(-\dfrac{3}{5}\right)\left(-\dfrac{5}{3}\right) = 1$ Multiplicative inverse property.

5.   Distributive Properties:

Distributive Properties

Distributive properties combine addition and multiplication. These properties are:

For any three real numbers a, b, and c

   $a(b + c) = ab + ac$ and $(b + c)a = ba + ca$

We say that multiplication distributes over addition. Using the above distributive properties we can easily establish that for all real numbers *a, b, c*

$$a(b - c) = ab - ac \qquad \text{and} \qquad (b - c)a = ba - ca$$

WARM-UP

11. Simplify in two ways as in Example 11.

   a) 3(2 + 5)

   b) 4(7 − 4)

   c) −2(2 − 7)

EXAMPLE 11   Evaluate the following in two ways using (i) the rules for operations with grouping symbols and (ii) the distributive property.

   a. 4(3 + 7)   **b.** 8(5 − 9)   **c.** −3(7 − 2)

Solutions:

   a. i) $4(\mathbf{3 + 7}) = 4 \cdot \mathbf{10} = 40$ Grouping symbol.

      ii) $4(3 + 7) = \mathbf{4} \cdot 3 + \mathbf{4} \cdot 7$ Distributive property.
         $= 12 + 28 = 40$

   b. i) $8(5 - 9) = 8\,(-4) = -32$ Grouping symbol.

      ii) $\mathbf{8}(5 - 9) = \mathbf{8} \cdot 5 - \mathbf{8} \cdot 9$ Distributive property.
         $= 40 - 72 = -32$

   c. i) $-3(7 - 2) = -3 \cdot 5 = -15$ Grouping symbol.

      ii) $\mathbf{-3}(7 - 2) = (\mathbf{-3}) \cdot 7 - (\mathbf{-3}) \cdot 2$ Distributive property.
         $= -21 - (-6)$
         $= -21 + 6 = -15$

The distributive properties can be extended to more than three numbers.

   i) $a(b + c + d) = ab + ac + ad,$
      $a(b + c + d + e) = ab + ac + ad + ae$

   ii) $(b + c + d)a = ba + ca + da,$
      $(b + c + d + e)a = ba + ca + da + ea$

12. Write without parentheses

   a) 4(3*x* − 2)

   b) 2(2 − 3*y*)

EXAMPLE 12   Write the following without parentheses.

   a. 3(5*y* − *z*)   **b.** −(4*x* − *t*)   **c.** −5(3*y* + 2*z* − 6)

Solutions:

   a. $\mathbf{3}(5y - z) = \mathbf{3}(5y) - \mathbf{3}z$ Distributive property.
      $= (3 \cdot 5)y - 3z$ Associative property.
      $= 15y - 3z$

   b. $-(4x - t) = -\mathbf{1}(4x - t)$
      $= (\mathbf{-1})\,(4x) - (\mathbf{-1})t$ Distributive property.
      $= (-1 \cdot 4)x - (-t)$ Associative property.
      $= -4x + t$

c. We use the extended distributive property.

$-5(3y + 2z - 6)$

$= (-5)(3y) + (-5)(2z) - (-5) \cdot 6$ Distributive property.

$= (-5 \cdot 3)y + (-5 \cdot 2)z - (-30)$ Associative property.

$= -15y - 10z + 30$

EXAMPLE 13 Identify the property demonstrated:

Commutative, Associative, Identity, Inverse or Distributive.

a. $\dfrac{-10}{11} + \dfrac{10}{11} = 0$ **b.** $4ts = 4st$

c. $5(2 + (-3)) = 5((-3) + 2)$

d. $5(2 + (-3)) = 10 + (-15)$ **e.** $1 \cdot x = x$

Solutions:

a. $\dfrac{-10}{11} + \dfrac{10}{11} = 0$ *Inverse property* for addition.

b. $4ts = 4st$ Only the order of *t s* is changed
Commutative property for multiplication.

c. $5(2 + (-3)) = 5((-3) + 2)$

Only the order of $2 + (-3)$ is changed
Commutative property for addition.

d. $5(2 + (-3)) = 10 + (-15)$ *Distributive property.*

e. $1 \cdot x = x$ *Identity property* for multiplication.

---

13. Identify the property demonstrated: Commutative, Associative, Identity, Inverse or Distributive.

a) $-5(2 \cdot 3) = (-5 \cdot 2)(-3)$

b) $-2x + 0 = -2x$

c) $-(x - 2y) = -x + 2y$

d) $\dfrac{-2}{3} \cdot \dfrac{-3}{2} = 1$

e) $x^2 + 3 + 2x = x^2 + 2x + 3$

Answers:

7. a) $7 + 9$ b) $5 \cdot 3$
   c) $4(-5)$ d) $(-8)(-7)$
8. a) $(5 + 3) + 2$ b) $(5 \cdot 6)(-7)$
   c) $[2(-3)] \cdot 5$
9. a) $0, 3$ b) $1, -8$ c) -4 d) $1, 8$
10. a) 6 b) $-\dfrac{9}{4}$
11. a) 21 b) 12 c) 10
12. a) $12x - 8$ b) $4 - 6y$
    c) $-15y - 15z$
13. a) Associative property
    b) Identity property
    c) Distributive property
    d) Identity property
    e) Commutative property

EXERCISE 1.5

B. In exercises 1-4, identify numbers which are

   (a) Whole numbers   (b) Integers   (c) Rational numbers

1. $\left\{ 0, \dfrac{3}{7}, -\dfrac{2}{3}, 4, -2.3, -8 \right\}$

2. $\left\{ \dfrac{5}{4}, \dfrac{9}{7}, -1.5, -2, -1 \right\}$

3. $\left\{ 1.4, -1, 5, 7, \dfrac{4}{5}, 11, \dfrac{1}{11} \right\}$

4. $\left\{ 1.2, -3.\overline{3}, 0, \dfrac{3}{13}, 1, 19, -19 \right\}$

In exercises 5-8, identify the appropriate set of numbers from the following list:

(a) Whole numbers ;　　　(b) Integers ;　　(c) Rational Numbers

5.　　Distances between planets　　　　　　　　　6.　　Daily Stock market activity

7.　　Seconds before and after take off of the space shuttle.

8.　　Vehicles available in a dealership for sale.

9.　　Graph the numbers on the number line : $-4, 2, 1, 3\frac{1}{2}, 4.25, -3$.

10.　　Graph the numbers on the number line : $4.5, -0.25, \frac{3}{8}, -\frac{6}{3}, 3\frac{1}{3}, 0, 2, -3$.

C.　**In exercises 11-26, determine whether or not the statement is true.**

11.　$5 \geq 4$　　12.　$-4 \leq -7$　　13.　$0 < 9$　　14.　$-4.3 \leq 1.5$　　15.　$7.5 > -11.9$　　16.　$\frac{1}{4} < \frac{1}{2}$

17.　$-6 < -13$　　18.　$5 \leq 5$　　19.　$3 \geq 5$　　20.　$4 \geq -5$　　21.　$-\frac{1}{3} < -\frac{1}{2}$　　22.　$-\frac{2}{3} < -1$

23.　$-\frac{1}{5} > -\frac{1}{2}$　　24.　$\frac{1}{5} < \frac{1}{2}$　　25.　$0 \geq -20$　　26.　$-\frac{3}{5} \geq -\frac{3}{5}$

D.　**In exercises 27-42, find the opposite of the given number.**

27.　6　　28.　-7　　29.　-6.32　　30.　0　　31.　$\frac{1}{2}$　　32.　-18　　33.　$\sqrt{3}$　　34.　$-\frac{2}{3}$

35.　$2\frac{1}{4}$　　36.　$-5\frac{1}{3}$　　37.　4.09　　38.　$-0.\overline{6}$　　39.　$-(-2)$　　40.　$-|-5|$　　41.　$-\left(-\frac{1}{3}\right)$　　42. $-(-3.7)$

E.　**In exercises 43-51, complete the statements demonstrating the identity property.**

43.　$\_\_ + (-8) = \_\_$　　　　　　44.　$0 + \_\_ = 0$　　　　　　45.　$7 + \_\_ = \_\_$

46.　$-\frac{5}{6} + \_\_ = \_\_$　　　　47.　$(-19) \cdot \_\_ = \_\_$　　　　48.　$1 \cdot \_\_ = \_\_$

49.　$-6 \cdot \_\_ = \_\_$　　　　　50.　$\_\_ \cdot (3) = \_\_$　　　　51.　$\_\_ \cdot \left(-\frac{2}{3}\right) = \_\_$

In exercises 52-61, complete the statement demonstrating the commutative property.

52.　$\left(6\frac{1}{5}\right)\left(-7\frac{1}{6}\right) = \_\_\_\_$　　　53.　$3 + (-7) = \_\_\_\_$　　54.　$-5 + 4 = \_\_\_\_$　　55.　$-6 + (-8) = \_\_\_\_$

56.　$(2) + \left(-\frac{1}{3}\right) = \_\_\_\_$　　　　57.　$\left(-1\frac{2}{3}\right) + \left(2\frac{1}{5}\right) = \_\_\_\_$　　58.　$(-3)(-7) = \_\_\_\_$

59.　$5 \cdot (-6) = \_\_\_\_$　　　　　60.　$(-12) \cdot 0 = \_\_\_\_$　　　　61.　$(-6) \cdot \left(-\frac{1}{3}\right) = \_\_\_\_$

In exercises 62-69, fill in the blanks so that the resulting statement is an example of the associative property.

62.　$(5 + 8) + (-3) = \_\_\_\_$　　　　63.　$4 + [6 + (-2)] = \_\_\_\_$　　　　64.　$\_\_(5 \cdot 7) = (6 \_\_) \cdot 7$

65.　$(-19 + 7) + 4 = \_\_\_\_$　　　　66.　$3 + [(-5) + 9] = \_\_\_\_$　　　　67.　$(-2) \cdot [4 \cdot (-8)] = \_\_\_\_$

68. __ $= [\,-9 + (-8)\,] + 4$　　　　**69.** $[61 + -\dfrac{2}{3}\,] + \left(-5\dfrac{1}{6}\right) = $ ___

In exercises 70-77, complete the statements demonstrating inverse property.

70. __ $+ -8 = $ __　　　**71.** $-19 \cdot$ __ $= $ __　　　**72.** $7 + $ __ $= $ __　　　**73.** $\dfrac{-5}{6} + $ __ $= $ __

74. __ $\cdot (-3) = $ __　　　**75.** $1 \cdot$ __ $= $ __　　　**76.** $-6 \cdot$ __ $= $ __　　　**77.** __ $\cdot \left(\dfrac{-2}{3}\right) = $ __

In exercises 78-84, identify the property demonstrated in the statement.

78. $4 \cdot \dfrac{1}{4} = 1$　　　**79.** $-7 + 7 = 0$　　　**80.** $\left(-\dfrac{2}{3}\right)\left(-\dfrac{3}{2}\right) = 1$　　**81.** $(-5) + 5 = 0$

82. $\dfrac{1}{11} \cdot 11 = 1$　　　**83.** $\dfrac{2}{9} + \left(-\dfrac{2}{9}\right) = 0$　　　**84.** $\left(1\dfrac{2}{3}\right)\left(\dfrac{3}{5}\right) = 1$

85. Compute $4 - (7 - 5)$ and $(4 - 7) - 5$, to verify that subtraction is not associative.

86. Compute $-3 - (9 - 6)$ and $(-3 - 9) - 6$, to verify that subtraction is not associative.

87. Compute $4 - 7$ and $7 - 4$, to verify that subtraction is not commutative.

88. Compute $\dfrac{1}{2} - \dfrac{1}{3}$ and $\dfrac{1}{3} - \dfrac{1}{2}$, to verify that subtraction is not commutative.

89. Compute $45 \div (5 \div 3)$ and $(45 \div 5) \div 3$, to verify that division is not associative.

90. Compute $\left(\dfrac{1}{3} \div 3\right) \div \dfrac{1}{2}$ and $\dfrac{1}{3} \div \left(3 \div \dfrac{1}{2}\right)$, to verify that division is not associative.

91. Compute $45 \div 5$ and $5 \div 45$, to verify that division is not commutative.

92. Compute $\dfrac{1}{6} \div \dfrac{1}{9}$ and $\dfrac{1}{9} \div \dfrac{1}{6}$, to verify that division is not commutative.

93. Evaluate $4 \div [36 + 8]$ and $4 \div 36 + 4 \div 8$, to verify that division does not distribute over addition.

94. Evaluate $2 - (6 + 9)$ and $2 - 6 + 2 - 9$, to verify that subtraction does not distributive over addition.

F. **In exercises 95-103, identify the property demonstrated ; Commutative, Associative, Identity, Inverse, or Distributive.**

95. $-\dfrac{4}{5} \cdot \dfrac{-5}{4} = 1$　　　**96.** $11(-5 + 2) = -55 + 22$　　　**97.** $-4(s - t) = -4s + 4t$

98. $-4 \cdot (5 \cdot 2) = (-4 \cdot 5)(-2)$　　**99.** $0 + \dfrac{1}{2} = \dfrac{1}{2}$　　　**100.** $0 + \dfrac{1}{2} = \dfrac{1}{2}$

101. $-\dfrac{4}{5} + \dfrac{4}{5} = 0$　　　**102.** $(^-1 + {}^-2) + {}^-3 = {}^-1 + (^-2 + {}^-3)$　　**103.** $5(x + y + 1) = 5x + 5y + 5$

1.6 TRANSLATIONS: STATEMENTS TO MATHEMATICAL EXPRESSIONS

A. TRANSLATE PHRASES

In order to solve application problems it is necessary to translate the word statements, and sentences into mathematical expressions and equations. For this we need to be familiar with the frequently used words that translate into operation symbol used in mathematical expressions. Some of these translations are listed in the following chart.

OPERATION VOCABULARY

ADDITION			SUBTRACTION		
More than	8 more than x	$x + 8$	Minus	x minus 2	$x - 2$
The sum of	the sum of x and z	$x + z$	Less than	7 less than t	$t - 7$
The total of	the total of 5 and y	$5 + y$	Subtracted from	5 subtracted from d	$d - 5$
plus	b plus seventeen	$b + 17$	Decreased by	m decreased by 3	$m - 3$
			The difference between	the difference between y and 4	$y - 4$
MULTIPLICATION			DIVISION		
Times	10 times t	$10\,t$	Divided by	x divided by 12	$\dfrac{x}{12}$
Of	one-half of x	$\dfrac{1}{2}x$	The quotient of	the quotient of y and z	$\dfrac{y}{z}$
The product of	the product of y and z	yz	The ratio of	the ratio of t and 9	$\dfrac{t}{9}$

Some phrases may involve unknown quantities that can take, or can be assigned any numerical value. In such situations we use letters of alphabet ($x, y, z, a, b, c\ldots$) to represent those unknown quantities. We call such a letter "**Variable**". The examples given below illustrate how variables are used to translate phrases into algebraic expressions.

EXAMPLE 1   Translate the following expressions into mathematical symbols.

a. **The sum** of *a number* and 11.

b. 3 **subtracted** from *a number*.

c. **The product** of 11 and *a number*.

d. **The quotient** of *a number* and 4.

e. **The quotient** of 4 and *a number*.

f. The sum of 5 **times** *a number* **and** 4.

g. **The difference** between **twice** *a number* and 7.

| Note | The word "number", without specification, means an unknown number. An *unspecified* number may be translated as x, y, z (any variable). |

e) The quotient of 10 and seven times a number.

f) 14 less then the product of nine and a number.

g) The difference between five times a number and 12.

Solutions:

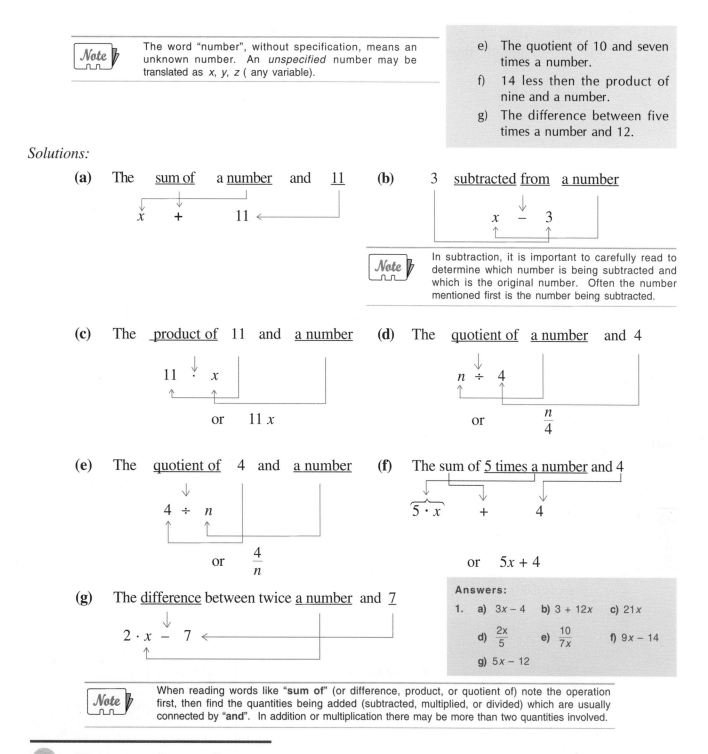

(a) The sum of a number and 11
$$x + 11$$

(b) 3 subtracted from a number
$$x - 3$$

| Note | In subtraction, it is important to carefully read to determine which number is being subtracted and which is the original number. Often the number mentioned first is the number being subtracted. |

(c) The product of 11 and a number
$$11 \cdot x$$
or $11x$

(d) The quotient of a number and 4
$$n \div 4$$
or $\dfrac{n}{4}$

(e) The quotient of 4 and a number
$$4 \div n$$
or $\dfrac{4}{n}$

(f) The sum of 5 times a number and 4
$$5 \cdot x + 4$$
or $5x + 4$

(g) The difference between twice a number and 7
$$2 \cdot x - 7$$

Answers:

1. a) $3x - 4$ b) $3 + 12x$ c) $21x$

   d) $\dfrac{2x}{5}$ e) $\dfrac{10}{7x}$ f) $9x - 14$

   g) $5x - 12$

| Note | When reading words like "**sum of**" (or difference, product, or quotient of) note the operation first, then find the quantities being added (subtracted, multiplied, or divided) which are usually connected by "**and**". In addition or multiplication there may be more than two quantities involved. |

B. **TRANSLATE SIMPLE STATEMENTS**

Word statements are usually complete sentences that translate into equations or inequalities.

- **Distinguish an Expression from an Equation**

Examples

1. The sum of four times a number and 7 is 91.

This means

the **sum** of **four times a number** and 7 is **91**

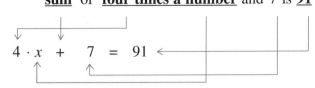

$$4 \cdot x + 7 = 91$$

Thus, the given **word statement** translates to the equation $4x + 7 = 91$. Words like **is, are, was, were, equals** are translated as "**=**".

2. Twice the **difference** of **a number** and **7 equals the sum** of **the number** and **20**.

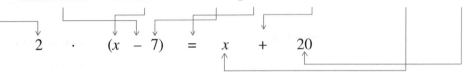

$$2 \cdot (x - 7) = x + 20$$

The difference between an expression and an equation is that an equation contains an '=' sign, and an expression does not contain '=' sign.

We observe that ; a **phrase** translates into an **expression**, and a **sentence** or a **statement** translates into an **equation**.

WARM-UP

2. Translate the following statements into symbols.

a) Thirteen increased by four equals seventeen.

b) Four times nine decreased by sixteen equals twenty.

c) Six multiplied by four equals twenty four.

d) Eighteen divided by three equals six.

EXAMPLE 2 Translate the following statements into symbols.

Solutions:

Statements	Conversion to symbols
a. Fourteen decreased by three equals eleven.	14 decreased by 3 equals 11. $$14 - 3 = 11$$
b. Two times five increased by seven equals seventeen.	2 times 5 increased by 7 equals 17. $$2 \cdot 5 + 7 = 17$$
c. Six divided by two is three.	6 divided by 2 is 3. $$6 \div 2 = 3$$
d. The quotient of eight and four is two.	8 divided by 4 is 2 $$8 \div 4 = 2$$

Some phrases may involve unknown quantities that can take, or can be assigned any numerical value. In such situations we use letters of alphabet ($x, y, z, a, b, c\ldots$) to represent those unknown quantities. We call such a letter "**Variable**". The examples given below illustrate how variables are used to translate phrases into algebraic expressions.

EXAMPLE 3 Decide whether the following is an equation or an expression.

a. $4x^2 - 5y$ b. $4x^2 - 5y = 0$

c. $7x^2 + 8x - 9$ d. $(3x + y)x - 2y$

Solutions: a. $4x^2 - 5y$ is an *expression*

b. $4x^2 - 5y = 0$ is an *equation*

c. $7x^2 + 8x - 9$ is an *expression*

d. $(3x + y)x - 2y$ is an *expression*

Note An expression corresponds to a *phrase* and an *equation* corresponds to a sentence.

- **The Solution of an equation**

A number is called the **solution** of an equation if the equation results in a true statement when the variable is replaced by this number.

To find out whether or not a number is a solution of an equation we use the following steps:

Step **1** Substitute the given number for the variable in the equation.

Step **2** Simplify the expressions on both sides of the equation.

If the simplification results in a true statement, the number is a solution, otherwise it is not a solution.

EXAMPLE 4 Given below is an equation and a number. Determine whether or not the number is a solution of the equation.

a. $4x + 7 = 91$; **21** b. $2(y - 7) = y + 20$; **25**

Solutions:

a. Substitute 21 for x in: $4x + 7 = 91$.

$$4 \cdot \mathbf{21} + 7 = 91$$
$$84 + 7 = 91$$
$$91 = 91 \quad \text{True!}$$

Therefore, 21 is a solution of the equation $4x + 7 = 91$

b. Substitute 25 for y in: $2(y - 7) = y + 20$

$$2(\mathbf{25} - 7) = \mathbf{25} + 20$$
$$2 \cdot 18 = 45$$
$$36 = 45 \quad \text{False!}$$

Therefore, 25 is not a solution of the given equation.

- **Identify a solution from a set of numbers**

A **set** is a well defined collection of objects. The objects belonging to the set are its **elements** or **members**. The set whose members are 1, 2, 3, 5 is written as {1, 2, 3, 5}. This set is a finite set with four elements in it.

To find the solution of an equation from a finite set of numbers, verify for each number in the set, one by one, whether or not it is a solution of the equation.

▀▀▀ **WARM-UP** ▀▀▀

5. Identify the solution from the given set.

a) $3x + 2 = 2x$; {0, 1, −2}

b) $4x − 12 = x$; {−1, 3, 4}

EXAMPLE 5   Identify the solution from a given set:

     a. $2x + 9 = 5x$; {0, −2 ,3}.

     b. $3x − 2 = 0$; {1, 4, −7}.

Solutions:

a. $x = 0$:   Substitute 0 for x in $2x+9=5x$. $2 \cdot 0 + 9 = 5 \cdot 0$

                 0 is not a solution. $0 + 9 = 0$ False

      $x = −2$: Substitute −2 for x. $2 \cdot (−2) + 9 = 5 \cdot (−2)$

                 −2 is not a solution. $5 = −10$ False

      $x = 3$:   Substitute 3 for x. $2 \cdot 3 + 9 = 5 \cdot 3$

                 3 is a solution. $15 = 15$ True

Therefore, 3 is the solution of $2x + 9 = 5x$ in the set {0, 2, 3}.

b. $x = 1$:   Substitute 1 for x in $3x−2 = 0$. $3 \cdot 1 − 2 = 0$

                1 is not a solution. $1 = 0$ False

      $x = 4$:   Substitute 4 for x. $3 \cdot 4 − 2 = 0$

                 4 is not a solution. $10 = 0$ False

      $x = −7$: Substitute −7 for x. $3 \cdot (−7) − 2 = 0$

                 −7 is not a solution $23 = 0$ False

Therefore, $3x − 2 = 0$ does not have a solution in {1, 4, −7}.

$\boxed{Note}$ An equation may have a solution outside a given set. For example, $\dfrac{2}{3}$ is a solution

of $3x − 2 = 0$ since $3\left(\dfrac{2}{3}\right) − 2 = 0$. However, $\dfrac{2}{3}$ is not in the set {1, 4, 7}.

▀▀▀ **WARM-UP** ▀▀▀

6. a) The product of 5 and a number is 30. Does this problem have a solution in the set {1, 3, 5, 6}? What is the solution?

EXAMPLE 6   The quotient of eighteen and three times a number is three. Does this problem have a solution in the set {1, 2, 3, 4}?

Solution:

    Step 1   Translate the statement into mathematical symbols. The statement is the same as:

The quotient of   18   and   3 times a number is 3.

$$18 \quad \div \quad (3 \cdot x) \qquad = \qquad 3$$

or $\qquad \dfrac{18}{3x} = 3$

Step 2 Take each number from the set $\{1, 2, 3, 4\}$ and examine whether it satisfies the equation (*i.e.*, whether it is a solution of the equation.)

The equation is $\dfrac{18}{3x} = 3$

Test $x = 1$: $\quad \dfrac{18}{3 \cdot 1} = 3 \quad \longrightarrow \quad \dfrac{18}{3} = 3 \quad \longrightarrow \quad 6 = 3$ False!

Test $x = 2$: $\quad \dfrac{18}{3 \cdot 2} = 3 \quad \longrightarrow \quad \dfrac{18}{6} = 3 \quad \longrightarrow \quad 3 = 3$ True!

Test $x = 3$: $\quad \dfrac{18}{3 \cdot 3} = 3 \quad \longrightarrow \quad \dfrac{18}{9} = 3 \quad \longrightarrow \quad 2 = 3$ False!

Test $x = 4$: $\quad \dfrac{18}{3 \cdot 4} = 3 \quad \longrightarrow \quad \dfrac{18}{12} = 3 \quad \longrightarrow \quad \dfrac{3}{2} = 3$ False!

Step 3 *Conclusion:*

Hence we find that there is a solution of the problem in the set $\{1, 2, 3, 4\}$. The solution is 2.

b) The quotient of three times a number and 5 is 6. Does this problem have a solution in the set $\{1, 4, 5, 7\}$?

Answers:

2. **a)** $13 + 4 = 17$ **b)** $4 \cdot 9 - 16 = 20$
    c) $6 \times 4 = 24$ **d)** $18 \div 3 = 6$
3. **a)** Expression **b)** Equation
    c) Expression **b)** Expression
4. **a)** No **b)** Yes
5. **a)** -2 **b)** 4
6. **a)** Yes; 6 **b)** No

C. TRANSLATE STATEMENTS OF INEQUALITY

Some phrases or statements may not directly translate into mathematical expressions or equations. The translation of words such as **less than, at least, more than** require special types of symbols, called inequality symbols, for the statement to be translated into mathematical inequality.

Some of the frequently used symbols together with well defined meaning for each are given in the following table.

Symbol	Meaning	Example	Verbal Statement
$\neq$	not equal to	$5 \neq 7$	5 is not equal to 7.
$<$	is less than	$-14 < -9$	-14 is less than -9
$>$	is greater than	$-8 > -30$	-8 is greater than -30.
$\leq$	is less than or equal to	$5 \leq 5$	5 is less than or equal to 5 [In this case 5 is equal to 5]
		$5 \leq 7$	5 is less than or equal to 7.
$\geq$	is greater than or equal to	$-5 \geq -5$	-5 is greater than or equal to -5 [In this case 5 is equal to 5]
		$6 \geq 4$	6 is greater than or equal to 4.

7. Which of the following statements are true and which are false?

a) $7 = 4$

b) $5 \neq 5$

c) $(9 + 2) < 13$

d) $(7 + 9) < (15 - 3)$

e) $(0 \div 5) < 4$

f) $(15 \div 3) > 3$

g) $(9 \times 4) > 25$

EXAMPLE 7 Determine which of the following statements are true and which are false.

a. $4 \neq 4$ b. $5 \neq 3$ c. $(4 + 2) > 7$

d. $(3 + 5) \leq (10 - 2)$ e. $(10 \div 2) > 5$

f. $(12 \div 2) > 5$ g. $(5 \times 4) \geq 8$

Solutions:

a. $4 \neq 4$ is **false**, since 4 equals itself.

b. $5 \neq 3$ is **true**, since 5 and 3 are not equal.

c. $(4 + 2) > 7$ is **false**, since 6 is less than 7.

d. $(3 + 5) \leq (10 - 2)$ is **true**, since $8 = 8$.

    Notice 8 is equal to itself. Therefore, we can also say 8 is less than or equal to 8.

e. $(10 \div 2) > 5$ is **false**, since 5 is equal to 5 and not greater than 5.

f. $(12 \div 2) > 5$ is **true**, since 6 is greater than 5.

g. $(5 \times 4) \geq 8$ is **true**, since 20 is greater than or equal to 8.

The statements '3 is less than 5' and '5 is greater than 3' convey the same meaning. Thus $3 < 5$ can also be written as $5 > 3$. It follows that $<$ changes to $>$ if the expressions on two sides are swapped. A similar conclusion holds for $\leq$ and $\geq$.

8. a) Express $5 < 9$ by using $>$.

b) Express $9 \geq 5$ by using $\leq$.

c) Express $25 > 21$ by using $<$.

EXAMPLE 8   a. Express $3 < 5$ by using $>$.

b. Express $7 \geq 5$ by using $\leq$.

c. Express $11 > 10$ by using $<$.

Solutions:

a. $3 < 5$ means   *"3 is less than 5"*. This is the same as *"5 is greater than 3"*. Therefore, $3 < 5 \rightarrow 5 > 3$.

b. $7 \geq 5$ means   *"7 is greater than or equal to 5"*. This is the same as *"5 is less than or equal to 7"*. Therefore, $7 \geq 5 \rightarrow 5 \leq 7$.

c. $11 > 10$ means   *"11 is greater than 10"*. This is the same as *"10 is less than 11"*. Thus, $11 > 10 \rightarrow 10 < 11$.

Answers:

7. a) False   b) False   c) True
   d) False   e) True   f) True
   g) True

8. a) $9 > 5$ b) $5 \leq 9$ c) $21 < 25$

D. EVALUATING ALGEBRAIC EXPRESSIONS

Variables are the building blocks for algebraic expressions. Recall that a variable is a symbol which is used to represent an unknown number. It is denoted by a letter such as: x, y, z, p, q, etc. Operations on variables are performed in the same way as operations on numbers.

For example,

    a) $x \cdot x$ is written as x^2.

    b) $2 \cdot x$, which is written as $2x$, represents the product of 2 and x.

    c) $x^2 + x$ means the sum of x^2 and x.

    d) $x - 2$ means 2 subtracted from x.

Algebraic expressions are created using variables, numbers, operations, and grouping symbols.

The following are examples of algebraic expressions:

$$3x^2 + 5, \quad x(x + 2), \quad 6x + 5yz - 7, \quad \text{and} \quad 5x^2 + (x - 1)2y + 4$$

An algebraic expression which involves only one variable is called an algebraic expression in one variable or specifically, an algebraic expression in x (the variable name). If there are two variables, x and y, then it is called an algebraic expression in two variables or an algebraic expression in x and y.

To find the value of an algebraic expression for given value(s) of the variable(s).

Procedure

> **Step 1** Replace the variable(s) by its given values.
> **Step 2** Simplify the resulting numerical expression.

EXAMPLE 9   Find the numerical values of:

    a. $3x$ when $x = {}^-2$

    b. $4y^2 + 5$ when $y = -\dfrac{3}{2}$

    c. $(3x - 2)^2 + 1$ when $x = 4$

    d. $\dfrac{4m^2 + 7m - 2}{2(m - 1)}$ when $m = 0.5$

WARM-UP

9.   Find the numerical value of:

    a) $5y$ for $y = -3$

    b) $2x^2 - 3$ for $x = -\dfrac{2}{3}$

Solutions:

    a.   **$3x$ when $x = {}^-2$**

        Step 1   Substitute $x = {}^-2$. $\left.\begin{array}{l} 3 \cdot ({}^-2) \\ = -6. \end{array}\right.$

        Step 2   Simplify.

    b.   **$4y^2 + 5$ when $y = -\dfrac{3}{2}$**

        Step 1   Substitute $y = -\dfrac{3}{2}$. $\left.\begin{array}{l} 4 \cdot \left(-\dfrac{3}{2}\right)^2 + 5 \\[2mm] = 4 \cdot \dfrac{9}{4} + 5 \\[2mm] = 9 + 5 = \mathbf{14}. \end{array}\right.$

        Step 2   Simplify.

c) $(4x-7)^2 + 4$ for $x = 1$

d) $\dfrac{2a^2 - 3a + 5}{2(a-1)}$ for $a = 1.5$

10. Evaluate:

a) $2a + 5b$ for $a = -3, b = 4$

b) $3x^2 + 4yz - 3$ for $x = -1,$
$y = 2, z = -2$

c) $(a^2 + 2b)(2b - 5)$ for $a = 2.5,$
$b = 7.6$

d) $\dfrac{x^2 + 2y^2}{x - 3y}$ for $x = 1, \ y = -1$

---

c. $(3x - 2)^2 + 1$ when $x = 4$

Step 1   Substitute $x = 4$. $(3 \cdot 4 - 2)^2 + 1$

Step 2   Simplify. $= (12 - 2)^2 + 1$

                               $= (10)^2 + 1$

                               $= 100 + 1 \ = \ \mathbf{101}$

d. $\dfrac{4m^2 + 7m - 2}{2(m-1)}$ when $m = \mathbf{0.5}$

Step 1   Substitute $m = \mathbf{0.5}$. $\dfrac{4 \cdot (\mathbf{0.5})^2 + 7 \cdot (\mathbf{0.5}) - 2}{2((\mathbf{0.5}) - 1)}$

Step 2   Simplify. $= \dfrac{4 \cdot (\mathbf{0.25}) + 7 \cdot (\mathbf{0.5}) - 2}{2(-\mathbf{0.5})}$

            $= \dfrac{1 + 3.5 - 2}{-1}$

            $= \dfrac{2.5}{-1} = \mathbf{-2.5}$

EXAMPLE 10   Evaluate the following expressions for the given values of the variables.

a. $3x - 5y$ **b.** $5x^2 - 2yz + 8$
for $x = -1.4, \ y = 2.3$ for $x = 3, \ y = 2, \ z = 4$

c. $(x^2 + 3y)(3y + 7)$ **d.** $\dfrac{x^2 - 3y^2}{5y + x}$
for $x = 1, \ y = 1$ for $x = 4, \ y = 2.$

Solutions:

a. $3x - 5y$ for $x = -\mathbf{1.4}$ and $y = \mathbf{2.3}$

    $3x - 5y$

    $= 3 \cdot (-\mathbf{1.4}) - 5 \cdot (\mathbf{2.3})$ Substitute values.

    $= -4.2 - 11.5 \ = \ \mathbf{-15.7}$ Simplify.

b. $5x^2 - 2yz + 8$ for $x = \mathbf{3}, y = \mathbf{2},$ and $z = \mathbf{4}$

    $= 5 \cdot \mathbf{3}^2 - 2 \cdot \mathbf{2} \cdot \mathbf{4} + 8$ Substitute values.

    $= 5 \cdot \mathbf{9} - 16 + 8$

    $= 45 - 16 + 8 = \mathbf{37}$ Simplify.

c. $(x^2 + 3y)(3y + 7)$ for $x = \mathbf{1}$ and $y = \mathbf{1}$

    $= (\mathbf{1}^2 + 3 \cdot \mathbf{1})(3 \cdot \mathbf{1} + 7)$

    $= (1 + 3)(3 + 7)$

    $= (4)(10) = \mathbf{40}$ Simplify.

d. $\dfrac{x^2 - 3y^2}{5y + x}$ for $x = 4$ and $y = 2$

$$= \dfrac{4^2 - 3 \cdot 2^2}{5 \cdot 2 + 4} \qquad \text{Substitute values.}$$

$$= \dfrac{16 - 3 \cdot 4}{10 + 4} = \dfrac{16 - 12}{14} = \dfrac{4}{14} = \dfrac{2}{7}$$

EXERCISE 1.6

A. In exercises 1-16, change the phrase to an algebraic expression. Use x to represent the unknown variable.

1.   Four times seven

2.   A number multiplied by two

3.   A number increased by nine

4.   Nine decreased by a number

5.   Seven decreased by twice a number

6.   Nine times a number added to seven

7.   Nine added to a number

8.   Nine added to the reciprocal of a number

9.   Quotient of eleven and a number

10.   Quotient of seven times a number and eight added to the number

11.   Twenty minus quotient of seven and a number

12.   Quotient of seven and sum of a number and eight

13.   Five added to the product of a number and two

14.   A number multiplied by ten decreased by square of the number

15.   Four added to three-fifths of a number

16.   Quotient of seven added to a number and ten decreased from the number.

B. In exercises 17-24, change the statement to an algebraic equation.

17.   Three times five added to four makes (equals) nineteen.

18.   Quotient of forty eight and twelve is equal to four.

19.   Three raised to fourth power is the same as nine squared.

20.   Twelve plus eighteen is equal to thirty five minus five.

21.   Seven multiplied by six is equal to eighty four divided by two.

22.   Six squared minus three squared equals twenty seven.

23.   Five times three subtracted from twenty is not equal to six.

24.   Six raised to third power minus four squared is equal to twice of ten squared.

In exercises 25-32, identify the given entity as an equation or an expression.

25. $3x^3 - 57x + y$

26. $2x + 7y = 5$

27. $4x^2 - 7x = \dfrac{8}{x+1}$

28. $8x + \dfrac{1}{x} = 6$

29. $5 + \dfrac{x}{3x-1} = 0$

30. $\dfrac{1}{x} + x = 20x^2$

31. $\dfrac{x^3 + 7x}{3x^2 + 5}$

32. $2x + 3y + 7 - 4z$

In exercises 33-43, find the solution, if any, of the equation in the set $\{2, 3, 5, 7, 10\}$.

33. $3x + 2 = 23$ **34.** $7x - 2 = 10$ **35.** $x^2 + 3x - 10 = 0$ **36.** $x^2 - 9x + 14 = 0$

37. $(3y + 4)(10 - y) = 0$ **38.** $(3y - 6)(y - 7) = 0$ **39.** $\dfrac{z + 6}{z - 1} = 8$ **40.** $z^2 - 4z + 3 = 0$

41. $6m + 2(m + 3) = 14$ **42.** $\dfrac{1}{2}y + \dfrac{1}{y} = \dfrac{3}{2}$ **43.** $2t + 1 - \dfrac{2}{t} = 4$

In exercises 44-58, change the word statement to an equation. Find the solution, if any, of the equation in the set $\{0, 1, 2, 4, 5\}$.

44. Sum of three times a number and four is nineteen.

45. Seven decreased from four times a number is one.

46. Difference of three times a number and ten equals twenty one.

47. Reciprocal of a number added to the number is one.

48. Quotient of sixteen and twice a number is four less than the number.

49. Sum of three and twice a number is twelve.

50. Five times a number exceeds three times the number by four.

51. Difference of three and twice a number is the number.

52. Nine and three times a number adds up to twenty-one.

53. Difference of square of a number and the number is zero.

54. Two times a number equals five times the number.

55. Quotient of two and a number is the sum of the number and its reciprocal.

56. Quotient of a number and eight is the quotient of two and the number.

57. Two times the square of a number decreased by one is the number.

58. Explain the difference between an algebraic expression and an equation.

C. In exercises 59 and 60, identify the symbol $=, \ne, <, \le, >,$ or $\ge$ that makes the statement true?

59. **a)** 3.........4 **b)** 5.........2 **c)** 4.........4

60. **a)** 5^2.........49 **b)** 8^2.........2^6 **c)** 4^3.........2^5

In exercises 61-68, rewrite the statements in a different way by changing the relational symbol.

61. $5 < 11$ **62.** $13 \ge 8$ **63.** $8 > 6$ **64.** $4 \le 7$

65. $7 < 15$ **66.** $12 \ge 12$ **67.** $4^2 \ge 3^2$ **68.** $6^2 \le 49$

In exercises 69-78, determine which statements are true and which are false.

69. $3 + 5 \times 2 > 15$ **70.** $6 - 2^2 < 13$ **71.** $4^2 + 5 = 21$ **72.** $6^3 - 5^2 = 10$

73. $7^2 + 8 \div 2 \ne 49$ **74.** $6^2 \ne 7 \cdot 4 \div 2$ **75.** $(6 - 3)(4 + 2) \le 15$

76. $(3^2 - 2^2)(8 - 5) \ge 18$ **77.** $1 + \dfrac{2}{3} + 4\dfrac{1}{3} = 6$ **78.** $5\dfrac{1}{6} - \dfrac{1}{2} + \dfrac{1}{3} = 5$

In exercises 79-90, translate the word statement into symbols.

79. Eight plus five is greater than ten.   **80.** Twelve minus ten is less than fifteen.

81. Twenty divided by four equals five.   **82.** Six multiplied by eight is greater than twelve.

83. Quotient of thirty and five is less than nine.   **84.** Twenty six divided by thirteen equals two.

85. Product of five and six is not equal to twenty one.

86. Nine decreased by five is less than or equal to four.

87. Seventeen minus two times five is greater than three.

88. Twenty two divided by two is less than three plus twelve.

89. Nine raised to fourth power is not the same as (is not equal to) four raised to ninth power.

90. Three to the fifth power plus seven is greater than two hundred.

D. In exercises 91-98, evaluate the expression for $x = {}^-2$ and $x = 9$.

91. $2x + 3$

92. $3x - 5$

93. $25 - 2x$

94. $\dfrac{x^2 + 1}{5}$

95. $\dfrac{4x - 3}{7x + 5}$

96. $\dfrac{2x^2 - 6}{x - 7}$

97. $\dfrac{x^2 + 2}{x + 10}$

98. $3 + \dfrac{5}{x} + \dfrac{4}{x^2}$

In exercises 99-104, evaluate the expression for the indicated value(s) of the variable(s).

99. $3m - 4m^2 + 1$; $m = \dfrac{1}{2}$

100. $y^3 + \dfrac{2}{y} + 3y^2$; $y = \dfrac{1}{3}$

101. $(4p + 7) \left\{ 5p^2 + 6p + \dfrac{4}{p} \right\}$; $p = 4$

102. $(6q^2 + 5)\left(q + \dfrac{1}{q} \right)$; $q = 3$

103. $3x + 7y^2$; $x = 1$, $y = 2$

104. $2x^3 + 5y^2$; $x = 2$, $y = 3$

1.7 SELF TEST

In exercises 1-5, find the opposite of the given number.

1. $-(-3)$

2. -7

3. $-[-(-8)]$

4. $-(-9)$

5. $-[(-11)]$

In exercises 6-8, graph the given integers on a number line.

6. $\{-5, -2, 1, 3, 6\}$

7. $\{-6, -4, -2, 0, 2, 4, 6\}$

8. $\{-7, -5, -3, 0, 3, 5, 7\}$

In exercises 9-12, find the indicated sum or difference.

9. $5 + 7$

10. $7 + (-9)$

11. $-5 + 20$

12. $-(-11) - 7$

In exercises 13-16, what are the possible values of n for which the given statement is true?

13. $|2n| = 1$

14. $|3n - 1| = -5$

15. $4 = |2n|$

16. $|2n - 1| = 5$

In exercises 17-24, evaluate the given expression.

17. $8 - 9 + 3 - 5$

18. $13 - 8 - 3 - 2$

19. $-7 - 87$

20. $22 - |-15|$

21. $-5(3) - 8 \div 4 + 1$

22. $-6(-2) - 9 \div 3 - 8$

23. $-3(4) + 8 \div 2 \times 4$

24. $(-10 \div 5) + (-6) + 2$

In exercises 25-29, apply the divisibility tests for 2, 3, 5, 6, and 8.

25. 80　　　　　　**26.** 525　　　　　　**27.** 184　　　　　　**28.** 120　　　　　　**29.** 250

In exercises 30-39, reduce the fractions to lowest terms.

30. $\dfrac{4}{6}$　　　　**31.** $\dfrac{15}{25}$　　　　**32.** $\dfrac{42}{72}$　　　　**33.** $\dfrac{125}{315}$　　　　**34.** $\dfrac{550}{900}$

35. $\dfrac{212}{320}$　　　　**36.** $\dfrac{160}{240}$　　　　**37.** $\dfrac{170}{850}$　　　　**38.** $\dfrac{3360}{3920}$　　　　**39.** $\dfrac{1450}{1700}$

In exercises 40-44, perform the operation(s) indicated and reduce the answer to lowest terms.

40. $\dfrac{25}{48} \cdot \dfrac{32}{50}$　　**41.** $\dfrac{4}{9} \cdot \dfrac{15}{25} \cdot \dfrac{30}{32}$　　**42.** $\left(\dfrac{-21}{14}\right)\left(\dfrac{-16}{28}\right)$　　**43.** $\dfrac{33}{35} \div \dfrac{44}{49}$　　**44.** $\left(-\dfrac{26}{33}\right) \div \left(\dfrac{39}{22}\right)$

In exercises 45-49, check whether the given fractions are equivalent.

45. $-\dfrac{4}{9}, \dfrac{-20}{45}$　　**46.** $-\dfrac{5}{7}, \dfrac{25}{35}$　　**47.** $\dfrac{8}{12}, \dfrac{14}{21}$　　**48.** $\dfrac{-12}{14}, \dfrac{18}{-21}$　　**49.** $\dfrac{6}{15}, \dfrac{16}{40}$

In exercises 50-52, list the group of fractions in increasing order.

50. $\dfrac{2}{3}, \dfrac{3}{4}, \dfrac{4}{5}$　　　　　　**51.** $\dfrac{1}{5}, \dfrac{1}{6}, \dfrac{1}{7}$　　　　　　**52.** $\dfrac{2}{3}, \dfrac{5}{9}, \dfrac{5}{12}$

In exercises 53-55, perform the operations indicated.

53. $\dfrac{2}{3} + \dfrac{3}{5} \cdot \dfrac{1}{2}$　　　　　　**54.** $\dfrac{7}{10} \times \dfrac{5}{6} - \dfrac{1}{6}$　　　　**55.** $1\dfrac{1}{2} - \left[\dfrac{5}{3} + \left(\dfrac{1}{3} - \dfrac{2}{3} \div \dfrac{4}{5} - \dfrac{3}{4} \cdot \dfrac{8}{12}\right)\right]$

56. Divide the difference of $2\dfrac{1}{4}$ and $\dfrac{3}{4}$ by the sum of $\dfrac{3}{4}$ and $\dfrac{5}{6}$.

57. Find the average of the following group of numbers:

　　(a) $2, \dfrac{5}{4}, 2\dfrac{1}{6}$　　　　**(b)** $\dfrac{5}{6}, 1, 1\dfrac{3}{8}, \dfrac{11}{12}$　　　　**(c)** $5\dfrac{1}{2}, 4\dfrac{2}{3}, 6\dfrac{1}{6}$

58. Give the word name for the following decimal numbers:

　　(a) 213.07　　　　**(b)** 123.456　　　　**(c)** 1,023,045,067.089　　　　**(d)** 789.003

59. Write the decimal numbers of the following word names:

　　(a) Forty-one and one hundredth　　　**(b)** One million, three hundred twenty-one and six thousandths.

60. Estimate the sum or difference, by rounding each number to its largest place (front-end rounding).

　　(a) $59,123 + 7,854$　　　**(b)** $0.9932 + 0.9512$　　　**(c)** $-36.673 + 39.999$　　　**(d)** $7,654.891 - 849.999$

61. Estimate the product, by rounding each number to its largest place (front-end rounding).

　　(a) 8.95×7.54　　　**(b)** 281.71×349.56　　　**(c)** $2,813.69 \times 84.99$

62. Estimate the quotient, by rounding the divisor to its largest place value (front-end rounding).

(a) $379.59 \div 49.89$ (b) $3,467.231 \div 459.513$ (c) $\dfrac{9,513.3}{.093}$

63. Multiply or divide a decimal by a power of 10.

(a) 345.23×10^3 (b) $9,932.56 \times 10^9$ (c) $\dfrac{314.835}{10^2}$ (d) $\dfrac{7,895.123}{10^6}$

64. Convert the following decimals to fractions:

(a) 5.4   (b) 0.003   (c) 9.999   (d) 1.6

(e) 2.675   (f) 3.125   (g) 5.1275

65. Convert the following decimals, fractions, improper fractions or mixed numbers to percents.

(a) 0.25   (b) 1.50   (c) $\dfrac{3}{5}$ (d) $\dfrac{7}{4}$ (e) $2\dfrac{1}{2}$ (f) $1\dfrac{4}{5}$

66. Convert the following percents to fractions and decimals:

(a) 25%   (b) 40%   (c) 120%   (d) 0.5%

67. A store offers 30% discount on the list price of all its goods. What do you save on the purchase of a T V if the list price is \$250? How much do you pay if the sales tax is 5% on the discounted price.

68. A sales representative gets 15% commission, on top of his salary, for all sales over \$2,500 during a month. What is his commission if his total sale during the month is \$8,500?

69. If \$300 is the actual amount of commission then what is the total sale if the commission rate is 15%?

In exercise 70-71, identify numbers which are

(a) whole numbers   **(b) integers**   **(c) rational numbers.**

70. $\left\{-3,\ 0,\ \dfrac{4}{5},\ -\dfrac{3}{4},\ -2.3,\ -8.\overline{3},\ 7.3\overline{69}\right\}$ **71.** $\left\{-\dfrac{4}{3},\ 1,\ 0.54,\ 0,\ -1,\ 3.\overline{4},\ 6.\overline{38}\right\}$

In exercise 72-76, find the opposite of the given number.

72. $\dfrac{-\sqrt{3}}{2}$ **73.** $-\left(-\dfrac{2}{3}\right)$ **74.** $-\left(-5\dfrac{1}{2}\right)$ **75.** $-3.8\overline{9}$ **76.** $-\left(-\sqrt{5}\right)$

In exercise 77-86, fill in the blank so that the resulting statement is true. Name the property of real numbers used ; Commutative, Associative, Identity, Inverse or Distributive.

77. $-3+4 \quad = \underline{\hspace{1cm}} + (-3)$ **78.** $(-4^2+7)+3^2 \quad = \underline{\hspace{1cm}} + (7+3^2)$

79. $-7+ \underline{\hspace{1cm}} = 0$ **80.** $(-5)(-7) \quad = \underline{\hspace{1cm}}(-5)$

81. $(-4) \underline{\hspace{1cm}} = -4$ **82.** $6 \underline{\hspace{1cm}} = 1$

83. $\{3(-5)\}(-7) = 3\{\underline{\hspace{1cm}}(-7)\}$ **84.** $3(4+5) \quad = 3\cdot 4 + \underline{\hspace{1cm}}\cdot 5$

85. $(6-5)\underline{\hspace{1cm}} = 6\cdot 4 - 5\cdot 4$ **86.** $5(2-\underline{\hspace{1cm}}+4) = 5\cdot 2 - 5\cdot 3 + 5\cdot 4$

87. Simplify the numeric expressions, using the rules for the order of operations.

(a) $3\cdot 4^2 - 4^2\cdot 6$ (b) $3-\left[2-5\left(5-3\right)\right]$ (c) $\dfrac{5-3\left(4^2-11\right)}{10-3^2}$ (d) $\left(6-5\times 2\right) \div \left[10 - \dfrac{4-3\cdot 2}{3^2-2}\right]$

Linear Equations and Inequalities in One Variable

Objective: Identify Terms & Numerical Coefficients

Verify Skill | Discussion | Example

Consider the algebraic expression :

$$3x^2 + 4x - 5$$

This expression has three terms.

1st term   2nd term   3rd term

$$3x^2 \quad + \quad 4x \quad + \quad (-5)$$

Each term, except the third term, has two factors or parts : a **number** and a variable part. The number is called the coefficient of the term. Terms such as the third term, having no variable part are called **constant** terms.

$$3x^2 \quad + \quad 4x \quad + \quad (-5)$$

Coefficient Variable Part   Coefficient Variable Part   Constant

Click or Press Spacebar to Continue   Copyright © 2005 Educo International, Inc.

2

LINEAR EQUATIONS AND INEQUALITIES IN ONE VARIABLE

INTRODUCTION

In Chapter 1 we learned about algebraic expressions and equations. In this chapter we will learn the techniques to solve simple equations and inequalities. This chapter is divided into eight sections.

2.1 SIMPLIFYING EXPRESSIONS

A. IDENTIFYING TERMS AND NUMERICAL COEFFICIENTS

Consider the algebraic expression: $3x^2 + 4x - 5$

This expression has three terms.

1st term	2nd term	3rd term
$3x^2$	$4x$	(-5)

Each term, except the third term, has two factors or parts: a number and a variable part. The number is called the **coefficient of the term**. Terms such as the third term, having no variable part are called **constant** terms.

> **OBJECTIVES** ▪ ■ ■ ■
>
> Upon completion of this section you will be able to:
>
> A. Identify terms and numerical coefficients;
>
> B. Identify and combine like terms;
>
> C. Simplify expressions; and
>
> D. Build expressions from word phrases.

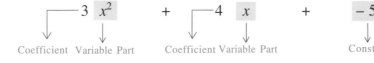

$$3\;\boxed{x^2}\quad +\quad 4\;\boxed{x}\quad +\quad \boxed{-5}$$

Coefficient Variable Part   Coefficient Variable Part   Constant

1. Identify the coefficient and variable part of the following terms.

   a) $13y$ b) $-9x^2$

   c) $\frac{1}{5}y$ d) $\frac{9}{y}$

Answers:

1. a) 13 and y b) -9 and x^2

   c) $\frac{1}{5}$ and y d) 9 and $\frac{1}{y}$

EXAMPLE 1 Identify the coefficient and variable part in the following terms.

   a. $3y$ **b.** $4x^2$ **c.** $\frac{2}{7}y$ **d.** $\frac{2}{y}$

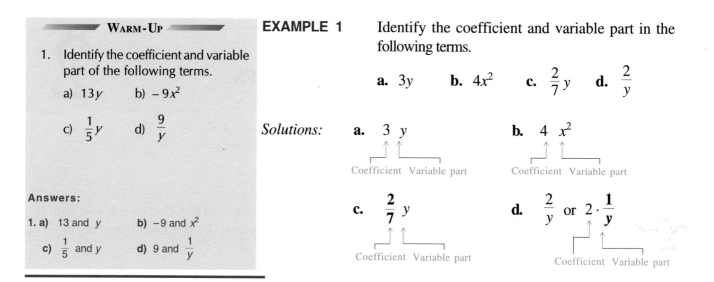

Solutions:

   a. $3 \; y$ Coefficient Variable part

   b. $4 \; x^2$ Coefficient Variable part

   c. $\frac{2}{7} \; y$ Coefficient Variable part

   d. $\frac{2}{y}$ or $2 \cdot \frac{1}{y}$ Coefficient Variable part

B. IDENTIFYING AND COMBINING LIKE TERMS

Terms which differ **only in numerical coefficients** and have identical variable parts are called **like terms**. Terms which are not like terms are called **unlike terms**. All constant terms are like terms.

2. Decide if the following pairs of terms are like terms.

   a) $2x^6$, $7x^6$

   b) $3x^3$, $3x^4$

   c) $15xz^3y$, $-13xyz^3$

EXAMPLE 2 Decide if the following pairs of terms are like terms.

   a. $3x^2$, $-4x^2$ **b.** $4x^3$, $4x^2$ **c.** $3xy^2z$, $-5xzy^2$

   d. $-5xy^2$, $5x^2y$ **e.** $3x^2$, $3y^2$ **f.** -18, $\frac{5}{8}$

Solutions:

   a. $3x^2$, $-4x^2$ $\rightarrow$ Terms

   $x^2 \qquad x^2$ $\rightarrow$ Variable Parts

   same

   Therefore, $3x^2$ and $-4x^2$ are **like terms**.

   b. $4x^3$, $\quad 4x^2$ $\rightarrow$ Terms

   $x^3 \qquad x^2$ $\rightarrow$ Variable Parts

   different

   Therefore, $4x^3$ and $4x^2$ are **unlike terms**.

   c. $3xy^2z$, $-5xzy^2$ $\rightarrow$ Terms

   $xy^2z \qquad xzy^2$ $\rightarrow$ Variable Parts

   same

   Therefore, $3xy^2z$ and $-5xzy^2$ are **like terms**.

d. $-5xy^2$, $5x^2y$ $\longrightarrow$ Terms

$\underbrace{xy^2 \qquad x^2y}_{\text{different}}$ $\longrightarrow$ Variable Parts

Therefore, $-5xy^2$ and $5x^2y$ are **unlike terms**.

e. $3x^2$, $3y^2$ $\longrightarrow$ Terms

$\underbrace{x^2 \qquad y^2}_{\text{different}}$ $\longrightarrow$ Variable Parts

Therefore, $3x^2$ and $3y^2$ are **unlike terms**.

f. -18, $\dfrac{5}{8}$ $\longrightarrow$ Terms

$\downarrow \quad \downarrow$

constants

Therefore, -18 and $\dfrac{5}{8}$ are **like terms**.

EXAMPLE 3   Combine like terms in the following algebraic expressions.

    a. $4x + 7x$ **b.** $-7p + 5p$

    c. $18t^2 - 21t^2$ **d.** $22y^2 + 10y - 30y^2$

    e. $-11q + 17 - 4q - 3$

Solutions:

To combine like terms, we add or subtract the coefficients.

We combine constant terms by adding or subtracting constants.

a. $4x + 7x = (4 + 7)x$
$$= 11x$$

b. $-7p + 5p = (-7 + 5)p$
$$= -2p$$

c. $18t^2 - 21t^2 = (18 - 21)t^2$
$$= -3t^2$$

d. $22y^2 + 10y - 30y^2 = 22y^2 - 30y^2 + 10y$
$$= (22 - 30)y^2 + 10y$$
$$= -8y^2 + 10y$$

e. $-11q + 17 - 4q - 3 = -11q - 4q + 17 - 3$
$$= (-11 - 4)q + (17 - 3)$$
$$= -15q + 14$$

d) $3x^2y$, $4xy^2$

e) $3r^2$, $2s^2$

f) -12, $\dfrac{9}{5}$

3.   Combine like terms.

   a) $8x + 11x$

   b) $-9z + 2z$

   c) $21r^2 - 32r^2$

   d) $3z^2 - 12z + 4z^2$

   e) $14 - 2m + 17 + 5m$

Answers:

  2.   a) Like   b) Unlike   c) Like
       d) Unlike   e) Unlike   f) Like

  3.   a) $19x$ b) $-7z$
       c) $-11r^2$ d) $7z^2 - 12z$
       e) $31 + 3m$

C. SIMPLIFYING EXPRESSIONS

To simplify expressions, we use the properties of addition and multiplication of real numbers. That is, we use the distributive property to get rid of parentheses and we combine like terms.

EXAMPLE 4   Simplify:

    a. $3x - 5 + 7$ **b.** $2(6y - 3z)$

    c. $7(-5k + 2) + 4$ **d.** $4a - 3(b - 5)$

    e. $3 \cdot 5 - 3(2m - 4)$

Solutions:

a. $3x - 5 + 7 = \mathbf{3x + 2}$ Combine like terms.

b. $\mathbf{2}(6y - 3z) = \mathbf{2} \cdot 6\,y - \mathbf{2} \cdot 3\,z$ Distributive Property.

              $= \mathbf{12y - 6z}$

c. $7(-5k + 2) + 4 = 7(-5k) + 7 \cdot 2 + 4$ Distributive Property.

                  $= -35\,k + 14 + 4$

                  $= \mathbf{-35k + 18}$ Combine like terms.

d. $4a - \mathbf{3}(b - 5) = 4a - \mathbf{3}(b) - \mathbf{3}(-5)$ Distributive Property.

               $= \mathbf{4a - 3b + 15}$

e. $3 \cdot 5 - \mathbf{3}(2m - 4) = 3 \cdot 5 - \mathbf{3}(2m) - \mathbf{3}(-4)$

                  $= 15 - 6m + 12$

                  $= 15 + 12 - 6m$

                  $= \mathbf{27 - 6m}$

D. BUILD EXPRESSIONS FROM WORD PHRASES

Recall that we discussed in Chapter 1, the translating of word phrases, and statements into algebraic expressions and equations. We continue the same discussion with slightly different word phrases and statements.

EXAMPLE 5   Find the sum of 5, seven times a number, and four times the number.

Solution: Assume that unknown number is x.

5 plus seven times a number plus four times the number.

    $5 \; + \; 7 \;\;\; \cdot \;\; x \;\;\;\;\; + \;\; 4 \;\; \cdot \;\;\;\;\; x$

Simplification:

    $5 + 7x + 4x = 5 + (7x + 4x)$

                  $= 5 + (7 + 4)x$

                  $= 5 + 11x$

EXAMPLE 6   Karen spends 10% of her paycheck on food, one fifteenth of the paycheck on clothing, 5% of the paycheck on utilities, 15% on rent, and one fourth on education. She also invests $200. If the total expenditure is $1,800, set up an equation that represents this information.

Solution:

Unknown: Let p represent the amount of paycheck.

Total expenses = 10% of p + $\dfrac{1}{15}$ of p + 5% of p + 15% of p + $\dfrac{1}{4}$ of p + 200

Since the total expenses **equal 1800**, we get:

$$\left(\frac{10}{100}\,p + \frac{1}{15}\,p + \frac{5}{100}\,p + \frac{15}{100}\,p + \frac{1}{4}\,p\right) + 200 = 1800$$

This equation is the conversion of the word problem into symbols.

We can now simplify this equation by combining like terms on the left side of the equation.

$$\underbrace{\left(\frac{10}{100} + \frac{1}{15} + \frac{5}{100} + \frac{15}{100} + \frac{1}{4}\right)}_{}p + 200 = 1800$$

$$\downarrow$$

$$\frac{37}{60} \cdot p + 200 = 1800$$

EXAMPLE 7   The sum of the following two quantities is 47.

   i.   Five multiplied by four minus a number.

   ii. The sum of seven and the number.

Set up an equation that represents this information.

Solution:

Unknown: a number = x

First Quantity : **5 multiplied** by four minus a number
$$= 5 \cdot (4 - x)$$

Second Quantity: **Sum** of 7 and the number = $7 + x$

The sum of $5(4 - x)$ and $(7 + x)$ is equal to 47.

Therefore $5(4 - x) + (7 + x) = 47$.

This equation is the conversion of the given word problem into symbols. We can now simplify this equation.

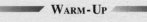
2.1 Simplifying Expressions

EXERCISE 2.1

A. In exercises 1-14, write down the numerical coefficient of each term.

1. $-15y^2z$ 2. $2xy$ 3. $6x$ 4. $-3lm$ 5. $-7mn$ 6. $20pqr$ 7. $4pq$

8. x^4y 9. $-m$ 10. $-2m^2n$ 11. x^5 12. $3y^4z^2$ 13. $-x^2yz$ 14. $-2^2xy^2z^3$

In exercises 15-28, identify the variable part and the numerical co-efficient.

15. $2x^2$ 16. $-p^2$ 17. $2xy$ 18. $-2xy^2$ 19. x^2y^2 20. $5x^2y$ 21. $-3y^2zx$

22. $10xyz$ 23. -7 24. $-x^2y^2z^2$ 25. x^2 26. 12 27. -2^2x^2y 28. $64pq^2r$

B. In exercises 29-40, determine if the pair of terms are like terms.

29. $3x, 7y$ 30. $-8p, 22p$ 31. $-4p, 8p$ 32. $12q, 2r$

33. $4m^2n, -m^2n$ 34. $8x^2y, -20x^2y$ 35. $5m^2n, 5mn^2$ 36. $-xyz, xyz$

37. $3, -5$ 38. $4^2x, -9x$ 39. $4z^3, -3z^2$ 40. $10x^2y, -10xy^2$

In exercises 41-72, simplify each expression by combining like terms.

41. $-7m + 4m$ 42. $20x - 7x$ 43. $5s + 6(s - 3)$ 44. $-8(p + 3) + 9p$

45. $15t^2 + 7(4 - t^2)$ 46. $-y^3 - 10(4 - y^3 + 10)$ 47. $2 + x + 15 - 7x$ 48. $2(-7 + z) + 10(2z - 3)$

49. $3y^2 + 7y + 8x - 4y + 5x - 2y^2$ 50. $-p^2 + q + 7p - 9q^2 - 10p$ 51. $3y - (2x + 2y) - 6x$

52. $2y - 6(y - 2) - 6x$ 53. $5y - 2(y - 3x) + 2(7x - y)$ 54. $3(y - 2y^2) + 4(7 - 5y) + 8(y^2 - 7)$

55. $2(z - z^2 + z^3) + 3(z - 2) + 9(-z^2 + 5)$ 56. $6(3p - 5) - (6p + 4)$ 57. $-6(-2pq + 3p) - 10(q + 2pq)$

58. $\dfrac{2}{3}x + \dfrac{1}{2}x - \dfrac{1}{3} - 2$ 59. $\dfrac{1}{3}(y + 3) + \dfrac{1}{2}(2x + 6)$ 60. $-6[3x + 2(7 - x)]$

61. $3[a + 3(a + 5)]$ 62. $-6[4y - 7(y + 7)]$ 63. $-6x - 3[2x - 5(x + 8)] - 6$

64. $\dfrac{3}{5}x - 3 - \dfrac{7}{4}x - 2$ 65. $\dfrac{1}{2}(x + 3) + \dfrac{1}{3}(3x + 6)$ 66. $2\left(3 - \dfrac{1}{3}x + 4y\right) + 6(x + 3y) - 9$

67. $\dfrac{12x}{5}\left(\dfrac{5}{12}\right) + (-6x)\left(-\dfrac{1}{6}\right)$ 68. $16x\left(\dfrac{1}{4}\right) - (-8x)\left(-\dfrac{3}{4}\right)$

69. $-\dfrac{8}{7}\left(\dfrac{7x^2}{8}\right) + \dfrac{1}{3}\left(3x^2\right) + \left(\dfrac{3x^2}{4}\right)\left(\dfrac{4}{3}\right)$ 70. $-\dfrac{3}{8}\left(24a^2\right) - \dfrac{1}{4}\left(-16a^2\right) + \left(\dfrac{3}{5}\right)\left(-5a^2\right)$

71. $0.4 + 2(x + 6) - 0.6 + 3$ 72. $0.5 + (2x^2y + 4y + 6x^2) - 0.25(4x^2y - 8y + 12x^2)$

C. In exercises 73-102, simplify the expression.

73. $5 + 3x + 4$ 74. $-6 - 2x + 9$ 75. $-6 + 5x - 15$ 76. $3 + 2x + 7x$

77. $7 - 3x - 9x$ 78. $8x - 16x - 3$ 79. $15 - 3x + 5x - 19$ 80. $-6x + 15 - 20 + 12x$

81. $-7 + 2x - 9 + 4x - 3x$ **82.** $-15x + 8 - 6 + 11x - 13$ **83.** $-4 - x - 3x - 9$ **84.** $-10 + 22x + 0 - 10x$

85. $4(5 - x) + 7$ **86.** $-2 + 5(-x + 3)$ **87.** $3(a - 5) + 4$

88. $-6(p + 10 - 2) + 3$ **89.** $6 - 2(x - 3)$ **90.** $8(7x + 0) - 3(2x + 5)$

91. $3(4 - x) + 2(x + 4)$ **92.** $7(-5x + 11) + 2(3x - 1) + 19$ **93.** $(3a + 8)2$

94. $(44x)\left(\dfrac{1}{11}\right)$ **95.** $(-4x)\left(\dfrac{1}{2}\right) + (22y)\left(\dfrac{1}{11}\right)$ **96.** $-\dfrac{3}{4}(-8x) + (-3x + 5)5$

97. $3\left(\dfrac{1}{3}x - 2x + \dfrac{1}{6}\right)$ **98.** $\dfrac{2}{5}(x - 5) - \dfrac{1}{5}(x + 20)$ **99.** $-\dfrac{1}{3}(3y - 6) + 4(y + 3)$

100. $3(2x^2 + 5x - 6)$ **101.** $4(3x^2 - 5x + 2)$ **102.** $-(5y^2 + 3y - 8)$

D. **In exercises 103-116, convert the word phrase into a mathematical expression. Use x as the variable, and simplify the resulting expression.**

103. The sum of a number and 8 times the number.

104. The sum of two consecutive integers.

105. For two consecutive integers, the sum of the smaller and twice the larger.

106. The product of two consecutive even integers.

107. Twice a number, decreased by 10.

108. The quotient of 6 and the sum of a number and 5.

109. The quotient of 6 more than two times a number, and the number.

110. The square of a number decreased by one sixth of the number.

111. The cube of a number decreased by the product of 10 and the number.

112. The ratio of four and 6 less than a number.

113. A number added to the difference of 4 and two times the number.

114. Sum of a number and −4 added to the difference of the number and 5.

115. The product of three times a number subtracted from 8, and the sum of the number and −4.

116. Five times a number added to twice the number and decreased by the difference of the number and 8.

2.2 SOLVING LINEAR EQUATIONS IN ONE VARIABLE

OBJECTIVES ■■■■

Upon completion of this section you will be able to:

A. Identify linear equations;

B. Verifying solutions;

C. Solve one-step equations;

D. Solve equations of the type $ax + b = c$;

E. Use the distributive property to solve equations; and

F. Solve general linear equations.

A. IDENTIFY LINEAR EQUATIONS

An equation of the type

$$3x + 4 = 0 \quad \text{or} \quad 4x - 5 = 7 - 9x$$

is a linear equation. The main characteristic of a linear equation is that the exponent of the **variable** part of any term on either side of the equation is "**one**". Also, there is no variable in the denominator.

───── WARM-UP ─────

1. Which of the following are linear equations?

   a) $11x + 5 = 0$

   b) $x^2 - 3x^4 = 6$

   c) $3(2x - 1) + 4x = 1$

Answers:

1. a) Linear equation

   b) Non-linear equation

   c) Linear equation

EXAMPLE 1 Which of the following are linear equations?

a. $4x - 7 = 2$ b. $3 + x^2 - x = 5$

c. $5(3 - x) + 7 = 2 + 2(x - 4)$

Solutions:

a. $4x - 7 = 2$ is a linear equation.

b. $3 + x^2 - x = 5$ is **not** a linear equation.

c. $15 - 5x + 7 = 2 + 2x - 8$ is a linear equation.

B. VERIFYING SOLUTIONS OF LINEAR EQUATIONS

A solution of a linear equation is any value of the unknown which when substituted in the equation makes the equation a true statement.

Illustrations :

1. $x = -2$ is a solution of $x + 2 = 0$, because $(-2) + 2 = 0$, which is true.

2. $x = 4$ is a solution of $x - 2 = 2$, because $(4) - 2 = 2$, or $2 = 2$, which is true.

3. $x = \frac{1}{3}$ is a solution of the equation $3x = 1$, because $3\left(\frac{1}{3}\right) = 1$, or $1 = 1$, which is true.

4. $x = \frac{1}{2}$ is a solution of the equation $4x + 3 = 5$, because $4\left(\frac{1}{2}\right) + 3 = 5$, or $2 + 3 = 5$, which is true.

EXAMPLE 2   Check whether the given value of the variable is a solution of the given equation.

   a. $x = 2$; $x - 2 = 0$ b. $y = -3$; $4y + 2 = 4$

   c. $x = \dfrac{5}{9}$; $\dfrac{3}{2}x - \dfrac{1}{2} = \dfrac{1}{3}$

   d. $p = 3.5$; $1.2\,p - 1.5 = 2.7$

Solutions:

   a. $x = 2$; $\boldsymbol{x} - 2 = 0$

   $\downarrow$

   $(\mathbf{2}) - 2 = 0$

   $\longrightarrow$ $0 = 0$,   which is **true**.

   Therefore, $x = 2$ is a solution of $x - 2 = 0$.

   b. $y = -3$; $4\boldsymbol{y} + 2 = 4$

   $\downarrow$

   $4(\mathbf{-3}) + 2 = 4$

   $\longrightarrow$ $-12 + 2 = 4$,   which is **false**.

   Therefore, $y = -3$ is not a solution of $4y + 2 = 4$.

   c. $x = \dfrac{5}{9}$; $\dfrac{3}{\mathbf{2}}x - \dfrac{1}{2} = \dfrac{1}{3}$

   $\downarrow$

   $\dfrac{\overset{1}{\cancel{3}}}{2}\left(\dfrac{5}{\underset{3}{\cancel{9}}}\right) - \dfrac{1}{2} = \dfrac{1}{3}$

   $\longrightarrow$ $\dfrac{5}{6} - \dfrac{1}{2} = \dfrac{1}{3}$

   $\longrightarrow$ $\dfrac{5 - 3}{6} = \dfrac{1}{3}$

   $\longrightarrow$ $\dfrac{2}{6} = \dfrac{1}{3}$, which is **true**.

   Therefore, $x = \dfrac{5}{9}$ is a solution of $\dfrac{3}{2}x - \dfrac{1}{2} = \dfrac{1}{3}$.

   d. $p = 3.5$; $1.2\,\boldsymbol{p} - 1.5 = 2.7$

   $\longrightarrow$ $1.2\,(\mathbf{3.5}) - 1.5 = 2.7$

   $\longrightarrow$ $4.20 - 1.5 = 2.7$

   $\longrightarrow$ $2.7 = 2.7$, which is **true**.

   Therefore, $p = 3.5$ is a solution of $1.2\,p - 1.5 = 2.7$.

C. SOLVE ONE-STEP EQUATIONS

Recall the following properties.

> **1. The Additive Inverse Property :** $a + (-a) = 0$

For example : $3 + (-3) = 0$, -3 is the Additive Inverse or **Opposite** of 3.

   $-5 + 5 = 0$ -5 is the Additive Inverse or **Opposite** of 5.

> **2. The Multiplicative Inverse Property :** $a \cdot \dfrac{1}{a} = 1$
> (Reciprocal Property)

For example : $2\left(\dfrac{1}{2}\right) = 1$; $\dfrac{2}{3}\left(\dfrac{3}{2}\right) = 1$; $-\dfrac{5}{3}\left(-\dfrac{3}{5}\right) = 1$

3. The Additive Identity Property: $a + 0 = 0 + a = a$
For Example : $3 + 0 = 0 + 3 = 3$

4. The Multiplicative Identity Property: $a \cdot 1 = 1 \cdot a = a$
For Example : $\dfrac{2}{3} \cdot 1 = 1 \cdot \dfrac{2}{3} = \dfrac{2}{3}$

5. The Addition property of equality: If the same number is added to both sides of an equation the sums are equal in value.

> **Addition Property of Equality :**
>
> For any three real numbers a, b, and c ;
>
> $a = b \longrightarrow a + c = b + c$

The resulting equations are called *equivalent equations*.
Equivalent equations have the same solutions.

We can use this property for solving linear equations of the type;

$$x + 4 = 5$$

Add -4 on both sides

$$x + 4 + (-4) = 5 + (-4)$$
$$\longrightarrow \quad x + 0 = 5 + (-4) \qquad \text{Recall } 4 + (-4) = 0.$$
$$\longrightarrow \quad x = 1 \qquad \text{Recall } x + 0 = x.$$

In general if we have an equation $x + a = b$ then we solve this equations by adding the opposite of a or $(-a)$ on both sides.

$$x + a = b$$
$$x + a + (-a) = b + (-a)$$
$$\longrightarrow \quad x + 0 = b - a \qquad [\,a + (-a) = 0\,]$$
$$\longrightarrow \quad x = b - a \qquad [\,x + 0 = x\,]$$

EXAMPLE 3   Solve for x : $x + \dfrac{3}{4} = -\dfrac{1}{4}$

Solution:

$$x + \frac{3}{4} + \left(-\mathbf{\frac{3}{4}}\right) = -\frac{1}{4} + \left(-\mathbf{\frac{3}{4}}\right) \quad \text{Add } -\tfrac{3}{4} \text{ on both sides.}$$
(Addition Property of Equality).

$$x + 0 = \frac{-4}{4} \qquad \text{Additive Inverse Property.}$$

$$x = -\mathbf{1} \qquad \text{Additive Identity Property.}$$

Check : $x = -1$; $x + \dfrac{3}{4} = -\dfrac{1}{4}$
$$\downarrow$$
$$-1 + \frac{3}{4} = -\frac{1}{4}$$
$$-\frac{1}{4} = -\frac{1}{4} \qquad \text{True}$$

WARM-UP

3. Solve for y : $y + \dfrac{5}{7} = -\dfrac{2}{7}$

EXAMPLE 4   Solve for x : $-3.5 = 2.7 + x$

Solution: $-3.5 = 2.7 + x$

$$-\mathbf{2.7} + (-3.5) = -\mathbf{2.7} + 2.7 + x \quad \text{Add} - 2.7 \text{ on both sides.}$$

$$-\mathbf{6.2} = x \qquad \text{(Addition Property of Equality).}$$

Check : $x = -6.2$; $-3.5 = 2.7 + x$
$$\downarrow$$
$$-3.5 = 2.7 + (-6.2)$$
$$-3.5 = -3.5 \qquad \text{True}$$

4. Solve for z : $-2.9 = 3.2 + z$

6. **Multiplication Property of Equality:**   If both sides of an equation are multiplied by the same number, the products are equal in value.

Multiplication Property of Equality:

For real numbers a, b, and c

$$a = b \;\Rightarrow\; ac = bc$$

We can use this property for solving equations of the type : $2x = 3$.

$$\left(\mathbf{\frac{1}{2}}\right)(2x) = \left(\mathbf{\frac{1}{2}}\right)(3) \qquad \text{Multiply both sides by } \tfrac{1}{2}.$$

$$\left(\frac{1}{2} \cdot 2\right)x = \frac{3}{2} \qquad \text{Associative property.}$$
(Multiplication Property of Equality)

$$1 \cdot x = \frac{3}{2} \qquad \tfrac{1}{2} \cdot 2 = 1$$

$$x = \frac{3}{2} \qquad 1 \cdot x = x$$

The equations $2x = 3$ and $x = \dfrac{3}{2}$ are equivalent equations. Equivalent equations have the same solutions. In general if we have an equations $ax = b$, then we solve the equation by multiplying both sides with $\dfrac{1}{a}$, the reciprocal of a.

$$a\,x = b$$

$$\longrightarrow \quad \frac{1}{a}\,(a\,x) = \frac{1}{a}\,b \qquad \text{Multiplication Property of Equality.}$$

$$\longrightarrow \quad \left(\frac{1}{a} \cdot a\right)x = \frac{b}{a} \qquad \text{Associative Property.}$$

$$\longrightarrow \quad 1 \cdot x = \frac{b}{a} \qquad \text{Multiplicative Inverse Property.}$$

$$\longrightarrow \quad x = \frac{b}{a} \qquad \text{Multiplicative Identity Property.}$$

=== WARM-UP ===

5. Solve for u: $-\dfrac{7}{9}u = 3$

EXAMPLE 5 Solve for x: $-\dfrac{2}{3}x = 5$

Solution:

$$-\frac{2}{3}x = 5 \qquad \text{Observe that } \left(-\frac{2}{3}\right)\left(-\frac{3}{2}\right)=1$$
Reciprocal Property.

$$\longrightarrow \quad \left(-\frac{3}{2}\right)\left(-\frac{2}{3}\right)x = \left(-\frac{3}{2}\right)\cdot 5 \qquad \text{Multiply both sides by } -\frac{3}{2}.$$
Multiplicative property of Equality.

$$\longrightarrow \quad 1 \cdot x = -\frac{15}{2} \qquad \text{Multiplicative Inverse Property.}$$

$$\longrightarrow \quad x = -\frac{15}{2} \qquad \text{Multiplicative Identity Property.}$$

Check : $\quad x = -\dfrac{15}{2} \; ; \; -\dfrac{2}{3}x = 5$

$$\downarrow$$

$$-\frac{2}{3}\left(-\frac{15}{2}\right) = 5$$

$$5 = 5 \quad \text{True}$$

7. **Division Property of Equality:** If both sides of an equation are divided by the same non-zero number, the quotients are equal in value.

Recall that $a \cdot \dfrac{1}{a} = 1$ \qquad Reciprocal Property.

An equivalent statement is that $\dfrac{a}{a} = 1$. \qquad any number divided by itself is 1.

Division Property of Equality :
For real numbers a, b, and c, $c \neq 0$,
$a = b \;\rightarrow\; \dfrac{a}{c} = \dfrac{b}{c}$

Since division by c is the same as multiplication by its reciprocal $\dfrac{1}{c}$, this is just another way to state the multiplication property of equality.

EXAMPLE 6   Solve for x : $-10x = 6.4$

Solution :

$$-10x = 6.4$$

$$\dfrac{-10x}{-10} = \dfrac{6.4}{-10} \qquad \text{Division Property of Equality.}$$

$$1 \cdot x = -0.64$$

$$x = -0.64$$

Check : $x = -0.64$; $-10x = 6.4$

$$-10(-0.64) = 6.4$$

$$6.4 = 6.4 \qquad \text{True}$$

WARM-UP

6. Solve for y : $-100\, y = 7.9$

Answers:

3. -1 4. -6.1 5. $-\dfrac{27}{7}$ 6. -0.079

D. SOLVING EQUATIONS OF THE TYPE $ax + b = c$

To solve equations of the type $ax + b = c$, we make use of both the Addition and Multiplication properties of equality.

Illustration : $3x + 4 = 9$

$$\longrightarrow \quad 3x + 4 + (-4) = 9 + (-4) \qquad \text{Addition Property of Equality.}$$

$$\longrightarrow \quad 3x + 0 = 5$$

$$\longrightarrow \quad 3x = 5 \qquad \text{Additive Inverse Property.}$$

$$\longrightarrow \quad \dfrac{3x}{3} = \dfrac{5}{3} \qquad \text{Division Property of Equality.}$$

$$\longrightarrow \quad x = \dfrac{5}{3}$$

EXAMPLE 7   Solve for p : $3p - 5 = 7$

Solution:

$$3p - 5 = 7$$

$$\longrightarrow \quad 3p - 5 + 5 = 7 + 5 \qquad \text{Addition Property of Equality.}$$

$$\longrightarrow \quad 3p = 12$$

$$\longrightarrow \quad \dfrac{3p}{3} = \dfrac{12}{3} \qquad \text{Division Property of Equality.}$$

$$\longrightarrow \quad p = 4$$

Check : $p = 4$; $3p - 5 = 7$

$$3(4) - 5 = 7$$

$$12 - 5 = 7 \quad \text{or} \quad 7 = 7 \qquad \text{True}$$

WARM-UP

7. Solve for q : $2q - 3 = 5$

8. Solve for y: $-3y + \dfrac{1}{4} = 1$

EXAMPLE 8   Solve for x: $-2x + \dfrac{1}{3} = \dfrac{1}{2}$

Solution: $\quad\quad -2x + \dfrac{1}{3} = \dfrac{1}{2}$

$\longrightarrow \quad -2x + \dfrac{1}{3} + \left(-\dfrac{\mathbf{1}}{\mathbf{3}}\right) = \dfrac{1}{2} + \left(-\dfrac{\mathbf{1}}{\mathbf{3}}\right)$ Addition Property of Equality.

$\longrightarrow \quad\quad\quad\quad -2x = \dfrac{1}{6}$ $\left(\dfrac{1}{2} - \dfrac{1}{3} = \dfrac{1}{6}\right)$

$\longrightarrow \quad\quad -\dfrac{\mathbf{1}}{\mathbf{2}}(-2x) = -\dfrac{\mathbf{1}}{\mathbf{2}}\left(\dfrac{1}{6}\right)$ Multiplication Property of Equality.

$\longrightarrow \quad\quad\quad\quad x = -\dfrac{\mathbf{1}}{\mathbf{12}}$ $-\dfrac{1}{2} \cdot (-2) = 1$

Check: $\quad x = -\dfrac{1}{12} \; ; \; -2x + \dfrac{1}{3} = \dfrac{1}{2}$

$\quad\quad\quad\quad\quad -2\left(-\dfrac{1}{12}\right) + \dfrac{1}{3} = \dfrac{1}{2}$

$\quad\quad\quad\quad\quad\quad\quad \dfrac{1}{6} + \dfrac{1}{3} = \dfrac{1}{2}$

$\quad\quad\quad\quad\quad\quad\quad\quad \dfrac{1}{2} = \dfrac{1}{2}$ True

9. Solve for z: $0.5z + 3 = -6.4$

EXAMPLE 9   Solve for x: $0.25x + 3.4 = -7$

Solution: $\quad 0.25x + 3.4 = -7$

$\longrightarrow \quad 0.25x + 3.4 + (\mathbf{-3.4}) = -7 + (\mathbf{-3.4})$ Addition Property of Equality.

$\longrightarrow \quad\quad\quad\quad 0.25x = -10.4$

$\longrightarrow \quad \dfrac{\mathbf{1}}{\mathbf{.25}}(.25x) = \dfrac{\mathbf{1}}{\mathbf{.25}}(-10.4)$ Multiplication Property of Equality.

$\longrightarrow \quad\quad\quad\quad x = \mathbf{-41.6}$

Check: $\quad x = -41.6 \, ; \, 0.25x + 3.4 = -7$

$\quad\quad\quad\quad 0.25(-41.6) + 3.4 = -7$

$\quad\quad\quad\quad\quad -10.4 + 3.4 = -7$

$\quad\quad\quad\quad\quad\quad\quad -7 = -7$ True

Answers:

7. 4   8. $-\dfrac{1}{4}$ 9. -18.8

E. USING THE DISTRIBUTIVE PROPERTY TO SOLVE EQUATIONS

Linear equations may involve expressions with grouping symbols. To solve such equations we make use of distributive property stated below :

> **Distributive Property :**
>
> If a, b, and c are any three real numbers then
>
> $$a(b + c) = a \cdot b + a \cdot c$$

Illustrations :

- $2(5 + 7) = 2 \cdot 5 + 2 \cdot 7$
  $2(12) = 10 + 14$
  $24 = 24$ True

- $3(x + 2) = 3 \cdot x + 3 \cdot 2$
  $= 3x + 6$

- $-2(2 + x) = (-2)(2) + (-2)(x)$
  $= -4 - 2x$

EXAMPLE 10   Solve the following equation for x.

$$3(x - 5) + 2x = 10$$

Solution:

$3(x - 5) + 2x$	$=$	10
$3x - 15 + 2x$	$=$	10 Distributive Property.
$3x + 2x - 15$	$=$	10 Associative Property.
$5x - 15$	$=$	10 Combine like terms.
$5x - 15 + \mathbf{15}$	$=$	$10 + \mathbf{15}$ Addition Property of Equality.
$5x$	$=$	25
$\dfrac{1}{5} \cdot 5x$	$=$	$\dfrac{1}{5} \cdot 25$ Multiplication Property of Equality.
x	$=$	$\mathbf{5}$

Check : $x = 5$; $3(x - 5) + 2x = 10$

$$3(5 - 5) + 2 \cdot 5 = 10$$

$$0 + 10 = 10 \quad \text{True}$$

F. SOLVE GENERAL LINEAR EQUATIONS

We refer to equations involving variables on both sides of the equation and possibly containing grouping symbols as general linear equations. We use the following four-step approach to solve such equations.

Procedure

Step 1	By using the distributive property and combining like terms, simplify both sides of the equation, if needed.
Step 2	Use the addition property of equality to move all variable terms on one side and constant terms on the other side. Simplify by combining like terms.
Step 3	Solve the equation using the multiplication property of equality.
Step 4	Check the solution using substitution.

WARM-UP

11. Solve for x.

$$9 - (5x + 4) = 2(x - 2) - 5$$

EXAMPLE 11 Solve the equation for x.

$$4 - (2x - 3) = 3(x + 2) + 4$$

Solution:

Step 1 Simplify both sides by using the distributive property and combining like terms.

$\longrightarrow \quad 4 - (2x - 3) = 3(x + 2) + 4$

$\longrightarrow \quad 4 - 2x + 3 = 3x + 6 + 4$

like terms   like terms

$$7 - 2x = 3x + 10$$

Step 2 Move variable terms to the left side and constant terms to the right side using the addition property of equality.

$$7 - 2x = 3x + 10$$

$$-3x + 7 - 2x = -3x + 3x + 10 \qquad \text{Add } -3x \text{ to both sides.}$$

like terms

$$-5x + 7 + (-7) = 10 + (-7) \qquad \text{Add } -7 \text{ to both sides.}$$

$$-5x = 3$$

Step 3 Use the multiplication property of equality to solve the equation.

$$\frac{1}{-5}(-5x) = \frac{1}{-5}(3)$$

$$1 \cdot x = -\frac{3}{5}$$

$$x = -\frac{3}{5}$$

Step 4 **Check:** $x = -\frac{3}{5}$; $4 - (2x - 3) = 3(x + 2) + 4$

$$4 - \left(-\frac{6}{5} - 3\right) = 3\left(-\frac{3}{5} + 2\right) + 4$$

$$4 + \frac{21}{5} = \frac{21}{5} + 4 \qquad \text{True}$$

Answer:

11. $x = 2$

A. **In exercises 1-12, identify the equation as linear or non-linear.**

1. $3x + 5 = 0$ 2. $3r + 9(r - 2) = 7$ 3. $3x^2 = 5$ 4. $y^2 + 2(y - 2) = 0$

5. $3(p + 5) = 4 - p$ 6. $(z + 2) - (2z + 3) = 0$ 7. $5(3y + 2) - 7y = 0$ 8. $z^3 + 2(z - 12) = 4z$

9. $5t = 0$ 10. $2(y^3 - 6) + 7(y^2 + 8) = 0$ 11. $3y^2 - 4y + 7 = 0$ 12. $y^3 = 1$

B. **In exercises 13-22, identify whether or not the given number is a solution of the equation.**

13. $2 \; ; x + 2 = 4$ 14. $-3 \; ; x - 3 = 6$ 15. $-5 \; ; x - 4 = -9$ 16. $4 \; ; 4x = 1$ 17. $\dfrac{1}{4} \; ; 2x - 8 = 0$

18. $7 \; ; 2x = 14$ 19. $-4 \; ; 4x + 2 = -14$ 20. $-3 \; ; 3x - 2 = -11$ 21. $\dfrac{1}{2} \; ; 4x - 5 = -3$ 22. $\dfrac{-2}{3} \; ; 2x + \dfrac{4}{3} = 0$

C. **In exercises 23-102, solve the equation.**

23. $x - 1 = 2$ 24. $x - 3 = 7$ 25. $x - 2 = -3$ 26. $x - 5 = -9$

27. $x - 5 = 11$ 28. $x - 3 = 15$ 29. $x - 7 = -10$ 30. $x - 9 = -14$

31. $x - 12 = 21$ 32. $x - 15 = -30$ 33. $x + 2 = 5$ 34. $x + 7 = 9$

35. $x + 3 = -2$ 36. $x + 6 = -1$ 37. $x + 4 = 13$ 38. $x + 8 = 20$

39. $x + 9 = -15$ 40. $x + 5 = -17$ 41. $x + 13 = 22$ 42. $x + 16 = -28$

43. $x + \dfrac{1}{2} = \dfrac{3}{2}$ 44. $x - \dfrac{1}{4} = \dfrac{3}{4}$ 45. $x - \dfrac{2}{3} = \dfrac{5}{3}$ 46. $x - \dfrac{2}{3} = \dfrac{7}{3}$

47. $x - \dfrac{2}{5} = \dfrac{7}{5}$ 48. $x + \dfrac{1}{2} = \dfrac{1}{4}$ 49. $x + \dfrac{1}{3} = \dfrac{1}{9}$ 50. $x + \dfrac{3}{4} = \dfrac{2}{3}$

51. $x + \dfrac{4}{5} = \dfrac{3}{2}$ 52. $x + \dfrac{4}{5} = \dfrac{2}{7}$ 53. $x - \dfrac{4}{9} = -\dfrac{5}{4}$ 54. $x + 1.2 = 2.4$

55. $x - 4.2 = 9.7$ 56. $x - 2.5 = 3.2$ 57. $x + 4.9 = -1.1$ 58. $x + 7.5 = 2.5$

59. $x - 2.9 = -4.3$ 60. $x - 9.2 = -2.5$ 61. $y - 11.9 = -14.2$ 62. $x + 19.2 = -5.9$

63. $x - 14.9 = -9.8$ 64. $2x = 3$ 65. $3x = 2$ 66. $3x = -5$

67. $5x = -9$ 68. $4x = 20$ 69. $7x = 14$ 70. $3x = -13$

71. $9x = -18$ 72. $12x = 24$ 73. $15x = -40$ 74. $-3x = 1$

75. $-7x = 5$ 76. $-2x = -7$ 77. $-9x = -3$ 78. $-10x = 20$

79. $-12x = 9$ 80. $-4x = -18$ 81. $-15x = -5$ 82. $-12x = 27$

83. $-20x = -35$ 84. $2x - 5 = 0$ 85. $3x - 6 = 0$ 86. $7x - 3 = 0$

87. $5x - 9 = 0$ 88. $4x - 12 = 0$ 89. $6x - 2 = 0$ 90. $8x - 24 = 0$

91. $14x - 22 = 0$ 92. $16x - 40 = 0$ 93. $24x - 18 = 0$ 94. $3x + 7 = 0$

95. $2x + 8 = 0$ 96. $7x + 5 = 0$ 97. $5x + 15 = 0$ 98. $12x + 4 = 0$

99. $7x + 28 = 0$ 100. $14x + 21 = 0$ 101. $25x + 20 = 0$ 102. $24x + 36 = 0$

D. In exercises 103-146, solve equation of the type $ax + b = c$.

103. $2x - 6 = 1$ **104.** $3x - 5 = 7$ **105.** $4x - 1 = -5$ **106.** $6x - 3 = -2$

107. $-7x - 10 = 4$ **108.** $-5x - 6 = 15$ **109.** $14x - 6 = -12$ **110.** $13x - 10 = -16$

111. $-15x - 11 = 14$ **112.** $-12x - 7 = 9$ **113.** $3x + 8 = 4$ **114.** $2x + 7 = 5$

115. $7x + 4 = -5$ **116.** $5x + 2 = -10$ **117.** $-4x + 1 = 10$ **118.** $-6x + 5 = 11$

119. $11x + 10 = 15$ **120.** $15x + 12 = 22$ **121.** $-10x + 16 = -12$ **122.** $-12x + 15 = -15$

123. $-39 + x = 3.9$ **124.** $-6.1 = x + 1.9$ **125.** $2 = \dfrac{a}{5}$ **126.** $-a = \dfrac{7}{2}$

127. $-\dfrac{1}{4}a = \dfrac{2}{5}$ **128.** $-0.22x = 11$ **129.** $12 = \dfrac{9}{5}y$ **130.** $-32.32 = -1.6x$

131. $\dfrac{x}{-5} = -10$ **132.** $-\dfrac{y}{6} = 6$ **133.** $-9 = 5 + x$ **134.** $\dfrac{4}{9} + a = -\dfrac{2}{9}$

135. $-15 = -\dfrac{3}{5}x$ **136.** $7x - 5x = 9$ **137.** $-4 = 8 + y$ **138.** $39.2 + a = -6.8$

139. $4.5 = 4.5 + 0.075x$ **140.** $5.7 + a = 6.2$ **141.** $2x + 5x = 3 + 4$ **142.** $3x + 7x = 6 + 5$

143. $6x - 4x = 7 + 5$ **144.** $8x - x = 2 + 7$ **145.** $5x + 7x = 12 - 6$ **146.** $9x + 2x = 14 - 8$

E. In exercises 147-160, use distributive property to solve the equation.

147. $2(x + 3) + x = 9$ **148.** $3(2x - 1) - x = 12$ **149.** $-4(x + 1) + 7x = 8$ **150.** $-5(x + 3) + 7x = -7$

151. $-2(5x + 6) + 6x = 3$ **152.** $-3(-2x + 3) - 3x = 4$ **153.** $5(x - 3) - 2x = 6$ **154.** $\dfrac{3}{2}(2x - 1) - x = \dfrac{5}{2}$

155. $\dfrac{4}{3}(3x - 1) - 2x = \dfrac{8}{3}$ **156.** $\dfrac{2}{5}(10x - 3) + x = \dfrac{9}{5}$ **157.** $\dfrac{1}{7}(14x - 11) - 3x = \dfrac{3}{7}$

158. $-\dfrac{3}{4}(8x - 3) + 7x = -\dfrac{3}{4}$ **159.** $\dfrac{3}{5}(x + 5) + \dfrac{2}{5}x = 8$ **160.** $\dfrac{3}{4}(-2x + 3) + \dfrac{7}{2}x = \dfrac{11}{4}$

F. In exercises 161-180, solve the equation.

161. $3(x + 2) = 2x - 3$ **162.** $2 + 3(x + 4) = x - 3$ **163.** $x - 2(x + 3) = 4 - 5x$ **164.** $3 - 2(x + 4) = 5 - 7x$

165. $4x - 2(x + 3) = 5 - 4x$ **166.** $2x - 5(4 - x) = 7 + 5x$ **167.** $6(2y - 1) - 5 = 7(3y - 2) - 24$

168. $-5(y + 2) + 7 - y = 3(y + 7)$ **169.** $-10z + 3(5 + 4z) = 2(3z + 3)$ **170.** $8(-2z + 5) = 7(2 + z) + 3(z - 1)$

171. $-5(2x + 9) - 6(3 - x) + 12(2x + 3) = 0$ **172.** $7(2t + 6) = 9(t + 3) - 5$ **173.** $3x - 2(3 + x) = 5 - 3(4 - x)$

174. $8 - 3(5x - 4) = 5(1 - x) - 10$ **175.** $10 + 2(3x - 8) = 12(1 + x) - 2(1 - x)$ **176.** $9y + 3(9 - y) = 6y - 10(y + 5)$

177. $-7(6y - 3) = 3y + 9y - 7$ **178.** $9(x - 1) = 4(x - 3)$ **179.** $-4(x + 1) = -3(x + 3)$ **180.** $-2(x - 6) = -5(x - 4)$

In exercises 181-187, translate the statement into an equation, and solve for the unknown number.

181. When a number is added to 7, the result is 10.

182. When a number is multiplied by -3, the result is 9.

183. Two times a number added to 10 is equal to the sum of the number and -5.

184. A number added to 7 is equal to the difference of three times the number and 7.

185. The sum of 2 consecutive integers is 11.

186. The sum of 2 consecutive even numbers is 6.

187. Two times the difference between a number and twenty is 4 times the number.

2.3 MORE ON SOLVING LINEAR EQUATIONS

In the last section we learned how to use the additive, multiplicative, and distributive properties to solve linear equations. In this section also, we will make use of these properties for solving linear equations involving fractions and decimals.

A. SOLVING LINEAR EQUATIONS WITH FRACTIONS AND DECIMALS

We use the same procedure as before for solving equations involving fractions and decimals, except for the following additional step.

Procedure

> ***Step 1 b*** After using the distributive property, if needed to remove parentheses, we remove fractions or decimals by multiplying both sides of the equation with the Least Common Denominator.

Equations with fractions can be difficult to solve. The difficulty is only due to the extra care that is required when computing fractions. To avoid this extra work, we multiply **all the terms, on both sides** of the equation, by the least common denominator of all the fractions. This produces an equivalent equation without any fractions. The same procedure is used if the equation contains decimal coefficients.

EXAMPLE 1   Solve for x: $\frac{2}{3}x + 4 = 5x - \frac{1}{3}$.

Solution: The least common denominator of all the fractions involved, $\frac{2}{3}$ and $\frac{1}{3}$, is 3.

$$\frac{2}{3}x + 4 = 5x - \frac{1}{3}$$

$$3 \cdot \frac{2}{3}x + 3 \cdot 4 = 3 \cdot 5x - 3 \cdot \frac{1}{3} \qquad \text{Multiply by the LCD.}$$

$$2x + 12 = 15x - 1$$

$$2x - 15x = -1 - 12 \qquad \text{Addition Property of equality.}$$

$$-13x = -13$$

$$x = \frac{-13}{-13} = 1 \qquad \text{Division Property of equality.}$$

Check : $x = 1$;

$$\frac{2}{3}x + 4 = 5x - \frac{1}{3}$$

$$\frac{2}{3}(1) + 4 = 5(1) - \frac{1}{3}$$

$$\frac{14}{3} = \frac{14}{3} \qquad \text{True}$$

WARM-UP

1. Solve for x.

$$\frac{4}{5}x - 3 = 2x - \frac{3}{5}$$

2. Solve for x:

$$\frac{2}{3}x - \frac{1}{6} = \frac{5}{2} - 3x$$

EXAMPLE 2   Solve for x: $\frac{3}{5}x - \frac{1}{10}x = x - \frac{5}{2}$

Solution: Multiply both sides by the LCD, 10.

$$\mathbf{10}\left(\frac{3}{5}x - \frac{1}{10}x\right) = \mathbf{10}\left(x - \frac{5}{2}\right)$$

$$\mathbf{10} \cdot \frac{3}{5}x - \mathbf{10} \cdot \frac{1}{10}x = \mathbf{10}x - \mathbf{10} \cdot \frac{5}{2}$$

$$6x - x = 10x - 25$$

$$5x = 10x - 25$$

$$\mathbf{-10}x + 5x = \mathbf{-10}x + 10x - 25$$

$$-5x = -25$$

$$-\frac{\mathbf{1}}{\mathbf{5}}(-5x) = -\frac{\mathbf{1}}{\mathbf{5}}(-25)$$

$$x = 5$$

Check : $x = 5$; $\frac{3}{5}x - \frac{1}{10}x = x - \frac{5}{2}$

$$\frac{3}{5}(5) - \frac{1}{10}(5) = 5 - \frac{5}{2}$$

$$3 - \frac{1}{2} = 5 - \frac{5}{2}$$

$$\frac{5}{2} = \frac{5}{2} \quad \text{True}$$

3. Solve for x:

$$.5x - 1.3 = 2.7 + 1.5x$$

EXAMPLE 3   Solve for x:

$$0.2x + 2.4 = 1.5 - 1.2x$$

Solution: There is only one decimal place in all the numbers in this equation. Therefore we multiply both sides of this equation by the LCD, 10.

$$\mathbf{10}(0.2x + 2.4) = \mathbf{10}(1.5 - 1.2x)$$

$$\mathbf{10}(0.2x) + \mathbf{10}(2.4) = \mathbf{10}(1.5) - \mathbf{10}(1.2x)$$

$$2x + 24 = 15 - 12x$$

$$2x + 12x = 15 - 24 \quad \text{Addition Property.}$$

$$14x = -9$$

$$x = -\frac{\mathbf{9}}{\mathbf{14}} \quad \text{Division Property.}$$

$Check:$ $x = -\dfrac{9}{14}$; $0.2x + 2.4$ $=$ $1.5 - 1.2x$

$$\dfrac{2}{10}\left(-\dfrac{9}{14}\right) + \dfrac{24}{10} = \dfrac{15}{10} - \dfrac{12}{10}\left(-\dfrac{9}{14}\right)$$

$$\dfrac{-18}{140} + \dfrac{24}{10} = \dfrac{15}{10} + \dfrac{108}{140}$$

$$\dfrac{318}{140} = \dfrac{318}{140} \quad \text{True}$$

EXAMPLE 4   Solve the equation :

$$0.03x + 0.065(5000 - x) = 255$$

Solution: $0.03x + 0.065(5000 - x) = 255$

$\longrightarrow$ $0.03x + 325 - 0.065x = 255$

$1000(0.03x + 325 - 0.065x) = 1000 \cdot 255$ Multiply both sides by the LCD ; 1000.

$1000 \cdot 0.03x + 1000 \cdot 325 - 1000 \cdot (0.065x) = 1000 \cdot 255$

$\longrightarrow$ $30x + 325000 - 65x = 255{,}000$

$\longrightarrow$ $325000 - 35x = 255{,}000$ Combine like terms.

$\longrightarrow$ $-35x = -70{,}000$ Addition Property.

$\longrightarrow$ $x = 2{,}000$ Division Property.

$Check:$ $x = 2000$; $0.03x + 0.065(5000 - x) = 255$

$\longrightarrow$ $0.03(2000) + 0.065(5000 - 2000) = 255$

$\longrightarrow$ $60 + 195 = 255$

$\longrightarrow$ $255 = 255$ True

B. Equations with No Solution or Many Solutions

All equations encountered so far had only one solution. We will now give an example of an equation which has *no solution* and an example of an equation which has *many solutions*.

An equation which is true for all real numbers, or has infinitely many solutions, is called an **identity**. An equation leading to a false statement is called a **contradiction** and has no solution.

EXAMPLE 5   Determine whether each of the following equations has only one solution, has no solution, or is an identity.

     a. $5(x - 1) = 4x - 1$

     b. $3(x + 4) + x = 4x + 12$

     c. $5(x - 1) + 9 = 5x + 1$

Warm-Up

5. Determine whether each of the following equations has only one solution, has no solution, or is an identity.

    a) $3(x - 2) = 9 + 2x$

    b) $5(3 - x) = 7 - 5x + 8$

    c) $7 - 4(x - 2) = 9 - 4x$

Answers:

5. a) Only one solution   b) Identity
   c) No solution

Solutions:

a.
$$
\begin{aligned}
5(x - 1) &= 4x - 1 \\
5x - 5 &= 4x - 1 \quad \text{Distributive Property.}\\
5x &= 4x - 1 + 5 \quad \text{Add 5 to both sides.}\\
5x &= 4x + 4 \quad \text{Combine like terms.}\\
5x - 4x &= 4x + 4 - 4x \quad \text{Add } -4x \text{ to both sides.}\\
x &= 4 \quad \text{Combine like terms.}
\end{aligned}
$$

Therefore, $x = 4$ is the only solution.

b.
$$
\begin{aligned}
3(x + 4) + x &= 4x + 12 \\
3x + 12 + x &= 4x + 12 \\
\mathbf{4x + 12} &= \mathbf{4x + 12}
\end{aligned}
$$

Notice that both sides are *identical*. Therefore whatever value we may assign to x, it will make the equation true. Thus, $3(x + 4) + x = 4x + 12$ has **infinitely many solutions**, and is therefore an *identity*.

c.
$$
\begin{aligned}
5(x - 1) + 9 &= 5x + 1 \\
5x - 5 + 9 &= 5x + 1 \\
5x + 4 &= 5x + 1 \\
-5x + 5x + 4 &= -5x + 5x + 1 \\
4 &= 1 \quad \text{False}
\end{aligned}
$$

Hence the given equation has **no solution,** and is therefore a **contradiction**.

EXERCISE 2.3

A. In exercises 1-47, solve the equation.

1. $8 - (6 - 2x) = 3x + 1$

2. $-4[2 - (6a + 1)] = 4 + [2(3a + 1)]$

3. $-2[3a - 2(4a - 1)] + 2 = 2a + 3 - 3$

4. $5 - (-y + 6) = 2(-y + 3) - 7(y + 1)$

5. $\dfrac{x}{3} = \dfrac{2}{3}$

6. $\dfrac{x}{2} = \dfrac{-3}{2}$

7. $\dfrac{x + 2}{5} = 6$

8. $\dfrac{x}{40} = \dfrac{-2}{25}$

9. $\dfrac{2x - 1}{4} = 7$

10. $\dfrac{3x}{4} = \dfrac{-2}{3}$

11. $\dfrac{2}{7} = -\dfrac{22}{3}x$

12. $-\dfrac{3}{5} = \dfrac{4x}{3}$

13. $\dfrac{x}{3} - \dfrac{5}{6} = -\dfrac{3}{2}$

14. $\dfrac{x}{8} + \dfrac{3}{4} = -\dfrac{5}{2}$

15. $\dfrac{x}{9} - \dfrac{2}{3} = \dfrac{1}{4}$

16. $\dfrac{x}{5} + \dfrac{3}{2} = \dfrac{3}{10}$

17. $\dfrac{x}{7} - \dfrac{1}{2} = \dfrac{1}{14}$

18. $\dfrac{x}{9} + \dfrac{1}{12} = -\dfrac{2}{15}$

19. $\dfrac{x}{6} - \dfrac{2}{9} = -\dfrac{5}{12}$

20. $x - 2 = 1.3$

21. $x + 5 = -2.9$

22. $\dfrac{2x}{3} - 1.2 = 0$

23. $\dfrac{5x}{4} + 3.2 = 0$

24. $x + 2.4 = 3.9$

25. $x - 2.7 = -4.2$

26. $2x - 3.2 = 9.8$

27. $1.2x - 2.3 = 9.7$

28. $\dfrac{1.2}{6} - x = -\dfrac{3.6}{6}$ **29.** $2(x-1.2)=7.8$ **30.** $\dfrac{4.8}{1.2} - 2.5x = \dfrac{-4.2}{0.2}$ **31.** $3.2\left(5 - \dfrac{x}{2}\right) = -\dfrac{4.8}{0.3}$

32. $\dfrac{x}{2} - 1.5 = 2.3$ **33.** $\dfrac{x+2}{5} = 0.06$ **34.** $\dfrac{2x-1}{4} = 0.7$ **35.** $\dfrac{3x}{4} - 1.2 = \dfrac{x}{3} + 2.5$

36. $\dfrac{1}{9}x + \left(x + \dfrac{5}{6}\right) = -\dfrac{1}{3}\left(x + \dfrac{1}{4}\right)$ **37.** $\dfrac{4}{5}x - \left(x + \dfrac{3}{2}\right) = \dfrac{1}{4}\left(x - \dfrac{1}{3}\right)$ **38.** $\dfrac{1}{2}x + 3\left(\dfrac{1}{4}x + 3\right) = 4$

39. $\dfrac{1}{3}x + 5\left(\dfrac{1}{6}x + 2\right) = 8$ **40.** $\dfrac{1}{8}x + 4\left(\dfrac{1}{6}x - 2\right) = 3$ **41.** $\dfrac{1}{5}x + 6\left(\dfrac{1}{2}x + 3\right) = -2$

42. $\dfrac{1}{6}x + 3\left(\dfrac{1}{9}x - 4\right) = 5$ **43.** $3 - \dfrac{4}{5}a = -\dfrac{3a}{4}$ **44.** $7 - \dfrac{5}{6}x = 3 - \dfrac{2x}{7}$

45. $\dfrac{x+2}{5} - \dfrac{x-3}{15} = \dfrac{x}{3}$ **46.** $\dfrac{1}{3}(2x-3) = \dfrac{1}{2}(x+4) - \dfrac{2}{5}(4-x)$ **47.** $\dfrac{5.4}{18} - 0.2(x-1.2) = \dfrac{2.3}{4}$

In exercises 48-65, solve the equation and check your answer.

48. $1.3y + 2.7 = 19.6$ **49.** $\dfrac{x}{3.05} - 1.06 = 2.3$ **50.** $1.7 = 0.5 + \dfrac{y}{1.03}$ **51.** $9x + 8.57 = -124.9$

52. $1.8w + 32 = 63.14$ **53.** $0.2(t+6.3) = 17.5$ **54.** $21.21 + 0.5x = 27.15$ **55.** $14.4 = 0.44x + 5.6$

56. $1.25t - 0.1 = 9$ **57.** $\dfrac{y}{12.1} - 0.06 = 1.04$ **58.** $12.50 = 80p - 130$ **59.** $5(x+3.7) = 27.05$

60. $\dfrac{w}{2.1} + 0.03 = 4.09$ **61.** $0.3x + 3.8 = 5.72 - 0.1x$ **62.** $0.1(x-15) + 0.3x = 0.116$

63. $13x - 8x = -35.45 + 10x$ **64.** $1.5x - 18.4 = 0.6x - 22.9$ **65.** $0.12x + 0.25x - 5.895 = 4.3x$

B. In exercises 66-85, determine whether the equation has only one solution, no solution, or is an identity.

66. $2x + x - 3 = 6$ **67.** $5(x+1) - x = 4x + 5$ **68.** $2(x+2) - 1 = x + 3$ **69.** $3 - 2(x+1) = 1 - 2x$

70. $3(x-2) + 5 = 3x + 1$ **71.** $2(x+3) - 4 = 2(x+1)$ **72.** $5(x-2) + 11 = 5x + 2$ **73.** $3x - 9 = 3(x-2) - 3$

74. $4(x+1) - x = 3x + 5$ **75.** $7x - 2 - 5x = 2x + 2$ **76.** $2(x+3) + 1 = 2(x+2)$ **77.** $3x + 4 = 2(x+2) + 1$

78. $\dfrac{3}{4}\left(\dfrac{8}{9}x + 4\right) = \dfrac{2}{3}x - 9$ **79.** $5\left(\dfrac{1}{6}x - 1\right) - \dfrac{x}{2} = \dfrac{x}{3} - 5$ **80.** $11 - \dfrac{3}{4}x = 3\left(\dfrac{x}{4} - 11\right)$

81. $\dfrac{9x-2}{3} + \dfrac{x}{2} = 4x - \dfrac{x}{2} + 1$ **82.** $0.25(x+7) - 1 = 0.25(x+3)$ **83.** $7.3x - 2 - 0.9x = 5x - 1.8 + 2(0.7x)$

84. $4(x-0.3) + 0.1 = x + 0.3$ **85.** $\dfrac{1}{2}\left(3.6x - \dfrac{1}{4}\right) = \dfrac{9}{5}x - 0.125$

2.4 APPLICATIONS OF LINEAR EQUATIONS

Upon completion of this section you will be able to:

A. Understand the process of solving an applied problem;

B. Solve problems involving one unknown quantity; and

C. Solve problems involving more than one unknown quantity.

A. SOLVING WORD PROBLEMS

We have already discussed how to translate words, phrases, and sentences into mathematical expressions and equations. We will now discuss some procedures to solve problems using a general and logical thought process.

Understand the problem, think of a plan, carry out the plan, and look back.

These procedures are summarized in the following steps.

Step 1	Read the problem carefully, and identify what is to be found *(the unknown)*. Choose a variable to represent the numerical value of the unknown quantity.
Step 2	Write down mathematical expressions for any other unknown quantities using the assigned variable. If possible, draw figures or diagrams. *Diagrams help us understand the problem better.*
Step 3	Translate the problem into an equation.
Step 4	Solve the equation.
Step 5	Answer the question asked. *Be sure that the answer makes sense and follows the logic of the question.*
Step 6	Verify your answer by using the *original* statement of the problem.

B. PROBLEMS INVOLVING ONLY ONE UNKNOWN QUANTITY

WARM-UP

1. The product of 3 and a number, decreased by 17, is 154. What is the number?

EXAMPLE 1 The product of 5 and a number, increased by 21, is 141. What is the number?

Solution:

Step 1 Let this number be x.

Step 2 There are no other unknown quantities involved.

Step 3 Translate the problem.

Product of 5 and a number, increased by 21 is 141

$$5x \qquad + \qquad 21 = 141$$

Step 4 Solve the equation:

$$5x + 21 = 141$$
$$5x + 21 - 21 = 141 - 21$$
$$5x = 120$$
$$\frac{5x}{5} = \frac{120}{5}$$
$$x = 24$$

Step 5   Answer the question. The required number is **24**.

Step 6   Verify your answer using the original statement.

Product of 5 and 24 is 120. 120 increased by 21 is 141.

Therefore, the answer is verified.

 There is a difference between the following two statements:

a. The product of 5 and a number increased by 21   when written as an expression is $5x + 21$.

b. The product of 5, and a number increased by 21   when written as an expression is $5(x + 21)$.

Compare the position of the comma in the statements.

EXAMPLE 2   If the sum of a number and 6 is multiplied by 5, the result is the same as 9 times the number decreased by 2. Find the number.

Solution:

Step 1   Let this number be x.

Step 2   There are no other unknown quantities involved.

Step 3   Translate the problem.

The sum of a number and 6 is multiplied by 5.

$(x + 6)$ $\cdot$ 5.

or $5(x + 6)$

Also, 9 times a number decreased by 2 gives us

$9x - 2$.

Therefore, the resulting equation is **$5(x + 6) = 9x - 2$**.

Step 4   Solve the equation :

$$5(x + 6) = 9x - 2$$
$$5x + 30 = 9x - 2$$
$$5x = 9x - 2 - 30$$
$$5x = 9x - 32$$
$$-9x + 5x = -32$$
$$-4x = -32$$
$$x = \frac{-32}{-4} \quad \text{or} \quad x = 8$$

Step 5   The required number is **8**.

Step 6   *Verification:*

Sum of 8 and 6 multiplied by 5 gives:

$(8 + 6)5 = 14(5) = $ **70**

Also, 9 times the number when decreased by 2 is:

$9(8) - 2 = 72 - 2 = $ **70**.

Both sides of the equation are equal. The answer is verified.

WARM-UP

2.   The sum of a number and 3, multiplied by 4 is the same as 3 times the number increased by 15. Find the number.

Answers:

1. 57   2. 3

C. PROBLEMS INVOLVING MORE THAN ONE UNKNOWN

WARM-UP

3. A piggy bank contains $8.00 in dimes and quarters. There are 10 more dimes than quarters. Find the number of dimes and quarters.

EXAMPLE 3 A purse contains $6.50 in quarters and dimes. There are 5 more quarters than dimes. Find the number of quarters and dimes.

Solution:

Step 1   There are 5 more quarters than dimes.

Let the number of dimes $= x$.

Step 2   The number of quarters $= x + 5$.

Step 3 x dimes have a value of $\$.10x$

$(x + 5)$ quarters have a value of $\$.25(x + 5)$

The total money in purse $= \$6.50$

The problem is translated into the following equation:

$$\$.10x + \$.25(x + 5) = \$6.50$$

$$.10x + .25x + 1.25 = 6.50$$

Step 4   The LCD of the decimal fractions is 100.

Multiply both sides by 100

$$100(.10x + .25x + 1.25) = 100(6.50)$$

$$\longrightarrow \quad 10x + 25x + 125 = 650$$

$$\longrightarrow \quad 35x + 125 = 650$$

$$\longrightarrow \quad 35x + 125 - \mathbf{125} = 650 - \mathbf{125}$$

$$\longrightarrow \quad 35x = 525$$

$$\longrightarrow \quad \frac{35}{35}x = \frac{525}{35}$$

$$x = \mathbf{15}$$

Step 5   Therefore, there are **15 dimes** and $15 + 5 = $ **20 quarters**.

Step 6   *Verification:*

i)   20 quarters is 5 more than 15 dimes

ii)   20 quarters $= 20 \cdot \$.25 = \$5.00$

15 dimes $= 15 \cdot \$.10 = \$1.50$

The total amount is $\$5 + \$1.50 = \$6.50$

The answer is verified.

EXAMPLE 4   The length of a rectangular piece of land is 60 yards more than two times its width. The perimeter is 540 yards. Find its dimensions.

Solution:

We are looking for length and width. The length is described in terms of the width.

Step 1   Let the width be x.

Step 2   The length, is 60 yards more than two times the width (x).

Therefore, the length $= 2x + 60$.

Step 3   Translate the problem.
Perimeter $= 2(\text{length}) + 2(\text{width})$
$540 = 2(2x + 60) + 2x$

Step 4   Solve the equation.

$$2(2x + 60) + 2x = 540$$
$$4x + 120 + 2x = 540$$
$$6x + 120 = 540$$
$$6x + 120 - 120 = 540 - 120$$
$$6x = 420$$
$$\frac{6x}{6} = \frac{420}{6}$$
$$x = \mathbf{70}$$

Step 5   width $= x = \mathbf{70}$ yards,

length $= 2x + 60 = 2(70) + 60$
$$= 140 + 60$$
$$= \mathbf{200} \text{ yards}$$

Therefore, the width is **70** yards and the length is **200** yards.

Step 6   *Verification:*

Perimeter $= 2(\text{length}) + 2(\text{width})$
$$= 2(\mathbf{200}) + 2(\mathbf{70}) = 400 + 140 = 540 \text{ yards}$$

EXAMPLE 5   Find the measure of an angle whose supplement is three times its complement.

Solution:

Step 1   Assume angle $= x$ degrees.

Step 2   Supplement $= (180 - x)°$ and
Complement $= (90 - x)°$

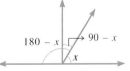

▰▰▰ **WARM-UP** ▰▰▰

4. The length of a rectangle is 3 yards more than four times its width. The perimeter is 96 yards. Find its dimensions in yards.

5. Find the measure of an angle whose supplement is twice its complement.

Step 3 Translate the problem.

The supplement is three times the complement.

$$180 - x = 3 \cdot (90 - x)$$

Step 4 Solve the equation.

$$180 - x = 3(90 - x)$$
$$180 - x = 270 - 3x \qquad \text{Subtract 180 from both sides.}$$
$$- x = 90 - 3x$$
$$- x + 3x = 90 \qquad \text{Add } 3x \text{ to both sides.}$$
$$2x = 90$$
$$x = 45 \qquad \text{Divide both sides by 2.}$$

Step 5 The measure of the angle is **45°**.

Step 6 *Verification:*

The supplement of $45° = 180° - 45° = \mathbf{135°}$

The complement of $45° = 90° - 45° = 45°$

Three times the complement $= 3(45)° = \mathbf{135°} = \mathbf{supplement}$

6. A television camera is sold for $350. If this item was on sale for a discount of 20%, find the original selling price of the television camera.

EXAMPLE 6 During a clearance sale, an electronic store sold a video cassette recorder for $225. If items on sale were discounted by 25%, find the original retail price of the video cassette recorder.

Solution:

Step 1 Let original retail price $= x$ dollars.

Step 2 Discount $= 25\%$ of $x = .25x$

Step 3 Translate the problem.

Discounted price = original retail price $-$ discount
Therefore, $225 = x - .25x$

Step 4 Solve the equation.
$$x - .25x = 225$$
$$.75x = 225$$
$$\frac{.75x}{.75} = \frac{225}{.75}$$
$$x = 300$$

Step 5 The original retail price of the video cassette recorder is **$300**.

Step 6   *Verification:*

$$25\% \text{ discount on } \$300 = 25\% \text{ of } 300$$
$$= .25(300)$$
$$= 75$$

Discounted price $= 300 - 75 = \textbf{\$225}$

EXAMPLE 7   A patient's temperature was taken at 7 a.m., 11 a.m., 3 p.m. and 7 p.m. The first, second, and fourth readings were 102° F, 101.5°F, and 102.5°F respectively. If the average of the four readings was 101.5°F, what was the third reading?

7. A student's scores for three exams were recorded to be 65, 85 and 90. If the average of four scores is 80, what was the fourth score?

Solution:

Step 1   Let third temperature reading $= x° \textbf{\textit{F}}$

Step 2   The average

$$= \frac{\text{sum of the four readings}}{4} = \frac{102 + 101.5 + x + 102.5}{4}$$

Time	Temperature
7 a.m.	102°
11 a.m.	101.5°
3 p.m.	$x°$
7 p.m.	102.5°

Step 3   Translate the problem. The average of the four readings is 101.5.

$$\frac{102 + 101.5 + 102.5 + x}{4} = 101.5$$

Step 4   Solve the equation.

$$\frac{102 + 101.5 + 102.5 + x}{4} = 101.5$$

$$\frac{x + 306}{4} = 101.5$$

$$4 \cdot \frac{x + 306}{4} = 4 \cdot 101.5 \qquad \text{Multiply both sides by 4}$$

$$x + 306 = 406 \qquad \text{Add } - 306 \text{ to both sides}$$

$$x = 100$$

Step 5   Third temperature was **100°F**.

Step 6   *Verification :*

The average of 102, 101.5, 100, 102.5

$$= \frac{102 + 101.5 + 100 + 102.5}{4} = \frac{406}{4} = 101.5$$

8. A lawn mower uses a mixture of gasoline and fuel. Each quart of fuel is mixed with three quarts of gasoline. If the tank holds 8 quarts of the mixture how many quarts each of fuel and gasoline are required to fill the tank completely?

EXAMPLE 8

A lawn mower uses a mixture of gasoline and oil. For each ounce of oil the mixture contains 15 ounces of gasoline. If the tank holds 80 ounces of the mixture, how many ounces each of oil and gasoline are required to fill the tank completely?

Solution:

Step 1 Let Oil required (in ounces) = x

Step 2 Gasoline required (in ounces) = $15x$

Step 3 Translate the problem.

The total amount of oil and gasoline is 80 ounces

$$x + 15x = 80$$

Step 4 Solve the equation

$$x + 15x = 80 \longrightarrow 16x = 80$$

$$\longrightarrow x = \frac{80}{16} \quad \text{or} \quad x = 5$$

Step 5 When the tank is full the quantity of oil required is 5 ounces and the quantity of gasoline required is $80 - 5 = $ **75 ounces**.

Step 6 *Verification:*

i) Gasoline 75 = **15**(5) = 15 times the amount of oil

ii) Total 75 + 5 = **80**

Answers:

3. 20 quarters, 30 dimes
4. Width : 9 yards, Length : 39 yards
5. Zero degree.
6. $437.50   7. 80
8. 6 quarts of gasoline; 2 quarts of fuel.

EXERCISE 2.4

B.

1. If 6 is added to a number, the result exceeds two times the number by 1. What is the number?

2. If the sum of an integer and 7 is multiplied by 3, the result is 6 times the original integer. Find the integer.

3. If 6 is multiplied by the difference between a number and 3, the result is the difference between 4 times the number and 2. Find the number.

4. Find a number which when subtracted from 4 times itself yields 36.

5. The difference of 4 times a number and 3 is the same as the difference of two times the number and 7. What is the number?

6. Find a number which when divided by 3 is equal to the sum of the number and 2.

7. The quotient of a number and 5 is the same as the product of the number and 5. Find the number.

8. The difference of five times a number and $\frac{1}{2}$ is equal to $\frac{1}{3}$ times the number. What is the number.

9. If a dozen rolls cost $2.16, find the price of one roll.

10. How many $6 hair dryers can be purchased with $256.80, if the tax is 7%.

C. 11. A purse contains $2.95 in quarters and dimes. The number of quarters exceeds the number of dimes by 2. Find the number of quarters and dimes in the purse.

12. A child has $10.45 in quarters and nickels in his piggy bank. If there are 11 more nickels than quarters, find the number of each type of coin in the piggy bank.

13. If ten pens cost $1.80, find the cost of one pen.

14. A purse contains $6 in quarters and dimes. The number of quarters is two times the number of dimes. Find the number of quarters and dimes in the purse.

15. The length of a rectangle is 3 cm less than four times its width. The perimeter of the rectangle is 34 cm. Find the dimensions of the rectangle.

16. A farmer plans to enclose a rectangular field by chain link fencing. The length of the field is 16 yards more than its width. If 140 yards of fencing is required, find the dimensions of the field.

17. A farmer has 38 more hens than roosters with 150 chickens in all. Find the number of hens and the number of roosters on the farm.

18. The length of a rectangular garden is 4 ft more than two times its width. If the perimeter of the garden is 32 ft, find its dimensions.

19. A strip of paper is 57 inches long. It is cut into three pieces. The longer piece is 10 inches longer than the middle-sized piece, and the shortest piece is 10 inches shorter than the middle-sized piece. Find the lengths of three pieces.

20. A lawn mower uses a mixture of gasoline and oil. For each ounce of oil, the mixture contains 16 ounces of gasoline. If the tank holds 85 ounces of mixture, how many ounces of oil and how many ounces of gasoline does it require when full.

21. Find the measure of an angle in degrees. It is given that the complement is one-half of the difference between the supplement and 25°.

22. The supplement of an angle is four times its complement. Find the measure of the angle.

23. A pharmacist found that he received $\frac{7}{5}$ times as many prescriptions for pain killers as he did for tranquilizers. If on a certain day the pharmacist received 72 prescriptions, how many prescriptions of each kind did he receive?

24. One side of a triangle is 1 meter more than two times the shortest side, while the second side is 3 meters more than the shortest side. The perimeter of the triangle is 24 meters. Find the length of each side.

25. The perimeter of an isosceles triangle is 42 centimeters. The two equal sides are 3 centimeters shorter than the base. Find the dimensions of the triangle.

26. Each of the equal sides of an isosceles triangle is 4 cm more than its base. If the perimeter of the triangle is 23 cm, find the lengths of the sides of the triangle.

27. The sum of the ages of a mother and a child is 40. If 4 years ago, the mother's age was seven times the child's age, how old are they?

28. A car dealer advertises a $7600 van at a 30% discount for $5500. Is the dealer telling the truth?

29. A furniture company declares a 30% discount on all items on Father's Day. The discounted price of a dining table is $280. What is the regular price of the dining table?

30. A company declares a discount of 20% on all items. A man buys a TV for $400. What was the regular price of TV.

31. Linda made 85, 84, and 78 on three of the four tests. If her average score for the four tests was 86, what was her score on the fourth test?

32. The average of three consecutive integers is 8. Find the integers.

33. The average of the ages of John, Smith and Singhania is 30 years. If the ages of John and Smith are 20 and 30 years respectively, find the age of Singhania.

34. The average maximum temperature of a city recorded on three consecutive days was 20°C. If the maximum temperature on first and third day was 18°C and 20°C, what was the maximum temperature on second day?

2.5 LITERAL EQUATIONS

A literal equation (*or a formula*) is a rule that expresses a relationship between two or more variables. For example, $A = LW$ expresses the relationship between the **A**rea, **L**ength, and **W**idth of a rectangle.

A. SOLVE FOR ONE VARIABLE, GIVEN THE VALUES OF OTHER VARIABLES

We use the following steps to solve literal equations.

Step **1**	Substitute the given values in the formula.
Step **2**	Solve the resulting equation.
Step **3**	Verify your answer.

WARM-UP

1. Find the value of the remaining variable.

a) $A = \frac{1}{2}bh$

$h = 5, A = 10$

EXAMPLE 1 Find the value of the remaining variable.

a. $A = \frac{1}{2}bh$; $A = 40$, $b = 10$

b. $A = \frac{1}{3}h(a + 4b + c)$;

$A = 20$, $h = 5$, $a = 1$, and $c = 1$

Solutions:

a. *Step* 1 Substitute $A = 40$ and $b = 10$ in $A = \frac{1}{2}bh$

We get $40 = \frac{1}{2}(10)h$.

Step 2 Solve: $\frac{1}{2}(10)h = 40$

$5h = 40$

$$\frac{5h}{5} = \frac{40}{5}$$

$$h = \mathbf{8}$$

Step 3   *Verification:*

Substitute $A = 40$, $b = 10$, and $h = 8$ in the formula.

$$A = \frac{1}{2}bh$$

$$40 = \frac{1}{2}(10)\,8$$

$$40 = 5(8)$$

$$40 = 40 \quad \text{True}$$

b.   *Step 1*   Substitute $A = 20$, $h = 5$, $a = 1$, and $c = 1$ in

$$A = \frac{1}{3}h\,(a + 4b + c)$$

We get $20 = \frac{1}{3}(5)\left(1 + 4b + 1\right)$

Step 2   Solve: $\frac{1}{3}(5)\left(1 + 4b + 1\right) = 20$

$$\frac{5}{3}\,(2 + 4b) = 20$$

$$\mathbf{3} \cdot \frac{5}{3}\,(2 + 4b) = \mathbf{3} \cdot 20$$

$$5(2 + 4b) = 60$$

$$10 + 20b = 60$$

$$20b = 50$$

$$b = \frac{50}{20}$$

$$b = \mathbf{2.5}$$

Step 3   *Verification:*

$$20 = \frac{1}{3}(5)\left(1 + 4(2.5) + 1\right)$$

$$20 = \frac{1}{3}(5)(12) \longrightarrow 20 = 20 \quad \text{True}$$

b) $A = \frac{1}{3}h(a + 4b + c)$

$a = 2,\; h = 1,\; c = 4,\; b = 0$

Answers:

1. **a)** $b = 4$ **b)** $A = 2$

B.   SOLVE FOR ONE VARIABLE IN TERMS OF OTHER VARIABLES

To solve a literal equation for a variable, use the following steps.

Step 1   Simplify both sides of the equation, if needed, using the distributive property. Remove fractions or decimals by multiplying both sides of the equation with the Least Common Denominator.

Step 2   Use the addition property of equality to move all the terms containing the variable, to be solved for, on one side of the equation and all other terms on the other side.

Step 3   Solve the equation using the multiplication property of equality.

2. The perimeter of a triangle is given by the formula $P = a + b + c$. Solve for b in terms of P, a, and c.

EXAMPLE 2 The perimeter of a rectangle is given by the formula $P = 2L + 2W$, where L is the length and W is the width. Solve for L in terms of P and W.

Solution:

$$P = 2L + 2W$$
$$P - 2W = 2L + 2W - 2W \qquad \text{Add } -2W \text{ to both sides.}$$
$$P - 2W = 2L$$
$$\frac{P - 2W}{2} = \frac{2L}{2} \qquad \text{Divide by 2.}$$
$$\text{or} \qquad L = \frac{P - 2W}{2} \qquad \text{Switch the sides.}$$

Note

If we multiply both sides by $\frac{1}{2}$ instead of dividing by 2, we get:

$$\frac{1}{2}(P - 2W) = \frac{1}{2}(2L)$$

$$\frac{1}{2}P - W = L \qquad \text{or} \qquad L = \frac{1}{2}P - W$$

Mathematicians favour the form of the answer in which the division (or fraction) is distributed to each term.

3. $5x = 2y + 8$.
   Solve for y.

EXAMPLE 3 Solve for the variable y in the equation
$$3x - 2y = 9.$$

Solution:

$$3x - 2y = 9$$
$$-3x + 3x - 2y = -3x + 9 \qquad \text{Add } -3x \text{ to both sides.}$$
$$-2y = -3x + 9$$

Divide both sides by -2, distributing the divisor.

$$\frac{-2y}{-2} = \frac{-3x}{-2} + \frac{9}{-2}$$

$$y = \frac{3x}{2} - \frac{9}{2}$$

4. Fahrenheit and Celsius scales of temperature are related by
$$F = \frac{9}{5}C + 32.$$
Express Celsius (C) in terms of Fahrenheit (F).

EXAMPLE 4 Fahrenheit and Celsius scales of temperature are related by the formula $C = \frac{5}{9}(F - 32)$. Solve for Fahrenheit (F) in terms of Celsius (C).

Solution:

$$C = \frac{5}{9}(F - 32)$$

$$C = \frac{5}{9}F - \frac{160}{9}$$

$$9 \cdot C = 9\left(\frac{5}{9}F - \frac{160}{9}\right) \qquad \text{Multiply both sides by the LCD, 9.}$$

$$9C = 5F - 160 \qquad \text{Add 160 to both sides.}$$

$$9C + 160 = 5F$$

$$\frac{1}{5}(9C + 160) = \frac{1}{5} \cdot 5F \qquad \text{Multiply both sides by } \tfrac{1}{5}.$$

$$\frac{9C}{5} + \frac{1}{5} \cdot 160 = F \qquad \text{Distributive Property.}$$

$$\frac{9C}{5} + 32 = F \qquad \text{Simplify.}$$

$$\text{or} \quad F = \frac{9}{5}C + 32 \qquad \text{Switch the sides.}$$

C. CONSECUTIVE INTEGERS AND FORMULAS

The examples given below explain the steps that should be followed to solve an application problem. These steps are essentially the same as those mentioned earlier in Section 2.4.

EXAMPLE 5 Given two consecutive integers. The sum of two times the first integer and three times the second integer is 48. Find the integers.

Solution:

Step 1   Let the first integer be x.

Step 2   The second integer is $x + 1$.

Step 3   Translate the problem

Two times the + Three times the
first integer   second integer   is   48.

$$2x \qquad + \qquad 3(x + 1) \qquad = \qquad 48$$

Step 4   Solve the equation.

$$2x + 3(x + 1) = 48$$
$$2x + 3x + 3 = 48$$
$$5x + 3 = 48$$
$$5x = 45 \quad \longrightarrow \quad x = 9$$

Step 5   Therefore, the integers are **9** and **10**.

Step 6   *Verification:*

$$2(9) + 3(9 + 1) = 48$$
$$18 + 30 = 48 \qquad \text{True}$$

EXAMPLE 6 A rectangular plot has an area of 500 yds². If the length of the plot is 25 yds, find the width.

Solution:

- Let the width = x.

- Draw a figure.

500 sq yds   W

L

- Use the formula for the area of a rectangle: $A = LW$

• Substitute the given values in the formula:
$$500 = 25 \cdot x$$

• Solve the equation.　　$25x = 500$
$$x = \frac{500}{25} \longrightarrow x = 20$$

• The width of the lot is **20 yds**.

• *Verification:*　　Length of the lot = 25 yds
Width of the lot = 20 yds
Thus, area of the lot = $25 \cdot 20$
= 500 yds^2　　True

---

7. If John has 2000 dollars available at the end of 20 years, with yearly simple interest rate of 5%, what is the principal that he invested?

EXAMPLE 7　　John wins $1000 in a state lottery. He decides to invest this money in a bank which pays 5% yearly simple interest. How long will it take for the money to double? Use $A = P + Prt$

Solution:

• Let the time taken to double the investment = t years.

• Since $1000 is invested ($P$), the final doubled amount (A) would be $2000.

• The final amount is given by the formula:
$$A = P + Prt$$

• Substitute the values: $P = 1000$, $A = 2000$
$$r = 5\% = .05, \text{ time} = t.$$
$$2000 = 1000 + 1000(.05)t$$

• Solve the equation:
$$1000 + 1000(0.05t) = 2000$$
$$1000 + 50t = 2000$$
$$50t = 1000 \quad \text{Add } -1000 \text{ to both sides.}$$
$$t = 20 \quad \text{Divide both sides by 50.}$$

• The investment will double in **20 years**.

• *Verification:*　The interest on $1000 at 5% in 20 years
$$= 1000(0.05)(20) = 1000.$$

The amount at the end of 20 years = Principal + Interest
$$= 1000 + 1000$$
$$= \$2000$$

---

8. If two vertical angles have the measure $(x + 27)°$ and $(5x - 13)°$ respectively, find the measure of these angles.

EXAMPLE 8　　If two vertical angles have measures $(5x - 27)°$, and $(3x + 11)°$ respectively, find the measure of these angles.

Solution:

• Draw the figure.　　$(5x - 27)° \times (3x + 11)°$

• The measures of vertical angles are equal.
Thus, $5x - 27 = 3x + 11$.

- Solve the equation.

$$5x - 27 = 3x + 11$$
$$2x - 27 = 11 \qquad \text{Add } -3x \text{ to both sides.}$$
$$2x = 38 \qquad \text{Add } 27 \text{ to both sides.}$$
$$x = \mathbf{19} \qquad \text{Divide both sides by 2.}$$

- The measure of each angle $= 5x - 27$
$$= 5(\mathbf{19}) - 27$$
$$= 95 - 27$$
$$= 68$$

*Therefore, the measure of each angle is **68°***

- *Verification:*

$$5x - 27 = 3x + 11$$
$$5(\mathbf{19}) - 27 = 3(\mathbf{19}) + 11$$
$$95 - 27 = 57 + 11$$
$$68 = 68 \qquad \text{True}$$

EXERCISE 2.5

A. In exercises 1-12, solve for the unknown.

1. $A = \dfrac{1}{2}h(b + c)$; $A = 30$, $b = 8$, $c = 7$

2. $A = \dfrac{1}{2}h(b + c)$; $A = 20$, $h = 5$, $b = 2$

3. $V = lwh$; $V = 80$; $l = 10, h = 2$

4. $V = lwh$; $V = 60$; $l = 8, w = 2$

5. $A = P + Prt$; $A = \$2440, r = 0.03, t = 20$ yr

6. $A = P + Prt$; $A = 2800, P = 400, r = 2$

7. $rp = rq + r$; $r = 20, p = 5$

8. $rp = q(r + 1)$; $p = 2, q = 3$

9. $C = \dfrac{5}{9}(F - 32)$; $C = 35$

10. $C = \dfrac{5}{9}(F - 32)$; $F = 50$

11. $V = \pi h^2\left(r - \dfrac{h}{3}\right)$, $h = 7, V = 308$ $\left[\text{Use } \dfrac{22}{7} \text{ for } \pi\right]$

12. $V = \pi h^2\left(r - \dfrac{h}{3}\right)$, $V = 180, h = 6,$ $\left[\text{Use } \dfrac{22}{7} \text{ for } \pi\right]$

B. In exercises 13-43, solve the equation for the indicated variable.

13. $x + 2y = 6$; for x

14. $2x - y = 3$; for y

15. $-2x + 3y = -5$; for x

16. $3x + 4y = -2$; for y

17. $y = -6x + 3$; for x

18. $-x = 5y - 3$; for y

19. $5y - 3x = -2$; for x

20. $-6x - 2y = 4$; for x

21. $-5x - 6y = 1$; for y

22. $2x = -4y - 5$; for y

23. $A = \dfrac{1}{2}bh$; for h

24. $A = \dfrac{1}{2}bh$; for b

25. $p = 2l + 2w$; for l

26. $p = 2l + 2w$; for w

27. $A = P + Prt$; for t

28. $A = P + Prt$; for r

29. $F = \dfrac{9}{5}C + 32$; for C

30. $9C = 5F - 160$; for F

31. $y = mx + b$; for m

32. $y = mx + b$; for x

33. $b = a + (n - 1)d$; for n

34. $b = a + d(n - 1)$; for d

35. $V = \dfrac{NRT}{P}$; for T

36. $F = \dfrac{am_1 m_2}{r_2}$; for m_1

37. $E = mc^2$; for m

38. $t = \dfrac{c - s}{r}$; for s

39. $T = fw - gm$; for w

40. $V = \dfrac{4}{3}\pi r^3$; for r^3

2.5   Literal Equations

93

41. $A = \dfrac{1}{2} h \left(b_1 + b_2 \right)$; for b_1 **42.** $\dfrac{3}{2} x - \dfrac{1}{3} y = 5$; for y **43.** $2x + 5y - 4 = 0$; for y

C. **44.** Find three consecutive integers whose sum is 36.

45. Find three consecutive natural numbers such that difference of four times the third number and three times the first number is twice the second number.

46. Find three consecutive integers such that three times the middle integer exceeds the sum of the other two by 15.

47. In the 1960 United States presidential election, John F. Kennedy received 84 more electoral votes than Richard M. Nixon. Together they received 522 electoral votes. How many votes did each candidate receive?

48. A rectangular lot has an area of 860 square yards. If the length of the lot is 43 yards. Find its width.

49. A rectangular lot has an area of 720 square yards. If the width of the lot is 24 yards, find its length.

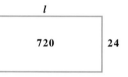

50. The perimeter of a sports complex, which is square in shape is 790 meters. Find the side of the sports complex.

51. The area of the trapezoid, shown in the figure, is 52 cm². Find the length of the base.

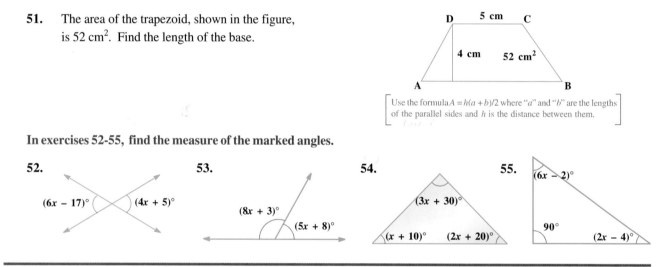

In exercises 52-55, find the measure of the marked angles.

52.   **53.**   **54.**   **55.**

2.6 RATIOS AND PROPORTIONS

OBJECTIVES ■■■■

Upon completion of this section you will be able to:

A. Write ratios;

B. Solve proportions; and

C. Solve applied problems involving ratios.

If for every three female members on a committee there are four male members, then the ratio of females to males on the committee is 3 : 4 or $\dfrac{3}{4}$. If a motor requires 3 ounces of oil for every 20 ounces of gasoline, then the ratio of oil to gasoline for the motor is 3:20 or 3/20. These are examples of ratios. Proportion is an equality relationship between two ratios. In this section, we examine some applications concerning ratios and proportions. Methods of solving equations can be effectively used to solve problems involving proportions.

A. WRITE RATIOS

A ratio is a quotient of two quantities. The ratio of a number a to a number b is written as: $a : b$ or $\dfrac{a}{b}$. Ratios are used to compare two numbers or two quantities. In order to compare two quantities using ratios, their units must be the same. We cannot compute ratio of a quantity in ounces to a quantity in gallons.

EXAMPLE 1   Write a ratio for each of the following.

      a.   Ratio of 4 dollars to 6 dollars

      b.   Ratio of 4 dimes to 3 quarters

Solutions:

a.   The ratio of 4 dollars to 6 dollars [same units] $= \dfrac{4}{6} = \dfrac{2}{3}$.

b.   The ratio of 4 dimes to 3 quarters [different units]. Since the units 'dimes' and 'quarters' are different we convert the quantities to a common unit, cents.

$$\frac{4 \text{ dimes}}{3 \text{ quarters}} = \frac{40 \text{ cents}}{75 \text{ cents}} = \frac{8}{15}.$$

B. PROPORTIONS

In the note above we observed that $\dfrac{40}{75} = \dfrac{8}{15}$. This is an example of a proportion.

A proportion is a statement which expresses equality of two ratios.

Notice that $\dfrac{a}{b} = \dfrac{c}{d} \longrightarrow \dfrac{a}{b}(bd) = \dfrac{c}{d}(bd) \longrightarrow ad = bc$

> **Rule : Cross Multiplication**
>
> The proportion $\dfrac{a}{b} = \dfrac{c}{d}$ can be tested by cross multiplication:
>
> $\dfrac{a}{b} \bowtie \dfrac{c}{d}$, ad and bc are called cross products.

If two ratios are equal, then their cross products must be equal: $ad = bc$.

EXAMPLE 2   Which of the following proportions are true statements?

    a. $\dfrac{3}{4} = \dfrac{7}{9}$ **b.** $\dfrac{15}{20} = \dfrac{24}{32}$

Solutions:

a. $\dfrac{3}{4} = \dfrac{7}{9} \longrightarrow 3 \cdot 9 = 7 \cdot 4 \longrightarrow 27 = 28$ *False*

Therefore, $\dfrac{3}{4} \neq \dfrac{7}{9}$ and the proportion is false.

b) $\dfrac{9}{12} = \dfrac{15}{20}$

b. $\dfrac{15}{20} = \dfrac{24}{32} \longrightarrow 15 \cdot 32 = 24 \cdot 20 \longrightarrow 480 = 480$ True

Therefore, $\dfrac{15}{20} = \dfrac{24}{32}$ and the *proportion is true*.

> *Note* The rule of cross multiplication simply expresses the fact that fractions are equivalent.

---

3. Find x in the following proportions.

a) $\dfrac{3}{5} = \dfrac{x}{15}$

EXAMPLE 3   Find x in the following proportions.

a. $\dfrac{25}{15} = \dfrac{x}{9}$ **b.** $\dfrac{24}{x+2} = \dfrac{4}{5}$

Solutions:

a. $\dfrac{25}{15} \bowtie \dfrac{x}{9} \longrightarrow 25 \cdot 9 = 15x \longrightarrow 225 = 15x$

$\longrightarrow 15x = 225$

$\longrightarrow x = \dfrac{225}{15}$

$\longrightarrow x = \mathbf{15}$

Verification: Substitute 15 for x in the proportion.

$\dfrac{25}{15} = \dfrac{15}{9} \longrightarrow \dfrac{5}{3} = \dfrac{5}{3}$ True

b) $\dfrac{27}{2x-1} = \dfrac{9}{8}$

b. $\dfrac{24}{x+2} \bowtie \dfrac{4}{5} \longrightarrow 24 \cdot 5 = 4x + 8$

$\longrightarrow 120 = 4x + 8$

$\longrightarrow 4x = 112$

$\longrightarrow x = \dfrac{112}{4} \longrightarrow x = \mathbf{28}$

Verification:

Substitute $x = 28$ in the proportion.

Answers:

2. a) False   b) True

3. a) $x = 9$ b) $x = 12.5$

$\dfrac{24}{28+2} = \dfrac{4}{5} \longrightarrow \dfrac{24}{30} = \dfrac{4}{5}$

$\longrightarrow \dfrac{4}{5} = \dfrac{4}{5}$ True

C. APPLICATIONS

Recall the six steps for solving word problems (Section 2.4).

Step 1	Read the problem carefully and identify the unknowns.
Step 2	Write down mathematical expressions for the unknowns.
Step 3	Translate the word problem into mathematical symbols.
Step 4	Solve the resulting equation.
Step 5	Respond to the question asked.
Step 6	Carry out the verification.

EXAMPLE 4   A university maintains a student-teacher ratio of
28 : 3. If a total of 4172 students are registered
for the next spring, how many teachers will be
needed to maintain the ratio?

Solution:

Step 1   Let the required number of teachers be x.

Step 2   The ratios of 28 : 3 and 4172 : x form a proportion.

Step 3   Therefore, $\dfrac{28}{3} = \dfrac{4172}{x}$ or $28x = 4\,172(3)$

Step 4   Solve the equation.

$$28x = 4172(3)$$
$$= 12516$$
$$x = \frac{12516}{28} \text{ or } x = \mathbf{447}$$

Step 5   Therefore, 447 teachers are required to maintain the
ratio 28 : 3.

Step 6   *Verification:*

$$\frac{4172}{447} = \frac{28}{3} \longrightarrow \frac{2 \cdot 2 \cdot 7 \cdot 149}{149 \cdot 3} = \frac{28}{3} \longrightarrow \frac{28}{3} = \frac{28}{3} \quad \text{True}$$

▬▬▬▬ ▶ **WARM-UP** ◀ ▬▬▬▬

4. A university maintains a student-teacher ratio of 30 : 3. If a total of 7260 students are registered for the next spring, how many teachers will be needed to maintain the ratio?

EXAMPLE 5   The distance between Jackson, Mississippi, and
Atlanta, Georgia, is 375 miles. On a certain
map, this is represented by a length of 9 inches.
Memphis, Tennessee, and Philadelphia,
Pennsylvania, are situated 1000 miles apart.
Find the length of the line that connects these
two cities on the map.

Solution:

• Let the length, which represents the distance between
Philadelphia and Memphis on the map, be x inches.

•

	Actual distance	Map distance
Jackson/Atlanta	375 mi	9 in
Memphis/Philadelphia	1000 mi	x in

• Thus, $\dfrac{375}{1000} = \dfrac{9}{x}$.

• Solve the equation. Multiply to get the cross products.

$$375x = 9000$$
$$x = 24 \qquad \text{Divide both sides by 375.}$$

5. The distance between Charlotte and Atlanta is 250 miles. On a certain map, this represents 6 inches. Concord, NC, and Columbus, GA, are situated 475 miles away. Find the length of the line that connects the two cities on the map.

- The length that represents the distance between Memphis and Philadelphia is **24 inches**.

- *Verification:*

$$\frac{375}{1000} = \frac{9}{24} \longrightarrow \frac{15}{40} = \frac{3}{8} \longrightarrow \frac{3}{8} = \frac{3}{8} \quad \text{True}$$

6. A tax payer pays a state tax of $300 on income of $9000. If the tax rate remains the same how much state tax would he have to pay if his income increases by 12,000.

EXAMPLE 6 A taxpayer pays a state tax of $500 on an income of $15000. If the tax rate remains the same, how much state tax would he have to pay if his income increases by $6000?

Solution:

- We have to find the tax on the increased income.

  Increased income = 15000 + 6000 = 21000

  Let the state tax on an income of $21000 = x dollars.

Income	Tax
$15,000	$500
$21,000	x

- $$\frac{15000}{21000} = \frac{500}{x}$$

- Solve the equation. Multiply to get the cross products.

  $$\frac{15000}{21000} = \frac{500}{x} \qquad \text{Reduce.}$$

  $$\frac{15}{21} = \frac{500}{x}$$

  $$\longrightarrow \quad 15x = 10500 \qquad \text{Divide both sides by 15.}$$

  $$\longrightarrow \quad x = 700$$

- Therefore, the state tax on the increased income is **$700**.

- *Verification:*

  $$\frac{15000}{21000} = \frac{500}{700} \longrightarrow \frac{15}{21} = \frac{5}{7} \longrightarrow \frac{5}{7} = \frac{5}{7} \quad \text{True}$$

7. The length and width of a rectangular field are in the ratio 4:3. If the perimeter of the field is 140 yards, find the length and width.

EXAMPLE 7 The length and width of a rectangular lot are in the ratio 5 : 3. If the perimeter of the lot is 800 yards, find the length and width.

Solution:

Step 1 The unknowns are the length and width of the rectangular lot.

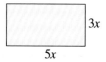

$3x$

$5x$

Step 2   The length and width of the
            lot are in the ratio 5 : 3.

            Let   length = 5x, width = 3x.

Step 3   The perimeter is 800 yards.

            Therefore, $5x + 5x + 3x + 3x = 800$

            [Perimeter = length + length + width + width]

Step 4   The resulting equation is

            $16x = 800 \longrightarrow x = \dfrac{800}{16} \longrightarrow x = 50$

Step 5   Length = 5x = 5 · 50 = **250 yards**

            Width = 3x = 3 · 50 = **150 yards**

Step 6   *Verification:*

            Perimeter = 250 + 250 + 150 + 150 = 800   True

            $\dfrac{\text{Length}}{\text{Width}} = \dfrac{250}{150} = \dfrac{5}{3}$ True

EXAMPLE 8   A certain mixture is made by mixing two
                 ingredients in the ratio 3 : 5. If it is required to
                 make 10 pounds of mixture, how much of each
                 ingredient will be needed.

Solution:

- Find the quantity of each of the ingredients.

  They are needed in the ratio 3 : 5.

- Let the required quantities of the two ingredients be 3x
  and 5x respectively.

- $3x + 5x = 10$

  $8x = 10$ Combine like terms.

  $x = \dfrac{10}{8}$

  $x = 1.25$

- Quantity of the first ingredient = 3x = 3(1.25)

                                     = **3.75 lbs**

  Quantity of the second ingredient = 5x = 5(1.25)

                                      = **6.25 lbs**

- *Verification :*

  Ratio of 3.75 to 6.25 = $\dfrac{3.75}{6.25} = \dfrac{375}{625} = \dfrac{3}{5}$ True

8. A certain mixture is made by
   mixing two ingredients in the ratio
   4 : 5. If it is required to make 20
   pounds of mixture, how much of
   each ingredient will be needed?

Answers:

4.   726 teachers
5.   11.40 inches
6. $700
7.   The length is 40 yards, width is 30
     yards.
8.   Quantity of first ingredient is 8.89,
     quantity of second ingredient is 11.11.

2.6   Ratios and Proportions

A. In exercises 1-20, change each ratio to a fraction and reduce the fraction. Write the ratio in the lowest terms.

1. 12 yards to 20 yards
2. 2 feet to 8 inches
3. 80°F to 60°F
4. 2 days to 8 days

5. 4 yards to 18 feet
6. 4 inches to 2 yards
7. 6 dimes to 9 nickels
8. 30 °C to 50 °C

9. 8 pints to 5 quarts
10. 2 days to 24 minutes
11. 6 days to 9 hours
12. 2 minutes to 45 seconds

13. 10 dimes to 12 nickels
14. 200 people to 60 people
15. 6 feet to 3 feet
16. 10 minutes to 10 seconds

17. 2 miles to 660 yards
   [1 mile = 1760 yards]
18. 800 m to 2 km
   [1 km = 1000 m]
19. 50 minutes to 2 hours
20. 20 ounces to 2 pounds

B. In exercises 21-32, determine if the proportion is true or false.

21. $\dfrac{4}{9} = \dfrac{24}{29}$
22. $\dfrac{2}{3} = \dfrac{16}{24}$
23. $\dfrac{4}{7} = \dfrac{12}{21}$
24. $\dfrac{5}{6} = \dfrac{10}{18}$
25. $\dfrac{6}{8} = \dfrac{9}{12}$
26. $\dfrac{8}{10} = \dfrac{16}{20}$

27. $\dfrac{7}{10} = \dfrac{10}{7}$
28. $\dfrac{2.5}{6} = \dfrac{1.5}{8}$
29. $\dfrac{7}{12} = \dfrac{3.5}{6}$
30. $\dfrac{10}{1.5} = \dfrac{6}{0.9}$
31. $\dfrac{9}{12.5} = \dfrac{18}{25}$
32. $\dfrac{4}{8} = \dfrac{8}{12}$

In exercises 33-55, find the value of the unknown from the given proportion.

33. $\dfrac{6}{5} = \dfrac{a}{20}$
34. $\dfrac{p}{6} = \dfrac{4}{3}$
35. $\dfrac{4}{7} = \dfrac{24}{k}$
36. $\dfrac{2}{2.5} = \dfrac{x}{10}$
37. $\dfrac{x}{14} = \dfrac{15}{21}$
38. $\dfrac{2.7}{6} = \dfrac{9}{r}$

39. $\dfrac{75}{y} = \dfrac{9}{12}$
40. $\dfrac{y}{6} = \dfrac{3.5}{7}$
41. $\dfrac{8}{5} = \dfrac{7}{k}$
42. $\dfrac{4}{5} = \dfrac{l}{9}$
43. $\dfrac{m}{5} = \dfrac{4}{7}$
44. $\dfrac{4}{z} = \dfrac{6.5}{1.3}$

45. $\dfrac{x}{30} = \dfrac{6}{18}$
46. $-\dfrac{2}{7} = \dfrac{x}{49}$
47. $\dfrac{4}{5} = \dfrac{x}{-100}$
48. $\dfrac{-\dfrac{2}{3}}{5} = \dfrac{2x}{\dfrac{1}{2}}$
49. $\dfrac{20}{-x} = \dfrac{5}{-4}$
50. $\dfrac{2}{x} = \dfrac{4}{x+4}$

51. $\dfrac{3}{2x-1} = \dfrac{4}{3x+2}$
52. $\dfrac{x-3}{2} = \dfrac{x+5}{3}$
53. $\dfrac{3x+1}{5} = \dfrac{4x-3}{6}$
54. $\dfrac{5x+4}{4} = \dfrac{4x+2}{3}$
55. $\dfrac{7x+8}{3} = \dfrac{5x+4}{2}$

C. Applications

56. 5 ounces of liver contains 37 grams of protein. How many ounces of liver will provide 111 gms of protein?

57. Sales tax on a $12 deep fryer is 90 cents. How much would the sales tax be on a typewriter which costs $104?

58. The distance between Birmingham, AL and Atlanta, GA is 150 miles. On a map it is shown by a length of 1.2 inches. On the same map the distance between Birmingham, AL and Jackson, MS is shown by a length of 2 inches. What is the distance between the two cities.

59. On a map, the distance from Atlanta, Georgia to Memphis, Tennessee is 3.4 cm and the distance from Atlanta to Chicago is 6.1 cm. Find the actual distance from Atlanta, Georgia to Memphis, if the actual distance from Atlanta to Chicago is 695 miles.

60. On a map, the distance from New York to Denver is 14 cm, and the distance from Washington D.C to New York is 2 cm. The actual distance from Washington D.C to New York is 252 miles. What is the distance from New York to Denver?

61. On a map, the distance from Boise ID to Los Angeles is 2.5 inches and the distance from Columbia SC to Las Vegas is 6.5 inches. The actual distance from Boise to Las Angeles is 837 miles. What is the distance from Columbia to Las Vegas?

62. Calzone State has a student-teacher ratio of 25 to 1.

   (a) Write this ratio as a fraction.

   (b) How large is the faculty, if the college has 32,600 students?

63. On a map 1 cm represents 85 miles. The distance between Washington D.C. and New York is 2.95 cm. How many miles apart are the cities?

64. On a map 1 inch represents 125 miles. The distance between two cities on the map is 3.25 inches. How many miles apart are the cities?

65. Which is a better buy for tomato ketchup? 15 ounces for $0.99 or 35 ounces for $2.19?

66. Which is a better buy for Grapefruit Juice? $4.99 for 33.5 oz or $6.99 for 45.75 oz.

67. One serving of fish steak is generally 0.45 lb of fish. How much fish steak is required for 35 servings.

68. If there are 8.9 calories of fat in one gram of fat, how many calories of fat are found in a potato with 0.45 gram of fat?

69. The tickets for a fashion show are sold for $75 each. If the light, music, and stage arrangements cost $5,750.50, and the hall rental costs $4,696.99, how many tickets must be sold to have a profit of $6,000.

70. The tickets for a dinner/dance are sold for $65 each. If the dinner costs $12.75 per head, music costs $450, and the hall rental costs $650, how many tickets must be sold to break even?

71. The tickets for a dinner/dance are sold for $55 each. If the dinner costs $13.75 per head, music costs $540, and the hall rental costs $559, how many tickets must be sold to have a minimum profit of $5,425.

72. If Bananas cost $0.45 per pound. How much can be purchased for $6.5?

73. Apples cost $0.99 per pound. How much can be purchased for $8?

74. Chicken costs $1.99 per pound. How much chicken can be purchased for $7.5?

75. Under typical conditions 1 ft of snow melts to 1.3 inches of water. To how many inches of water will 7.5 ft of snow melt?

76. To control a fever, a doctor suggests that a child should be given 1 mg of Tylenol for every 0.07 kg body weight. If the dosage is proportional to the child's weight, how much Tylenol is recommended for a child who weighs 25.5 kg?

77. An 8.5 lb turkey breast contains 35 servings of meat. How many pounds of turkey breast would be needed for 55 servings?

78. Tires are often priced according to the number of miles they are expected to be driven. Suppose a tire priced at $69.99 is expected to be driven 35,000 mi. How much would you pay for a tire that is expected to be driven 45,000 miles?

79. A tree casts a shadow that is 20 ft long. At the same time, the shadow cast by a 6 ft man is 8 ft long. Find the height of the tree.

80. A house is 16 m tall. Its shadow is 8 m long and at the same time the shadow of a nearby building is 42 m long. What is the height of the other building?

81. A 6 feet man casts a 4 feet shadow. At the same time a building casts a 30 feet shadow. Determine the height of the building.

82. Bill is 68 inches tall. His shadow is 58 inches long. At the same time, the length of the shadow of a pine tree is 270 inches. How tall is the pine tree?

83. A small tree 15 feet high casts a shadow which is 12 feet long. How long is the shadow of another tree which is 9 ft 7 inches long?

2.7 APPLICATIONS (CONTINUED)

Upon completion of this section you will be able to solve word problems involving mixtures, percents, simple interest, profit/loss, distance, rate and time.

In this section we will extend the techniques learned so far to solve additional application problems. Recall the steps for solving word problems. In more challenging problems, it can be very helpful to organize data in tables and to use diagrams whenever appropriate.

WARM-UP

1. How many pounds of Chinese coffee costing $10 per pound must be mixed with 30 lbs. of Colombian coffee costing $5 per pound to produce a mixture worth $8.00 per pound?

EXAMPLE 1   How many pounds of Brazilian coffee costing $6 per pound must be mixed with 27 lbs of Colombian coffee costing $4 per pound to produce a mixture costing $4.50 per pound.

Solution:

- Let the quantity of Brazilian coffee needed to be mixed = x lbs.

- Make a table

Coffee	Unit price	Amount	Total cost
Brazilian	$ 6/lb	x lbs	$6x$
Columbian	$ 4/lb	27 lbs	(4×27)
Mixture	$ 4.50/lb	$x + 27$ lbs	$4.5(x+27)$

- Brazilian coffee: Quantity = x lbs ; cost = $6x$

  Colombian Coffee: Quantity = 27 lbs ; cost = $4(27)$

  Total cost = **$6x + 4(27)$**

  Quantity of Mixture: $x + 27$ lbs ;

  Total cost = **$4.50(x + 27)$**

- $6x + 4(27) = 4.50(x + 27)$, since the mixture is obtained by simply adding the two ingredients.

- Solve the equation.

  $$6x + 108 = 4.50x + 121.50$$ Add $-4.50\,x$ and -108 to both sides.

  $$6x - 4.50x = 121.50 - 108$$

  $$1.5x = 13.5$$ Divide both sides by 1.5.

  $$x = \textbf{9 lbs}$$

- **9 lbs** of Brazilian coffee should be mixed with 27 lbs of Colombian coffee so that the mixture costs $4.50 per pound.

- *Verification:*

  Cost of 9 lbs of Brazilian coffee = $6 \cdot 9 = \$54$
  Cost of 27 lbs of Colombian coffee = $4 \cdot 27 = \$108$
  Cost of the mixture ($9 + 27 = 36$ lbs) = $(4.50)\,36$
                                          = $\$162$
  $\$54 + \$108$ = $\$162$ True

EXAMPLE 2   A 40% acid solution is mixed with a 75% acid solution to produce 140 liters of a 50% acid solution. How many liters of each acid solution was mixed?

Solution:

- Let the quantity of 40% acid solution be x liters. Then the quantity of 75% acid solution is $140 - x$ liters.

- Make a table

% Acid	Amount	Total Acid
0.40	x Liters	$0.40x\,l$
0.75	$(140-x)\,l$	$0.75(140-x)\,l$
Total = 0.50	$140\,l$	$0.50(140)\,l$

- 40% means 0.40 ; 50% means 0.50; and 75% means 0.75.

- The acid in the final solution comes from the acid in the solutions mixed.

  The problem translates to :

  $(40\%$ of $x) + (75\%$ of $(140 - x)) = (50\%$ of $140)$

  or $0.4x + 0.75(140 - x) = 0.5(140)$

- Solve the equation.

  $0.4x + \mathbf{0.75}\,(140) - \mathbf{0.75}x = 0.5(140)$

  $-0.35x + (0.75)\,(140) = 0.5\,(140)$

  $\longrightarrow \quad -0.35x + 105 = 70$

  $\longrightarrow \quad -0.35x = 70 - 105$

  $\longrightarrow \quad -0.35x = -35$ Multiply by -100.

  $\longrightarrow \quad 35x = 3500$

  $\longrightarrow \quad x = 100$

- 40% acid solution $= x = \mathbf{100\ liters}$

  75% acid solution $= 140 - x = 140 - 100 = \mathbf{40\ liters}$

- *Verification:*

  40% of 100 liters $= 0.4\,(100) = 40$ liters of acid.

  75% of 40 liters $= 0.75(40) = 30$ liters of acid.

  50% of 140 liters $= 0.5(140) = 70$ liters of acid.

  $40 + 30 = 70$ True

EXAMPLE 3   A store marks up a 20% for profit on a television and sells it for $ 270. How much did the television cost the store?

Solution: Let the cost price of the television be x dollars.

Profit marked up on the television $= 20\%$ of $x = 0.2x$

2. A 15% acid solution is mixed with a 60% acid solution to produce 90 liters of a 50% acid solution. How many liters of each acid solution was mixed?

3. A certain store marks up 30% profit on a television and sells it for $210. What was the cost of the television to the store?

Selling price = cost price + profit = $x + 0.2x$

$$= (1 + 0.2)x = 1.2x$$

Model for the problem

Profit % × Cost = Profit		
20%	x	$0.2x$

Cost + Profit = Sales Price		
x	$0.2x$	$x + 0.2x = 1.2x$

Therefore,

$1.2x = 270$ Divide both side by 1.2.

$x = 225$

Therefore, the cost of the television was **$225**.

4. Leslie invested $6000 at 15% per year. How much money should she invest at 10% per year so that the annual income from the two investments is 12%?

EXAMPLE 4   Leslie invested $5000 at 5% per year. How much money should she invest at 8% per year so that the annual income from the two investments is 6%?

Solution:

Let the investment at 8%   = x dollars

Income from x dollars at 8% = $0.08x$

Income from $5000 at 5%   = $5000(0.05)\,(1)$ (I = PRT)

       = $250   T = 1 year

Total desired income = 6% of the total investment

       = $0.06\,(x + 5000)$

Model for the solution

Investment	Rate × Amount = Interest		
8% investment	0.08	x	$0.08x$
5% investment	0.05	5000	$5000(.05) = \$250$
Total 6% investment	0.06	$x + 5000$	$(x+5000)(0.06)$

Total income = income from $5000 at 5% + income from x at 8%.

or $0.06(x + 5000) = 5000(0.05) + 0.08x$

$0.06x + 300 = 250 + 0.08x$ Add $-.08x$ and -300 to both sides.

$0.06x - 0.08x = 250 - 300$

$-0.02x = -50$ Multiply by -100 on both sides.

$x = 2{,}500$

Therefore, Leslie should invest **$2,500** at 8%.

To verify, fill in all missing numbers in the table and check that the total interest is really 6% of the investments.

EXAMPLE 5   A part of $6000 was invested at 6% annual interest and the remaining at 7% annual interest. At the end of one year, the total amount received was $6395. How much money was invested at each rate?

Solution: Suppose x dollars were invested at 6%.

Then the amount invested at $7\% = 6000 - x$, since the total investment is $6000.

Model for the Problem

Investment	Rate	× Amount	= Interest
6% investment	0.06	x	$0.06x$
7% investment	0.07	$6000-x$	$0.07(6000 - x)$
Total Interest		$0.06x + 0.07(6000 - x) = 395$	

Interest from 6% investment $= x \, (0.06) \, (1) = 0.06x$

Interest from 7% invement
$$= (6000 - x) \, (0.07) \, (1) = (6000 - x) \, (0.07)$$

Total interest earned $= \$6395 - \$6000 = \$395$

Therefore, the sum of the interest earned must be $395.

$$
\begin{aligned}
0.06x + 0.07(6000 - x) &= \$395 \\
0.06x + 420 - 0.07x &= 395 \\
420 - 0.01x &= 395 \\
-0.01x &= -25 \\
x &= 2500
\end{aligned}
$$

Therefore, **$2,500** was invested at 6% and the remaining **$3,500** [= 6,000 – 2,500] was invested at 7%.

To verify, fill in all the missing values in the table and check that the total amount at the end of the year is $6,395.

EXAMPLE 6   John has to attend a meeting 150 miles away from home. The meeting starts at 10 a.m. If John drives at an average speed of 60 miles per hour, at what time should he leave home to be at the meeting just in time?

Solution: Suppose John takes t hours to drive to the scheduled place.

Rate	× Time	= Distance
60	$\cdot \quad t$	$= \quad 150$

Therefore, $60t = 150$ or $t = 2.5$ hr
$$= 2 \text{ hrs and } 30 \text{ min.}$$

Hence, John must leave 2 hrs and 30 minutes before 10:00 a.m., that is at 7:30 a.m.

WARM-UP

5. A part of $8000 was invested at 4% annual interest and the rest at 5% annual interest. If at the end of one year, the total amount received was $8380. How much money was invested at each rate?

6. Peter has to attend a meeting 200 miles away from his place. The meeting starts at 11 a.m. If Peter drives at an average speed of 50 miles per hour, at what time should he leave this place to be just at the meeting?

7. A second train leaves City A for City B four hours after the first train. The first train travels at an average speed of 75 mile per hour. How long will it take the second train to overtake the first train if the second train travels at an average speed of 85 miles per hour?

EXAMPLE 7 Two trains leave Chicago for New York. The second train leaves one hour after the first train. The first train travels at an average speed of 60 miles an hour. How long will it take the second train to overtake the first train if the second train travels at an average speed of 80 miles per hour?

Solution:

Suppose the second train has traveled t hours before it catches up the first train. While the second train travels t hours, the first train would have traveled $(t + 1)$ hours. *When the two trains meet, they would have traveled the same distance.*

Train	Rate	× Time	= Distance
First	60	$t + 1$	$60(t + 1)$
Second	80	t	$80t$

Therefore, when the trains meet

$$80t = 60(t + 1) \longrightarrow 80t = 60t + 60$$
$$\longrightarrow 20t = 60$$
$$\longrightarrow t = 3$$

It will take the second train **3 hours to overtake the first**.

8. Two cyclist start out at the same time and travel towards each other from points that are 170 miles apart. The first cyclist travels at an average speed of 40 miles/hr and the second travels at an average speed of 45 miles an hour. After how many hours will they meet?

EXAMPLE 8 Two cyclists start out at the same time and travel towards each other from points that are 140 miles apart. The first cyclist travels at an average speed of 30 miles per hour, and the second travels at an average speed of 40 miles an hour. After how many hours will they meet?

Solution: Suppose the two cyclists meet after t hours.

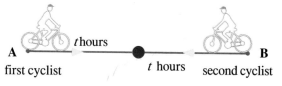

A first cyclist t hours t hours second cyclist B

The sum of distances covered by the two cyclists in t hours equals the distance between two points, *i.e.* 140 miles.

Cyclist	Rate	× Time	= Distance
First	30	t	$30t$
Second	40	t	$40t$

Therefore, when they meet.

$$30t + 40t = 140$$
$$70t = 140$$
$$t = 2 \text{ hours}$$

The two cyclists will meet after **2 hours**.

Answers:

1. 45 lbs.
2. 20 liters of 15% solution, 70 liters of 60% solution
3. $161.54   4. $9000
5. $2000 at 4% ; $6000 at 5%
6. At 7 a.m.   7. $t = 30$ hrs
8. $t = 2$ hrs.

1. Caramels costing $1.75 per pound are mixed with cream chocolates costing $2 per pound to make a 5 pound mixture that will be sold at $1.90 per pound. How many pounds of each are needed?

2. How many Caramels costing $2 per pound must be mixed with 20 cream chocolates worth $2.5 per pound to produce a mixture costing $2.25 per pound?

3. A grocer notices that he has 20 pounds of cashews that are not selling for their cost of $6 a pound. He mixes these cashews with peanuts to sell the mixture for $3 per pound. If the peanuts sell for $1.50 a pound, how many pounds of peanuts are needed?

4. Cream has approximately 22% butterfat. How many gallons of cream must be mixed with 2% milk to give 20 gallons of milk containing 4% butterfat?

5. How many gallons of milk with 4% butterfat must be mixed with 3 gallons of cream with 20% butterfat to produce milk containing 5% butterfat?

6. How much pure acid must be mixed with 60 liters of 65% acid solution to obtain a new solution that is 75% acid?

7. 20 litres of pure acid is mixed with 70% acid solution to have a new solution with 80% acid. How many litres of solution with 70% acid are needed?

8. How much water must be added to dilute 10 quarts of 18% iodine solution, so that the resulting solution will be 15% iodine?

9. How many quarts of a solution with 18% iodine must be added to 40 quarts of water to have a resulting solution with 10% iodine?

10. How many gallons of water must be added to 50 gallons of alcohol, so that the resulting solution has 75% alcohol content? (*Note*: Water is 0% alcohol).

11. An automobile dealer has $600,000 invested in compact cars and mid-size cars. The profit on the sale of the compact cars is 1%, and the profit on the sale of midsize cars is 16%. How much did the dealer invest in midsize cars if the overall profit on the total investment is 12%.

12. A film shop carrying black and white, and color films has $4000 in inventory. Profit on black and white films is 12% and the profit on color films is 21%. If the annual profit on color films is $150 less than the annual profit on black and white films, how much was spent in each type of film?

13. A shopkeeper sells a VCR for $200 at a loss of 20%. Find the original price of the VCR.

14. A man invested a total of $15000 in two ventures. In one he made a profit of 8% and in the other he suffered a loss of 4%. His net income from the two investments for the year was $240. How much did he invest in each venture?

15. Torrance split an inheritance between two investments, one paying 7% and the other paying 10%. He invested twice as much at 10% as at 7%. The combined annual income from two investments was $4050. How much did Torrance inherit?

16. A man invests some money at 5% per year and some at 8% per year. If the amount invested at 8% is three times that at 5% and his total annual income is $580, find the two investments.

17. Hesse wishes to earn $3500 per year in supplemental income from an inheritance of $40,000. He puts $10,000 in a bank paying 8%. What rate must he earn on the remainder so that his annual income is $3500?

18. Two planes leave the same airport at the same time and travel in the same direction. One plane flies at an average speed of 480 miles per hour and the other at 400 miles per hour. After how many hours will they be 300 miles apart?

19. A boat makes a round trip from mainland to a fishing village in 6 hours. If the average speed of the boat while going to the village is 15 miles per hour, and the average speed while returning is 12 miles per hour, find the distance between the village and the mainland.

20. A second train leaves Atlanta for New York two hours after the first train. The first train travels at an average speed of 80 miles per hour. How long will it take the second train to overtake the first train if the second train travels at an average speed of 100 miles per hour.

21. Linda and Kevin went on vacation. They drove to the airport to catch a plane. With an average speed of 55 miles per hour it took them two hours to reach the airport. Their plane cruised at an average speed of 450 miles per hour. How long were they in the air if they traveled a total of 1460 miles?

22. Two cyclists start out at the same time towards each other from points 150 miles apart. After how many hours will they cross each other if the first and the second cyclist travels respectively at speeds of 40 miles and 50 miles respectively.

23. A motorboat can go 18 miles per hour in still water. If it can go 80 miles downstream in 4 hours, find the speed of the current. (Speed of the boat downstream = speed of the boat in still water + speed of the current.)

24. A motorboat can go 24 miles per hour in still water. If it can go 100 miles upstream in 5 hours, find the speed of the current. (Speed of the boat upstream = speed of boat in still water – speed of the current)

25. At 4 p.m. a plane leaves San Francisco for Boston, traveling at an average speed of 500 miles per hour. Two hours later a plane departs from Boston to San Francisco traveling on air-route at an average of 400 miles per hour. The cities are 3700 miles apart, at what time do the planes pass each other? Disregard the time difference between two cities.

26. A runner and a biker start from the same point and travel in opposite directions. The biker travels 3 times faster than the runner. In 2 hours they are 80 miles apart. Find the speed, of both of them.

27. On a 300 miles trip, a small plane flew at an average speed of 110 mph and then reduced its speed to 80 mph for the remainder of the trip. The trip took a total of 3 hours. For how long did the plane fly at 80 mph.

28. A car traveling 80 mph overtakes a cyclist riding at a rate of 20 mph. If the cyclist had 2 hour head start, how far from starting point does the car overtake the cyclist?

29. Two cyclists start at the same time from opposite ends of 22 miles road. Both are riding the cycle at 10 mph. How long after they begin will they meet ?

30. A bus leaves Las Vegas at 11 a.m. and travels 65 mph. At noon, a car leaves same place (Las Vegas) and travels 85 mph. At what time does the car overtake the bus?

31. How many gallons of 25% acid solution must be mixed with 6 gal of 35% solution to make 28% acid solution?

32. How many ounces of pure water must be added to 20 oz of pure alcohol to make a solution that is 60% alcohol?

33. A coffee that is 20% java beans is blended with a coffee that is 15% java beans. How many pounds of each coffee are used to make 5 lb of coffee that is 18% java beans ?

34. Steve invested a portion of $20,000 in a 8% annual simple interest account and the rest in a 7% annual simple interest mutual fund. The two investments earn $1500 in interest. How much was invested in each account ?

35. A man invested 55% of his money in an account that earns 8.25% annual simple interest. The remainder of the cash was placed in an account that earns 10% annual interest. The interest earned in one year was $5,800. Find the total amount invested.

36. An investment of $3,500 is made at an annual simple interest rate of 8%. How much money is invested at an annual simple interest rate of 12% if the total interest earned is 9% of the total investment ? Round your answer to a whole number.

2.8 SOLUTIONS OF LINEAR INEQUALITIES

Recall the following facts.

1. If we plot two numbers on a number line, the number on the right is greater , and the number on the left is smaller.

2. The inequality symbols for two numbers or expressions are:

$a < b$ $\longrightarrow$ a " is less than" b
$a \leq b$ $\longrightarrow$ a " is less than or equal to " b
$a > b$ $\longrightarrow$ a " is greater than" b
$a \geq b$ $\longrightarrow$ a " is greater than or equal to " b
$a \neq b$ $\longrightarrow$ a " is not equal to " b

A. INTERVALS AND THEIR GRAPHS

Some Graphs of intervals and their representations in two different forms are given below.

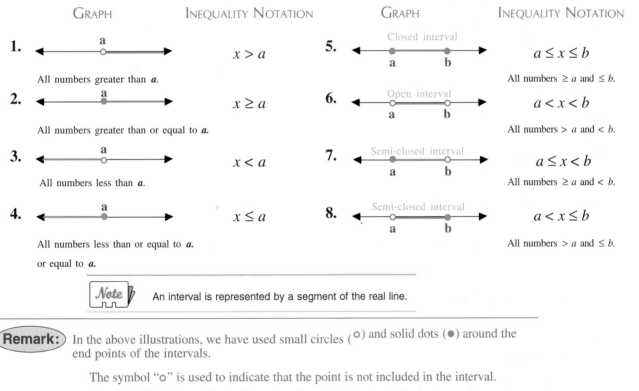

	GRAPH	INEQUALITY NOTATION
1.	All numbers greater than **a**.	$x > a$
2.	All numbers greater than or equal to **a**.	$x \geq a$
3.	All numbers less than **a**.	$x < a$
4.	All numbers less than or equal to **a**. or equal to **a**.	$x \leq a$

	GRAPH	INEQUALITY NOTATION
5.	Closed interval — All numbers $\geq a$ and $\leq b$.	$a \leq x \leq b$
6.	Open interval — All numbers $> a$ and $< b$.	$a < x < b$
7.	Semi-closed interval — All numbers $\geq a$ and $< b$.	$a \leq x < b$
8.	Semi-closed interval — All numbers $> a$ and $\leq b$.	$a < x \leq b$

> **Note** An interval is represented by a segment of the real line.

Remark: In the above illustrations, we have used small circles (○) and solid dots (●) around the end points of the intervals.

The symbol "○" is used to indicate that the point is not included in the interval.

The symbol "●" is used to indicate that the point is included in the interval.

Sometimes we use a different symbol, instead of ○ and ●, as illustrated below.

Symbol "○" is used for ") " or " (" depending on whether it is for left or right end point.

Symbol ● is used for " [" or "] " depending on whether it is for left or right end point.

1. Graph the intervals

a) $x > 4$

b) $x \geq 4$

c) $x < 4$

d) $x \leq 4$

2. Graph the intervals

a) $4 \leq x \leq 6$

EXAMPLE 1   Graph the intervals.

    a. $x > -3$ **b.** $x \geq -3$

    c. $x < -3$ **d.** $x \leq -3$

Solutions:

    a. $x > -3$

    Step 1   Mark -3 on the real line.

               Mark -3 by an *open circle* since -3 is not included.

    Step 2   Since all numbers greater than -3 lie to its right, the graph of $x > -3$ is shaded to the right of -3.

    b. $x \geq -3$

            The graph of this inequality is similar to the graph of $x > -3$ except that -3 is also a part of the graph of the solution.

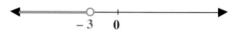

    c.   The graph of $x < -3$ is shown below.

            Notice that all the numbers which are less than -3 lie to its left, and -3 is *not included*.

    d. $x \leq -3$

            The graph of this inequality is similar to the graph of $x < -3$ except that -3 is also a part of the graph of the solution.

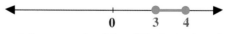

EXAMPLE 2   Graph the intervals.

    a. $3 \leq x \leq 4$ **b.** $3 < x < 4$

    c. $3 \leq x < 4$ **d.** $3 < x \leq 4$

Solutions:

    a. $3 \leq x \leq 4$ is an example of a **closed interval**. It represents the set of all real numbers between 3 and 4, *including both 3 and 4. Filled circles represent inclusion of the end points.*

    Step 1   Mark the numbers 3 and 4 on the real line.

            3 and 4 are marked by *filled circles* since these points are included in $3 \leq x \leq 4$

Step 2   *Shade the line segment joining 3 and 4. This line segment is the graph of the* interval $3 \leq x \leq 4$.

b.   **$3 < x < 4$** is an example of an open interval. This includes all real numbers between 3 and 4; the end points 3 and 4 are **not included**. *Open circles indicate that the end points are not included.*

Step 1   Mark the numbers 3 and 4 on the real line.

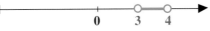

3 and 4 are marked by *open circles* to emphasize that these points are *not included*.

Step 2   Shade the line segment joining 3 and 4. The shaded region is the graph of the interval $3 < x < 4$.

c.   **$3 \leq x < 4$** is *closed* on the left, since 3 is *included* in $3 \leq x < 4$ and *open* on the right, since 4 is *not included*.

Step 1   Mark 3 and 4 on the real line,

mark 3 by a filled circle since the interval is closed at 3 and mark 4 by an open circle since the interval is open at 4.

Step 2   Shade the line segment between 3 and 4. The shaded region is the graph of the interval $3 \leq x < 4$.

d.   **$3 < x \leq 4$** is closed on the right since 4 is *included* and open on the left since 3 is *not included*.

Step 1   Mark 3 and 4 on the real line,

mark 3 by an *open circle* since the interval is *open* at 3 and mark 4 by a *filled circle* since the interval is *closed* at 4.

Step 2   Shade the line segment joining 3 and 4. The shaded region is the graph of the interval $3 < x \leq 4$.

EXAMPLE 3   Given the graph of an inequality as an interval on a line. Write its equivalent algebraic form.

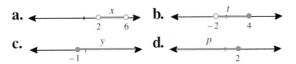

b) $4 < x < 6$

c) $4 \leq x < 6$

d) $4 < x \leq 6$

3.   Given the graph of an inequality as an interval on a line, write its equivalent algebraic form.

a)

2.8   Solutions of Linear Inequalities

111

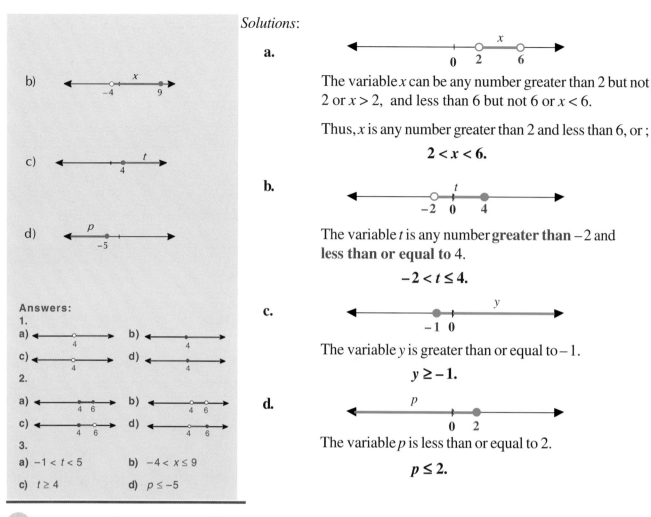

Solutions:

a.

The variable x can be any number greater than 2 but not 2 or $x > 2$, and less than 6 but not 6 or $x < 6$.

Thus, x is any number greater than 2 and less than 6, or ;

$$2 < x < 6.$$

b.

The variable t is any number **greater than** -2 and **less than or equal to** 4.

$$-2 < t \le 4.$$

c.

The variable y is greater than or equal to -1.

$$y \ge -1.$$

d.

The variable p is less than or equal to 2.

$$p \le 2.$$

B. ADDITION PROPERTY OF INEQUALITY

The solution set of an inequality is the set of all those real numbers which make the inequality true. The inequality $x < 3$ is true for all real numbers less than 3. Inequalities are solved in the same way as equations.

A linear inequality is said to have been solved when it is reduced to the forms:

$$x < k, \quad x \le k, \quad x > k \quad \text{or} \quad x \ge k.$$

This reduced form is called the **solution** of the inequality.

We will need some properties of inequalities in order to solve inequalities.

> **Addition Property of Inequality:**
>
> For any three real numbers a, b, c:
>
> **(i)** $a < b \longrightarrow a + c < b + c$ **(ii)** $a \le b \longrightarrow a + c \le b + c$
>
> **(iii)** $a > b \longrightarrow a + c > b + c$ **(iv)** $a \ge b \longrightarrow a + c \ge b + c$

Note ┐ The addition property of inequality asserts that an inequality does not change when the same number is added to both sides of the inequality.

EXAMPLE 4   Solve the inequalities.

$$\textbf{a. } 3 + 4x < 3x + 10 \quad \textbf{b. } -4 + 5x \le 6x + 9$$

Solutions:

a.
$$3 + 4x < 3x + 10$$
$$-3 + 3 + 4x < -3 + 3x + 10 \qquad \text{Add } -3 \text{ to both sides.}$$
$$4x < 3x + 7 \qquad \text{Simplify.}$$
$$-3x + 4x < -3x + 3x + 7 \qquad \text{Add } -3x \text{ to both sides.}$$
$$x < 7 \qquad \text{Simplify.}$$

The graph of the solution is:

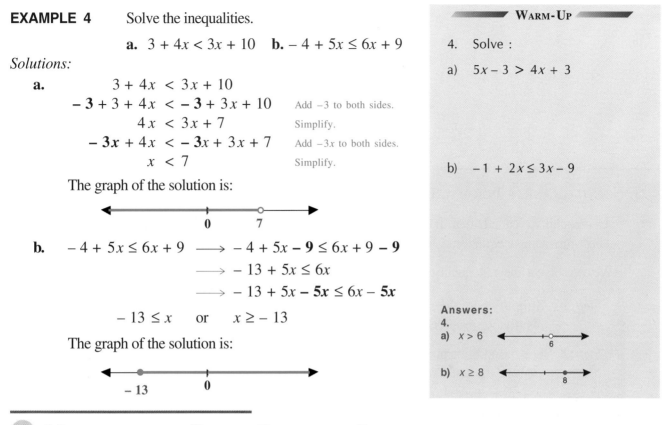

b.
$$-4 + 5x \le 6x + 9 \longrightarrow -4 + 5x - 9 \le 6x + 9 - 9$$
$$\longrightarrow -13 + 5x \le 6x$$
$$\longrightarrow -13 + 5x - 5x \le 6x - 5x$$
$$-13 \le x \quad \text{or} \quad x \ge -13$$

The graph of the solution is:

WARM-UP

4. Solve :

a) $5x - 3 > 4x + 3$

b) $-1 + 2x \le 3x - 9$

Answers:
4.
a) $x > 6$
b) $x \ge 8$

C.   MULTIPLICATION OR DIVISION PROPERTY OF INEQUALITY

Multiplication or division by a positive number on both sides of an inequality does not affect the solution of the inequality. In other words if $a > 0$ (**positive number**) then :

(i) $b < c \longrightarrow ab < ac$ (ii) $b \le c \longrightarrow ab \le ac$

(iii) $b > c \longrightarrow ab > ac$ (iv) $b \ge c \longrightarrow ab \ge ac$

Multiplication or division by a *negative* number *reverses* the inequality symbol.

- $-2 < 1 \longrightarrow 2 > -1$
  becomes
  Multiply by **−1**

- $3 > -7 \longrightarrow (\textbf{−2})3 < (\textbf{−2})(-7)$
  becomes
  Multiply by **−2**

Multiplication or division with a negative number on both sides changes $<$ to $>$ and $>$ to $<$.

EXAMPLE 5   Solve the inequalities. Graph the solution.

$$\textbf{a. } 4r \le 16 \qquad \textbf{b. } -3r > 15$$

Solutions:

a. $4r \le 16$ Divide by 4.

$$\frac{4r}{4} \le \frac{16}{4} \longrightarrow r \le 4$$

The graph of the solution is :

WARM-UP

5. Solve the inequalities. Graph the solution.

a) $5r \ge 20$

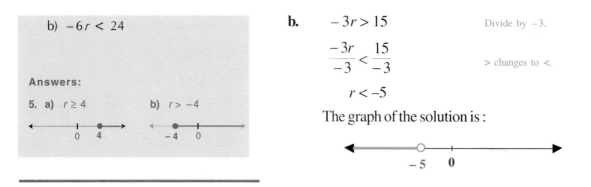

b) $-6r < 24$

Answers:

5. a) $r \geq 4$

b) $r > -4$

b. $-3r > 15$ Divide by -3.

$$\frac{-3r}{-3} < \frac{15}{-3}$$ $>$ changes to $<$.

$$r < -5$$

The graph of the solution is :

D. SOLVING LINEAR INEQUALITIES

An inequality is called **linear** if on changing the *inequality* sign ($<$, $\leq$, $>$, or $\geq$) with an *equality sign* ($=$), it becomes a linear equation.

We can solve a linear inequality using the following steps.

> *Step* **1**   Simplify both sides of the inequality by using the associative, commutative, distributive properties of real numbers, and combining like terms.
>
> *Step* **2**   Use the addition property of inequality to isolate the variable term on the left side and the constants on the right side of the inequality.
>
> *Step* **3**   Use the multiplication or division property of inequality to isolate the variable on one side of the inequality.
>
>   Recall, the **inequality is reversed if we multiply or divide both sides by a negative number.**
>
> *Step* **4**   Graph the inequality obtained in Step 3.

6. Solve the inequalities and graph the solutions.

a) $3x < 4(x - 1) + 1$

EXAMPLE 6   Solve the inequalities, and graph the solutions.

     a. $5x < 3(x - 4) + 7$

     b. $4x + 5 \geq 7(2x - 3) + 1$

Solutions:

     a. $5x < 3(x - 4) + 7$

         Step 1 $5x < 3(x - 4) + 7$

                       $5x < 3x - 12 + 7$ Simplify.

         Step 2 $5x < 3x - 5$

                $-3x + 5x < -3x + 3x - 5$

                       $2x < -5$ Addition Property.

         Step 3 $\dfrac{2x}{2} < \dfrac{-5}{2}$ Division Property.

                       $x < -\dfrac{5}{2}$

Step 4   The solution is $x < -\dfrac{5}{2}$.

The graph of the solution is :

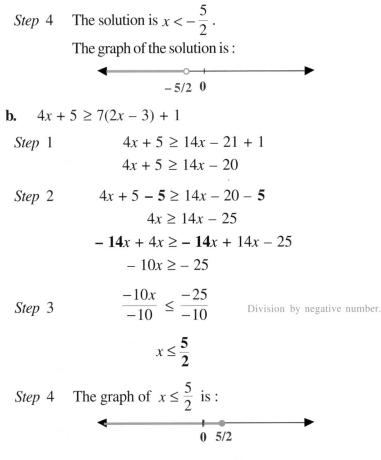

b. $4x + 5 \geq 7(2x - 3) + 1$

Step 1 $4x + 5 \geq 14x - 21 + 1$

$4x + 5 \geq 14x - 20$

Step 2 $4x + 5 - \mathbf{5} \geq 14x - 20 - \mathbf{5}$

$4x \geq 14x - 25$

$-\mathbf{14}x + 4x \geq -\mathbf{14}x + 14x - 25$

$-10x \geq -25$

Step 3 $\dfrac{-10x}{-10} \leq \dfrac{-25}{-10}$ Division by negative number.

$x \leq \dfrac{\mathbf{5}}{\mathbf{2}}$

Step 4   The graph of $x \leq \dfrac{5}{2}$ is :

EXAMPLE 7   Solve the inequality $\dfrac{3}{4}x - 4 < \dfrac{4}{5}x + 1$ and graph the solution.

Solution:

$\dfrac{3}{4}x - 4 < \dfrac{4}{5}x + 1$

This is an inequality which involves fractions.

Multiply both sides by the *least common denominator of the fractions, which is 20.*

$\mathbf{20}\left(\dfrac{3}{4}x - 4\right) < \mathbf{20}\left(\dfrac{4}{5}x + 1\right)$ Multiplication Property.

$\mathbf{20}\left(\dfrac{3}{4}x\right) - \mathbf{20}(4) < \mathbf{20}\left(\dfrac{4}{5}\right)x + \mathbf{20}(1)$

$15x - 80 < 16x + 20$

$-x < 100$

$x > \mathbf{-100}$ Multiply by -1.

We may use a calculator to solve an inequality.
See example 1 and 2 of Section 2.8 in Appendix B.

b) $7x - 6 \geq 5(3x + 9) + 5$

7.   Solve the inequality and graph the soluiton.

$\dfrac{5}{3}x - 2 > \dfrac{17}{7}x + 4$

Answers:
6.
a) $x > 3$ b) $x \leq -7$

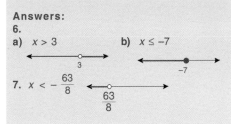

7. $x < -\dfrac{63}{8}$

E. THREE PART INEQUALITIES

Inequalities indicating that a number is between two given numbers are examples of three-part inequalities. Three part inequalities can be solved by using the addition and multiplication properties. These properties are used to reduce the given inequality to the form:

$$a < x < b \quad or \quad a < x \leq b \quad or \quad a \leq x \leq b \quad or \quad a \leq x < b.$$

The final solution to three part inequality is re-written so that the numbers are written in increasing order, or the smallest number is always on the left. Recall:

$$2 < x \quad \longrightarrow \quad x > 2$$

The point of the inequality symbol always points toward the smaller number.

$$3 > x > -2 \quad \longrightarrow \quad \mathbf{-2 < x < 3}$$

Both these inequalities are equivalent and we can read both as:

"x greater than -2 and x less than 3".

But it is desirable to express the solution of the type

$$3 > x > -2 \quad as \quad -2 < x < 3$$

because -2 is to the left of 3 on the number line.

WARM-UP

8. Solve the inequalities. Graph the solution.

a) $6 < 3x < 9$

b) $-12 < -6x < 24$

EXAMPLE 8 Solve the following three part inequalities and graph the solutions.

a. $4 < 2x < 6$ **b.** $-8 < -4x \leq 12$

Solutions:

a. $4 < 2x < 6$

$$\frac{4}{2} < \frac{2x}{2} < \frac{6}{2} \qquad \text{Multiplication Property.}$$

$$\mathbf{2 < x < 3}$$

The graph of the solution is :

b. $-8 < -4x \leq 12 \quad \longrightarrow \quad \dfrac{-8}{-4} > \dfrac{-4x}{-4} \geq \dfrac{12}{-4}$ Notice the inequality symbols are changed.

$$\longrightarrow \quad 2 > x \geq -3$$

$$\longrightarrow \quad \mathbf{-3 \leq x < 2} \quad \text{Rewrite with smaller number on left side.}$$

The graph of the solution is :

EXAMPLE 9 Solve the following three part inequalities

a. $-3 \le 1 - 2x \le 6$ **b.** $5 \le 3x - 1 < 11$

Solutions:

a. $-3 \le 1 - 2x \le 6$

$\mathbf{-1} - 3 \le \mathbf{-1} + 1 - 2x \le \mathbf{-1} + 6$ Add −1; Addition Property.

$-4 \le -2x \le 5$

$\frac{-4}{-2} \ge \frac{-2x}{-2} \ge \frac{5}{-2}$ Division Property, −2 is negative, and the inequalities are reversed.

$2 \ge x \ge -\frac{5}{2}$ Rewrite with smaller number on the left.

$-\frac{5}{2} \le x \le 2$

The graph of the solution $-\frac{5}{2} \le x \le 2$ is:

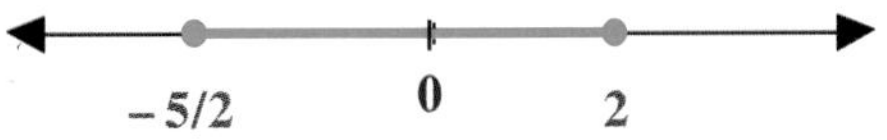

b. $5 \le 3x - 1 < 11$

$5 + \mathbf{1} \le 3x < 11 + \mathbf{1}$

$6 \le 3x < 12$

$\frac{6}{3} \le \frac{3x}{3} < \frac{12}{3}$ Divide by 3.

$2 \le x < 4$

The graph of the solution $2 \le x < 4$ is:

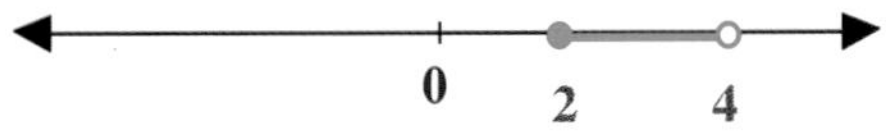

WARM-UP

9. a) $-2 \le 2 - 2x \le 6$

b) $7 < 4x - 3 \le 13$

Answers:

8. a) $2 < x < 3$

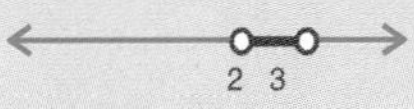

b) $-4 < x < 2$

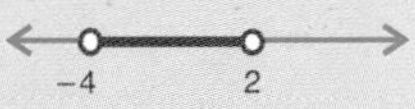

9. a) $-2 \le x \le 2$

b) $\frac{5}{2} < x \le 4$

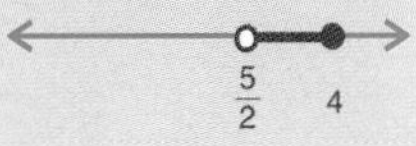

F. TRANSLATING STATEMENTS OF INEQUALITY

There are many different phrases that indicate a statement of inequality, such as

"is at most" , **"is greater than"** , **"is no more than"** , **"is at least"** , **"is less than"**.

Usually a problem involving an inequality includes a simple statement of the inequality relationship. For example, in a perimeter problem, you may be told: "The perimeter is at least 400 yards".

To determine how to write this, ask yourself which of the following are allowed:

$$P < 400 \text{ yd}$$

$$P > 400 \text{ yd}$$

$$P = 400 \text{ yd}$$

If P is at least 400 yards, then P can be greater than 400 yd or equal to 400 yd. But P cannot be less than 400 yds. Therefore $P \ge 400$ is the statement of the inequality.

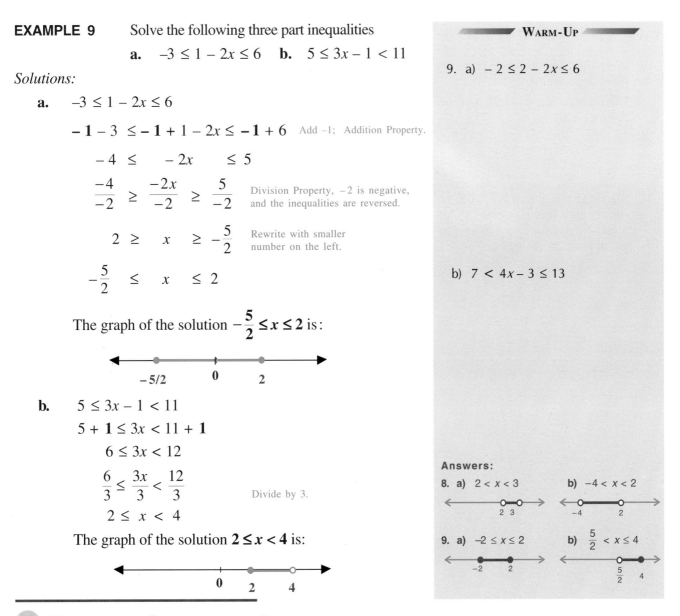

10. Write the inequality to express the following statement.

The number of applicants, A, is no more than 80.

11. Manda scored grades of 78, 65, 43 on her first three exams. What must she make in her last test to get at least an average of 70?

Answers:

10. $A \leq 80$

11. Greater than or equal to 94.

EXAMPLE 10   Write an inequality to express the following statement. The temperature exceeded 115° all day.

Solution: The temperature (t) exceeded 115° all day.

If t exceeded 115° then $t > 115°$. The other two statements.

$t < 115°$ and $t = 115°$ cannot be true.

EXAMPLE 11   Classie has test grades of 78, 84, and 76 on the first three tests in her pre-algebra class. What are the possible scores she can make on the fourth test in order to make at least a letter grade of "B" after the fourth test. A letter grade "B" means an average of at least 80.

Solution: Total earning of five employees

Average of at least 80 $\longrightarrow$ Average ≥ 80

Suppose the score that Classie makes on the fourth test $= x$.

The average of the four tests $= \dfrac{78 + 84 + 76 + x}{4}$.

Classie's grade will be at least 'B' if

$$\dfrac{78 + 84 + 76 + x}{4} \geq 80 \qquad \text{Average is atleast 80.}$$

$$\dfrac{238 + x}{4} \geq 80$$

$$238 + x \geq 320 \qquad \text{Multiply both sides by 4.}$$

$$x \geq 82 \qquad \text{Add } -238.$$

Classie needs to score **at least 82** on the fourth test.

EXERCISE 2.8

A.   In exercises 1-24, graph the interval, or find the inequality in algebraic form from its graph.

1. $x \geq 4$ 2. $x \geq -2$ 3. $x > -3$ 4. $x > 1$ 5. $x < 0$ 6. $x < 2$

7. $x \leq -1$ 8. $x \leq 4$ 9. $-3 < x \leq 7$ 10. $-5 < x \leq 0$ 11. $0 \leq x \leq 6$ 12. $-1 \leq x \leq 1$

13. $-5 < x \leq -2$ 14. $-2 < x \leq 1$ 15. $-2 \leq x < 0$ 16. $1 \leq x < 3$ 17.

18.

19.

20.

21.

22.
9

23.
−12

24.
6

B. In exercises 25-64, solve the inequality.

25. $x + 2 < 3$ **26.** $x - 3 < 4$ **27.** $x + 5 \le -2$ **28.** $x - 4 \le -6$ **29.** $x + 1 \le -8$

30. $x + 6 < -1$ **31.** $x - 2 < 7$ **32.** $x + 7 \le 5$ **33.** $x - 6 \le 4$ **34.** $x - 5 < -7$

35. $x + 5 > 1$ **36.** $x + 4 > -2$ **37.** $x + 8 \ge 6$ **38.** $x - 6 \ge 5$ **39.** $x - 2 > 7$

40. $x - 4 \ge -5$ **41.** $x - 9 > -6$ **42.** $x + 7 \ge -5$ **43.** $x + 6 > -6$ **44.** $x - 8 \ge 5$

45. $2x + 1 < 5$ **46.** $3x - 1 \le 2$ **47.** $6x + 4 \le 3$ **48.** $5x + 4 < -1$ **49.** $7x - 2 \le 6$

50. $4x - 5 < -4$ **51.** $8x - 4 \le 7$ **52.** $9x - 8 < -7$ **53.** $7x - 6 \le -4$ **54.** $6x + 5 < -8$

55. $3x + 0.1 > 0.4$ **56.** $0.2x - 4 \le 6$ **57.** $0.5x - 4 > 6$ **58.** $4x + 3.8 \ge -1$ **59.** $7x - 0.7 \le -4.9$

60. $8x + 3.1 > -1.7$ **61.** $9x - 4 > -0.4$ **62.** $6x + 2 \ge 5.6$ **63.** $0.4x - 5.2 > 4$ **64.** $8x + 1.2 \ge -8.4$

C. In exercises 65-78, solve the inequality and graph the solution.

65. $-7p < 4p + 22$ **66.** $8(x - 1) < 2(x - 4) + 6$ **67.** $5(x - 1) \le 3x + 1$

68. $9(x - 2) - 7(x - 2) \le 0$ **69.** $5 - (2 - z) > 3z + 5$ **70.** $2(3 - y) - 7 > -2(2 + y) + y$

71. $4(2 - 3k) \ge 9 - 5(2k - 1)$ **72.** $5(2k - 3) \ge -9 + 4(k + 2) + 4$ **73.** $10x + 5 - (x - 15) \le x + 3 - 23$

74. $7(y + 3) - 2(-y + 7) \le 3y + 13$ **75.** $x + (x - 5) \ge x$ **76.** $(2x + 9) - (3x + 7) \ge 5x - 10$

77. $(x + 3) - (x - 3) > x + 1$ **78.** $3(x + 2) - 3(-x + 6) > 2(x - 4)$

D. In exercises 79-94, solve the inequality.

79. $-(x + 4) \le (2x + 5)$ **80.** $-2(2 - x) < 3x + 1$ **81.** $-4(-5 - x) > 3(x + 2) + x - 1$

82. $20 + 4x > 4x$ **83.** $4x + \dfrac{7}{8} > 2x + \dfrac{1}{4}$ **84.** $x + \dfrac{5}{12} \ge 2x - \dfrac{3}{4}$

85. $3y - \dfrac{1}{2} < y - \dfrac{3}{4}$ **86.** $4(-4 + x) > 3(x - 1) + 6 + x$ **87.** $6(x + 1) \ge 5 + (x + 3) - 3x$

88. $-2(-3x - 10) < -5(x - 2) + 3$ **89.** $\dfrac{1}{2}(5x - 7) \le -\dfrac{1}{4}(6 - 2x)$ **90.** $\dfrac{1}{5}(6 - 4d) < \dfrac{2}{5}(6d + 3)$

91. $6x + 4 - 3 < 5 + \dfrac{2}{5}(3 - 2x)$ **92.** $\dfrac{3}{5}(15 - 10a) - 2 \le \dfrac{3}{8}(8a - 16) + 5$

93. $4[2(x + 2) - (3 - x)] > 6(x + 3)$ **94.** $3(b - 6) \le 5[2(b - 1) - 3(1 + b)]$

E. In exercises 95-117, solve the three-part inequality.

95. $3 < x + 2 < 5$ **96.** $4 < x - 6 < 7$ **97.** $-2 \le x + 7 < 4$ **98.** $-1 \le x - 5 < 5$

99. $-3 < x + 6 \le -1$ **100.** $-5 < x - 8 \le -2$ **101.** $2 < x - 7 \le 8$ **102.** $-6 \le x + 5 \le 2$

103. $-7 \le x + 4 \le -2$ **104.** $-5 \le x - 7 \le 5$ **105.** $4 < 2x + 1 \le 5$ **106.** $2 < 3x - 2 \le 6$

107. $-2 < 4x - 5 \le 6$ **108.** $-6 \le 5x + 3 < -2$ **109.** $-1 \le 7x + 2 < 5$ **110.** $-7 \le 6x - 4 < -2$

111. $4 \le 8x - 1 \le 7$ **112.** $6 \le 6x + 4 \le 9$ **113.** $-4 \le 8x + 6 \le 6$ **114.** $-2 < 7x - 8 \le 4$

115. $-9 < 9x - 5 \le -8$ **116.** $-6 \le -3(x - 4) < 24$ **117.** $-2 < -2(x + 5) \le 10$

F. In exercises 118-125, use the inequality to express the statement in symbols.

118. The profit (P) must be at least $ 50,000.

119. The population (P) varied from 1,000 to 15,000 in the rural towns.

120. No more than 5 tutors (T) will be hired.

121. Between 50 and 100 students (S) were expected to attend the orientation session.

122. No fewer than 20 cakes (C) were made each hour.

123. The area (A) must be at least 4,000 square miles but less than 9,000 square miles.

124. The cost (C) must be kept below $90.

125. The final exam should count between 15% and 25% of the final (F) grade.

In exercises 126-142, setup and solve the inequalities to solve the problem.

126. The $19 wholesale cost of a clock radio added to the profit must not be more than $32 or the radio will not sell. What is the possible profit?

127. The $225 wholesale cost of a computer and the profit must not be more than $300 or the computer will not sell. What is the possible profit?

128. Lawanda has test scores of 70, 77, 85. What score on the fourth test would give her an average of 80 or better?

129. Lisa invests $10,000 at 8% annual simple interest. How much more should she invest at 9% so that her annual interest will exceed $1250?

130. The length of a rectangle is 5 feet greater than its width. If the perimeter must be at least 38 feet, but no more than 62 feet, find possible values of the width.

131. A student has test scores of 85, 75, and 98 on the first three tests. A letter grade of 'A' means an average of 90 or more. Can the student make an 'A' after the fourth test?

132. A student has test scores of 70, 75, 90 in the first three tests. What score on the fourth test would give an average of 80 or better?

133. John has test scores of 80, 78,79 in the first three tests. What score on the fourth test would give him an average of 85 or better.

134. A student has test scores of 81, 80, 82, 83 in first four tests of Pre-algebra. What score on the fifth test would give an average score of 85 or better.

135. The cost of renting a truck is $39.99 for the first hour and $19.99 for each additional hour. How long can a person have the truck if the cost is to be less than $120.

136. Eric can afford to spend no more than $350 on a stereo system and some compact discs. If the stereo cost $180 and the discs are $9 each, find the greatest number of discs he can buy.

137. Suppose that a long distance telephone call costs 30 cents for the first three minutes and 11 cents for each additional minute. For how many minutes can a person talk for less than $2.50.

138. If a long distance telephone call costs $\$0.6$ for the first 5 minutes and $\$0.14$ for each additional minute, for how many minutes can a person talk for less than $\$5$.

139. The number 23.7 lies between 23 and 24 and 35.8 lies between 35 and 36. Write the range of the estimate of the product 23.7×35.8 as a three-parts inequality.

140. What is the range of the estimate of the product 73.5×86.6? (Use a three part inequality)

141. Ken is 6 years younger than his cousin Rager. The sum of their ages does not exceed 40. What is the maximum possible age of Rager?

142. The amount of current used in operating a certain electrical appliance must be in the range of 7 to 9.5A. If 12 such appliances are to be used, what is the range of total current being used?

2.9 CHAPTER SUMMARY

EXAMPLES

1. We can simplify expressions by combining like terms.

1. $\underbrace{2x + 3x} \underbrace{- 7 + 9} = 5x + 2$

2. Addition Property:

The **same** number may be added to each side of an equation.

2.
$$2x + 3 = 0$$
$$2x + 3 + (-3) = 0 + (-3)$$
$$2x = -3$$

3. Multiplication (or Division) Property:

Both sides of an equation may be multiplied (or divided) by the **same non-zero** number. All terms on both sides are multiplied (or divided) by that number.

3.
$$2x = -3$$
$$\frac{1}{2} \cdot 2x = \frac{1}{2} \cdot (-3)$$
$$x = -\frac{3}{2}$$

4. Steps for solving a Linear Equation:

Step 1 Use the distributive property and/or combine like terms on each side and simplify.

Step 2 Eliminate fractions or decimals by multiply both sides by LCD.

Step 3 Use the addition property to move all variable terms to one side and constant terms to the other side.

Step 4 Isolate the variable using the multiplication property of equality.

Step 5 Verify the solution by substituting it in the original equation.

4.
$$2x + 4x - 3 = x + 3 + 7$$
$$6x - 3 = x + 10$$
$$6x - 3 + 3 = x + 10 + 3$$
$$6x = x + 13$$
$$6x + (-x) = x + 13 + (-x)$$
$$5x = 13$$
$$\frac{1}{5}(5x) = \frac{1}{5} \cdot 13 \rightarrow x = \frac{13}{5}$$

Verification: $x = \frac{13}{5}$; $6x - 3 = x + 10$

$$6\left(\frac{13}{5}\right) - 3 = \frac{13}{5} + 10$$
$$\rightarrow \frac{78}{5} - 3 = \frac{13}{5} + 10$$
$$\rightarrow \frac{63}{5} = \frac{63}{5} \quad \text{True}$$

5. An equation which on simplification becomes a **true statement** is called an identity. An **identity** is true for all real numbers.

6. An equation which on simplification leads to a **false statement** has **no solution**. Such an equation is called a **contradiction**.

7. **To solve a word problem involving linear equations,** read the problem carefully and use the following steps:

Step **1**   Identify the unknown and choose a variable to represent the unknown.

Step **2**   Write down mathematical expression for any other unknown quantities using the variable. If possible, draw diagram or organize the information in a table.

Step **3**   Translate the problem into an equation.

Step **4**   Solve the equation.

Step **5**   Answer the question asked. Make sure the solution makes sense in reference to the question.

Step **6**   Verify your answer by using the original statement of the problem.

EXAMPLES

8. Given $3xy + 4x^2 = 4x - 4$, find y when $x = 2$

$$3(2)y + 4(2)^2 = 4(2) - 4$$
$$\rightarrow \quad 6y + 16 = 8 - 4$$
$$\rightarrow \quad 6y + 16 = 4 \rightarrow 6y = -12 \rightarrow y = -2$$

9. Solve for F ; $\quad C = \dfrac{5}{9}(F - 32)$

$$\rightarrow \qquad C = \frac{5F}{9} - \frac{160}{9}$$
$$\rightarrow \qquad 9C = 5F - 160$$
$$\rightarrow \quad 5F - 160 = 9C$$
$$\rightarrow \qquad 5F = 9C + 160 \rightarrow F = \frac{9}{5}C + 32$$

10. Ratio of 5 cents to 2 dollars is:

$$\frac{5 \text{ cents}}{2 \text{ dollars}} = \frac{5 \text{ cents}}{200 \text{ cents}} = \frac{5}{200} = \frac{1}{40}$$

11. Ms. Tonya earns \$150 working 12 hours a week. How much does she earn if she works 18 hours?

Suppose Ms. Tonya earns x dollars working 18 hours a week. Then

$$\frac{x}{150} = \frac{18 \text{ hours}}{12 \text{ hours}} \qquad \text{Cross multiply.}$$

$$12 \cdot x = 2700 \rightarrow x = 225$$

She earns \$225 working 18 hours a week.

LITERAL EQUATIONS

8. If values of all but one variable in a formula are given, then the value of the remaining variable can be found by substituting the given values into the formula and solving for the remaining variable.

9. A formula or equation can be solved for a specified variable by treating all other variables as constants and then solving the resulting equation for the specified variable.

RATIOS AND PROPORTIONS

10. To calculate a ratio of two quantities, they must be expressed in the same units.

11. **A proportion is a statement** that two ratios or fractions are equal. We can use the method of cross multiplication for solving a proportion.

12. **Addition Property:** If the same number is added to each side of an inequality, the inequality does not change.

12. $3x + 4 \leq 3$

$\rightarrow \qquad 3x + 4 + (-4) \leq 3 + (-4)$

$\rightarrow \qquad\qquad\qquad 3x \leq -1$

13. **Multiplication Property:** Multiplying (or dividing) both sides of an inequality by a negative number reverses the order relation of inequality. Multiplying both sides by a positive number does not change the order relation ($<$ or $>$).

13. $-3x \leq 1$

Observe the change of symbol.

$\rightarrow \qquad \dfrac{1}{-3}(-3x) \geq \dfrac{1}{-3}(1)$

$\rightarrow \qquad\qquad x \geq -\dfrac{1}{3}$

14. **To solve and graph an inequality**

Step **1** Use the distributive property and/or combine like terms on both sides.

Step **2** Eliminate fractions or decimals by multiplying both sides by the LCD.

Step **3** Use the addition property of inequalities to move all variable terms to one side and constant terms to the other side.

Step **4** Use the multiplication property of inequalities to isolate the variable.

Step **5** Graph the inequality.

14. Solve $3x + 1 \leq x - 4$

$3x + 1 + (-1) \leq x - 4 + (-1)$

$\rightarrow \qquad\quad 3x \leq x - 5$

$\rightarrow \qquad 3x + (-x) \leq x - 5 + (-x)$

$\rightarrow \qquad\qquad 2x \leq -5$

$\dfrac{1}{2}(2x) \leq \dfrac{1}{2}(-5) \rightarrow x \leq \dfrac{-5}{2}$

$-5/2 \qquad 0$

2.10 REVIEW EXERCISES

In exercises 1-12, combine like terms and simplify wherever possible.

1. $7x + 4x - 7$
2. $3x - 9x + 5$
3. $3x - 7 + 2x - 15$
4. $-2x - 3x + 2 + 5$

5. $5 - 2x + 9 - 4x$
6. $3(x - 1) + 2(-x + 5)$
7. $2(4 - x) + 9x$
8. $-2(2x + 6) - 9 + 3(x + 2)$

9. $x^2 + 3x - 5 - 5(3 - 4x)$
10. $5x^2 + 2x + 6 + (4x + 3)$
11. $-(4z + 6) + 3(z - 4)$
12. $x^2 + 4x + 4(x^2 - 2x + 1)$

In exercises 13-27, solve the equation.

13. $k + 5 = 7$
14. $5 - x = 9$
15. $3x = 4$
16. $-2x = 9$

17. $2x - 4 = 10$
18. $7 - 4x = 11$
19. $-11 + 2x = 1$
20. $10y + 5 = 17$

21. $12z - 11 = 61$
22. $-2z + 3 = 9$
23. $2p + 3 = 3(p - 5)$
24. $2(x - 3) + 4(x - 12) = -2(x + 27)$

25. $4(x - 1) + 2(x - 1) = 3(x + 1)$
26. $\dfrac{1}{3}m - \dfrac{1}{2}m = 4$
27. $\dfrac{1}{4}x + \dfrac{1}{2}x = 2$

In exercises 28-32, solve the word problem.

28. When five is subtracted from three times a number, the result is nineteen. Find the number.

29. Three times a number added to four is twice the number. Find the number.

30. The supplement of an angle measures seven times its complement. Find the measure of the angle.

31. The supplement of an angle is four times its complement. Find the measure of the angle.

32. The sum of the ages of a father and his son is 70. The age of the father is 10 years more than twice the age of the son. Find the age of each of them.

In exercises 33-40, solve the formula for the specified variable.

33. $V = abh$; for h **34.** $2x - 3y = 4$; for y **35.** $2x - 3y = 4$; for x **36.** $4x + y = 9$; for y

37. $\dfrac{x}{2} - \dfrac{a}{5} = 3$; for a **38.** $\dfrac{5}{a} + \dfrac{1}{b} = 7$; for b **39.** $\dfrac{4}{a} + \dfrac{3}{b} = \dfrac{1}{c}$; for a **40.** $\dfrac{1}{x} + \dfrac{y}{2} = 3$; for x

In exercises 41-48, write the ratio and reduce them to lowest terms, wherever possible.

41. 16 feet to 24 feet   **42.** 60 inches to 7 feet   **43.** 2 dollars to 25 cents   **44.** 2 km to 200 meter
[1 km = 1000 meters]

45. 5 dimes to 4 nickels   **46.** 27 inches to 5 feet   **47.** 2 yards to 4 inches   **48.** 1 hour to 25 minutes

In exercises 49-54, identify proportion.

49. $\dfrac{1}{2} = \dfrac{2}{4}$ **50.** $\dfrac{5}{15} = \dfrac{1}{3}$ **51.** $\dfrac{13}{25} = \dfrac{23}{45}$ **52.** $\dfrac{15}{24} = \dfrac{35}{56}$ **53.** $\dfrac{8}{64} = \dfrac{12}{96}$ **54.** $\dfrac{10}{25} = \dfrac{26}{40}$

In exercises 55-62, solve the proportion.

55. $\dfrac{x}{5} = \dfrac{4}{10}$ **56.** $\dfrac{3}{5} = \dfrac{x}{15}$ **57.** $\dfrac{3}{x} = \dfrac{4}{5}$ **58.** $\dfrac{2}{x} = \dfrac{3}{5}$

59. $\dfrac{x-1}{2} = \dfrac{5}{8}$ **60.** $\dfrac{x}{3} = \dfrac{2x-1}{5}$ **61.** $\dfrac{2x-3}{5} = \dfrac{x-6}{-2}$ **62.** $\dfrac{4x+1}{3} = \dfrac{x+5}{2}$

In exercises 63-68, solve the word problem.

63. One quart of oil must be mixed with 20 quarts of gasoline. How much oil is needed for 150 quarts of gasoline?

64. Perimeter of a triangle is 38 inches. Longest side of the triangle is 1 inch less than twice the smallest side. Third side is 3 inches more than the smallest side. Find the lengths of the three sides of the triangle.

65. Two air planes leave San Francisco at the same time in opposite directions. They fly with a speed of 350 miles per hour and 440 miles per hour respectively. In how many hours will they be 1,580 miles apart?

66. John invests a part of his savings of $5,000 at 6% and the remaining at 7%. The total annual income from the interest is $324. Find the amount of each of the two investments.

67. The distance between two cities on a road map is 12 centimeters. The two cities are actually 150 miles apart. What is the actual distance between two cities which are joined by a 21 centimeter line on this map?

68. Two trains are 480 miles apart. They start at the same time, and travel towards one another. The difference between the speeds of the two trains is 20 miles per hour. If the two trains meet after four hours, find the speed of the faster train.

In exercises 69-77, solve the inequality and graph the solution set.

69. $3 + x \geq -9$ **70.** $3 - x \geq 5$ **71.** $3x \leq 9$

72. $-3x \leq 12$ **73.** $4x + 3 < 5$ **74.** $4 - 5x > 24$

75. $2x + 7 \leq 5(x - 4)$ **76.** $4 - 5k - 3(2k - 7) > -(k + 2)$ **77.** $-7 < 3m + 5 \leq 14$

78. The perimeter of a given square is at most 120 feet. Find the possible values for the length of a side.

2.11 SELF TEST

In exercises 1-4, simplify by combining like terms.

1. $-4x + 7y + 2(3x - 5) + 7$

2. $2(x + 2) - 3(y + 2) + 7$

3. $3(x - y) + 4(y - x) - 5(x + y)$

4. $6(x + 2y) + 3(y + 4x) - 9(x + 2)$

In exercises 5-14, solve the equation.

5. $4(p + 3) + 7 = 3p - 1$

6. $6(x - 2) - 2(x + 1) = 4$

7. $\frac{3}{4}y - 2 = 3$

8. $\frac{1}{4}x + 2 = \frac{1}{3}$

9. $0.1(x + 70) + 0.3x = -1$

10. $0.2(x + 9) - 0.5x = 2$

11. $4(3x - 5) - 3(x + 2) = 9x + 5$

12. $3(2x - 5) + 6(x + 4) = 13x + 3$

13. $3z + 2(z - 4) = 5z - 8$

14. $(6z + 3) - (z + 4) = 2z + 8$

In exercises 15-18, solve the proportion.

15. $\frac{x}{7} = \frac{42}{21}$

16. $\frac{y}{-7} = \frac{12}{6}$

17. $\frac{2m - 1}{5} = \frac{3m + 1}{3}$

18. $\frac{4m + 2}{3} = \frac{6m + 1}{2}$

19. When three times a number is added to 7, the result is 18. Find the number.

20. The perimeter of a rectangle is 36 cm. The length of the rectangle is 4 cm more than its width. Find the dimensions of the rectangle.

21. Given that $(x - 35)°$ and $(65 + 2x)°$ are supplementary angles, determine x.

22. If $(x + 20)°$ and $(2x - 20)°$ are complementary angles, determine x.

23. Solve the formula $S = 2(ab + bh + ah)$ for h.

24. How many liters of 30% chemical solution must be mixed with 30 liters of 70% solution to get a 60% mixture?

25. Willie invests some money at 7.5%. He also invests $4,000 less than this amount at 6.5%. His total annual income from the interest of these two investments is $1,000. How much money is invested at each rate?

In exercises 26-33, solve the inequality and graph the solution.

26. $-3p > 15$

27. $5x < 20$

28. $2x + 7 \leq -5 + x$

29. $-3x + 9 \geq 3 + x$

30. $3(a + 2) - 5a \leq 4(2a - 3)$

31. $2(a - 2) + 4a > 2(2a + 1)$

32. $-6 \leq 3 - 3k < 15$

33. $-2 \leq 4k + 2 \leq 10$

In exercises 34-37, find the inequality from the graph of its solution.

34.
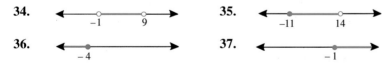

35.

36.

37.

38. Lisa has scores 85, 93, and 89 on her first three tests in Algebra. What possible scores on the fourth test will enable her to achieve an average of 90 or more on the four tests? Assume that her scores cannot be fractional numbers.

Linear Equations and Inequalities in Two Variable

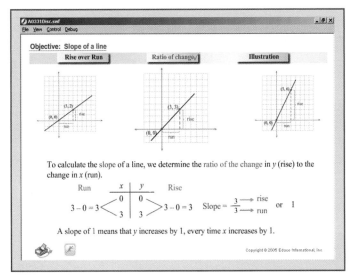

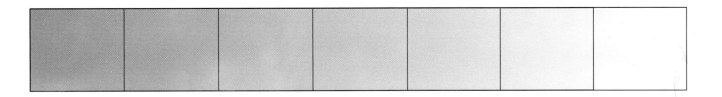

LINEAR EQUATIONS AND INEQUALITIES IN TWO VARIABLES

3

This Chapter is divided into the following sections:

3.1 LINEAR EQUATIONS IN TWO VARIABLES

Equations like $3x + 4 = 0$ are called *linear equations in one variable*. Equations like : $y = 3x + 4$ and $4x + 5y = 1$ are examples of linear equations in two variables.

An equation in two variables, say x and y, is called linear if it can be written in the form $ax + by = c$, where a, b and c are real numbers, and both a or b are not zero. Thus $2x - 7y = 1$ is a linear equation in x and y and $3q + p = 5$ is a linear equation in p and q.

OBJECTIVES ■■■■

Upon completion of this section you will be able to:

A. Write a solution of a linear equation;

B. Complete a table of values of solutions;

C. Plot ordered pairs; and

D. Identify the relationship between the components of ordered pairs.

A. SOLUTIONS OF A LINEAR EQUATION

A **solution** of a linear equation in two variables is a pair of numbers, one for each variable, which when substituted for the respective variables makes the equation true.

For example, $2x + 3y = 1$ is satisfied by $x = 2$ and $y = -1$.

$$2(2) + 3(-1) = 1 \quad \longrightarrow \quad 4 - 3 = 1 \qquad \text{True}$$

Thus, the pair $x = 2$ and $y = -1$ is a solution of $2x + 3y = 1$.

This is also expressed by saying that the *ordered pair* $(x, y) = (2, -1)$ is a solution of $2x + 3y = 1$.

We may check whether or not the ordered pair is a solution of the given equation by using calculator. See example 1 of section 3.1 in Appendix B.

Remark: An ordered pair is a pair (a, b) of numbers for which the order of appearance of the two numbers a and b is important. Thus, $(2, -1)$ is not the same as $(-1, 2)$. For an ordered pair (a, b), a is called the ***x*-coordinate**, and b is called the ***y*-coordinate**. In general, letters representing components of an ordered pair are in alphabetical order.

A linear equation in two variables has infinitely many solutions.

1. Verify that $x = 2$, $y = 2$, and $x = 4$, $y = -1$, both are the solutions of the equation $3x + 2y = 10$.

2. Identify whether the given ordered pair is a solution of the indicated equation.

a) $(3, 1)$; $2x - y = 4$

b) $(1, 2)$; $x - y = -1$

c) $(2, 5)$; $3x - y = 1$

Answers:

1. Yes

2. a) No   b) Yes   c) Yes

EXAMPLE 1   Verify that $x = 2$, $y = 3$ and $y = -1$, $x = 4$, are both solutions of the equation $2x + y = 7$. Write these solutions as ordered pairs of numbers.

Solution:

Verification : $x = 2$, $y = 3$:

Substitute these values in $2x + y = 7$

$2 \cdot 2 + 3 = 7 \longrightarrow 7 = 7$ True

Therefore, $x = 2$, $y = 3$ is a solution of $2x + y = 7$.

This solution is written as $(2, 3)$.

Again, substitute $y = -1$, $x = 4$ in the equation.

$$2x + y = 7$$
$$2 \cdot 4 + (-1) = 7$$
$$7 = 7 \qquad \text{True}$$

Therefore, $y = -1$ and $x = 4$ is also a solution of $2x + y = 7$. This solution is written as $(4, -1)$, and not as $(-1, 4)$, since the x comes first in the alphabetical order.

EXAMPLE 2   Identify whether the given ordered pair is a solution of the indicated equation.

a. $(-4, 5)$; $2x - y = 10$

b. $(1, 1)$; $x - y = 0$

c. $(1, 3)$; $2y - x = 5$

Solutions:

a. $(-4, 5)$; $2x - y = 10$

Substitute -4 for x and 5 for y.

$2(-4) - 5 = 10 \longrightarrow -8 - 5 = 10$

$\longrightarrow \qquad -13 = 10$ False

Therefore, $(-4, 5)$ **is not a solution** of $2x - y = 10$.

b. $(1, 1)$; $x - y = 0$

Substitute 1 for x and 1 for y.

$1 - 1 = 0 \longrightarrow 0 = 0$ True

Therefore, $(1, 1)$ **is a solution** of $x - y = 0$.

c. $(1, 3)$; $2y - x = 5$

Substitute 1 for x and 3 for y.

$2 \cdot 3 - 1 = 5 \longrightarrow 5 = 5$ True

Therefore, $(1, 3)$ **is a solution** of $2y - x = 5$.

B. COMPLETING A TABLE OF VALUES

One way to graph an equation, in two variables, is to construct a table of values. This can be done by substituting the value of one variable into the equation, and solving for the other.

EXAMPLE 3   For the equation $2x + 5y - 3 = 0$, find the missing coordinate of the ordered pairs, in order, for these pairs to be solutions.

   a. $(-3, ?)$ **b.** $(?, 5)$

Solutions:

a. $(-3, ?)$:

$$2x + 5y - 3 = 0, \qquad \text{First coordinate is } -3.$$
$$2(-3) + 5y - 3 = 0, \qquad \text{Substitute } -3 \text{ for } x.$$
$$-6 + 5y - 3 = 0$$
$$5y - 9 = 0$$
$$5y = 9 \;\longrightarrow\; y = \frac{9}{5}$$

Thus, the completed ordered pair is $\left(-3, \dfrac{9}{5}\right)$.

b. $(?, 5)$:

$$2x + 5y - 3 = 0, \qquad \text{Second coordinate is 5.}$$
$$2x + 5 \cdot 5 - 3 = 0, \qquad \text{Substitute 5 for } y.$$
$$2x + 22 = 0$$
$$2x = -22 \;\longrightarrow\; x = -11$$

Thus, the completed ordered pair is **(-11, 5)**.

In order to complete the table of values, we must complete the ordered pairs as shown in the following examples.

EXAMPLE 4   Complete the given table of values for the equation $2x + y = 7$.

x	y
-1	—
2	—
5	—
—	3
—	-2

Solution:

When **x is -1;**
$$2(-1) + y = 7 \quad\longrightarrow\quad -2 + y = 7 \quad\longrightarrow\quad y = 9.$$

When **x is 2;**
$$2 \cdot 2 + y = 7 \quad\longrightarrow\quad 4 + y = 7 \quad\longrightarrow\quad y = 3.$$

When **x is 5;**
$$2 \cdot 5 + y = 7 \quad\longrightarrow\quad 10 + y = 7 \quad\longrightarrow\quad y = -3.$$

━━━ **WARM-UP** ━━━

3. For the equation $3x + 4y + 6 = 0$, find the missing coordinate of the ordered pairs, in order, for these pairs to be the solutions.

   a) $(-4, ?)$

   b) $(?, 3)$

4. Compute the given table of values for the equation $4x + 3y = 11$.

x	y
—	1
-3	--
4	--
2	--
—	0

When **y is 3;**

$2x + 3 = 7 \quad \longrightarrow \quad 2x = 4 \quad \longrightarrow \quad x = 2$

When **y is –2;**

$2x + (-2) = 7 \quad \longrightarrow \quad 2x = 9 \quad \longrightarrow \quad x = 4.5$

Therefore, the completed table of values is:

x	y
–1	**9**
2	**3**
5	**–3**
2	3
4.5	–2

5. Complete the following table of values for the equation $x = -2$.

x	y
__	4
__	–4
__	0
__	5

Answers:

3. a) $\frac{3}{2}$ b) –6

4.

x	y
2	1
–3	7.67
4	–1.67
2	1
2.75	0

5.

x	y
–2	4
–2	–4
–2	0
–2	5

EXAMPLE 5   Complete the following table of values for the equation $x = 3$.

x	y
__	–3
__	0
__	5

Solution:

Since the given equation $x = 3$ does not contain y. It can be written as $x + 0 \cdot y = 3$. The value of x remains 3 for all values of y. Therefore, the completed table of values is:

x	y
3	–3
3	0
3	5

C. PLOTTING ORDERED PAIRS

When two intersecting number lines, one horizontal and another vertical, are drawn in the plane, the plane is divided into four regions [Figure 3.1]. Each of these regions is called a **quadrant.** A coordinate system can be set up, such that:

(a) the point of intersection of these lines represents zero on both number lines.

(b) numbers to the right of zero on the horizontal number line are positive.

(c) numbers above zero on the vertical line are positive.

- The horizontal number line is called the **x-axis.**
- The vertical line is called the **y-axis.**
- The x-axis and y-axis together constitute the **rectangular coordinate system.**
- The point of intersection is called the **origin.**
- The quadrants are numbered as shown in Figure 3.1.

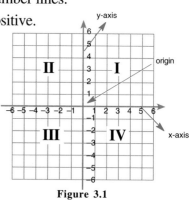

Figure 3.1

Note Quadrants are numbered with Roman numerals in the counter-clockwise direction.

Every ordered pair of real numbers represents a point on the plane. The point represented by (*a*, *b*) is said to have *a* as its **x-coordinate** and *b* as its **y-coordinate.** In general, *a* and *b* are called the **coordinates** of the point.

A point with coordinates (*a*, *b*) is plotted as follows:

1. Mark *a* on the *x*-axis.

2. Go *b* units vertically upwards from *a* if *b* is *positive,* or *b* units vertically downwards if *b* is *negative.* If *b* is zero, then the point marked at *a* on the *x*-axis is the required point.

EXAMPLE 6   Plot the following points on a coordinate plane:

  a. (2, 4)   **b.** (–2, 5)   **c.** (–5, –7)

  d. $\left(\frac{5}{2}, -1\right)$ **e.** (3, 0)   **f.** (0, –2)

Solutions:

  a. (2, 4):   Locate the point representing 2 on the *x*-axis. Since 4 is positive, move *vertically upwards* 4 units from this point. The point A in Figure 3.2 is the graph of (2, 4).

  b. (–2, 5):   Locate the point representing –2 on the *x*-axis. Since 5 is positive, move 5 units *vertically upwards.* The point B in Figure 3.2 is the graph of (–2, 5).

  c. (–5, –7):   Locate the point representing –5 on the *x*-axis. Since –7 is negative, move *vertically downwards* 7 units from this point. The point *C* in Figure 3.2 is the graph of (–5, –7).

  d. $\left(\frac{5}{2}, -1\right)$:   Locate the point representing $\frac{5}{2}$ on the *x*-axis.

    Since –1 is negative, move *vertically downwards* 1 unit from this point. The point *D* in Figure 3.2 is the graph of (5/2, –1).

  e. (3, 0):   Locate the point representing 3 on the *x*-axis. This is the point whose coordinates are (3, 0). The point E in Figure 3.2 is the graph of (3, 0).

  f. (0, –2):   Locate the point representing zero on *x*-axis. Since –2 is negative, move vertically downwards 2 units from this point. The point F in Figure 3.2 is the graph of the point (0, –2). Figure 3.2 is the graph of (0, –2).

WARM-UP

6. Plot the following points :

  a) A (3, 3)

  b) B (2, – 2)

  c) C (0, 5)

  d) D (– 3, 0)

  e) E (– 4, – 2)

  f) F (– 2, – 5)

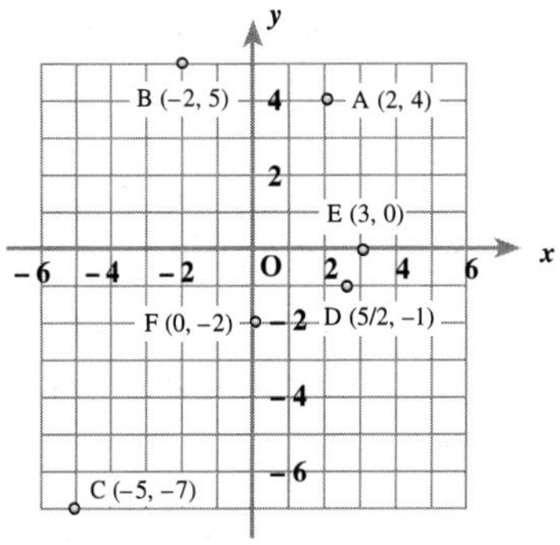

Figure 3.2

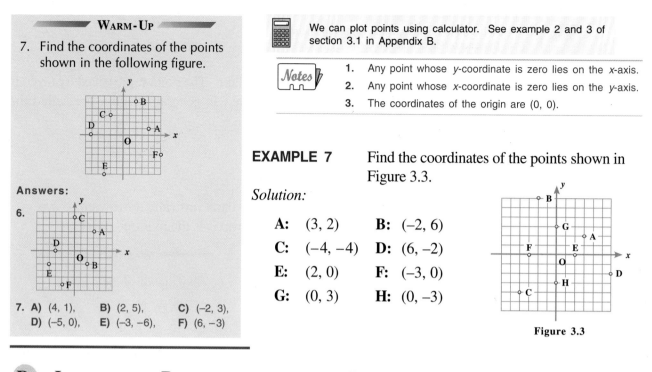

WARM-UP

7. Find the coordinates of the points shown in the following figure.

We can plot points using calculator. See example 2 and 3 of section 3.1 in Appendix B.

Notes

1. Any point whose *y*-coordinate is zero lies on the *x*-axis.
2. Any point whose *x*-coordinate is zero lies on the *y*-axis.
3. The coordinates of the origin are (0, 0).

Answers:

6.

7. A) (4, 1),   B) (2, 5),   C) (−2, 3),
   D) (−5, 0),   E) (−3, −6),   F) (6, −3)

EXAMPLE 7   Find the coordinates of the points shown in Figure 3.3.

Solution:

A:	(3, 2)	**B:**	(−2, 6)
C:	(−4, −4)	**D:**	(6, −2)
E:	(2, 0)	**F:**	(−3, 0)
G:	(0, 3)	**H:**	(0, −3)

Figure 3.3

D. IDENTIFY THE RELATIONSHIP BETWEEN COORDINATES OF ORDERED PAIRS

Consider the following collection of ordered pairs, and :

a) identify the relationship, if any, between the *x* and *y* coordinates,

b) plot the points, or the ordered pairs, and

c) observe the pattern of the plots.

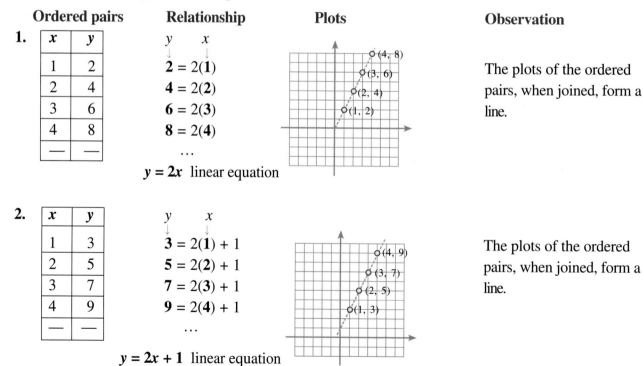

Ordered pairs

1.

x	y
1	2
2	4
3	6
4	8
—	—

Relationship

y   x
↓   ↓
2 = 2(**1**)
4 = 2(**2**)
6 = 2(**3**)
8 = 2(**4**)
...

$y = 2x$ linear equation

Plots

Observation

The plots of the ordered pairs, when joined, form a line.

2.

x	y
1	3
2	5
3	7
4	9
—	—

y   x
↓   ↓
3 = 2(**1**) + 1
5 = 2(**2**) + 1
7 = 2(**3**) + 1
9 = 2(**4**) + 1
...

$y = 2x + 1$ linear equation

The plots of the ordered pairs, when joined, form a line.

3.

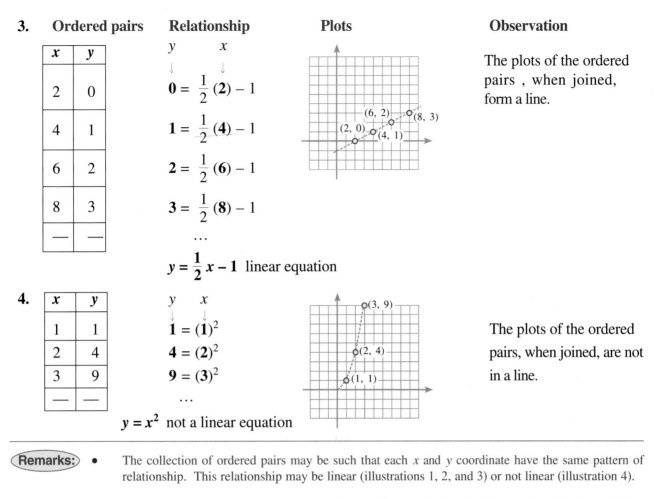

Ordered pairs	Relationship	Plots	Observation

3.

x	y
2	0
4	1
6	2
8	3
—	—

$$y \qquad x$$
$$\downarrow \qquad \downarrow$$

$$\mathbf{0} = \frac{1}{2}\,(\mathbf{2}) - 1$$

$$\mathbf{1} = \frac{1}{2}\,(\mathbf{4}) - 1$$

$$\mathbf{2} = \frac{1}{2}\,(\mathbf{6}) - 1$$

$$\mathbf{3} = \frac{1}{2}\,(\mathbf{8}) - 1$$

$$\dots$$

$$y = \frac{1}{2}\,x - 1 \text{ linear equation}$$

The plots of the ordered pairs , when joined, form a line.

4.

x	y
1	1
2	4
3	9
—	—

$$y \qquad x$$
$$\downarrow \qquad \downarrow$$

$$\mathbf{1} = (\mathbf{1})^2$$

$$\mathbf{4} = (\mathbf{2})^2$$

$$\mathbf{9} = (\mathbf{3})^2$$

$$\dots$$

$$y = x^2 \text{ not a linear equation}$$

The plots of the ordered pairs, when joined, are not in a line.

Remarks:

- The collection of ordered pairs may be such that each x and y coordinate have the same pattern of relationship. This relationship may be linear (illustrations 1, 2, and 3) or not linear (illustration 4).

- If the relationship between x and y coordinates of the ordered pairs is linear then the plots of these points (ordered pairs) are in a straight line.

EXAMPLE 8 Identify the relationship between the coordinates of the ordered pairs.

a.

x	y
1	3
2	6
3	9

b.

x	y
−1	2
−2	4
−3	6

c.

x	y
1	2
2	5
3	8

Solutions:

a.

x	y
1	3
2	6
3	9

$$y \qquad x$$
$$\downarrow \qquad \downarrow$$

$$\begin{rcases} \mathbf{3} = 3(\mathbf{1}) \\ \mathbf{6} = 3(\mathbf{2}) \\ \mathbf{9} = 3(\mathbf{3}) \end{rcases} \longrightarrow y = 3x$$

The relationship between x and y coordinates is $y = 3x$.

WARM-UP

8. Identify the relationship between the coordinates of the ordered pairs.

a)

x	y
1	7
2	14
3	21

b)

x	y
−1	−1
−2	−3
−3	−5

b.

x	y
-1	2
-2	4
-3	6

$$\begin{array}{l} 2 = -2(-1) \\ 4 = -2(-2) \\ 6 = -2(-3) \end{array} \Bigg\} \longrightarrow y = -2x$$

The relationship between x and y coordinates is $y = -2x$.

c.

x	y
1	2
2	5
3	8

$$\begin{array}{l} 2 = 3(1) - 1 \\ 5 = 3(2) - 1 \\ 8 = 3(3) - 1 \end{array} \Bigg\} \longrightarrow y = 3x - 1$$

The relationship between x and y coordinates is $y = 3x - 1$.

EXERCISE 3.1

A. In exercises 1-15, determine whether or not the given ordered pair is a solution of the given equation.

1. $x + 3y = 5$; $(1, 2)$
2. $2x + y = 4$; $(2, 0)$
3. $2x - 5y = 7$; $(6, 1)$
4. $3x + 2y = 4$; $(2, 1)$
5. $2x + 5y + 10 = 0$; $(-5, 0)$
6. $3x + y - 4 = 0$; $(2, 1)$
7. $3x - 2y = 12$; $(0, 6)$
8. $2x - y = 4$; $(0, -4)$
9. $x = 5$; $(7, 0)$
10. $y = 4$; $(0, 4)$
11. $x + 3 = 0$; $(-3, 2)$
12. $x - 4 = 0$; $(4, 0)$
13. $2x = 3y$; $(6, 4)$
14. $3x = 4y$; $(4, 3)$
15. $y = 1$; $(3, 1)$

In exercises 16-29, complete the ordered pair so that it represents a solution for the given equation.

16. $(4, ?)$; $x - 3y = 2$
17. $(?, 2)$; $2x + y = 2$
18. $(-3, ?)$; $2x + y = 5$
19. $(?, 0)$; $x - 2y = 1$
20. $(?, 2)$; $x = 8$
21. $(0, ?)$; $y = 7$
22. $(?, -4)$; $2x + 3y = 8$
23. $(?, 2)$; $3x - y = 4$
24. $(0, ?)$; $3x + 5y = 10$
25. $(?, 0)$; $2x - 7y = 4$
26. $(?, 0)$; $2x + 7y + 10 = 0$
27. $(2, ?)$; $3x - y + 2 = 0$
28. $(-2, ?)$; $2x + 7y = 10$
29. $(?, -1)$; $x + 4y = 5$

B. In exercises 30-49, complete the table of values so that each ordered pair in the table represents a solution for the given equation.

30. $3x - 5y = 15$;

x	y
0	—
—	0
4	—
—	3

31. $2x + 3y = 6$;

x	y
—	0
0	—
—	4
6	—

32. $x - 2y = 3$;

x	y
-1	—
3	—
—	2
—	-1

33. $x + 2y = 2$;

x	y
0	—
2	—
—	4
—	3

34. $y + 3 = 4x$;

x	y
-2	—
0	—
5	—

35. $y - 1 = 3x$;

x	y
—	4
—	13
—	16

36. $2x + 5y = 10$;

x	y
0	—
—	0
—	4

37. $3x - 2y = 6$;

x	y
—	3
0	—
—	0

38. $3x + 2y = 6$;

x	y
-2	—
—	3
2	—

39. $x + 3y = 4$;

x	y
1	—
—	0
-2	—

40. $3x + 6y = 12$;

x	y
—	0
0	—
2	—

41. $3x + y = 6$;

x	y
0	—
—	0
—	3

42. $x + 2y = 4$;

x	y
4	—
—	2
2	—

43. $2x - y = 3$;

x	y
1	—
—	1
−1	—

44. $2x + 8 = 4y$;

x	y
−4	—
0	—
—	1

45. $-x + 2y = 4$;

x	y
—	0
—	2
—	3

46. $2x + y = 8$;

x	y
—	0
1	—
2	—

47. $x = 5$;

x	y
—	−3
—	4
—	7

48. $y = 4$;

x	y
3	—
2	—
−1	—

49. $y + 4 = 0$;

x	y
0	—
−1	—
4	—

C. 50. Plot the ordered pairs on the same coordinate system.

(a) $(3, -2)$ **(b)** $(2, 4)$ **(c)** $(-2, 3)$ **(d)** $(-3, -2)$ **(e)** $(5, 0)$ **(f)** $(0, 5)$

51. Plot the ordered pairs on the same coordinate system.

(a) $(2, -3)$ **(b)** $(-4, 7)$ **(c)** $(3, 5)$ **(d)** $(6, 2)$ **(e)** $(-6, 2)$ **(f)** $(0, 0)$

52. Plot the ordered pairs on the same coordinate system.

(a) $(0, 4)$ **(b)** $(4, 0)$ **(c)** $(4, -4)$ **(d)** $(-2, 0)$ **(e)** $(0, -2)$ **(f)** $(-4, 4)$

53. Plot the ordered pairs on the same coordinate system.

(a) $(-4, 0)$ **(b)** $(0, 5)$ **(c)** $(-2, 2)$ **(d)** $(3, 0)$ **(e)** $(0, -5)$ **(f)** $(-3, -5)$

54. Without plotting the point, determine the quadrant in which the point lies.

(a) $(-4, 3)$ **(b)** $(4, -3)$ **(c)** $(-4, -3)$ **(d)** $(4, 3)$

55. Without plotting the point, determine the quadrant in which the point lies.

(a) $(4, 5)$ **(b)** $(-3, -7)$ **(c)** $(4, -2)$ **(d)** $(-3, 2)$

56 Determine whether the following points lie on the x-axis or the y-axis, or neither.

(a) $(4, 0)$ **(b)** $(0, 3)$ **(c)** $(4, -4)$ **(d)** $(0, -2)$ **(e)** $(-5, 0)$ **(f)** $(2, 3)$

57. Determine whether the following points lie on the x-axis or the y-axis, or neither.

(a) $(-3, 0)$ **(b)** $(0, -1)$ **(c)** $(5, 0)$ **(d)** $(2, -3)$ **(e)** $(0, 4)$ **(f)** $(1, 4)$

In exercises 58-63, determine the coordinates of each of the points shown in the figure.

58.   **59.**   **60.**

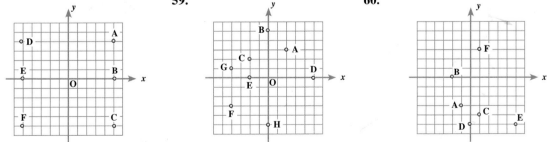

61.

62.

63.

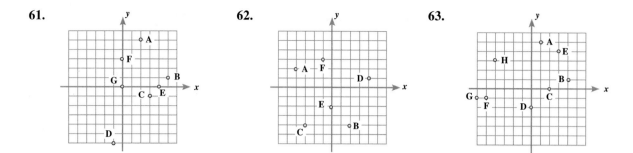

D. In exercises 64-88, find the relationship between the coordinates of the collection of order pairs.

64.

x	y
1	0
2	2
3	4
4	6

65.

x	y
1	-2
2	-4
3	-6
4	-8

66.

x	y
-1	3
-2	6
2	-6
3	-9

67.

x	y
2	0
4	1
6	2
8	3

68.

x	y
1	1
2	3
3	5
4	7

69.

x	y
0	2
1	4
-1	0

70.

x	y
1	-1
2	1
3	3

71.

x	y
0	1
1	3
2	5

72.

x	y
0	-2
1	0
2	2
3	4

73.

x	y
1	1
2	4
3	7

74.

x	y
2	5
3	8
4	11

75.

x	y
1	4
2	5
3	6

76.

x	y
1	-1
2	1
3	3
4	5

77.

x	y
0	-2
1	1
2	4
3	7

78.

x	y
0	-5
1	-1
2	3
3	7

79.

x	y
0	-3
1	-2
4	1

80.

x	y
1	2
4	-1
6	-3

81.

x	y
0	-4
3	2
4	4

82.

x	y
0	3
2	0
4	-3

83.

x	y
0	-3
1	1
2	5

84.

x	y
1	-1
2	-2
3	-3

85.

x	y
0	-2
3	-1
6	0

86.

x	y
1	4
2	8
3	12

87.

x	y
0	4
3	2
6	0

88.

x	y
2	-1
5	0
8	1

3.2 GRAPHING LINEAR EQUATIONS IN TWO VARIABLES

In this section, we will learn how to graph a linear equation. We will learn to graph the linear equation using two methods:

1. by making a table of *x*-values and *y*-values, and

2. by using the intercepts.

A. GRAPHING A LINEAR EQUATION USING POINTS

The **graph** of a linear equation is a line such that the ordered pairs representing points on the line are the solutions of the equation and the ordered pairs not on the line are not the solutions of the equation.

A general strategy for graphing a linear equation in *x* and *y* consists of three steps.

> *Step* 1   Construct a table of several *x* and *y* values for the equation, and obtain the corresponding ordered pairs (x, y).
>
> *Step* 2   Plot the ordered pairs, obtained in step 1, on a coordinate system.
>
> *Step* 3   Draw a smooth line passing through the points, plotted in step 2.

In section 3.4, we will see that the equation associated with a straight line is linear in *x* and *y*. Conversely, it can be shown that the graph of any linear equation in two variables is a straight line. Since a straight line can be graphed with only two points on it, it is enough to make a table consisting of two *x*-values and *y*-values for graphing a linear equation. However, it is recommended to make a table of *three* values. This will prevent errors.

A general procedure to graph a *linear equation* in *x* and *y* consists of the following steps:

> *Step* 1   Construct a table of three ordered pairs as solutions of the equation.
>
> *Step* 2   Graph the three points.
>
> *Step* 3   Draw a straight line passing through the three points.

Notes
1. Since plotting a point with fractional coordinates is more difficult, it is easier if the table of values avoids fractions.

2. As far as possible, the *x* or *y* values should be chosen so that the resulting points are not too close to each other.

EXAMPLE 1   Graph the line $2x - 3y = 0$ using points.

Solution:

Step 1   Construct a table of *three* *x*-values and *y*-values for the equation $2x - 3y = 0$.

x	*y*
0	0
3	2
−3	−2

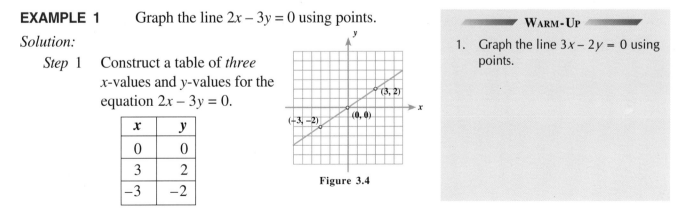

Figure 3.4

Step 2   Plot the points (0, 0),(3, 2),(–3, –2).

Step 3   Draw the straight line passing through the three points.

Notes

1. Observe that the graph of 2x – 3y = 0 is a line passing through the origin.

2. For all real numbers **a**, **b** (both not zero), the graph of a linear equation with no constant term (**ax** + **by** = **0**) is a straight line passing through the origin.

3. We may graph a line using calculator. See examples 1-3 of section 3.2 in Appendix B.

2. Graph the equation $y = 2x + 2$ using points.

EXAMPLE 2   Graph the equation $2x + 3y = 6$ using points.

Solution:

Step 1   Construct a table of x-values and y-values for the equation $2x + 3y = 6$.

x	y
0	2
3	0
6	–2

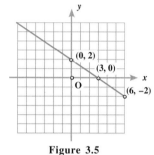

Figure 3.5

Step 2   Plot the points (0, 2), (3, 0), (6, –2)

Step 3   Draw the line passing through the three points.

3. Graph the equation $x = -4$ using points.

EXAMPLE 3   Graph the equation $x = 4$ using points.

Solution:

Step 1   Construct a table of three x-values and y-values for the equation $x = 4$. Observe that for the equation $x = 4$, all ordered pairs have a constant value (4) of x, and y can have any value.

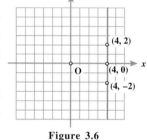

Figure 3.6

x	y
4	0
4	2
4	–2

Step 2   Plot the points (4, 0), (4,2), (4, –2).

Step 3   Draw the line through the three points.

Notes

1. Observe that the graph of $x = 4$ is a vertical line passing through (4, 0).

2. The graph of a linear equation $x = k$, where k is a constant is a **vertical** line through the point (k, 0). In particular, the graph of $x = 0$ is the y-axis.

EXAMPLE 4   Graph the equation $y + 4 = 0$ using points.

Solution:

Observe that $y + 4 = 0$ can be rewritten as $y = -4$.

Step 1   Construct a table of *three* x-values and y-values for the equation $y = -4$.

x	y
0	−4
3	−4
5	−4

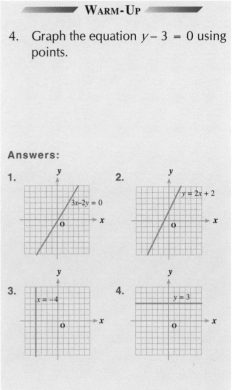

Figure 3.7

Step 2   Plot the points: $(0, -4), (3, -4), (5, -4)$.

Step 3   Draw the straight line passing through the three points.

Notes
1.   Observe that the graph of $y = -4$ is a horizontal line through $(0, -4)$.

2.   The graph of the linear equation $y = k$, where k is a constant, is a **horizontal** line through the point $(0, k)$. In particular, the graph of $y = 0$ is the x-axis.

•   **INTERCEPTS**

Consider the graph in example 2 (Figure 3.5). Notice that the graph crosses the x-axis at $(3, 0)$ and the y-axis at $(0, 2)$. The point $(3, 0)$ is the **x-intercept** of the graph. Similarly, the point $(0, 2)$ is the **y-intercept** of the graph.

> •   To find the **x-intercept**, substitute 0 for **y** in the given equation and solve for **x**.
>
> •   To find the **y-intercept**, substitute 0 for **x** in the given equation and solve for **y**.

Observations

1.   The graph of a linear equation of the form x = k (no y-term) has the x-intercept (k, 0), and it has no y-intercept. For example, the x-intercept of x + 2 = 0 is (−2, 0).

2.   The graph of a linear equation of the form y = k (no x-term) has a y-intercept (0, k), and it has no x-intercept. For example, the y-intercept of y = 3 is (0, 3).

3.   The graph of a linear equation of the form ax + by = 0 (no constant term) has an x-intercept (0, 0), and a y-intercept (0, 0).

B.   **USING INTERCEPTS TO GRAPH A LINEAR EQUATION**

For an equation of the form $ax + by + c = 0$ with a, b, and c all non-zero, we can use the intercepts to draw the graph.

> *Step* 1   Find the x-intercept.
>
> *Step* 2   Find the y-intercept.
>
> *Step* 3   Find another point for a check.
>
> *Step* 4   Plot the three points and draw a straight line through them.

3.2   Graphing Linear Equations in Two Variables

5. Find the intercepts for the graph of $2x - y = 6$.

EXAMPLE 5   Find the intercepts for the graph of $x - 2y = 6$. Draw the graph.

Solution:

Step 1   **x-intercept:** substitute 0 for y.

$x - 2 \cdot 0 = 6 \longrightarrow x = 6$

The x-intercept is (6, 0).

x	y
6	0
0	-3
2	-2

Step 2   **y-intercept:** substitute 0 for x.

$0 - 2y = 6 \longrightarrow y = -3$

The y-intercept is (0, -3)

Step 3   Check point :

If $x = 2$, then

$\mathbf{2} - 2y = 6 \longrightarrow -2y = 4$

$\longrightarrow y = -2$

Then, (2, -2) is another point on the graph.

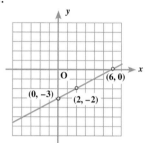

Figure 3.8

Step 4   Plot the points (6, 0), (0, -3), (2, -2), and draw a straight line through them (Figure 3.8).

6. Graph the linear equation using intercepts: $y = \dfrac{x}{2} - 1$

EXAMPLE 6   Graph the linear equation $3y = 5x - 2$ by finding the intercepts.

Solution:

x-intercept:

x	y
2/5	0
0	-2/3

$3 \cdot (0) = 5x - 2 \quad {\scriptstyle (y=0)}$

$5x - 2 = 0$

$5x = 2$

$x = \dfrac{2}{5}$

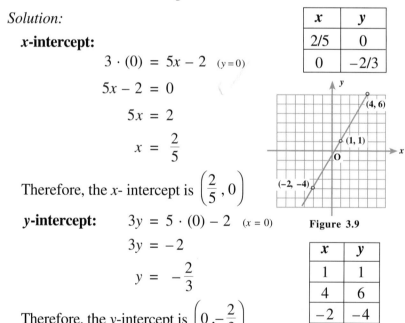

Figure 3.9

Therefore, the x- intercept is $\left(\dfrac{2}{5}, 0\right)$

y-intercept: $3y = 5 \cdot (0) - 2 \quad {\scriptstyle (x=0)}$

$3y = -2$

$y = -\dfrac{2}{3}$

x	y
1	1
4	6
-2	-4

Therefore, the y-intercept is $\left(0, -\dfrac{2}{3}\right)$

Since the x-intercept and the y-intercept are fractional numbers, which are usually difficult to plot exactly, we try to construct a table of *three* x-values and y-values for the equation $3y = 5x - 2$.

We plot the points (1, 1), (4, 6), (-2, -4), and draw a straight line joining these points (Figure 3.9).

Answers:

5. (3, 0) and (0, -6)

6. (0, -1) and (2, 0)

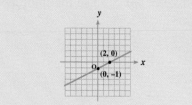

EXERCISE 3.2

A. In exercises 1-20, complete the table of *x*-values and *y*-values for the given equation. Draw the graph of the equation by plotting these points.

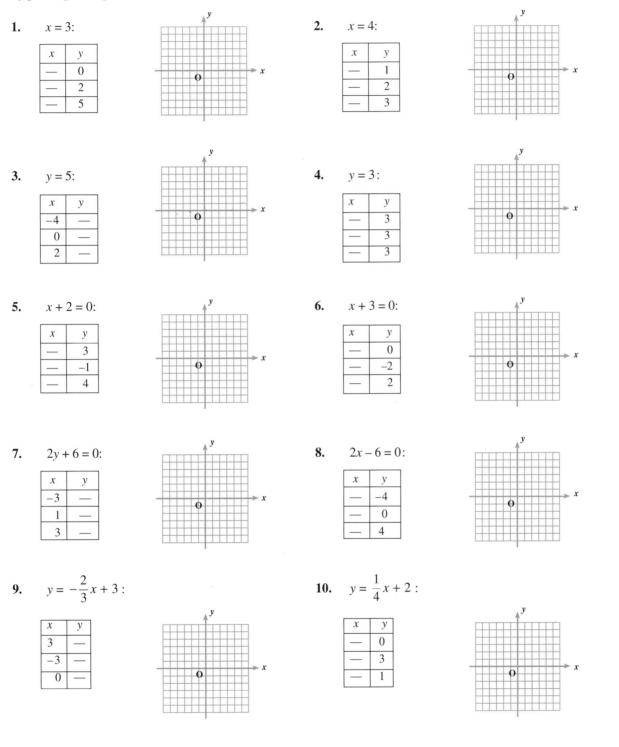

1. $x = 3$:

x	y
—	0
—	2
—	5

2. $x = 4$:

x	y
—	1
—	2
—	3

3. $y = 5$:

x	y
−4	—
0	—
2	—

4. $y = 3$:

x	y
—	3
—	3
—	3

5. $x + 2 = 0$:

x	y
—	3
—	−1
—	4

6. $x + 3 = 0$:

x	y
—	0
—	−2
—	2

7. $2y + 6 = 0$:

x	y
−3	—
1	—
3	—

8. $2x − 6 = 0$:

x	y
—	−4
—	0
—	4

9. $y = -\dfrac{2}{3}x + 3$:

x	y
3	—
−3	—
0	—

10. $y = \dfrac{1}{4}x + 2$:

x	y
—	0
—	3
—	1

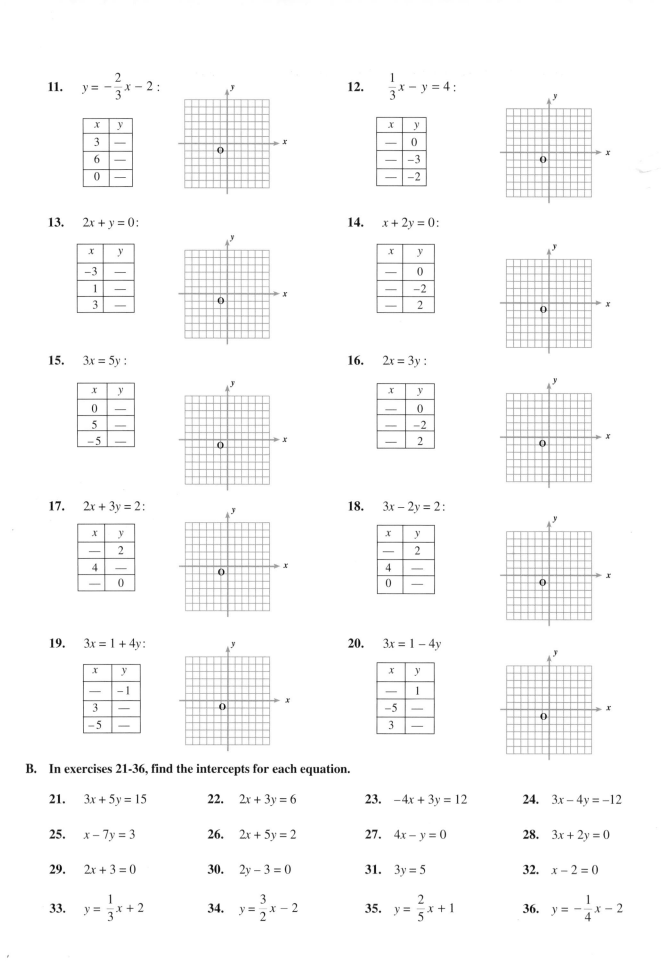

11. $y = -\dfrac{2}{3}x - 2$:

x	y
3	—
6	—
0	—

12. $\dfrac{1}{3}x - y = 4$:

x	y
—	0
—	-3
—	-2

13. $2x + y = 0$:

x	y
-3	—
1	—
3	—

14. $x + 2y = 0$:

x	y
—	0
—	-2
—	2

15. $3x = 5y$:

x	y
0	—
5	—
-5	—

16. $2x = 3y$:

x	y
—	0
—	-2
—	2

17. $2x + 3y = 2$:

x	y
—	2
4	—
—	0

18. $3x - 2y = 2$:

x	y
—	2
4	—
0	—

19. $3x = 1 + 4y$:

x	y
—	-1
3	—
-5	—

20. $3x = 1 - 4y$

x	y
—	1
-5	—
3	—

B. **In exercises 21-36, find the intercepts for each equation.**

21. $3x + 5y = 15$

22. $2x + 3y = 6$

23. $-4x + 3y = 12$

24. $3x - 4y = -12$

25. $x - 7y = 3$

26. $2x + 5y = 2$

27. $4x - y = 0$

28. $3x + 2y = 0$

29. $2x + 3 = 0$

30. $2y - 3 = 0$

31. $3y = 5$

32. $x - 2 = 0$

33. $y = \dfrac{1}{3}x + 2$

34. $y = \dfrac{3}{2}x - 2$

35. $y = \dfrac{2}{5}x + 1$

36. $y = -\dfrac{1}{4}x - 2$

In exercises 37-60, graph the linear equation. Use the intercepts wherever convenient.

37. $x + 2y = 4$

38. $x - 2y = 5$

39. $2x - 3y = 6$

40. $y = 2x + 3$

41. $2x + 3y = 5$

42. $2x - 3y = 1$

43. $x = 3y + 2$

44. $2x = y - 2$

45. $x = -3$

46. $y = -2$

47. $y + 1 = 0$

48. $x - 2 = 0$

49. $x + y + 4 = 0$

50. $x - y - 3 = 0$

51. $3x - y = 4$

52. $2x + y = 3$

53. $x = 0$

54. $y + 4 = 0$

55. $y = 0$

56. $y - 5 = 0$

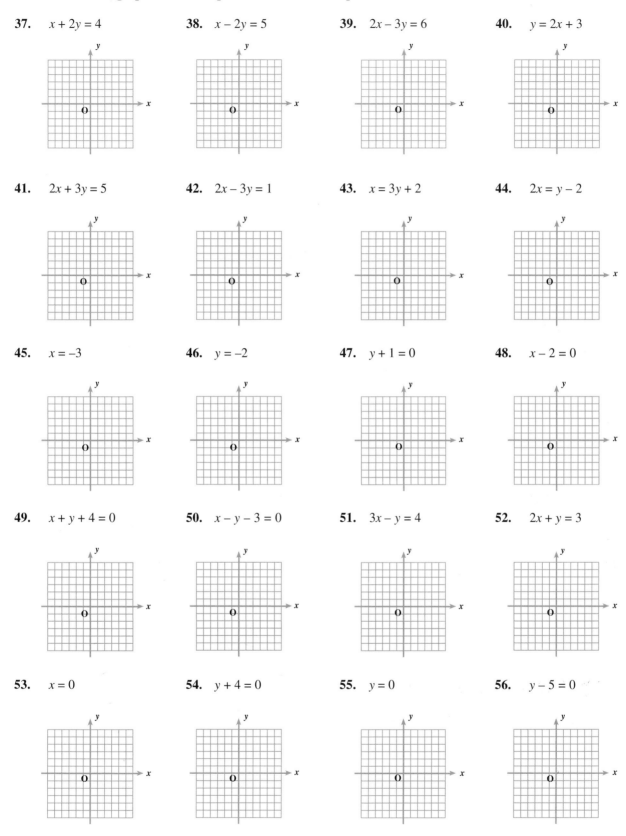

57. $4x + 3y = 12$ **58.** $x - 2y = 4$ **59.** $5x - 2y = 10$ **60.** $-x + 2y = 4$

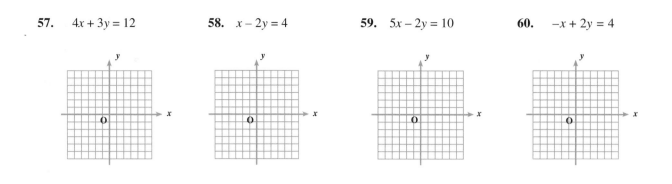

3.3 SLOPE OF A LINE

OBJECTIVES ■■■■

Upon completion of this section you will be able to:

A. Find the slope of a line through two given points;

B. Find the slope from the equation of a line; and

C. Use the slope to determine whether two lines are parallel or perpendicular.

A. SLOPE OF A LINE

a) The slope of a line is a measure of its steepness. It is measured by comparing its rise to its run, using a ratio or a fraction. Observe the rise and run between two points on the lines in the following figures.

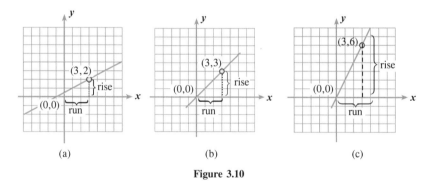

(a)   (b)   (c)

Figure 3.10

In Figure 3.10(a), the rise is 2 units and the run is 3 units.

The slope is $\frac{2}{3}$ $\longrightarrow$ rise
$\longrightarrow$ run

In Figure 3.10(b), the rise is 3 units and the run is 3 units.

The slope is $\frac{3}{3}$ $\longrightarrow$ rise   or   1
$\longrightarrow$ run

In Figure 3.10(c), the rise is 6 units and the run is 3 units.

The slope is $\frac{6}{3}$ $\longrightarrow$ rise   or   2
$\longrightarrow$ run

b) To calculate slope of a line, we determine the ratio of the change in y (rise) to the change in x (run).

Figure 3.10 (a)

Run	x	y	Rise

$$3 - 0 = 3 \left\langle \begin{array}{c|c} 0 & 0 \\ \hline 3 & 2 \end{array} \right\rangle 2 - 0 = 2$$

$$\text{slope} = \frac{\text{Rise}}{\text{Run}} = \frac{2}{3}$$

Figure 3.10 (b)

Run	x	y	Rise

$$3 - 0 = 3 \left\langle \begin{array}{c|c} 0 & 0 \\ \hline 3 & 3 \end{array} \right\rangle 3 - 0 = 3$$

$$\text{slope} = \frac{\text{Rise}}{\text{Run}} = \frac{3}{3} = 1$$

Figure 3.10 (c)

Run	x	y	Rise

$$3 - 0 = 3 \left\langle \begin{array}{c|c} 0 & 0 \\ \hline 3 & 6 \end{array} \right\rangle 6 - 0 = 6$$

$$\text{slope} = \frac{\text{Rise}}{\text{Run}} = \frac{6}{3} = 2$$

A slope of $\frac{2}{3}$ means that y increases by 2, every time x increases by 3.

A slope of 1 means that y increases by 1, every time x increases by 1.

A slope of 2 means that y increases by 2, every time x increases by 1.

c) Given any two points on a line, we can determine the slope of that line. Let $P(x_1, y_1)$ and $Q(x_2, y_2)$ be any two points as shown in Figure 3.11.

Run	x	y	Rise

$$x_2 - x_1 \left\langle \begin{array}{c|c} x_1 & y_1 \\ \hline x_2 & y_2 \end{array} \right\rangle y_2 - y_1$$

$$\text{slope} = \frac{y_2 - y_1}{x_2 - x_1}$$

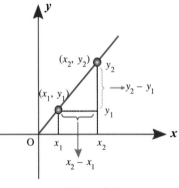

Figure 3.11

d) The slope of a line is constant, no matter which two points are selected on a line. The ratio of the difference of y-coordinates (rise) and the difference of x-coordinates (run) is same for any two points on a line.

> The **slope**, m, of a line passing through the points (x_1, y_1) and (x_2, y_2) is:
>
> $$m = \frac{y_2 - y_1}{x_2 - x_1} \quad \text{if} \quad x_1 \neq x_2.$$

e) If the x-coordinates of two points are equal then the line must be vertical (parallel to y-axis). Consider the two points $(3, 2)$ and $(3, -1)$ and a line passing through these points (Figure 3.12).

x	y
3	2
3	-1

Observe that $x = 3$ for all points on this line. The slope of this line is

$$m = \frac{-1 - 2}{3 - 3} = \frac{-3}{0} \longrightarrow \text{ the slope is } \textbf{undefined.}$$

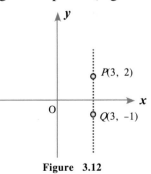

Figure 3.12

A Vertical line has the following characteristics:

1. the same x-coordinate for all points on the line;

2. an equation of the form $x = k$, where k is constant; and

3. slope that is undefined.

f) If two points on a line have equal y-coordinates, the line must be horizontal, parallel to x-axis.

Consider the two points $Q(2, 3)$ and $P(-1, 3)$ and a line passing through these points (Figure 3.13).

x	y
−1	3
2	3

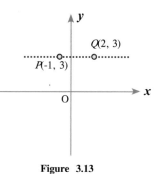

Observe that $y = 3$ for all points on this line.
The slope of this line is

$$m = \frac{3-3}{2-(-1)} = \frac{0}{3} = 0. \longrightarrow \text{the slope is } 0.$$

A Horizontal line has the following characteristics:

1. the same y-coordinate for all points on it;

2. an equation of the form $y = k$, where k is constant; and

3. slope equal to 0.

Figure 3.13

▼ **WARM-UP** ▼

1. Find the slope of line through following pair of points:

   a) $(2, 4)$ and $(-1, 1)$

   b) $(1, 5)$ and $(-1, -1)$

EXAMPLE 1 Find the slope of each of the following lines. Draw the graph of these lines.

   a. The line through $(3, 5)$ and $(2, -1)$.

   b. The line through $(2, -3)$ and $(-1, 2)$.

Solutions:

To draw these lines, plot the two given points and join them by a straight line, see Figures 3.14 and 3.15.

a. $\text{Slope} = \dfrac{-1-5}{2-3} = \dfrac{-6}{-1} = 6$ **b.** $\text{Slope} = \dfrac{2-(-3)}{-1-2} = \dfrac{5}{-3} = -\dfrac{5}{3}$

1.a **1.b**

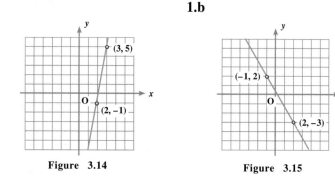

Figure 3.14   Figure 3.15

Observations

In Example 1(a), the slope is positive and the line rises from left to right.

In Example 1(b), the slope is negative, and the line falls from left to right.

- If the slope of a line is *positive*, then it *rises* from left to right.
- If the slope of a line is *negative*, then it *falls* from left to right.

EXAMPLE 2 Find the slopes of the lines through the points.

  a. (3, 5), (6, 7) **b.** (1, 4), (3, 4)

  c. (2, −1), (2, 0)

Solutions:

a. (3, 5), (6, 7) : $slope = \dfrac{7-5}{6-3} = \dfrac{2}{3}$

b. (1, 4), (3, 4) : $slope = \dfrac{4-4}{3-1} = \dfrac{0}{2} = 0$ Horizontal line.

c. (2, −1), (2, 0) : $slope = \dfrac{0-(-1)}{2-2} = \dfrac{1}{0}$ Undefined vertical line.

EXAMPLE 3 Given four lines whose slopes are:

  a. 4 **b.** not defined **c.** $-\dfrac{1}{3}$ **d.** 0.

  Determine which of these lines is:

  i) Rising from the left to right.

  ii) Falling from left to right.

  iii) Vertical. **iv)** Horizontal.

Solutions:

 a. Since the slope is positive, the line is **rising** from left to right.

 b. Since the slope is not defined, the line is **vertical**.

 c. Since the slope is negative, the line is **falling** from left to right.

 d. Since the slope is zero, the line is a **horizontal line**.

EXAMPLE 4 For the lines shown on the graph, provide the following information about their slopes.

  i) Slope is positive. **ii)** Slope is negative

  iii) Slope is undefined. **iv)** Slope is zero.

---

2. Find the slope of the lines through the given points.

 a) (3, 8) and (4, 5)

 b) (3, −1) and (1, −1)

 c) (3, 6) and (3, 13)

3. Given four lines whose slopes are:

 a) 0 b) $\dfrac{1}{2}$ c) − 3 d) not defined

 Determine which of these lines is:

 i. falling from left to right.

 ii. vertical.

 iii. rising from left to right.

 iv. horizontal.

4. Describe the slope of the following lines:

 a) horizontal line

 b) line rising from left to right

 c) line falling from left to right

 d) vertical line

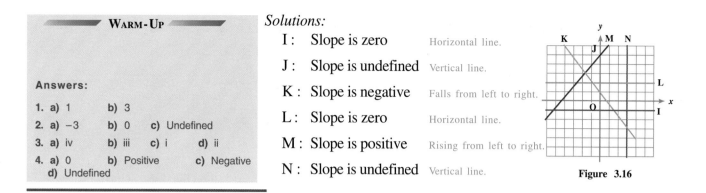

WARM-UP

Answers:

1. **a)** 1   **b)** 3
2. **a)** −3   **b)** 0   **c)** Undefined
3. **a)** iv   **b)** iii   **c)** i   **d)** ii
4. **a)** 0   **b)** Positive   **c)** Negative
   d) Undefined

Solutions:

I : Slope is zero   Horizontal line.

J : Slope is undefined   Vertical line.

K : Slope is negative   Falls from left to right.

L : Slope is zero   Horizontal line.

M : Slope is positive   Rising from left to right.

N : Slope is undefined   Vertical line.

Figure 3.16

B. FINDING THE SLOPE OF A LINE FROM THE EQUATION OF THE LINE

We know that the graph of a linear equation is a line. Linear equations can be written in one of the two forms:

  i) $x = a$ (if the **y** term is absent)

  ii) $y = mx + b$ (if the **y** term is present).

The slope of a line can be determined directly from its equation.

  • The slope of the vertical line with equation $x = a$ is **undefined**.

  • The slope of the line with equation $y = mx + b$ is **m**.

The following examples provide verification of the above statements.

WARM-UP

5. For each of the following equations, take any two points on the line and calculate the slope.

   a) $y = 3$

   b) $y = 2x + 5$

EXAMPLE 5 For each of the following equations, take any two points on the line and calculate the slope.

  a. $x = -2$ **b.** $y = 3x + 1$ **c.** $y = -4$

Solutions:

  a. $x = -2$:   (–2, 1), (–2, 0) are two points on the graph of $x = -2$.

$$Slope = \frac{0-1}{-2-(-2)} = \frac{-1}{0} \qquad \text{Undefined.}$$

Therefore, the slope of $x = -2$ is undefined.

Notice that graph of $x = -2$ is a vertical line. Therefore, there is no y-intercept.

  b. $y = 3x + 1$:   (1, 4) and (0, 1) are two points on the graph of $y = 3x + 1$.

$$Slope = \frac{1-4}{0-1} = \frac{-3}{-1} = 3$$

We observe that the coefficient of x in the equation $y = 3x + 1$ is also 3.

c. **y = –4 is equivalent to y = 0x – 4:** (1, –4) and (2, –4) are any two points on the graph of $y = 0x - 4$.

$$Slope = \frac{-4 - (-4)}{2 - 1} = \frac{0}{1} = 0$$

We observe that the coefficient of x in $y = \mathbf{0}x - 4$ or $y = -4$ is also 0.

Note ▷ For a linear equation in the form $y = \mathbf{m}x + \mathbf{b}$, the slope of the line is the coefficient of x, $\mathbf{m}$ in this case.

EXAMPLE 6   Determine the slopes of the following lines.

a. $y = 4x - 2$ **b.** $3y + 5x = 0$

c. $\dfrac{x}{3} - \dfrac{y}{4} = 4$ **d.** $3x - 2y + 6 = 0$

e. $3x + 5 = 0$

Solutions:

a. $y = 4x - 2$

Slope = coefficient of x = **4**.

b. $3y + 5x = 0$

$$3y = -5x \qquad \text{Solve for } y.$$

$$y = -\frac{5}{3}x$$

Slope = coefficient of x = $-\dfrac{5}{3}$

c. $\dfrac{x}{3} - \dfrac{y}{5} = 4$

Solve for y.

$$5x - 3y = 60 \qquad \text{Multiply by the LCD, 15.}$$

$$-3y = 60 - 5x \qquad \text{Solve for } y.$$

$$-3y = -5x + 60$$

$$y = \frac{5}{3}x - 20 \qquad \text{Divide by } -3.$$

Slope = coefficient of x = $\dfrac{5}{3}$

d. $3x - 2y + 6 = 0$

$$-2y = -3x - 6 \qquad \text{Solve for } y.$$

$$y = \frac{3}{2}x + 3$$

Slope = coefficient of x = $\dfrac{3}{2}$.

6. Determine the slope of following lines.

a) $y = 3x - 3$

b) $2y = 5x - 4$

c) $\dfrac{x}{4} - \dfrac{y}{3} = -2$

d) $3x - 2y - 6 = 0$

e. $3x + 5 = 0$

$3x + 5 = 0$ cannot be solved for y since it does not contain y-term. The equation $3x + 5 = 0$ can be written in the form $x = -\dfrac{5}{3}$, which is a vertical line. Hence, the slope is undefined.

C. SLOPE OF PARALLEL AND PERPENDICULAR LINES

Recall that two lines are said to be **parallel** if they do not intersect. The lines $y = 3x - 5$ and $y = 3x + 1$ have the same slope. The graphs of these lines are shown on the same coordinate system in Figure 3.17. The two lines are parallel.

Any two non-vertical lines are parallel if and only if they have the same slope.

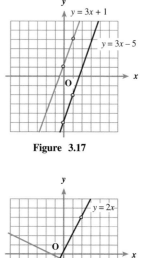

Figure 3.17

Next, consider the graphs of $-2y = x + 1$, and $y = 2x$.

Solving for y, we get $\left(-\dfrac{1}{2}\right)(-2y) = -\dfrac{1}{2}(x + 1)$, and $y = 2x$

$\rightarrow \quad y = -\dfrac{1}{2}x - \dfrac{1}{2}$, and $y = 2x$

Notice that their slopes are respectively $-\dfrac{1}{2}$ and 2. The product of their slopes is $\left(\dfrac{-1}{2}\right)(2) = -1$.

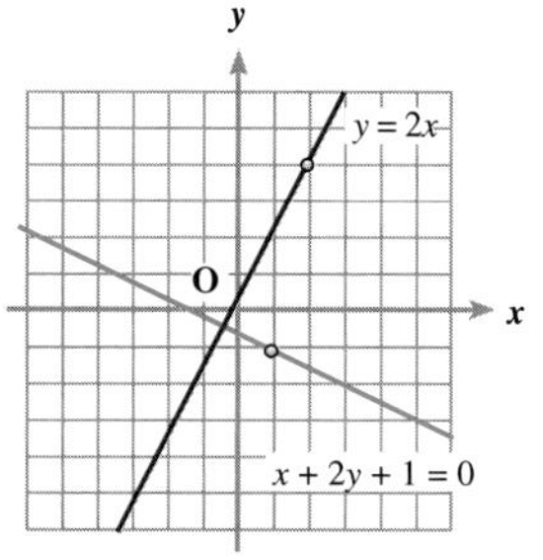

Figure 3.18

The two lines as shown in Figure 3.18 are perpendicular.

Any two lines, neither of which is horizontal or vertical, are perpendicular if and only if the *product of their slopes is –1.*

- Two *non-vertical* lines are parallel if and only if they have the same slope.
- Two lines, *neither of which is vertical or horizontal*, are perpendicular if and only if the product of their slopes is –1. We also say that the two slopes are negative reciprocals of each other.
- Any horizontal line and any vertical line are perpendicular to each other.
- All vertical lines are parallel to each other.

WARM-UP

7. Determine whether the following pair of lines is parallel, perpendicular or neither.

a) $5x + 3y = 8$
    $3x + 4y = 5$

EXAMPLE 7   Determine whether each of the following pairs of lines is parallel, perpendicular, or neither.

a. $3x + 2y = 4$ **b.** $2x + 3y = 3$
       $4x + 6y = 3$ $2y = 3x - 4$

c. $4x + 6y = 3$
       $6x + 9y = 7$

Solutions:

a.

$3x + 2y = 4$ <small>Solve for y.</small>	$4x + 6y = 3$ <small>Solve for y.</small>
$2y = -3x + 4$	$6y = -4x + 3$
$y = -\dfrac{3}{2}x + 2$	$y = -\dfrac{4}{6}x + \dfrac{3}{6}$
Slope $= -\dfrac{3}{2}$	Slope $= -\dfrac{4}{6} = -\dfrac{2}{3}$

The slopes are neither equal nor their product is –1.

Therefore, $3x + 2y = 4$ and $4x + 6y = 3$ are neither parallel nor perpendicular.

b.

$2x + 3y = 3$ <small>Solve for y.</small>	$2y = 3x - 4$ <small>Solve for y.</small>
$3y = -2x + 3$	$y = \dfrac{3}{2}x - 2$
$y = -\dfrac{2}{3}x + 1$	Slope $= \dfrac{3}{2}$
Slope $= -\dfrac{2}{3}$	

b) $5x + 3y = 8$
$\quad 3x - 5y = 5$

The product of the slopes of the two lines $= \left(-\dfrac{2}{3}\right)\cdot\left(\dfrac{3}{2}\right) = -1$.

Therefore, the two lines are perpendicular.

c) $5x + 3y = 8$
$\quad 10x + 6y = 11$

c.

$4x + 6y = 3$ <small>Solve for y.</small>	$6x + 9y = 7$ <small>Solve for y.</small>
$6y = -4x + 3$	$9y = -6x + 7$
$y = \dfrac{-4}{6}x + \dfrac{3}{6}$	$y = \dfrac{-6}{9}x + \dfrac{7}{9}$
$y = -\dfrac{2}{3}x + \dfrac{1}{2}$	$y = -\dfrac{2}{3}x + \dfrac{7}{9}$.
Slope $= -\dfrac{2}{3}$.	Slope $= -\dfrac{2}{3}$.

The slopes of $4x + 6y = 3$ and $6x + 9y = 7$ are equal. Therefore, the two lines are parallel.

Answers:

7. **a)** Neither parallel nor perpendicular.
   b) Perpendicular.
   c) Parallel.

EXERCISE 3.3

A. **In exercises 1-16, find the slope of the line passing through the given pair of points.**

1. $(3, 2), (-2, 4)$	**2.** $(2, 3), (-2, 4)$	**3.** $(1, -1), (-1, 1)$	**4.** $(2, 1), (1, -2)$
5. $(-2, 3), (-2, 5)$	**6.** $(2, -3)\ (3, 4)$	**7.** $(4, 1), (-5, 1)$	**8.** $(3, -1), (2, 4)$
9. $(3, 0), (0, 4)$	**10.** $(0, 3), (5, 0)$	**11.** $(3, 0), (3, -3)$	**12.** $(5, 1), (0, -2)$
13. $(1, 4), (5, -3)$	**14.** $(2, 3), (-4, 2)$	**15.** $(3, -1), (1, -2)$	**16.** $(-4, 1), (-2, 3)$

B. **In exercises 17-32, find the slope of the line.**

17. $y = 4x - 1$ **18.** $y = -3x + 1$ **19.** $3x + 5y = 1$ **20.** $2x - 3y = 2$

21. $2x = y + 1$ **22.** $3x - y = 2$ **23.** $-2x + 4y = 7$ **24.** $3x + 4y = 2$

25. $3x - y = 2$ **26.** $2x + y = 3$ **27.** $3x + 3y = 1$ **28.** $4x - 5y = 2$

29. $2x - 3y + 4 = 0$ **30.** $2y - 3x + 5 = 0$ **31.** $2x + 3y + 5 = 0$ **32.** $3y - 2x + 4 = 0$

33.   **Consider the lines A, B, C, D, and E in the figure. For each line, determine which of the following is true.**

    I.   The slope is positive.

    II.   The slope is negative.

    III.   The slope is zero.

    IV.   The slope is not defined.

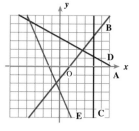

34.   **Consider the lines A, B, C, D, and E in the figure. For each line, determine which of the following is true.**

    I.   The slope is positive.

    II.   The slope is negative.

    III.   The slope is zero.

    IV.   The slope is not defined.

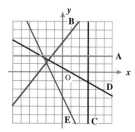

In exercises 35-42, without drawing the graph of the line, determine whether the line is rising or falling from left to right.

35. $3x = 4y - 7$ **36.** $2x - 3y = 7$ **37.** $2x + 3y = 9$ **38.** $3x + 4y = 5$

39. $5y - 4x + 1 = 0$ **40.** $3x - 4y - 1 = 0$ **41.** $x + 7y - 2 = 0$ **42.** $2x + 3y + 2 = 0$

C. **In exercises 43-50, two points on each line are given. Use these points to find the slope and verify that:**
(1) the slopes of parallel lines are equal, and (2) the product of the slopes of perpendicular lines is -1.

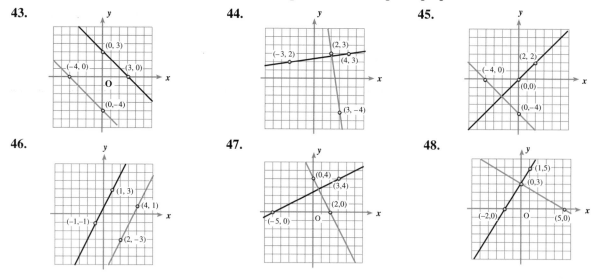

49.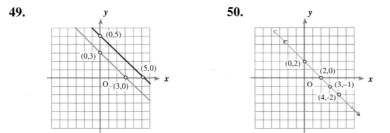

50.

In exercises 51-78, determine whether the pair of lines is parallel, perpendicular or neither.

51. $y = 3x + 7$
$y = 3x - 5$

52. $y = 2x - 7$
$y = 2x + 1$

53. $y = 2x + 1$
$2y = -1$

54. $y - 3x - 1 = 0$
$3y + 2 = 0$

55. $3y + 5x = 1$
$5y - 3x + 4 = 0$

56. $2y + 3x = 1$
$3y - 2x = 1$

57. $2y = 4x + 7$
$4y + 2x = 0$

58. $3y = 5x + 7$
$5y + 3x = 2$

59. $2x + 3y = 4$
$6y = 5 - 4x$

60. $x + 2y - 5 = 0$
$4y = 7 - 2x$

61. $7y + 2x = 4$
$7y = 1 + 2x$

62. $3y - 4x = 3$
$3y = 3 - 4x$

63. $y = \dfrac{1}{3}x + 6$
$2y = 6x - 1$

64. $6y - 5 = -9x$
$y = -\dfrac{3}{2} + 1$

65. $3x + 2y = 10$
$y = \dfrac{3}{2}x + 4$

66. $2x + y = 10$
$y = \dfrac{1}{2}x - 6$

67. $-5x - 4y = 2$
$y = \dfrac{4}{5}x + 3$

68. $y = \dfrac{1}{3}x + 1$
$y - 3x = 2$

69. $y = 2x + \dfrac{1}{5}$
$-2x - y = 4$

70. $2x + 3y = 9$
$4x + 6y = 13$

71. $2x + 3y = 9$
$3x - 2y = 12$

72. $y = 2x - \dfrac{1}{3}$
$6x - 3y - 1 = 0$

73. $x - 2y + 3 = 0$
$2x + y + 9 = 0$

74. $y = 2x + \dfrac{3}{2}$
$y = -\dfrac{1}{2}x - \dfrac{1}{2}$

75. $y = -x + y$
$y = x - 7$

76. $7x - 2y = 4$
$y = \dfrac{7}{2}x - 2$

77. $2x - 9y = 1$
$9x + 2y = 18$

78. $2y = 4x + 1$
$y = 2x + 3$

3.4 EQUATION OF A LINE

OBJECTIVES ■■■■

Upon completion of this section you will be able to:

A. Write the equation of a line, given its slope and *y*-intercept;

B. Graph a line, given the slope and *y*-intercept;

C. Write the equation of a line in slope-intercept or standard form;

D. Write the equation of a line, given its slope and a point on the line; and

E. Write the equation of a line, given two points on the line.

In this section, we will learn how to find the equation of a line and its graph under some given conditions.

A. SLOPE-INTERCEPT FORM OF A LINE

From the last section we know that for the equation $y = mx + b$, *m* (the coefficient of *x*) is its slope. What does *b* represent?

Notice that when $x = 0$, $y = m \cdot 0 + b = b \rightarrow (0, b)$ is the *y*-intercept of the line.

[Recall that the *y*-intercept of a line is obtained by substituting zero for *x* and solving for *y*.]

> The equation $y = mx + b$ is called the *slope-intercept* form of the equation of a line. Here, the slope is *m* and the *y*-intercept is $(0, b)$.

WARM-UP

1. Find the equation of a line, given that:

a) Slope = –3, *y*-intercept is (0, 2)

b) Slope = $\frac{3}{5}$, *y*-intercept is (0, 3)

Answers:

1. a) $y = -3x + 2$ b) $y = \frac{3}{5}x + 3$

EXAMPLE 1   Find the equation of a line given that:

a. slope = –2, *y*-intercept is (0, 4).

b. slope = $\frac{5}{3}$, *y*-intercept is (0, –3).

Solutions:

Since we are given the slope and *y*-intercept, we will use the slope-intercept form to find the equation of the lines.

a.   Let the equation of the line be $y = mx + b$.

Here, slope = $m = -2$, and   Given.

y-intercept = $(0, b) = (0, 4)$.   Given.

Therefore, $b = 4$.

Hence, the equation of the line is $y = -2x + 4$.

b.   Let the equation of the line be $y = mx + b$.

Here, slope = $m = \frac{5}{3}$, and   Given.

y-intercept = $(0, b) = (0, -3)$.   Given.

Therefore, $b = -3$.

Hence, the equation of the line is $y = \frac{5}{3}x - 3$

B. GRAPHING A LINE IN THE SLOPE INTERCEPT FORM

Recall that the general method to graph a line, when the equation of the line is given, is to first find three points on the line, plot them, and join them by a straight line. However, when the equation is given in the slope-intercept form, we can use the slope and the intercept directly to draw the graph. We demonstrate this with the help of the following examples.

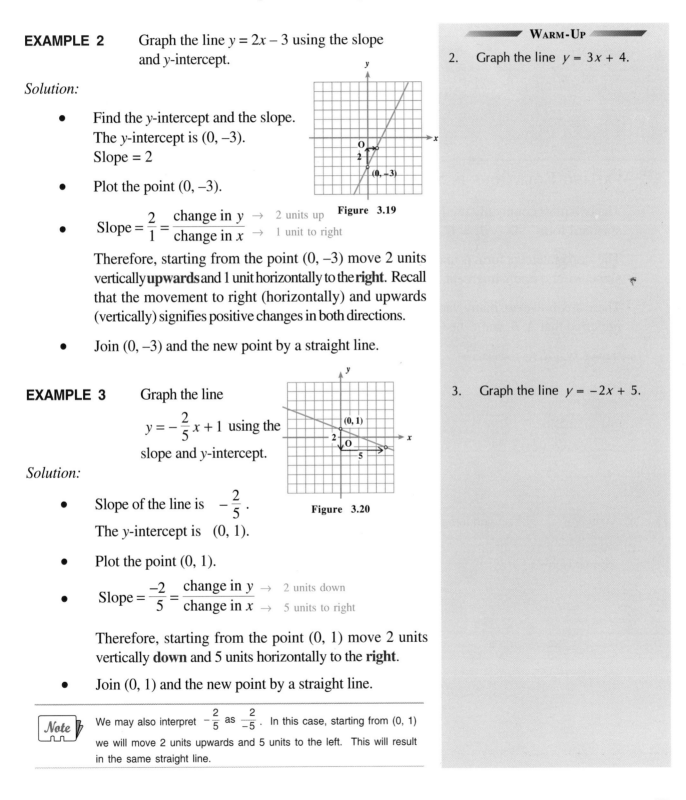

EXAMPLE 2   Graph the line $y = 2x - 3$ using the slope and y-intercept.

Solution:

- Find the y-intercept and the slope.
  The y-intercept is $(0, -3)$.
  Slope = 2

- Plot the point $(0, -3)$.

- Slope $= \dfrac{2}{1} = \dfrac{\text{change in } y}{\text{change in } x}$ → 2 units up
  → 1 unit to right

  Figure 3.19

  Therefore, starting from the point $(0, -3)$ move 2 units vertically **upwards** and 1 unit horizontally to the **right**. Recall that the movement to right (horizontally) and upwards (vertically) signifies positive changes in both directions.

- Join $(0, -3)$ and the new point by a straight line.

EXAMPLE 3   Graph the line

$y = -\dfrac{2}{5}x + 1$ using the

slope and y-intercept.

Solution:

- Slope of the line is $-\dfrac{2}{5}$.
  The y-intercept is $(0, 1)$.

- Plot the point $(0, 1)$.

- Slope $= \dfrac{-2}{5} = \dfrac{\text{change in } y}{\text{change in } x}$ → 2 units down
  → 5 units to right

  Figure 3.20

  Therefore, starting from the point $(0, 1)$ move 2 units vertically **down** and 5 units horizontally to the **right**.

- Join $(0, 1)$ and the new point by a straight line.

Note We may also interpret $-\dfrac{2}{5}$ as $\dfrac{2}{-5}$. In this case, starting from $(0, 1)$ we will move 2 units upwards and 5 units to the left. This will result in the same straight line.

WARM-UP

2.   Graph the line $y = 3x + 4$.

3.   Graph the line $y = -2x + 5$.

4. Graph the line with slope 1.5 and passing through (2, 1).

Answers:

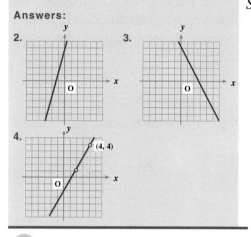

2.

3.

4. (4, 4)

EXAMPLE 4 Graph the line with slope –3 and passing through (2, 2).

Solution:

Plot the point (2, 2).

Slope = –3 = $\dfrac{-3}{1}$.

Starting from the point (2, 2) move 3 units vertically **downwards** and 1 unit horizontally to the **right**. Join the two points.

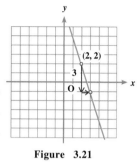

(2, 2)

3

Figure 3.21

C. WRITING EQUATIONS IN SLOPE-INTERCEPT OR STANDARD FORM

The two most commonly used forms for linear equations are the slope-intercept form, $y = mx + b$, and standard form, $Ax + By = C$.

The slope-intercept form is unique for each line since any line (other than a vertical line) has only one slope, m, and one y-intercept, $(0, b)$. **Note**: This form is used with graphing calculators.

There are, however, many variations for the standard form $Ax + By = C$ for any line. Generally it is preferred that A, B, and C be integers, and A, a positive integer. We will follow these practices.

5. Write $x - 4y = 3$ in slope intercept form.

6. a. Write $y = \dfrac{4}{3}x$ in standard form.

   b. Write $y = 2.1x - .45$ in standard form.

EXAMPLE 5 Write $2x - 5y + 7 = 0$ in slope intercept form.

Solution:

Solve for y: $2x - 5y + 7 = 0$

$$\underline{-2x \qquad -7 = -2x - 7}$$ Add $-2x$ and -7 to both sides.

$$-5y \quad\; = -2x - 7$$

$$y = \frac{2}{5}x + \frac{7}{5}$$ Divide both sides by -5.

EXAMPLE 6 Write the equation in standard form.

  a. $y = \dfrac{2}{3}x - \dfrac{4}{5}$ b. $y = 0.81x + 25$

Solutions:

  a. $y = \dfrac{2}{3}x - \dfrac{4}{5}$

Clear the fractions by multiplying both sides by the least common denominator, **15**.

$$\mathbf{15} \cdot y = \frac{\mathbf{15}}{1} \cdot \frac{2}{3} \cdot x - \frac{\mathbf{15}}{1} \cdot \frac{4}{5}$$ Distributive property.

$$15y = 10x - 12$$ Simplify.

$$-10x + 15y = -12$$ Add $-10x$ to each side.

$$10x - 15y = 12$$ Multiply both sides by -1.

b. $y = 0.81x + 25$

$\qquad 100\,y = 81x + 2500$ Multiply by the LCD, 100.

$\qquad -2500 = 81x - 100y$ Add $-100\,y$ and -2500 to both sides.

$\qquad 81x - 100y = -2500$ Switch the sides.

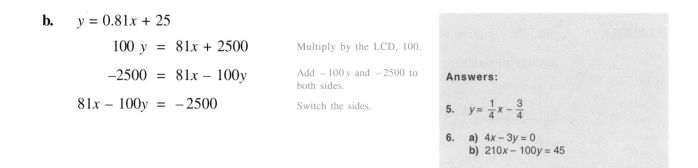

D. EQUATION OF A LINE GIVEN THE SLOPE AND ANY POINT ON THE LINE

In the slope intercept form of the equation $y = mx + b$ of a line, x and y are *variables* but m and b are *constants*. Every line, except vertical lines, has only one value of slope (m) and only one y-intercept $(0, b)$.

Recall that an equation of a line is the relationship between x and y coordinates of all the points on the graph of that line. The equation is completely determined if we know the value of the constants, m and b. These constants may be given directly as in example 1 or may be obtained as in example 5 below.

We may find the equation of a line, given its slope and any one point, using "**Slope-point**" form of the equation of a line as discussed below.

Consider the line **L** (Figure 3.22). Let its slope be m and $A(x_1, y_1)$ be any given fixed point on this line. Let $P(x, y)$ be any general point on **L**.

As illustrated in the Figure 3.22,

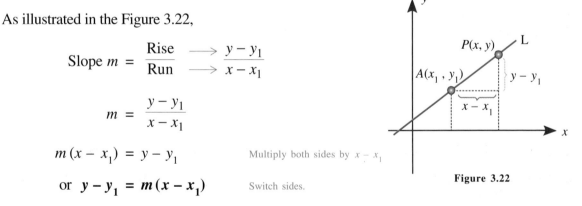

$\qquad$ Slope $m = \dfrac{\text{Rise}}{\text{Run}} \longrightarrow \dfrac{y - y_1}{x - x_1}$

$\qquad\qquad m = \dfrac{y - y_1}{x - x_1}$

$\qquad\quad m(x - x_1) = y - y_1$ Multiply both sides by $x - x_1$

$\qquad$ or $\; y - y_1 = m(x - x_1)$ Switch sides.

Figure 3.22

This is the standard "**Slope-point**" form of the equation of a line.

> If a line with slope m passes through a fixed point (x_1, y_1) then its equation is :
> $$y - y_1 = m(x - x_1)$$

EXAMPLE 7   Find the equation of the line with slope $-\dfrac{1}{2}$ and passing through $(3, -1)$.

Solution:

$m = -\dfrac{1}{2}$, fixed point is $(\mathbf{3, -1})$ then the equation of the line is:

$$y - (\mathbf{-1}) = -\frac{1}{2}(x - \mathbf{3})$$

$$y + 1 = -\frac{1}{2}(x - 3)$$

$$y + 1 = -\frac{1}{2}x + \frac{3}{2} \qquad \text{Add } -1 \text{ on both sides.}$$

$${-1} \phantom{-\frac{1}{2}x + } {-1}$$

$$y = -\frac{1}{2}x + \frac{1}{2} \qquad ...(2)$$

EXAMPLE 8   Find the equation of the line:

    a.   passing through $(4, 5)$ and parallel to $2x - 3y = 4$.

    b.   passing through $(-2, 1)$ and *perpendicular to* $4x + 7y + 3 = 0$.

Solutions:

    a.   Write $2x - 3y = 4$ in the form $y = mx + b$

$$2x - 3y = 4$$

$$-3y = -2x + 4$$

$$y = \frac{2}{3}x - \frac{4}{3}$$

The slope of $2x - 3y = 4$ is $\dfrac{2}{3}$.

Since the line in question is parallel to $2x - 3y = 4$, its slope is also $\dfrac{2}{3}$.

Therefore, we must find the equation of the line with slope $\dfrac{2}{3}$, and passing through $(\mathbf{4, 5})$.

We use "**Slope-point**" form of the equation of the line.

8. Find the equation of the line:

a) passing through $(2, -3)$ and parallel to $x + 3y = 6$.

b) passing through (3, 5) and
perpendicular to $2x + 5y = 7$.

$$y - 5 = \frac{2}{3}(x - 4)$$

$$y - 5 = \frac{2}{3}x - \frac{8}{3}$$ Add 5 on both sides.

$$\underset{+5}{\qquad} \qquad \underset{+5}{\qquad} \qquad -\frac{8}{3} + 5 = \frac{-8 + 15}{3} = \frac{7}{3}$$

$$y = \frac{2}{3}x + \frac{7}{3}$$

Verify that the point (4, 5) satisfies this equation.

b. Write $4x + 7y + 3 = 0$ in slope-intercept form.

$$\begin{array}{ll} 4x + 7y + 3 = 0 & \text{Add } -4x \text{ and } -3 \text{ to both sides.} \\ -4x \qquad\qquad -3 = -4x - 3 \\ \hline \qquad 7y \qquad = -4x - 3 \\ \qquad y = -\frac{4}{7}x - \frac{3}{7} & \text{Divide both sides by 7.} \end{array}$$

The slope of $4x + 7y + 3 = 0$ is $-\frac{4}{7}$. Let the slope of the desired line be m. Since the two lines are perpendicular,

$$-\frac{4}{7} \cdot m = -1$$

or $\qquad m = \frac{7}{4}$,   Negative reciprocal of $-\frac{4}{7}$.

We now find the equation of the line with the slope $\frac{7}{4}$ and passing through the point **(–2, 1).**

We use "Slope-point" form of the equation of the line.

$$y - 1 = \frac{7}{4}(x - (-2))$$

$$\underset{+1}{\qquad} \qquad \underset{+1}{\qquad}$$

$$y - 1 = \frac{7}{4}x + \frac{7}{2}$$ Add 1 on both sides.

$$\frac{7}{2} + 1 = \frac{7}{2} + \frac{2}{2} = \frac{9}{2}$$

$$y = \frac{7}{4}x + \frac{9}{2}$$

Verify that the point (–2, 1) satisfies this equation.

Answers:

7. $y = -\frac{3}{2}x + 10$ 8. a) $y = -\frac{1}{3}x - \frac{7}{3}$

   b) $y = \frac{5}{2}x - \frac{5}{2}$

E. EQUATION OF A LINE IN TWO-POINT FORM

Knowing two points on a line allows us to sketch the line. (See Figure 3.23). If we can sketch the line, then we have enough information to write the equation of the line.

We use the slope formula, $m = \dfrac{\text{Rise}}{\text{Run}} = \dfrac{y_2 - y_1}{x_2 - x_1}$ and the "Slope-point" form of the line to find the equation. The slope of the line passing through (1, 2) and (3, 4) is:

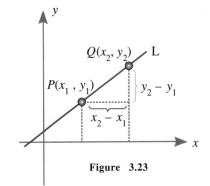

Figure 3.23

3.4   Equation of a Line

$$m = \frac{y_2 - y_1}{x_2 - x_1}$$

$$m = \frac{4 - 2}{3 - 1} = \frac{2}{2} = 1 \quad \longrightarrow \quad m = 1$$

We are given two points on the line.

Use one of the two points, say **(1, 2)** with slope $m = 1$ to find the equation of the line.
Use "**Slope-point**" form of the equation of the line.

$$y - 2 = \mathbf{1}(x - \mathbf{1}) \quad \longrightarrow \quad y - 2 = x - 1 \qquad \text{Add 2 on both sides.}$$

$$\longrightarrow \quad \boldsymbol{y = x + 1}$$

Using the second point (3, 4) would give the same result. Substitute $x = \mathbf{3}$, $y = \mathbf{4}$, and $m = 1$ in Slope-point form:

$$y - 4 = 1(x - 3) \quad \longrightarrow \quad y - 4 = x - 3 \qquad \text{Add 4 on both sides.}$$

$$\longrightarrow \quad \boldsymbol{y = x + 1}$$

Observe that we get the same equation.

Use either of the two points. It makes no difference, because both points are on the line.

WARM-UP

9. Find the equation of a line passing through (–1, 2) and (4, 5).

Answer:

9. $y = \frac{3}{5}x + \frac{13}{5}$ or $3x - 5y = -13$

EXAMPLE 9 Find the equation of a line passing through (–2, 5) and (3, 4).

Solution: Since two points on the line are known, we use the slope formula to determine the slope.

$$m = \frac{y_2 - y_1}{x_2 - x_1}$$

$$= \frac{4 - 5}{3 - (-2)} = \frac{-1}{5}$$

We will use the point (3, 4) and the slope $m = -\frac{1}{5}$ to find the equation.

$$y - 4 = -\frac{1}{5}(x - 3)$$

$$y - 4 = -\frac{1}{5}x + \frac{3}{5} \qquad \text{Add 4 on both sides.}$$

$$\underset{+4}{} \qquad \underset{+4}{} \qquad \frac{3}{5} + 4 = \frac{3}{5} + \frac{20}{5} = \frac{23}{5}$$

$$y = -\frac{1}{5}x + \frac{23}{5}$$

We now rewrite this equation in standard form.

$$5y = -x + 23 \qquad \text{Multiply both sides by 5.}$$

$$\underset{+x}{} \qquad \underset{+x}{}$$

$$x + 5y = 23 \qquad \text{Add } x \text{ on both sides.}$$

A. In exercises 1-10, find the equation of a line.

1. Slope = 2, y – intercept (0, 3)

2. Slope = $\dfrac{5}{2}$, y – intercept (0, –1)

3. Slope = –3, y – intercept (0, –2)

4. Slope = –5, y – intercept $\left(0, \dfrac{1}{2}\right)$

5. Slope = –1, y – intercept $\left(0, \dfrac{2}{3}\right)$

6. Slope = $-\dfrac{1}{3}$, y – intercept $\left(0, \dfrac{3}{2}\right)$

7. Slope = $\dfrac{3}{5}$ y – intercept (0, 4)

8. Slope = $\dfrac{-3}{2}$, y – intercept (0, 5)

9. Slope = 0 y – intercept $\left(0, -\dfrac{1}{2}\right)$

10. Slope = 2, y – intercept $\left(0, -\dfrac{3}{2}\right)$

B. In exercises 11-22, graph the line for which the slope m and one of its points are given.

11. $m = \dfrac{3}{2}$; (– 4, 2)

12. $m = 2$; (2, 4)

13. $m = -\dfrac{5}{2}$; (1, 1)

14. $m = -\dfrac{3}{2}$; (2, –2)

15. $m = 0$; (2, 1)

16. $m = -3$; (3, 4)

17. m = undefined; (3, –1)

18. $m = 0$; (–1, –3)

19. $m = 3$; (2, 5)

20. m = undefined; (4, 1)

21. $m = -2$; (–2, –1)

22. $m = \dfrac{5}{2}$; (4, –2)

C. In exercises 23-30, rewrite the equation in slope-intercept form.

23. $x - y = 3$

24. $y - x = 4$

25. $3x - 5y = 4$

26. $2x + 3y = 5$

27. $2x + 7y - 9 = 0$

28. $3x - 4y + 9 = 0$

29. $4x - 2y - 5 = 0$

30. $6x - 3y + 7 = 0$

In exercises 31-38, rewrite the equation in standard form.

31. $y = 2x - 11$

32. $y = -7x$

33. $y = \dfrac{3}{4}x - \dfrac{7}{8}$

34. $y = 2x + \dfrac{9}{2}$

35. $y = 0.65x + 5$

36. $y = 2.2x - 0.75$

37. $y = \dfrac{4}{5}x + 0.85$

38. $y = 0.75x - \dfrac{5}{4}$

D. In exercises 39-54, find the equation of the line in slope-intercept form with a given slope and passing through a given point.

39. $m = 4$; (–1, 2)

40. $m = -2$; (2, 1)

41. $m = -3$; (2, 5)

42. $m = \dfrac{1}{2}$; (3, 1)

43. $m = -\dfrac{4}{5}$; (1, 0)

44. $m = -5$; (3, 0)

45. $m = 0$; $\left(\dfrac{5}{3}, -\dfrac{3}{7}\right)$

46. $m = \dfrac{1}{2}$; $\left(\dfrac{3}{2}, -\dfrac{1}{2}\right)$

47. $m = \dfrac{5}{2}$; (2, 5)

48. $m = 0$; (1, 2)

49. $m = -\dfrac{2}{3}$; $\left(\dfrac{1}{2}, \dfrac{3}{4}\right)$

50. $m = -\dfrac{1}{2}$; (2, –3)

51. $m = -\dfrac{7}{9}$; (4, 0)

52. $m = \dfrac{3}{2}$; (–2, 0)

53. $m = -\dfrac{4}{7}$; (6,0)

54. $m = -\dfrac{8}{9}$; (5,0)

E **In exercises 55-66, find the equation of the line with the given two points, in the standard form.**

55. $(-1, 2), (2, 3)$ **56.** $(2, 1), (-3, 4)$ **57.** $(1, 0), (0, 5)$ **58.** $(0, 2), (3, 1)$

59. $(-4, 3), (3, -4)$ **60.** $(-2, -3), (1, 2)$ **61.** $\left(\frac{1}{3}, 1\right), \left(\frac{2}{3}, \frac{4}{3}\right)$ **62.** $\left(3, \frac{1}{3}\right), \left(-\frac{1}{3}, \frac{2}{3}\right)$

63. $\left(-\frac{1}{5}, \frac{2}{3}\right), \left(\frac{3}{5}, 4\right)$ **64.** $(0, 2), (2, 0)$ **65.** $\left(-\frac{2}{3}, -\frac{3}{5}\right), \left(\frac{7}{3}, \frac{12}{5}\right)$ **66.** $\left(\frac{5}{4}, \frac{4}{5}\right), \left(\frac{13}{4}, \frac{9}{5}\right)$

In exercises 67-80, find the equation of the line, in the standard form with the given conditions.

67. Passes through $(2, 1)$ and is parallel to the line $4x - 3y = 1$.

68. Passes through $(1, 1)$ and is parallel to the line $4x + 4y + 7 = 0$

69. Passes through $(-3, 2)$ and is perpendicular to the line $2x + y = 3$.

70. Passes through $(4, -5)$ and is perpendicular to the line $3x + 4y + 5 = 0$

71. Passes through $(4, 3)$ and is perpendicular to $3x - 2y + 4 = 0$.

72. Passes through $(-1, 4)$ and is parallel to $2x + 5y = 7$.

73. Passes through $(4, 3)$ and is parallel to $3x - 2y + 4 = 0$.

74. Passes through $(2, 3)$ and is perpendicular to the straight line $4x - 3y = 10$.

75. Passes through $(2, 4)$ and is parallel to the straight line $2x + y = 3$.

76. Passes through $(-2, 2)$ and is perpendicular to the straight line $-6x + 2y = 5$.

77. Passes through $(3, 3)$ and is parallel to the straight line $6x + 3y = 9$.

78. Passes through $(-5, -4)$ and is perpendicular to the straight line $y = 2x$.

79. Passes through $(4, -3)$ and is parallel to the straight line $y = -5x + 1$.

80. Passes through $(6, -4)$ and is perpendicular to the straight line $4x = 2y - 3$.

3.5 GRAPHING LINEAR INEQUALITIES IN TWO VARIABLES

In Chapter 2, we learned how to solve linear inequalities in one variable. In this section, we will learn to solve linear inequalities in two variables. Recall that the process of solving and graphing a linear inequality in one variable makes use of the solution of the *corresponding linear equation*. In just the same way, the process of solving and graphing linear inequalities in two variables uses the graphing of the *corresponding equations*.

OBJECTIVES ■■■■

Upon completion of this section you will be able graph linear inequalities in two variables.

GRAPHING INEQUALITIES

A linear inequality involving two variables can be solved for "*y*" just like linear equations. The resulting inequality is of the form

$$y \begin{Bmatrix} > \\ \geq \\ < \\ \leq \end{Bmatrix} mx + b$$

We are familiar with the equation, $y = mx + b$ related to this inequality. The graph of this linear equation is a straight line. The line divides the plane into two regions. These regions are marked I and II as in Figure 3.24.

BASIC PRINCIPLES

- All points in one of the two regions satisfy $y > mx + b$.
- All points in the other region satisfy $y < mx + b$.
- All points on the line satisfy $y = mx + b$. The line forms the boundary between the two regions.

To graph an inequality in two variables we use the following steps.

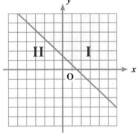

Figure 3.24

Step 1	Solve the inequality for *y*, being careful with order relation. Recall that the order relation changes if you multiply or divide by a negative number.
Step 2	Graph the related equation, $y = mx + b$. Use a dotted line if the inequality excludes "equals" (< or >), and solid line if the inequality includes "equals" (≤ or ≥).
Step 3	Identify the region containing solutions. If the inequality is simplified to $y > mx + b$ then use arrows vertically upward from the points on the boundary. For $y < mx + b$, use arrows vertically downward from points on the boundary.

1. Graph the inequality
   $3x - 2y > 5$

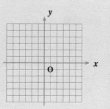

EXAMPLE 1   Graph the inequality $2x - y > 3$.

Solution:

- Solve for y.

$$2x - y > 3$$
$$-y > -2x + 3 \quad \text{Add } -2x \text{ on both sides.}$$
$$y < 2x - 3 \quad \text{Multiply both sides by } -1.$$

x	y
0	−3
2	1
1	−1

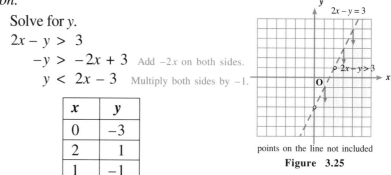

points on the line not included
Figure 3.25

- Graph the related line $y = 2x - 3$ as a **dotted** line, since "equals" is excluded from the inequality, by plotting the three points.

- To identify the region containing solutions for $y < 2x - 3$, draw arrows from points on the line vertically downward and shade the region below the line.

    We can graph the solution of an inequality using a graphing calculator. See examples 1 and 2 of Section 3.5 in Appendix B.

2. Graph the inequality $y \geq \dfrac{3}{2}x$

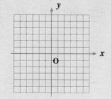

EXAMPLE 2   Graph the inequality $y \geq 3x$.

Solution:

- Solve for y. $y \geq 3x$

- Graph the line $y = 3x$ as a **solid** line, since the inequality includes "equals".

x	y
0	0
1	3
−1	−3

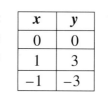

Figure 3.26

- To identify the region containing solutions for $y \geq 3x$, draw arrows from points on the line vertically upward and shade the region above the line.

3. Graph the inequality $3y > 7$

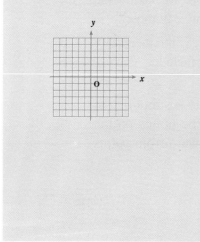

EXAMPLE 3   Graph the inequality $2y < 5$.

Solution:

- Solve for y. $2y < 5$

$$y < \frac{5}{2}.$$

- Graph the line $y = \dfrac{5}{2}$ as a dotted line, since the inequality excludes "equals". Note that this is a horizontal line.

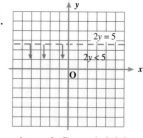

points on the line not included.
Figure 3.27

- To identify the region containing solutions for $y < \dfrac{5}{2}$, draw arrows from points on the line vertically downward and shade the region.

EXAMPLE 4   Graph the inequality $x \geq 5$.

Solution:

This is a special case, but similar to Example 3.

Graph the line $x = 5$ as a solid line, since the inequality includes "equals". All points on this line have their x-coordinate equal to 5. It is a vertical line through $(5, 0)$.

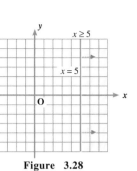

Figure 3.28

All points with $x > 5$ are to the right of $x = 5$. Shade the region to the right of the solid vertical line. The solution includes the line and the shaded region. Observe that all ordered pairs in this solution region have x-coordinates greater than or equal to 5.

___

Note   Compare the graph of the inequality $x \geq 5$ when considered in only one variable (Figure 3.29) with the graph $x \geq 5$ when it is considered in two variables (Figure 3.28). Notice that in two variables $x \geq 5 \rightarrow x + 0 \cdot y \geq 5$.

$x \geq 5$

0   5

Figure 3.29

___

We may use a graphing calculator to graph linear inequalities in two variables. See examples 1 and 2 of Section 3.5 in Appendix B.

WARM-UP

4.   Graph the inequality $x \geq 3$

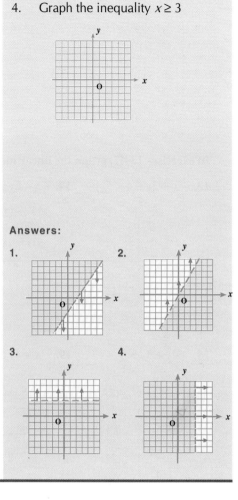

Answers:

1.   2.

3.   4.

EXERCISE 3.5

In exercises 1-12, identify which side of the lines should be shaded to represent the solution region of the given inequality.

1. $x + y > 3$ 2. $x + y \leq 3$ 3. $2y - x \leq 5$ 4. $2x + 3y \geq 6$

5. $3x - 4y \geq 12$ 6. $y \leq 4$ 7. $3x + y < 0$ 8. $x > 3$

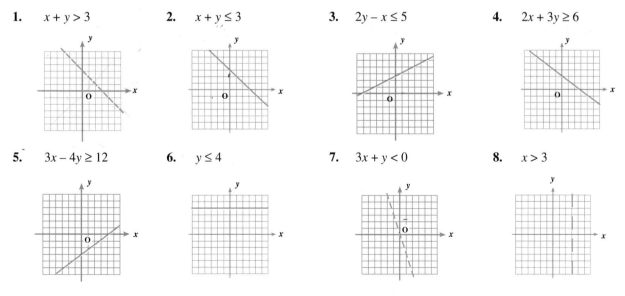

3.5 Graphing Linear Inequalities in Two Variables

9. $x > -2$

10. $3x + 5y - 15 < 0$

11. $y \le 0$

12. $2x + 3y \ge 12$

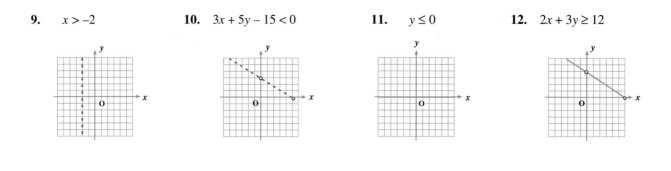

In exercises 13-47, graph the linear inequality.

13. $x + 2y \le 4$

14. $x - 2y \le 4$

15. $3x - 2y > 2$

16. $x + y \le 5$

17. $2x - y \le -3$

18. $2x + 3y > 3$

19. $x + 4y \ge 5$

20. $-5x + 4y < 0$

21. $x < y$

22. $x - 3y \ge 6$

23. $3x \ge y$

24. $x \ge 3$

25. $2x \ge -5$

26. $2x \le 4$

27. $y < 5$

28. $x \ge y$

29. $3x + 7y > 21$

30. $y - x \le 6$

31. $2x + 3y < 6$

32. $2y - 3x - 6 \ge 0$

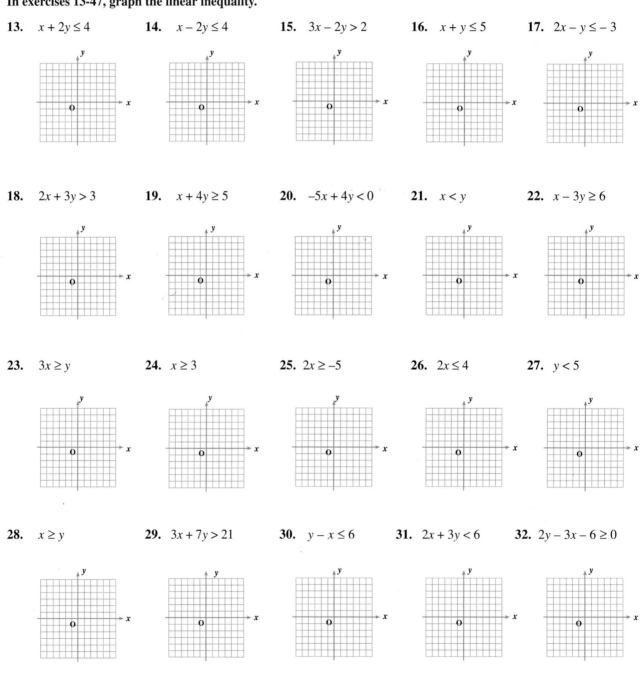

33. $y < 5x + 2$

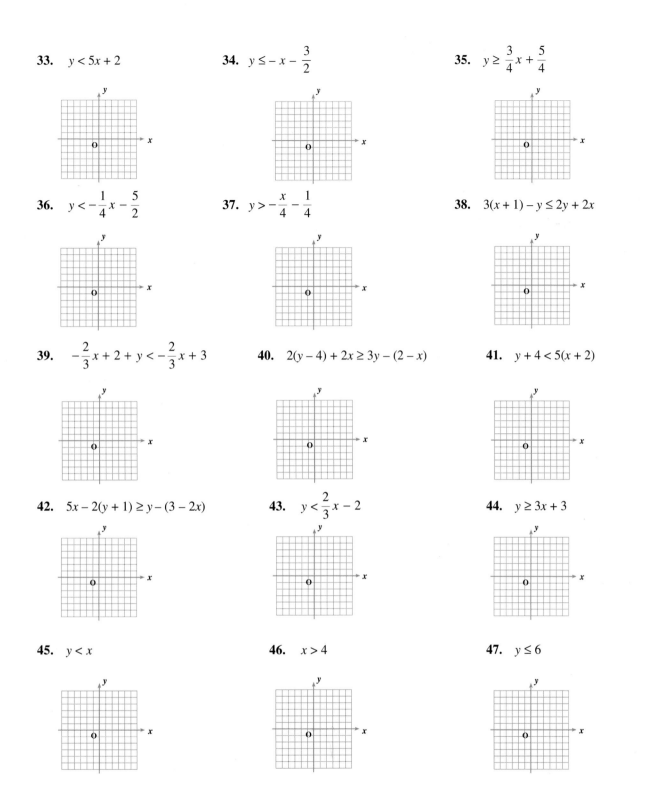

34. $y \leq -x - \dfrac{3}{2}$

35. $y \geq \dfrac{3}{4}x + \dfrac{5}{4}$

36. $y < -\dfrac{1}{4}x - \dfrac{5}{2}$

37. $y > -\dfrac{x}{4} - \dfrac{1}{4}$

38. $3(x + 1) - y \leq 2y + 2x$

39. $-\dfrac{2}{3}x + 2 + y < -\dfrac{2}{3}x + 3$

40. $2(y - 4) + 2x \geq 3y - (2 - x)$

41. $y + 4 < 5(x + 2)$

42. $5x - 2(y + 1) \geq y - (3 - 2x)$

43. $y < \dfrac{2}{3}x - 2$

44. $y \geq 3x + 3$

45. $y < x$

46. $x > 4$

47. $y \leq 6$

3.6 FUNCTIONS AND RELATIONS

OBJECTIVES ■■■■

Upon completion of this section you will be able to:

A. Understand the definition of a relation;

B. Understand the definition of a function;

C. Graph a relation;

D. Understand the vertical line test; and

E. Use the $f(x)$ notation.

The concept of a function is very important in mathematics. A function is a rule that assigns *exactly one* element y in a set Y to each element x in set X. For example, the equation $y = 3x + 5$ is a rule which assigns to each real number x exactly one real number, namely "five more than three times x". A function can be compared to an input/output machine.

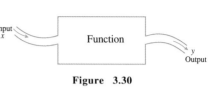

Figure 3.30

A more general concept is that of a relation. In this section, we study relations and functions.

A. DEFINITION OF A RELATION

Consider the following examples:

(i) When a ball is thrown upwards with a certain velocity, the height of the ball above the ground changes as time changes. Suppose the height, h, of the ball above the ground, measured in feet, for time t, measured in seconds, is given by the formula :

$$h = 100\,t - 16\,t^2$$

For each value of t, we can get a value for h. For example, when $t = 2$ sec,

$$h = 100 \cdot 2 - 16 \cdot 2^2 = 136 \text{ ft.}$$

This solution can be expressed as the ordered pair (2, 136). The set of all such ordered pairs represents a relationship between the height of the ball above the ground and the time taken to get to that position.

(ii) Consider assigning to each numerical age, the number of persons living in a town who are of that age. Both the age and the number of persons are whole numbers. The ordered pair (50, 160) would represent the age 50 years, and the total of 160 citizens of the town who are 50 years old. The set of all such ordered pairs expresses the relationship between age and population.

Any set of ordered pairs is called a **relation**. The set of all *first coordinates* in the ordered pairs of a relation is called its **domain**, and the set of all *second coordinates* is called its **range**.

EXAMPLE 1 Find the domain and range of the relation given by the following set of ordered pairs.

{(–3, 1), (0, 2), (–3, 2), (1, 1), (2, 3), (4, –1)}.

Solution:

Domain = the set of all first coordinates

= { –3, 0, 1, 2, 4}

Range = the set of all second coordinates = {–1, 1, 2, 3}

Sometimes it is convenient to represent a relation graphically. For example, the relation in Example 1 above can be graphed as in Figure 3.31.

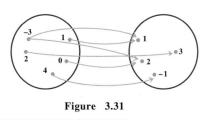

Figure 3.31

B. DEFINITION OF A FUNCTION

A function is a special type of relation. Notice that in example 1, the number –3 was associated with *two* elements, namely, 1 and 2. Such a situation is not permissible if a relation is to qualify for a function.

A **function** is a set of ordered pairs in which each distinct first coordinate is assigned to only one second coordinate.

> *Note* — By definition every function is a relation. However, some relations may not be functions. The relation in example 1 is not a function.

Many functions have an infinite number of ordered pairs. Since the set of such ordered pairs cannot be listed, we use an equation to define a function. This provides the rule for associating second coordinates with first coordinates. We will use equations in x and y, where x represents the first coordinate, and y represents the second coordinate.

EXAMPLES OF FUNCTIONS:

1. $y = \left| x \right|$ is a function. Some of the ordered pairs are:

    (0,0), (–1, 1), (1, 1), (– 4, 4), (5, 5), (–5, 5). Every real number has only one absolute value associated with it.

2. The equation $y = \dfrac{9}{5}x + 32$ expresses a relationship between the Fahrenheit scale of temperature y and the Celsius scale of temperature x. For example, (10, 50) is an element of the function defined by $y = \dfrac{9}{5}x + 32$. This expresses the fact that the value 10°C for x corresponds to exactly one value of y, namely 50° F.

C. GRAPH OF A RELATION

We have seen that many relations and consequently functions are defined by equations in two variables, say x and y. The graph of such a relation, or a function, is the set of all ordered pairs (x, y) which constitute the relation. In order to draw the graph of a relation we follow the steps listed below.

1. Use the equation to determine several ordered pairs (x, y) for different values of x.
2. Plot the points (x, y).
3. Join the points by a smooth curve.

This curve is the graph of the relation.

3.6 Functions and Relations

2. Draw the graph of the relation
    $y = 3x + 2$.

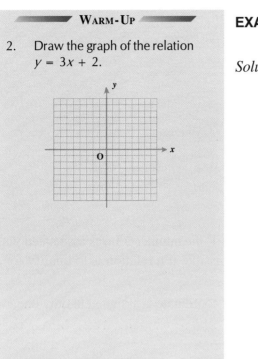

3. Draw the graph of the relation
    defined by $y^2 = 4x$.

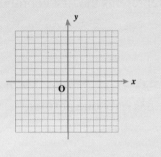

4. Draw the graph of the relation defined
    by the equation $y = |x - 2|$.

EXAMPLE 2   Draw the graph of the relation defined by
$y = 2x - 3$.

Solution: We recognize that the graph of the equation
$y = 2x - 3$ is a straight line. **This is an example
of a function** because this equation gives exactly
one value of y for every value of x.

We use the equation $y = 2x - 3$ to obtain the
following ordered pairs.

x	y	(x, y)
-2	-7	$(-2, -7)$
-1	-5	$(-1, -5)$
0	-3	$(0, -3)$
1	-1	$(1, -1)$
2	1	$(2, 1)$
3	3	$(3, 3)$

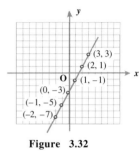

Figure 3.32

Graph of the relation $y = 2x - 3$

EXAMPLE 3   Draw the graph of the relation defined by $y^2 = x$.

Solution: **This equation does not define a function**
because for every positive value of x there are
two values of y.

$$x = 9 \rightarrow y = +3 \text{ or } -3$$

We use the equation $y^2 = x$ to obtain the
following ordered pairs.

x	y	(x, y)
9	-3	$(9, -3)$
9	3	$(9, 3)$
4	-2	$(4, -2)$
4	2	$(4, 2)$
1	-1	$(1, -1)$
1	1	$(1, 1)$
0	0	$(0, 0)$

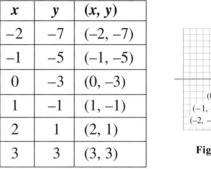

Figure 3.33

Graph of the relation $y^2 = x$

EXAMPLE 4   Draw the graph of the relation defined by the
equation $y = |x|$.

Solution: **This equation defines a function** because
exactly one value of y, corresponds to each value
of x.

We use the equation $y = |x|$ to obtain the following ordered pairs.

x	y	(x, y)
-3	3	$(-3, 3)$
-2	2	$(-2, 2)$
-1	1	$(-1, 1)$
0	0	$(0, 0)$
1	1	$(1, 1)$
2	2	$(2, 2)$
3	3	$(3, 3)$

Figure 3.34

Graph of the relation $y = |x|$

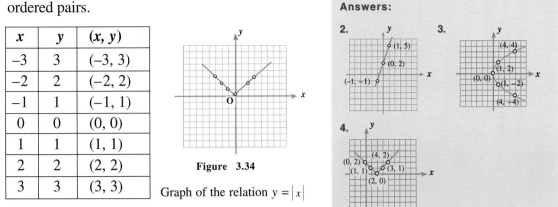

Answers:

2.

3.

4.

D. VERTICAL LINE TEST

Some equations will not represent functions. Consider the equation $y^2 = x$ of example 2. This equation defines a relation which is not a function because $(1, 1)$ and $(1, -1)$ are both ordered pairs belonging to this relation. The **graph** of an equation can be used to test whether the equation represents a function. This can be done with the *vertical line test*. The vertical line test is based on the defining property of the function that *no element in the domain corresponds to more than one element in the range.*

Vertical Line Test: If any vertical line intersects, or meets the graph of an equation in at most one point, then the equation defines a function.

EXAMPLE 5 The graphs of some equations are given below. Determine whether or not the relation defined by each of these graphs is a function.

Solutions:

a.

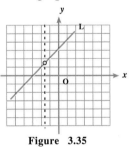

Figure 3.35

Function: No vertical line intersects the non-vertical line (L) in more than one point.

b.

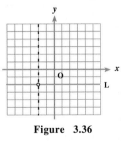

Figure 3.36

Function: No vertical line intersects the horizontal line (L) in more than one point.

━━━ **WARM-UP** ━━━

5. The graphs of some equations are given below. Determine whether the relation is a function or not.

a)

b)

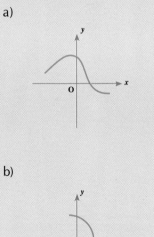

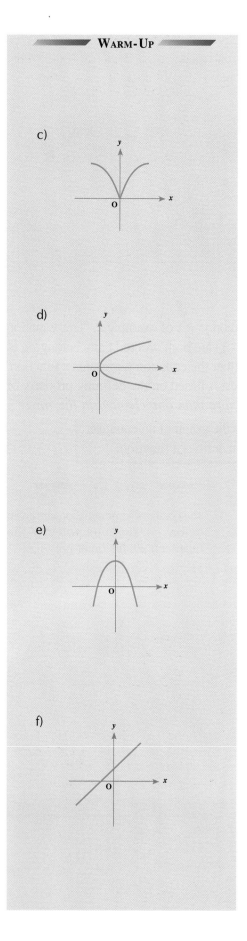

c)

d)

e)

f)

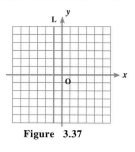

c.

Figure 3.37

Not a function: The graph itself is a vertical line (L). This line meets itself at infinitely many points.

d.

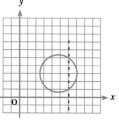

Figure 3.38

Not a function: There are vertical lines which cut the circle in two points.

e.

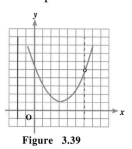

Figure 3.39

Function: No vertical line intersects the graph in more than one point.

f.

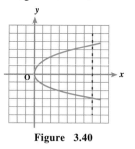

Figure 3.40

Not a function: There are vertical lines which intersect the graph in more than one point.

EXAMPLE 6   Sketch the graph and determine whether or not the equation represents a function.

   a. $y = 3x - 5$ **b.** $y = 3$ **c.** $y = x^2$

   d. $y^2 = x$ **e.** $x = 4$

Solutions:

a. ***Function:*** Graph $y = 3x - 5$.

x	y
0	−5
1	−2
2	1

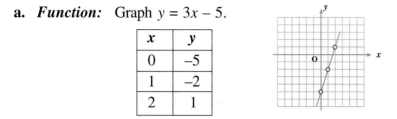

This non-vertical line passes the vertical line test.

b. ***Function:*** The graph of $y = 3$ is a horizontal line. It passes the vertical line test.

x	y
0	3
1	3
2	3

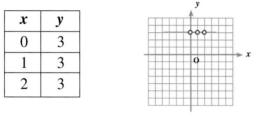

c. ***Function:*** The graph of $y = x^2$ passes the vertical line test.

x	y
−2	4
−1	1
0	0
1	1
2	4

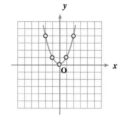

d. ***Not a function:*** The graph of $y^2 = x$ does not pass the vertical line test.

x	y
4	−2
1	−1
0	0
1	1
4	2

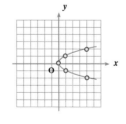

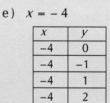
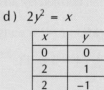
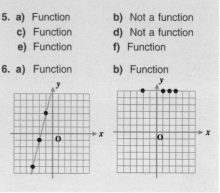

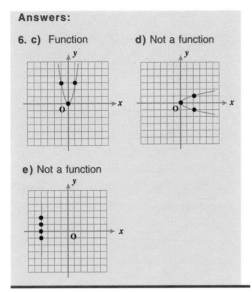
e. *Not a function:* The graph of $x = 4$ is a vertical line itself. It does not pass the vertical line test because on one vertical line there are infinitely many points.

x	y
4	0
4	1
4	2

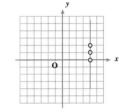

E. FUNCTIONAL NOTATION

The function $y = 3x - 1$ may be written as $f(x) = 3x - 1$. The expression $f(x)$ is read as "f of x". In this notation:

    (i) f is the name of the function.

    (ii) x is an element of the domain.

    (iii) $f(x)$ is the unique value corresponding to x in the domain.

Since $f(x)$ is defined by an algebraic expression, $f(a)$ is found by substituting a for x in the expression.

In this notation $f(4)$ means the value of the function corresponding to 4 in the domain.

    $f(4) = 3 \cdot 4 - 1 = 11$.   Thus "$f$ of 4 equals 11".

EXAMPLE 7   For the function $f(x) = 3x^2 + 4x - 1$, find

    a. $f(-3)$ **b.** $f(0)$ **c.** $f(5)$

Solutions: $f(x) = 3x^2 + 4x - 1$

  a. $f(-3) = 3(-3)^2 + 4(-3) - 1$

          $= 3 \cdot 9 + 4 \cdot (-3) - 1 = \mathbf{14}$

  b. $f(0) = 3 \cdot 0^2 + 4 \cdot 0 - 1 = \mathbf{-1}$

  c. $f(5) = 3(5)^2 + 4(5) - 1 = 3(25) + 20 - 1$

          $= 75 + 20 - 1 = \mathbf{94}$

🖩   We make use of the calculator to evaluate a function. See example 1 of Section 3.6 in Appendix B.

B. In exercises 1-14, determine which of the relations is a function? Find the domain and the range in each case.

1. $\{(-2, 2), (-1, 0), (-3, 0), (-1, 5), (0,0)\}$

2. $\{(1, 5), (2, 5), (3, 6), (4, 7)\}$

3. $\{(3, 1), (2, 0), (-2, -4), (4, 2)\}$

4. $\{(1, 6), (2, 6), (1, 5), (3, 5), (4, 5)\}$

5. $\{(-1, 1), (-2, 2), (0, 0), (1, 1) (2, 2)\}$

6. $\{(1, 5), (1, 6), (2, 5), (2, 7), (3, 6), (4, 7)\}$

7. $\{(-1, 1), (-2, 4), (0, 0), (1, 1) (2, 4)\}$

8. $\{(2, 3), (3, 4), (4, 5), (5, 6)\}$

9. $\{(4, 2), (1, -1), (0, 0), (9, -3) (9, 3)\}$

10. $\{(-1, 0), (1, 2), (2, 3), (3, 4)\}$

11.

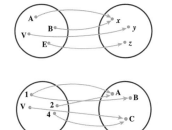

12.

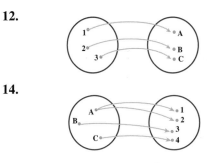

13.

14.

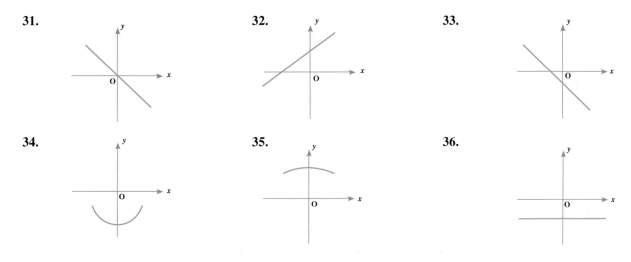

C. In exercises 15-30, determine whether or not the equation describes a function.

15. $y = -2x + 1$

16. $y = 5x + 1$

17. $y = 3x + \dfrac{1}{2}$

18. $y = -7$

19. $4x + 3y - 7 = 0$

20. $y^2 = 2x$

21. $x = -3$

22. $y = \dfrac{1}{2}x^2$

23. $y = -4$

24. $x = 7$

25. $y = x^2$

26. $y = \dfrac{1}{4x + 3}$

27. $y = \dfrac{1}{3x + 1}$

28. $x + 3y = 5$

29. $y = \dfrac{4x}{x^2 + 2}$

30. $y = \dfrac{2x}{3 + x^2}$

D. In exercises 31-44, identify whether or not the relation defined by the graph is a function.

31.

32.

33.

34.

35.

36.

37. **38.** **39.**

40. **41.** **42.**

43. **44.**

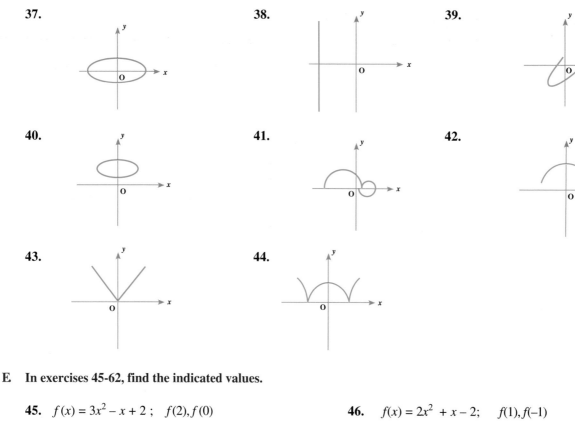

E **In exercises 45-62, find the indicated values.**

45. $f(x) = 3x^2 - x + 2$; $f(2), f(0)$

46. $f(x) = 2x^2 + x - 2$; $f(1), f(-1)$

47. $g(x) = -3 |x|$; $g(-2), g(0), g(3)$

48. $g(x) = 3x + 4; g\left(\dfrac{1}{2}\right), g(-4)$

49. $h(x) = 4x + 5$; $h(5), h(-3)$

50. $h(x) = -3x^2 + 2x$; $h(-2), h(0)$

51. $f(x) = -3x^2 + 5x$; $f(4), f(-4)$

52. $f(x) = \dfrac{5}{5 + x^2}$; $f(-2), f(1)$

53. $P(x) = \dfrac{3}{x^2 + 1}$; $P(-2), P(0), P(-1)$

54. $g(x) = -(x + 5)^2$; $g(0), g(-1), g(2)$

55. $Q(x) = -(x - 3)^2$; $Q(3), Q(-3), Q(0)$

56. $h(x) = -5|x|$; $h(1), h(-1), h\left(\dfrac{1}{5}\right)$

57. $f(x) = \dfrac{1}{4}x - 2$; $f(-2), f(0), f(40)$

58. $f(x) = \dfrac{2}{3}x^2 + \dfrac{1}{2}x - 4$; $f(3), f(1), f(-1)$

59. $g(x) = \dfrac{-x^2 + 4}{-3}$; $g(0), g(-2), g\left(\dfrac{1}{3}\right)$

60. $h(x) = \dfrac{-2x^2 + 4x}{-3}$; $h(1), h\left(-\dfrac{1}{2}\right), h(0)$

61. $f(x) = \dfrac{4x^2 - 1}{3x}$; $f(1), f(-2), f\left(\dfrac{1}{3}\right)$

62. $f(x) = \dfrac{-\left(x^2 + 2x + 1\right)}{4}$; $f(0), f(-1), f(2)$

3.7 CHAPTER SUMMARY

LINEAR EQUATIONS IN TWO VARIABLES

1. An ordered pair is a solution of an equation in two variables if it makes the equation a true statement.

2. A linear equation in two variables has infinitely many solutions.

GRAPHING EQUATIONS

3. The graph of $x = k$ is a vertical line through $(k, 0)$.

4. The graph of $y = k$ is a horizontal line through $(0, k)$.

5. To graph a linear equation in two variables x and y:

   - find three ordered pairs satisfying the linear equation,

   - plot the corresponding points, and

   - draw a straight line through the three points.

SLOPE OF A LINE

6. The slope of a non-vertical line passing through (x_1, y_1) and (x_2, y_2) is given by:

$$m = \frac{y_2 - y_1}{x_2 - x_1} \qquad (x_1 \neq x_2)$$

7. The slope of a vertical line is **undefined**. The x-coordinates of all points on this line are the same.

8. The slope of a *horizontal* line is 0. The y-coordinates of all points on this line are the same.

9. To find the slope of a line from its equation:

   - Solve the equation for y in the form $y = mx + b$

   - The slope is the coefficient (m) of x in the new equation.

10. Two non-vertical lines are parallel if and only if they have the same slope.

Examples

1. $(2, 1)$ is a solution of $x + 2y = 4$, since $2 + 2(1) = 4$ is **true.**

2. $(1, 3), (2, 5), (3, 7) \ldots$ are all solutions of $2x - y + 1 = 0$.

3. The graph of $x = 2$ is a line joining points $(2, 0), (2, 1), (2, 2) \ldots$ These points are on vertical line.

4. The graph of $y = 3$ is a line joining points $(0, 3), (1, 3), (2, 3) \ldots$ These points are on a horizontal line.

5. Graph the equation $2x + y = 2$.

x	y	(x, y)
0	2	(0, 2)
1	0	(1, 0)
2	–2	(2, –2)

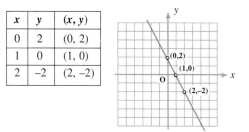

6. Slope of a line passing through $(2, 1)$, and $(0, 3)$ is:

$$\text{Slope} = \frac{3-1}{0-2} = \frac{2}{-2} = -1$$

7. The slope of $x = 4$ is not defined. All x-coordinates equal 4. Hence the denominator of the slope ratio is zero.

8. The slope of $y = 3$ is zero. All y-coordinates are equal to 3. Hence the numerator of the slope ratio is zero.

9. Find the slope of $2x + y = 3$

   $2x + y = 3 \rightarrow y = -2x + 3$

   Slope = **–2**

10. The two lines $y = 2x + 3$ and $y = 2x - 5$ are parallel because slope of each line is 2.

11. Two lines $y = 2x + 3$ and $y = -\frac{1}{2}x + 3$ are perpendicular because $(2)\left(-\frac{1}{2}\right) = -1$.

11. The slopes of two perpendicular lines are the negative reciprocals of each other.

   Alternatively, two non-vertical lines are perpendicular if and only if the product of their slopes is -1.

EQUATIONS OF A LINE

12. The equation of a line with slope $= 3$ and intercept $(0, 2)$ is $y = 3x + 2$.

12. • **Slope-Intercept Form:**

   If m is the slope and $(0, b)$ the y-intercept of a line, then its equation is $y = mx + b$.

• Find the equation of a line with slope $= 2$ and passing through $(1, 3)$.

$$y = mx + b, \ m = 2, \ x = 1, \ y = 3$$
$$3 = 2 \cdot 1 + b$$
$$b = 1$$
$$y = 2x + 1$$
$$\text{or} \quad y - 3 = 2(x - 1)$$
$$= 2x - 2$$
$$y = 2x + 1$$

• **Equation of a line given the slope and any point on the line.**

   We use slope-intercept form, $y = mx + b$.

   To find b, we substitute the value of m, x, and y in $y = mx + b$ and solve for b.

   We may use the "**Slope-point**" form to find the equation. If m is the slope and (x_1, y_1) is any point on line then the equation is $y - y_1 = m(x - x_1)$.

• The equation is $y = \frac{4}{3}x - \frac{10}{3}$

Multiply by the LCD, 3, to get:

$$3y = 4x - 10$$

Add $-4x$ to both sides, then multiply by -1.

$$4x - 3y = 10$$

• **Writing Equations in Slope Intercept Form or Standard Form**

   To write a linear equation in slope-intercept form, $y = mx + b$, solve for y.

   To write a linear equation in the standard form

   $Ax + By = C$, first clear the equation of fractions by multiplying by the LCD.

   Then use the addition principle to move all variable terms to the left side and all constant terms to the right side. Multiply by -1 if the first term (x-term) has a negative coefficient.

• Find the equation of a line passing through $(1, -2)$ and $(4, 2)$.

$$m = \frac{2 - (-2)}{4 - 1} = \frac{2 + 2}{3} = \frac{4}{3}$$

Substituting $m = \frac{4}{3}$, $x = 1$, and $y = -2$ in

$$y - y_1 = m(x - x_1)$$
$$y - (-2) = \frac{4}{3}(x - 1)$$
$$y + 2 = \frac{4}{3}x - \frac{4}{3}$$

• **Equation of Line given two points**

   If two points (x_1, y_1) and (x_2, y_2) are known, first determine the slope using the slope formula

   $m = \dfrac{y_2 - y_1}{x_2 - x_1}$. Then substitute the value of m and one of the ordered pairs for x and y in the formula $y - y_1 = m(x - x_1)$ and simplify to express this equation as $y = mx + b$.

$$y = \frac{4}{3}x - \frac{4}{3} - 2$$

$$y = \frac{4}{3}x - \frac{10}{3}$$

Equation of the line is

$$y = \frac{4}{3}x - \frac{10}{3} \quad \text{or} \quad 4x - 3y = 10$$

GRAPHING LINEAR INEQUALITIES

13. The steps to solve a linear inequality in two variables:

* Solve for y, being careful to change the order of relation whenever multiplying or dividing by a negative number.

* Graph the related line, $y = mx + b$, using **dotted** line if the inequality excludes "equals" ($<$, $>$), or a **solid** line if the inequality includes "equals" ($\geq$, $\leq$).

* Draw arrows vertically **up** and shade the region above the line if the inequality is $>$ or $\geq$, and draw arrows vertically **down** and shade the region below the line if the inequality is $<$ or $\leq$.

* As a special case, if the inequality has no y variable, solve for x and graph the line $x = k$. Shade to the right or left of the line as indicated by the inequality.

13. Solve $2x - y \leq 1$

$$2x - y \leq 1$$

$$-y \leq -2x + 1$$

$$y \geq 2x - 1$$

Graph the boundary line $y = 2x - 1$

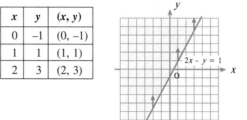

x	y	(x, y)
0	−1	(0, −1)
1	1	(1, 1)
2	3	(2, 3)

The inequality is $y \geq 2x - 1$. Draw arrows vertically up from the line and shade the upper region.

FUNCTIONS AND RELATIONS

14. A **function** is a set of ordered pairs in which each first coordinate (x-coordinate) has only one second coordinate (y-coordinate).

14. $\{(2, 3), (3, 4), (4, 5), (-1, 0)\}$ represents a function because for each x there is a unique y.

$\{(1,2), (1, -2), (3, 1)\}$
is not a function because for $x = 1$
there are two distinct values of y, 2 and −2.

15. The set of first coordinates of the ordered pairs of a relation is called its **domain**, and the set of second coordinates is called the *range*.

15. The domain of $\{(2, 3), (3, 4), (4, 5), (-1, 0)\}$ is $\{2, 3, 4, -1\}$

16. To draw the graph of a relation defined by an equation:

a. Use the equation to determine several ordered pairs (x, y).

b. Plot the points (x, y).

c. Join the points by a smooth curve or line.

16. **Draw the graph of the relation $y = |x + 1|$**

x	y	(x, y)
−2	−1	(−2, −1)
−1	0	(−1, 0)
0	1	(0, 1)
1	2	(1, 2)
2	3	(2, 3)

17.

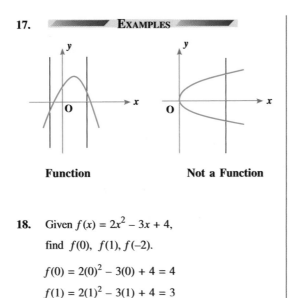

Function   Not a Function

17. **Vertical Line Test:** If all vertical lines intersect or meet the graph of an equation in at most one point, then the equation defines a function.

18. Given $f(x) = 2x^2 - 3x + 4$,

find $f(0)$, $f(1)$, $f(-2)$.

$f(0) = 2(0)^2 - 3(0) + 4 = 4$

$f(1) = 2(1)^2 - 3(1) + 4 = 3$

$f(-2) = 2(-2)^2 - 3(-2) + 4 = 18$

18. We can find the value of a function, $f(x)$, for any value of x by substituting the value of x into the function.

3.8 REVIEW EXERCISES

In exercises 1-6, determine whether or not the indicated ordered pair is a solution of the given equation.

1. $-3x + 4y = 10$; $(-2, 1)$ **2.** $3x - 2y = 5$; $(2, -3)$ **3.** $5x + 7y = 2$; $(1, -1)$

4. $3x - 2y = 4$; $(0, -2)$ **5.** $2x = 5y$; $(10, 4)$ **6.** $3x - 2y = 0$; $(2, 3)$

In exercises 7-10, complete the ordered pair so that it is a solution of the indicated equation.

7. $x + 3y = 5$; $(?, -2)$ **8.** $x - 2y = 6$; $(0, ?)$

9. $2x - 3y = 7$; $(-4, ?)$ **10.** $3x + 2y = 7$; $\left(\dfrac{1}{3}, ?\right)$

In exercises 11-22, complete the table of values for the given equation.

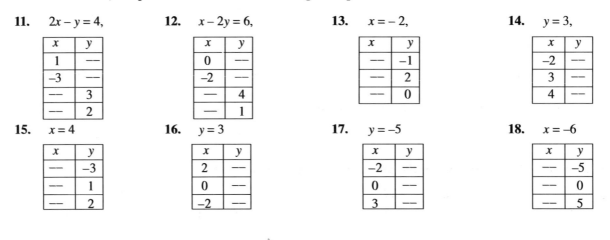

11. $2x - y = 4$,

x	y
1	—
-3	—
—	3
—	2

12. $x - 2y = 6$,

x	y
0	—
-2	—
—	4
—	1

13. $x = -2$,

x	y
—	-1
—	2
—	0

14. $y = 3$,

x	y
-2	—
3	—
4	—

15. $x = 4$

x	y
—	-3
—	1
—	2

16. $y = 3$

x	y
2	—
0	—
-2	—

17. $y = -5$

x	y
-2	—
0	—
3	—

18. $x = -6$

x	y
—	-5
—	0
—	5

19. $2x = 3y$

x	y
−3	−−
−−	0
−−	2

20. $x = 2y$

x	y
0	−−
−−	2
−3	−−

21. $3x + 4y = 1$

x	y
−1	−−
3	−−
−5	−−

22. $x − y = 2$

x	y
0	−−
2	−−
−4	−−

23. Plot the following ordered pairs on the same coordinate system.

   (a) (−1, 3)   **(b)** (2, 5)   **(c)** (3, −7)   **(d)** (−4, −1)   **(e)** (3, 0)   **(f)** (0, −2)   **(g)** (0, 0)

24. Plot the following ordered pairs on the same coordinate system.

   (a) (4, −2)   **(b)** (−4, −2)   **(c)** (−4, 2)   **(d)** (4, 2)   **(e)** (0, −4)   **(f)** (−4, 0)   **(g)** (−7, −7)

25. Determine the coordinates of each of the points shown in the figure.

26. Determine the coordinates of each of the points shown in the figure.

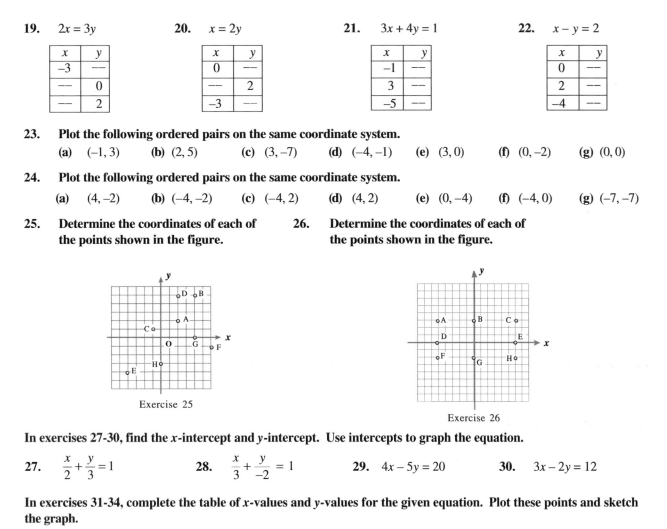

Exercise 25

Exercise 26

In exercises 27-30, find the *x*-intercept and *y*-intercept. Use intercepts to graph the equation.

27. $\dfrac{x}{2} + \dfrac{y}{3} = 1$ **28.** $\dfrac{x}{3} + \dfrac{y}{-2} = 1$ **29.** $4x − 5y = 20$ **30.** $3x − 2y = 12$

In exercises 31-34, complete the table of *x*-values and *y*-values for the given equation. Plot these points and sketch the graph.

31. $y = x^2$

x	y
−1	−−
−2	−−
1	−−
2	−−

32. $y = −x^2$

x	y
−2	−−
−1	−−
1	−−
2	−−

33. $y = x^2 − 2x + 2$

x	y
0	−−
−1	−−
1	−−
−2	−−
2	−−
3	−−

34. $y = x^2 + 2x + 2$

x	y
0	−−
−1	−−
1	−−
2	−−
−2	−−
−3	−−

In exercises 35-38, find the slope of the line passing through the pairs of points.

35. (−2, 4) (3, 9)   **36.** (2, 3), (−2, 3)   **37.** (3, 5) , (6, 1)   **38.** (1, 2), (3, 4)

In exercises 39-42, find the slope of the line and the *y*-intercept.

39. $3x = 4y + 1$ **40.** $3y + 4x = 1$ **41.** $2x + 5y + 3 = 0$ **42.** $2x = 3y − 1$

In exercises 43-50, identify whether the pair of lines are parallel, perpendicular, or neither.

43. $y = 3x + 7$
    $3y = x − 7$

44. $x + y = 0$
    $x − y = 0$

45. $2y − 5x = 1$
    $6y = 15x + 11$

46. $x − 2y = 7$
    $4y − 2x = 13$

47.	$x + 3y = 5$	48.	$2x - 3y - 7 = 0$	49.	$2x - y = 0$	50.	$4x - 3y = 10$
	$3x = y + 1$		$3x + 2y = 8$		$x + 2y + 1 = 0$		$3x + 4y = 18$

In exercises 51-70, find the equation of the line using the given information.

51. Slope $= -3$, y - intercept $(0, 0)$.　　　**52.** Slope $= \dfrac{5}{2}$, y - intercept $(0, 5)$

53. Slope $= \dfrac{5}{7}$, y - intercept $(0, -3)$.　　**54.** Slope $= -2$, y - intercept $\left(0, \dfrac{1}{2}\right)$

55. Slope $= 0$, passes through $(3, 5)$.　　　**56.** Slope $= \dfrac{-3}{2}$, passes through $(0, 5)$.

57. Slope $= \dfrac{2}{3}$, passes through $(-2, 3)$.　　**58.** Slope $= -2$, passes through $(2, -3)$.

59. Passes through the points $(2, 5)$ and $(3, 3)$.　　**60.** Passes through the points $(3, 1)$ and $(1, 2)$.

61. Passes through $(3, -1)$ and is parallel to the line $2y + 6x = 9$.

62. Passes through $(1, -2)$ and is parallel to the line $2x + 3y = 4$.

63. Passes through $(-1, 1)$ and is perpendicular to $4y = 3x + 5$.

64. Passes through $(0, 1)$ and is perpendicular to $x + 3y = 5$.

65. Slope $= \dfrac{1}{3}$, passes through $(-2, 4)$.　　**66.** Slope $= -2$, passes through $(1, -3)$.

67. Slope $=$ undefined, passes through $(0, 0)$.　　**68.** Slope $= 0$, passes through $\left(3, -\dfrac{1}{2}\right)$.

69. Passes through $(-2, -3)$ and $(1, -4)$.　　**70.** Passes through $(0, 2)$ and $(4, 0)$.

In exercises 71-80, graph the linear inequality.

71.	$2x - y \le 1$	72.	$x - 2y > 2$	73.	$x + 2y \ge 5$	74.	$x + 3y \le 0$
75.	$\dfrac{x}{3} + \dfrac{y}{2} < 1$	76.	$\dfrac{x}{2} + \dfrac{y}{4} > 1$	77.	$y > 3x$	78.	$x < 2y$
79.	$y < -4$	80.	$x + 5 \ge 0$				

In exercises 81-84, identify whether or not the relation is a function? Also determine the domain and the range in each case.

81. $\{(2, 1), (3, 1), (4, -1), (2, 2)\}$　　　**82.** $\{(1, 2), (3, -4), (4, -5), (5, -6)\}$

83. $\{(0, 0), (1, 1), (2, 1), (-1, 0), (-2, 3)\}$　　**84.** $\{(5, -2), (6, -1), (7, 0), (5, 2)\}$

In exercises 85-91, draw the graph of the given relation.

85.	$y > 4 - 3x$	86.	$y < 3x + 4$	87.	$y^2 < -4$	88.	$y^2 = 4(1 - x^2)$
89.	$y = |x| - 3$	90.	$y \ge 2x + 1$	91.	$y = |x + 1|$		

In exercises 92-94, use the vertical line test to determine whether or not the relation is a function.

92.

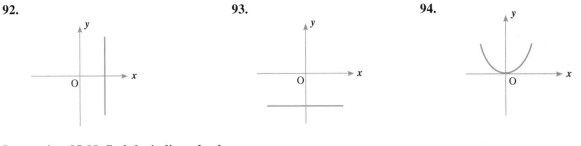

93.

94.

In exercises 95-98, find the indicated values:

95. $f(x) = 2x^2 + 3$; $f(0), f(-5)$

96. $h(x) = \dfrac{x}{2x+1}$; $h(0), h(3)$

97. $f(x) = |x| - 1$; $f(-5), f(3)$

98. $P(x) = 0.95x$; $P(6), P(20)$

3.9 SELF TEST

1. Complete the ordered pairs for the given equation.
$3x - 2y = 11$; $(-1, ?)$, $(2, ?)$, $(?, 2)$, $(?, -1)$

2. Complete the ordered pairs for the given equation.
$2x + 3y = 6$; $(3, ?)$, $(0, ?)$, $(4, ?)$, $(?, 1)$

In exercises 3-10, graph the linear equations. Find the *y*-intercept where indicated.

3. $3x = y$; *y*-intercept

4. $2x + y = 4$; *y*-intercept

5. $5x + 2y = 1$

6. $2x + 3y = 6$

7. $x + 2 = 0$; *y*-intercept

8. $y - 2 = 0$, *y*-intercept

9. $y = -3$; *y*-intercept

10. $x = -5$; *y*-intercept

In exercises 11-18, find the slope of the line. Also determine the y-intercept where indicated.

11. Passing through $(-1, 5)$ and $(4, 7)$

12. Passing through $(2, 3)$ and $(0, 1)$

13. $2y + 3 = 0$; *y*-intercept

14. $3x - y = 2$; *y*-intercept

15. $3x - 5 = 0$; *y*-intercept

16. $x - y = 2$; *y*-intercept

17. $2y + 3x = 7$; *y*-intercept

18. $5x + y = -2$; *y*-intercept

In exercises 19-24, graph the lines.

19. $2y = x + 6$

20. $2x = y + 3$

21. Slope = -2, passing through $(1, 2)$

22. Slope = 4, passing through $(0, 2)$

23. Passing through $(-1, 3)$, and $(2, 4)$

24. Passing through $(2, -1)$ and $(3, -2)$

In exercises 25-28, graph the linear inequality in two variables:

25. $2x - y \le 4$

26. $x - y \ge 3$

27. $x + y > 7$

28. $x + 2y < 3$

In exercises 29-32, identify whether or not the relation is a function? Also find the domain and range in each case?

29. $\{(-3, -2), (-1, -3), (-2, -3), (0, -1), (0, 4)\}$

30. $\{(-1, 0), (1, 2), (2, 3), (3, -4)\}$

31. $\{(2, 3), (4, 3), (6, -3), (7, 0)\}.$

32. $\{(3, 2), (4, 5) (5, 6), (3, -2)\}$

In exercises 33-38, identify whether or not the graph is a function.

33.

34.

35.

36.

37.

38.

In exercises 39-42, identify whether or not the equation represents a function.

39. $x^2 + y^2 = 1$

40. $y^2 = 4x$

41. $\dfrac{2}{3} x = 4 - 5y$

42. $3y - \dfrac{2}{5} x = 5$

In exercises 43-44, find the indicated values.

43. $f(x) = \dfrac{x^2 + 1}{-3x}$; $f(0), f(-2)$

44. $f(x) = \dfrac{(x - 3)(x + 2)}{2x - 3}$; $f(3), f(-1)$

Systems of Linear Equations and Inequalities

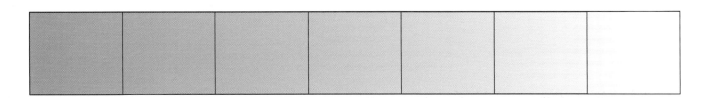

Objective: Intersecting, Parallel, and Coincident Lines

| Verify Skill | Discussion 1 | Discussion 2 | Example |

When we draw the graphs of two *linear equations* or two lines on the same *coordinate system*, we have one of the following three possibilities:

- The two lines intersect
- The lines are parallel
- The lines coincide

If the two lines *intersect* then the point of *intersection* is the only solution of the system.

- A system of equations is said to be *independent* and *consistent* if it has exactly one solution.

- The graphs of the *equations* of such a system are *distinct intersecting lines*.

Intersection Point

Copyright © 2005 Edvoo International, Inc.

4

SYSTEMS OF LINEAR EQUATIONS AND INEQUALITIES

Linear systems of equations and inequalities occur frequently in the solutions of problems related to science, social science, and business. In this chapter, we will only consider systems of two linear equations or inequalities in two variables and study different methods of solving such systems. In real life situations, however, the number of variables and equations can be very large and can be easily solved with the help of computers. Computer methods are based on algorithms which have their roots in the methods that will be investigated in this chapter.

This chapter is divided into five sections:

4.1 *Solutions using Graphs of Lines;*

4.2 *Solutions using Substitution;*

4.3 *Solutions using Elimination by Addition;*

4.4 *Solving Systems of Linear Inequalities; and*

4.5 *Applications*

4.1 SOLUTIONS USING GRAPHS OF LINES

A system of linear equations in two unknowns consists of two or more linear equations that describe relationships between x and y.

Consider the following system of linear equations in x and y.

$$3x + 5y = 2$$
$$4x - 2y = -6$$

We have seen in chapter 3, that a single equation has infinitely many solutions. In fact, for any value of x, a value of y can be obtained from the equation. However, if two linear equations are considered simultaneously, there may only be one ordered pair which is a solution of both equations. For example, $(-1, 1)$ is a solution of both equations in the above system.

$$3(-1) + 5(1) = 2 \qquad \text{True}$$
$$4(-1) - 2(1) = -6 \qquad \text{True}$$

Such an ordered pair of numbers is called a solution of the system.

The **solution of a system** is an ordered pair that is a solution of each equation in the system.

OBJECTIVES ■■■■

Upon completion of this section you will be able to:

A. Determine whether or not an ordered pair is a solution of a system of linear equations;

B. Solve linear systems by graphing; and

C. Identify whether the graph of a system of two linear equations consists of intersecting, parallel, or coincident lines and find the number of solutions to the system.

A. IDENTIFYING A SOLUTION OF A SYSTEM OF LINEAR EQUATIONS

An ordered pair (a, b) is a solution of a system of linear equations in two variables x and y if $x = a$ and $y = b$ satisfy each linear equation of the system.

EXAMPLE 1   Identify whether the indicated ordered pair is a solution of the given system.

a. $3x - 4y = 11$ $(1, -2)$
    $3x + y = 1$

b. $3x - 2y = 0$ $(2, 3)$
    $4x - 3y = 1$

c. $2x + y = 3$ $(1, -1)$
    $x - y = 0$

Solutions:

To decide whether an ordered pair is a solution of a system of linear equations, substitute the value for the variables in each equation of the system.

a.   Substitute **1** for x and **-2** for y.

$$
\begin{array}{c|c}
3x - 4y = 11 & 3x + y = 1 \\
3(\mathbf{1}) - 4(\mathbf{-2}) = 11 & 3(\mathbf{1}) + (\mathbf{-2}) = 1 \\
3 + 8 = 11 & 3 - 2 = 1 \\
11 = 11 \quad \text{True} & 1 = 1 \quad \text{True}
\end{array}
$$

$(1, -2)$ *satisfies both* equations.

Therefore, $(1, -2)$ is a *solution* of the system.

b.   Substitute **2** for x and **3** for y.

$$
\begin{array}{c|c}
3x - 2y = 0 & 4x - 3y = 1 \\
3(2) - 2(3) = 0 & 4(2) - 3(3) = 1 \\
6 - 6 = 0 & 8 - 9 = 1 \\
0 = 0 \quad \text{True} & -1 = 1 \quad \text{False}
\end{array}
$$

$(2, 3)$ *does not satisfy both* equations.

Therefore, it is *not a solution* of the system.

c.   Substitute **1** for x and **-1** for y.

$$
\begin{array}{c|c}
2x + y = 3 & x - y = 0 \\
2(\mathbf{1}) + (\mathbf{-1}) = 3 & 1(\mathbf{1}) - (\mathbf{-1}) = 0 \\
2 - 1 = 3 & 1 + 1 = 0 \\
1 = 3 \quad \text{False} & 2 = 0 \quad \text{False}
\end{array}
$$

$(1, -1)$ *does not satisfy either* equation.

Therefore, it is *not a solution* of the system.

B.   SOLVE LINEAR SYSTEMS USING GRAPHING

There are several methods which can be used to solve a system of linear equations. We will study three of these methods in this chapter. In this section, we will learn how to solve a system of linear equations by graphing both equations on the same coordinate system. A solution of the system must be a point on the graph of each line because it must satisfy each equation. Since two different lines can intersect in at most one point, we have the following conclusion.

> A system of linear equations *can have only one solution* if the graphs of the equations are different non-parallel lines.

EXAMPLE 2 Solve the following systems of equations by graphing.

a.	$x + 3y = 4$	**b.** $3x - y = 7$
	$2x - y = 1$	$x + y = 1$

Solutions:

We will graph each of the equations of the system on the same coordinate system. The coordinates of the point of intersection, if any, form the solution of the system.

To draw the graph, we make a table of three ordered pairs for each equation.

It is convenient to graph, if the ordered paires of numbers are integers. To do this, we identify values of x that gives y as an integer.

a. For $x + 3y = 4$, identify those values of x for which y or $\dfrac{4 - x}{3}$ is an integer.

For $x = 1$, $y = \dfrac{4 - 1}{3} = \dfrac{3}{3} = 1$. Therefore **(1, 1)** is a point on the line.

For $x = 4$, $y = \dfrac{4 - 4}{3} = \dfrac{0}{3} = 0$. Therefore **(4, 0)** is a point on the line.

For $x = -2$, $y = \dfrac{4 - (-2)}{3} = \dfrac{6}{3} = 2$. Therefore **(–2, 2)** is a point on the line.

• For $2x - y = 1$, identify those values of x for which $y = 2x - 1$ is an integer.

For $x = 0$, $y = 2(0) - 1 = $ **–1**

For $x = 1$, $y = 2((1) - 1) = $ **1**

For $x = 2$, $y = 2(2) - 1 = $ **3**

Table for $x + 3y = 4$

x	y
1	1
4	0
−2	2

Table for $2x - y = 1$

x	y
0	−1
1	1
2	3

Note, the ordered pair (1, 1) is found in both tables.

4.1   Solutions Using Graphs of Lines

The graphs are shown in Figure 4.1. They intersect at (1,1). Therefore, (1,1) is the solution of the system. Verify, by substituting 1 for x and 1 for y in the two equations, that both equations are satisfied.

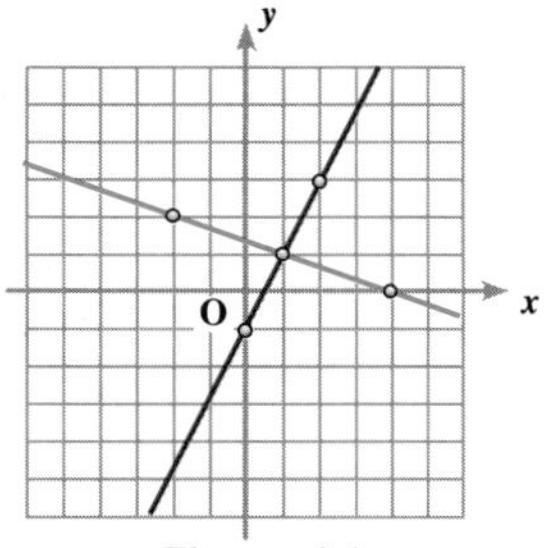

Figure 4.1

See examples 1-4 of section 4.1 in Appendix B for solving systems of equations using a calculator.

b) $x + 3y = -5$
$x - y = 7$

b.

Table for $3x - y = 7$

x	y
0	−7
3	2
1	−4

Table for $x + y = 1$

x	y
0	1
1	0
−1	2

The graphs are shown in Figure 4.2. They intersect at $(2, -1)$. Therefore, $(2, -1)$ is a solution of the system. Verify, by substituting 2 for x and −1 for y in the two equations, that $(2, -1)$ is a solution of both equations.

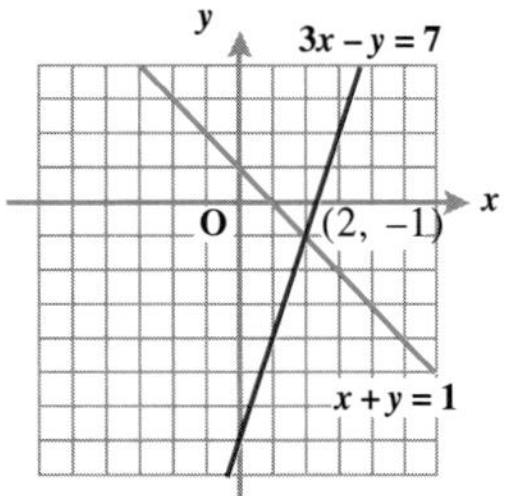

Figure 4.2

Note

When finding a solution by graphing, it is very important to verify the solution. In most cases, it may not be possible to determine the exact coordinates of the point of intersection from the graph. In such cases the solution obtained from the graph will only be an *approximation* of the solution.

To solve a system of equations graphically using a calculator, see example 4 of Section 4.1 in Appendix B.

Answers:

2. a) (0, −2) b) (4, −3)

C. INTERSECTING, PARALLEL, AND COINCIDENT LINES

When we draw the graphs of two linear equations or two lines on the same coordinate system, we have one of the following three possibilities:

1. the two lines intersect,   **2. the lines are parallel, or**   **3. the lines coincide**

1.   If the two lines intersect then the **point of intersection is the only solution of the system. (Figure 4.3)**

   A system of equations is said to be **independent** and **consistent** if it has *exactly one solution*. The graphs of the equations of such a system are distinct intersecting lines.

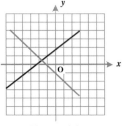

Figure 4.3

2. If the two lines are **parallel**, then the **lines do not intersect and the system has** *no solution* **(Figure 4.4).**

A system of equations is said to be **inconsistent** if it has *no solution*. The graphs of the equations of such a system are a pair of distinct and parallel lines.

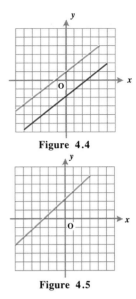

Figure 4.4

3. If the two lines are **coincident** (the same line), then **every point on the line is a solution of the system (Figure 4.5).** There are infinitely many solutions.

A system of equations is said to be **dependent** if the system of equations has infinitely many solutions. The graphs of the equations of such a system are the same line.

> *Note* Two equations will represent the same line if one equation can be obtained from the other by multiplying it by a suitable number. For example consider $4x - 6y = 8$ and $2x - 3y = 4$. Notice $4x - 6y = 8$ can be obtained by multiplying both sides of $2x - 3y = 4$ by 2.

Figure 4.5

EXAMPLE 3 Graph each of the following systems of equations. Determine whether the lines are intersecting, parallel, or coincident.

a. $2x + 3y = 6$
$4x + 6y = 24$

b. $2x + y = 1$
$x - 2y = 7$

c. $3x - 2y = 5$
$6x = 4y + 10$

Solutions:

a. Table for $2x + 3y = 6$

x	y
0	2
3	0
−3	4

Table for $4x + 6y = 24$

x	y
0	4
6	0
3	2

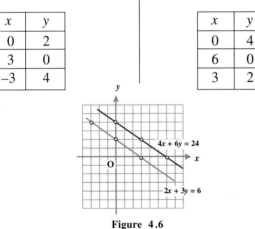

Figure 4.6

The two lines are parallel. The system has no solution.

b. Table for $2x + y = 1$

x	y
0	1
−1	3
1	−1

Table for $x - 2y = 7$

x	y
1	−3
−1	−4
3	−2

━━━━━ **WARM-UP** ━━━━━

3. Graph each of the following systems of equations. Determine whether the lines are intersecting, parallel, or coincident.

a. $y = -\dfrac{3}{2}x + 8$

$y = -\dfrac{3}{2}x + \dfrac{25}{2}$

b. $x - 3y = 9$
$3x + y = 2$

The two lines intersect. Therefore, the system has only one solution. The solution is $x \approx 2$ and $y \approx -2.6$.

Exact solution is $(1.8, -2.6)$.

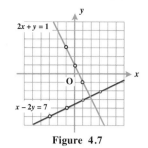

Figure 4.7

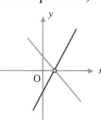

(2,–2.6) is only an approximate solution.

c. $y = \dfrac{4}{5}x - \dfrac{7}{5}$

$4x - 5y = 7$

c. Table for $3x - 2y = 5$

x	y
3	2
1	-1
-1	-4

Table for $6x = 4y + 10$

x	y
2	1/2
1	-1
0	$-5/2$

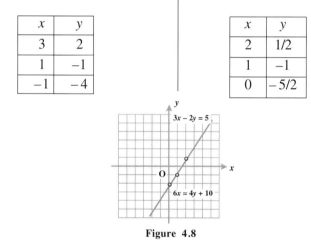

Figure 4.8

Answers:

3. **a)** The two lines are parallel so the system is inconsistent and has no solution.

b) The two lines are perpendicular and intersect.
The system has only one solution.

c) The two lines are coincident and the system is dependent.
The system has an infinite number of solutions.

The two lines are identical. Therefore, the system is dependent. In fact, every point on this line is a solution of the system. Observe that the equations $6x = 4y + 10$ and $3x - 2y = 5$ are equivalent. When both sides of first equation, $3x - 2y = 5$, are multiplied by 2, we get the second equation, $6x = 4y + 10$.

 Examples 2 and 3 of section 4.1 in Appendix B explain how to find, using calculator, whether the graphs are parallel, intersecting, or coincident.

We can identify the nature of the system of linear equations in a relatively simpler way by writing the equations of the lines in slope-intercept form and using the following observations.

- Parallel lines have the same slope and different y-intercepts.

- Intersecting lines have different slopes.

- Coincident lines, since their graph is the same line, have the same slope and the same y-intercept. (identical equations).

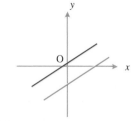

Same slope, different y-intercept
Lines are Parallel

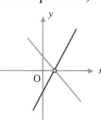

Different slope
Lines are Different

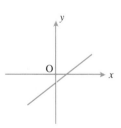

Same slope, same y-intercept.
Lines are Coincident

By writing each line in slope-intercept form ($y = mx + b$), we can determine the graph of the system, and the number of solutions to the system. We illustrate this by repeating example 3 as example 4, below.

EXAMPLE 4   Solve each equation for y to get the slope-intercept form, $y = mx + b$. Determine whether the lines in each system are intersecting, parallel, or coincident. Indicate the number of solutions for each system.

    a. $2x + 3y = 6$ **b.** $2x + y = 1$ **c.** $3x - 2y = 5$

          $4x + 6y = 24$ $x - 2y = 7$ $6x = 4y + 10$

Solutions:

    a.   Solve for y: $2x + 3y = 6$ $\longrightarrow$ $y = -\dfrac{2}{3}x + 2$

                     $4x + 6y = 24$ $\longrightarrow$ $y = -\dfrac{2}{3}x + 4$

These lines are not the same since they have different y-intercepts: $(0, 2)$ and $(0, 4)$. They do have the same slope; $m = -\dfrac{2}{3}$.

The lines are parallel and the system has no solution.

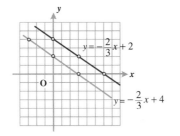

    b.   Solve for y: $2x + y = 1$ $\longrightarrow$ $y = -2x + 1$

                     $x - 2y = 7$ $\longrightarrow$ $y = \dfrac{1}{2}x - \dfrac{7}{2}$

These lines have different slopes. So, they are non-parallel lines. They intersect at a single point. The system has one solution.

    c.   Solve for y: $3x - 2y = 5$ $\longrightarrow$ $y = \dfrac{3}{2}x - \dfrac{5}{2}$

                     $6x = 4y + 10$ $\longrightarrow$ $y = \dfrac{3}{2}x - \dfrac{5}{2}$

The equations in slope-intercept form are identical. This means the graphs are the same line (coincident lines) and there are infinitely many solutions to the system.

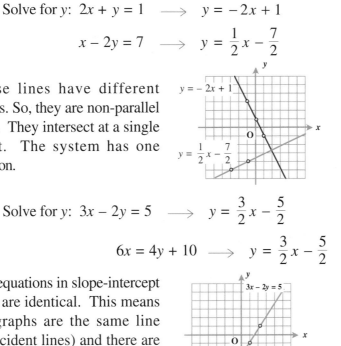

A. In exercises 1-18, identify whether the indicated ordered pair is a solution of the given system.

1. $\left.\begin{array}{l} 4x - 3y = 6 \\ x + 2y = 7 \end{array}\right\}$ (3, 2)

2. $\left.\begin{array}{l} y + 3x = 26 \\ 3y - x = 18 \end{array}\right\}$ (6, 8)

3. $\left.\begin{array}{l} 3x - y + 4 = 0 \\ 2x + 5y = 3 \end{array}\right\}$ (−1, 1)

4. $\left.\begin{array}{l} x + 7y = 22 \\ y + 3x = 26 \end{array}\right\}$ (8, 2)

5. $\left.\begin{array}{l} -2x + 5y = 1 \\ x - 4y = 3 \end{array}\right\}$ (2, -1)

6. $\left.\begin{array}{l} 3y = x + 18 \\ x + y = 6 \end{array}\right\}$ (0, 1)

7. $\left.\begin{array}{l} 3x + 2y = 0 \\ 2x = 3y - 5 \end{array}\right\}$ (−2, −3)

8. $\left.\begin{array}{l} x - 2y = 6 \\ 2x + y = 7 \end{array}\right\}$ (2, 3)

9. $\left.\begin{array}{l} 4x + 3y = 15 \\ x - y + 5 = 10 \end{array}\right\}$ (0, 5)

10. $\left.\begin{array}{l} 3x - 2y = 4 \\ x + y = 6 \end{array}\right\}$ (2, −3)

11. $\left.\begin{array}{l} 3x + y = 5 \\ 2y = 10 - 6x \end{array}\right\}$ (1, 2)

12. $\left.\begin{array}{l} 7y = 22 - x \\ 3y = x + 18 \end{array}\right\}$ (−6, 4)

13. $\left.\begin{array}{l} 2x - y = -4 \\ 2x - y = 1 \end{array}\right\}$ (0, 4)

14. $\left.\begin{array}{l} 2x - 3y = 6 \\ 2x + 3y = 10 \end{array}\right\}$ (3, −2)

15. $\left.\begin{array}{l} 3x - 2y = 6 \\ 9x - 4y = 24 \end{array}\right\}$ (4, 3)

16. $\left.\begin{array}{l} x + 2y = 9 \\ x - 2y = 1 \end{array}\right\}$ (5, 2)

17. $\left.\begin{array}{l} 2x + y = -1 \\ x + 2y = 4 \end{array}\right\}$ (−2, 3)

18. $\left.\begin{array}{l} x - y = -2 \\ x + 2y = -2 \end{array}\right\}$ (−2, 0)

B. In exercises 19-42, solve the system of equations by graphing. Identify whether the lines are intersecting, parallel, or coincident.

19. $x - 2y = 2$
$x + 2y = 6$

20. $x + y = 3$
$2x + 5y = 12$

21. $4x + y = 5$
$3x = 2y + 12$

22. $2x + 3y = 13$
$5x - 2y = 4$

23. $2x + y = 5$
$y = 3$

24. $3x - 5y = -1$
$2x - y = -3$

25. $x - 2y = 2$
$2x = 4y - 2$

26. $2x + 3y = 12$
$3y + 2x = 6$

27. $2x - 3y = 4$
$y = -2$

28. $x = 3$
$y = 2$

29. $3x = 5 - 2y$
$3x + 2y = 7$

30. $5x + 2y = 1$
$4x - 3y = 10$

31. $x = 3y - 1$
$x = 2y$

32. $2x + 3y = 0$
$2x - 3y = -4$

33. $2x = 5y - 4$
$3x - 5y = -1$

34. $4x - 3y = -1$
$3y + 8x = 4$

35. $3x + 5y = 8$
$6x = 16 - 10y$

36. $2x + 7y = 10$
$10x + 35y = 50$

37. $2x + 4y = 12$
$5x + 4y = 30$

38. $2x + 10 = 6y$
$9y = 3x + 15$

39. $x = 4$
$3x - 2y = 4$

40. $3y = 2x + 6$
$4x - 6y = -1$

41. $3x - 5y = -5$
$3x - 5y = -5$

42. $4x + y = 5$
$2x + y = 3$

C. In exercises 43-62, solve for y to express the equation in slope-intercept form. Determine whether the lines are parallel, intersecting or coincident.

43. $3x = 4y + 7$
$y = x + 7$

44. $x + 3y = 20$
$x - y = 4$

45. $2y + 5x = 8$
$5y - 2x = 1$

46. $2x - y = 3$
$4x + y = 3$

47. $2x = 3y + 2$
$-6x + 9y = 5$

48. $3x - 4y = 12$
$6x - 8y = 48$

49. $2x - y = 4$
$y = 2x + 9$

50. $3y + 2x = 24$
$2x + 3y = 12$

51. $x - y = 0$
$x - y = 1$

52. $2x + y = 6$
$x + y = 4$

53. $x - y = 1$
$x + y = 1$

54. $x + 2y = 3$
$2x + 4y = 8$

55. $y = x$
$2x + y = 2$

56. $3x + y = 6$
$3x + 6y = 18$

57. $x - y = 4$
$y = 0$

58. $x + 2y = 4$
$2x - y = 3$

59. $2x + 3y = 7$
$4x = 14 - 6y$

60. $y = 3x - 2$
$2y = 6x - 4$

61. $\dfrac{3}{5}x + \dfrac{7}{3}y = 10$

$\dfrac{4}{7}x + \dfrac{2}{3}y = -5$

62. $6y + 4x = 10$
$9y + 6x = 15$

4.2 SOLUTIONS USING SUBSTITUTION

The graphing method provides visualization, but it has its limitations. Sometimes it may be difficult to read the exact values of the coordinates of the point of intersection from the graph. In this section we study the first of the two algebraic methods, namely the **substitution method**.

A. SOLVING USING SUBSTITUTION

The following steps may be used in solving a system by the method of substitution.

> *Step* 1 Solve one of the equations for either of the two variables in terms of the other variable.
>
> *Step* 2 Substitute the solution for this variable in the other equation. This results in an equation in one variable.
>
> *Step* 3 Solve the equation obtained in step 2.
>
> *Step* 4 Substitute the value obtained in step 3 into any one of the two equations involving both variables, and solve for the second variable.
>
> *Step* 5 Check the solution for (x, y) by substituting it into both of the original equations.

EXAMPLE 1   Solve the system $3x - 5y = -6$
                                    $x + 3y = 2$

Solution:

- Solve the second equation for x.
$$x + 3y = 2 \quad \longrightarrow \quad x = 2 - 3y \qquad \ldots(1)$$

- Substitute $2 - 3y$ for x in the first equation.
$$3x - 5y = -6 \quad \longrightarrow \quad 3(2 - 3y) - 5y = -6$$

- $6 - 9y - 5y = -6$

    $6 - 14y = -6$

    $-14y = -12$

    $y = \dfrac{-12}{-14}$

    $y = \dfrac{6}{7}$

- Substitute $\dfrac{6}{7}$ for y in equation (1): $x = 2 - 3y$.

$$x = 2 - 3\left(\frac{6}{7}\right) = 2 - \frac{18}{7} = -\frac{4}{7}$$

Therefore, $\left(-\frac{4}{7}, \frac{6}{7}\right)$ is a solution of the system.

• **Check:**

Substitute $\frac{-4}{7}$ for x and $\frac{6}{7}$ for y in the original equations, and verify that both equations are satisfied. You may use a calculator or proceed as follows.

$3x - 5y = -6$	$x + 3y = 2$
$3\left(-\frac{4}{7}\right) - 5\left(\frac{6}{7}\right) = -6$	$-\frac{4}{7} + 3\left(\frac{6}{7}\right) = 2$
$\frac{-12}{7} - \frac{30}{7} = -6$	$\frac{-4}{7} + \frac{18}{7} = 2$
$\frac{-42}{7} = -6$	$\frac{14}{7} = 2$
$-6 = -6$ **True**	$2 = 2$ **True**

Notes

1. This example shows that the substitution method can be employed where the graphing method may give only an approximate answer. Notice that it is difficult to read $-\frac{4}{7}$ or $\frac{6}{7}$ from a graph. The substitution method gave an exact solution.

2. The substitution method is best used when it is easy to solve for a variable, i.e. when the coefficient of one of the variables in one of the two equation is 1 or –1.

2. Solve
$$x + 2y = 4$$
$$3x + 4y = 6$$

EXAMPLE 2　　Solve the system　$2x - y = 5$
$$4x + 3y = 4$$

Solution:

• Solve the first equation for y:

$$2x - y = 5 \longrightarrow \boldsymbol{y = 2x - 5} \qquad \ldots(1)$$

• Substitute this expression for y in the second equation

$$4x + 3y = 4 \longrightarrow 4x + 3(\boldsymbol{2x - 5}) = 4$$

• Solve the equation in step 2 for x.

$$4x + 6x - 15 = 4 \quad \text{or} \quad 10x = 19 \longrightarrow \boldsymbol{x = \frac{19}{10}}$$

• Substitute $\frac{19}{10}$ for x in equation (1);

$$y = 2x - 5$$

$$y = 2\left(\frac{19}{10}\right) - 5 \qquad \text{Substitute for } x.$$

$$y = \frac{19}{5} - 5$$

$$y = -\frac{6}{5}$$

Therefore, the solution is $\left(\frac{19}{10}, -\frac{6}{5}\right)$.

- *Check:*

  Substitute $x = \frac{19}{10}$ and $y = -\frac{6}{5}$ in both original equations.

$2x - y = 5$	$4x + 3y = 4$
$2\left(\frac{19}{10}\right) - \left(-\frac{6}{5}\right) = 5$	$4\left(\frac{19}{10}\right) + 3\left(-\frac{6}{5}\right) = 4$
$\frac{19}{5} + \frac{6}{5} = 5$	$\frac{38}{5} - \frac{18}{5} = 4$
$\frac{25}{5} = 5$	$\frac{20}{5} = 4$
$5 = 5$ **True**	$4 = 4$ **True**

EXAMPLE 3   Solve: $1.5x - y = -3$
$$-5x + 4y = 16$$

Solution:

- $-y = -1.5x - 3$ Solve first equation for y.
  $y = \mathbf{1.5x + 3}$ ...(1)

- $-5x + 4(\mathbf{1.5x + 3}) = 16$ Substitute expression for y in second equation.

- $-5x + 6x + 12 = 16$ Solve for x.
  $$x = 16 - 12$$
  $$x = \mathbf{4}$$

- Substitute $x = \mathbf{4}$ in equation (1)
  $$y = 1.5(\mathbf{4}) + 3$$
  $$y = 9$$

- Check the solution $(4, 9)$ by substituting it into the *original* system of equations.

WARM-UP

3. Solve
    $x + 1.5y = -8$
    $4x - 5y = 12$

B. PARALLEL AND COINCIDENT LINES

EXAMPLE 4   Solve the following system of linear equations.
$$x - 5y = 7$$
$$10y = 2x + 5$$

Solution:

- $x - 5y = 7$ Solve the first equation for x.
  $x = \mathbf{5y + 7}$

WARM-UP

4. Solve
    $x - 5y = 7$
    $15y = 3x - 9$

• Substitute for x in the second equation.

$$10y = 2x + 5 \longrightarrow 10y = 2(\mathbf{5y + 7}) + 5$$
$$10y = 10y + 14 + 5$$
$$\mathbf{0 = 19}$$

• This is a **False** statement. Hence the system has no solution, *i.e.* the system is **inconsistent**. The graph of the system consists of two parallel lines.

We may verify this by solving for y to obtain the slope-intercept form, and by comparing their slopes.

5. Solve
$$3x + 4y = 13$$
$$16y = 52 - 12x$$

EXAMPLE 5   Solve the system. $2x + 3y = 6$
$$9y = 18 - 6x$$

Solution: Solve the second equation for y.

• $9y = 18 - 6x$

$$y = \frac{\mathbf{18 - 6x}}{\mathbf{9}}$$

$$y = 2 - \frac{2}{3}x$$

• Substitute for y in the first equation:

$$2x + 3y = 6$$

$$2x + 3\left(2 - \frac{2}{3}x\right) = 6$$

• $2x + 6 - 2x = 6$

$$6 = 6 \qquad \text{True for any } x.$$

This is a true statement but contains no variables for which to solve. This means that the system is **dependent**. If solving leads to an *identity* $(0 = 0)$, then the graph of the system consists of two coincident lines.

Answers:

1. $(2, 0)$ 2. $(-2, 3)$
3. $(-2, -4)$ 4. No solution.
5. Any point on the coincident lines.

By solving each equation for y to get the slope-intercept form, we get $y = -\frac{2}{3}x + 2$ and $y = -\frac{2}{3}x + 2$. The two lines have the same slope and the same y-intercept.

If solving a system leads to a false statement (contradiction), the system is inconsistent, there is no solution, and the lines are parallel.

If solving a system leads to a true statement (identity), the system is dependent with infinitely many solutions, and the lines are coincident.

A. In exercises 1-30, solve the system of equations using substitution method.

1. $x + y = 5$
    $x - y = 1$

2. $x - y = -1$
    $3x - 5y = -1$

3. $x - y = 5$
    $3x + 2y = 10$

4. $x = 2 + y$
    $2x + 3y = 4$

5. $2x - y = -5$
    $4x + y = 2$

6. $2x + y = 11$
    $x = 18 - 3y$

7. $x + 2y = 9$
    $x = 2y + 1$

8. $2x + 3y = 7$
    $6x - y = 1$

9. $2x + y = 5$
    $x + 3y = 0$

10. $x + 2y = 4$
    $2x + y = 8$

11. $2x + y = 3$
    $2y = -4x + 6$

12. $2x = 4 + y$
    $4x - 2y = 10$

13. $x - y = 3$
    $3y = x$

14. $y - 1.2x = 0.4$
    $6y - 5x = 9$

15. $2x + y = -4$
    $x - 2y = -7$

16. $x + 1.5y = 0$
    $3x + 4y = 5$

17. $4x + y = 5$
    $x - 3 = 0$

18. $2x + y = -4$
    $3y = 5x - 1$

19. $3x + 5y = 10$
    $y = 2$

20. $3x - 7y + 10 = 0$
    $y - 2x - 3 = 0$

21. $4y + x = 13$
    $3x - 2y = -6$

22. $5x + 3y = 6$
    $x = 3y + 5$

23. $2x - y = 6$
    $6x - 5y = -2$

24. $x = 4 - y$
    $4x + 4y = 16$

25. $x = 3y$
    $9y - 3x = 12$

26. $x + y = 7$
    $3x + 2y = 19$

27. $3x - 2y = 0$
    $x - 2.5y = -5.5$

28. $2x - 7y = -3$
    $x + 3y = 5$

29. $2x - 3y = 4$
    $8x = 12 + 2y$

30. $3y = x - 6$
    $x - 3y = 6$

B. In exercises 31-65, solve the system of equations using substitution method. Using the solution, identify whether the graph of the system consists of intersecting, parallel, or coincident lines.

31. $x = y + 4$
    $3x + 7y = -18$

32. $x - y = 3$
    $3x - 3y = 12$

33. $x + 2y = 5$
    $x = 2y + 1$

34. $2x - 5y = 6$
    $3x + 4y = 8$

35. $2x - 3y = 7$
    $5x + 3y = 7$

36. $x + y = 3$
    $2x - y = 12$

37. $8x + 3y = 4$
    $-x + .75y = .25$

38. $2x + y = 12$
    $2x - y = 4$

39. $2x - 2y = -2$
    $x + 3y = 5$

40. $3x - 5y + 1 = 0$
    $x - y + 1 = 0$

41. $9x + 7y = 4$
    $1.5x + 4y = 3.5$

42. $4x + y = 10$
    $3x - 5y = -4$

43. $2x = 10y + 14$
    $6x - 2y = 2x + 28$

44. $x = 2y + 7$
    $x = 3y - 1$

45. $y = -3x + 1$
    $-y = -2x + 3$

46. $4x + 7y = 10$
    $x + 1.75y = 2.5$

47. $x + y = 5$
    $.4x + .18y = 1.6$

48. $1.5x + 0.2y = .1$
    $x + 0.5y = -2.5$

49. $0.25x + 0.5y = 5$
    $1.5x - 0.2y = 14$

50. $0.2x - 0.3y = .7$
    $0.3x + 0.5y = .1$

51. $1.5x - y = 1$
    $6x = 4y + 7$

52. $x + y - 7 = 0$
    $5x + 12y - 7 = 0$

53. $2x + y = 6$
    $3y = 18 - 6x$

54. $2x - y - 3.7 = 0$
    $y - 5x = -11.2$

55. $x + y = -1.2$
    $2x + 3y = -4.8$

56. $2x - 3y = -3$
    $18x + 30y = 11$

57. $6x + 6y = -19$
    $6x + 2y = -9$

58. $2x + 3y = 0.1$
    $2x + 3y = 0.1$

59. $2x + 3y = 0.1$
    $3x - 2y = -10.9$

60. $x - 2.2y = 4.3$
    $x + 1.1y = -1.1$

61. $x = 2.3y + 1$
    $2x - 4.6y = 3$

62. $x + y = 90$
    $x - y = 32.4$

63. $x - y = 45.6$
    $x + y = 180$

64. $0.2x + 0.5y = 1.6$
    $-0.3x + 0.4y = -0.1$

65. $2.1x - 0.6y = 8.4$
    $-1.5x - 0.3y = -6$

4.3 SOLUTIONS USING ELIMINATION BY ADDITION

Upon completion of this section you will be able to:

A. Solve linear systems by the addition method ; and

B. Determine whether the graphs of a linear system represent parallel, intersecting or coincident lines by the addition method.

A. ELIMINATION BY ADDITION METHOD

The second method to solve a system of linear equations is called the **Elimination by Addition Method.** We replace the original system of equations by an equivalent system in such a way that the coefficients of one of the variables in the two equations are opposites of each other. Adding the respective sides of the equations of the equivalent system eliminates this variable. This facilitates the solution of the other variable. The following steps may be used to solve a linear system of equations by the addition method.

Step 1 Write both equations in standard form $ax + by = c$. It is important that each variable term occupies the same position in both equations.

Step 2 Multiply both sides of one or both equations by suitable numbers so that the coefficients of either x or y in the resulting equations are opposites of each other.

Step 3 Add the two equations. This will result in an equation in only one variable, as the other variable term is eliminated.

Step 4 Solve the equation obtained in step 3.

Step 5 Substitute the value obtained in step 4 in any equation that contains both variables. Find the value of *other variable*.

Step 6 Check the answer.

Note ✏ In some cases, it may be more convenient to repeat steps 2-4 for the other variable instead of doing step 5.

WARM-UP

1. Solve
$$5x - 4y = 12$$
$$-5x + 2y = 4$$

EXAMPLE 1   Solve $4x - 3y = 15$
$$-2x + 3y = -9$$

Solution:

- Both equations are already in the form $ax + by = c$.
- The coefficients of y are already -3 and 3.
- Add the two equations.

$$\begin{array}{rcl} 4x - 3y &=& 15 \\ -2x + 3y &=& -9 \\ \hline 2x &=& 6 \end{array}$$

- Solve $2x = 6$
$$x = 3$$

- Substitute $x = 3$ into any of the equations containing both x and y. Let us substitute 3 for x in the second equation.

$$\begin{array}{rcl} -2x + 3y &=& -9 \\ -2(3) + 3y &=& -9 \\ 3y &=& -3 \\ y &=& -1 \end{array}$$

- We may verify that $(3, -1)$ satisfies both equations. Therefore, the solution is $(3, -1)$

| Note | The substitution method for the above example will involve fractions. Using the addition method is preferred. |

EXAMPLE 2   Solve: $2x + 5y + 5 = 0$ ...(1)

$2y = 3x + 17$ ...(2)

Solution:

- Rewrite both equations in the form $ax + by = c$

$2x + 5y = -5$

$-3x + 2y = 17$

- Let us eliminate x. The least common multiple of the coefficients of x is 6. Since one of the coefficients is already negative, we can multiply equation (1) by 3 and equation (2) by 2.

$$2x + 5y = -5 \xrightarrow{(3)} 6x + 15y = -15$$
$$-3x + 2y = 17 \xrightarrow{(2)} -6x + 4y = 34$$

- Add the two equations. $\overline{\qquad 19y = 19}$

- Solve for y: $19y = 19$

$y = \mathbf{1}$

- Substitute 1 for $\mathbf{y}$ in any one of the equations containing both variables. We will use $2x + 5y = -5$.

$$2x + 5(\mathbf{1}) = -5$$
$$2x = -10$$
$$x = -5$$

- Verify that $(-5, 1)$ is a solution of the *original* system.

$2(-5) + 5(1) + 5 = 0$ True

$2(1) = 3(-5) + 17.$ True

Caution: Checking in only one equation is not sufficient. An incorrect answer often satisfies one equation and not the other. Always check both.

EXAMPLE 3   Solve: $5x = 11y + 2$ ...(1)

$3x + 7y = 5$ ...(2)

Solution:

- Rewrite the equations in standard form.

$5x - 11y = 2$

$3x + 7y = 5$

- Eliminate x. The LCM of the coefficients of x is 15. We multiply equation (1) by 3 and equation (2) by -5.

2. Solve

$3x + 7y - 62 = 0$

$y = 2x + 4$

3. Solve

$x - 4y = -3$

$4x + 5y = 2$

$$5x - 11y = 2 \quad \xrightarrow{(3)} \quad 15x - 33y = 6$$
$$3x + 7y = 5 \quad \xrightarrow{(-5)} \quad -15x - 35y = -25$$

- Add the two equations. $-68y = -19$

- Solve for y. $y = \dfrac{19}{68}$

Note ⮞ Substituting $y = \dfrac{19}{68}$ into any of the previous equations requires calculations with fractions. In such a case, it is easier to repeat steps 2, 3, and 4 to eliminate y.

- The lcm of 11 and 7 is 77, so multiply equation (1) by 7 and equation (2) by 11.

$$5x - 11y = 2 \quad \xrightarrow{(7)} \quad 35x - 77y = 14$$
$$3x + 7y = 5 \quad \xrightarrow{(+\,11)} \quad \underline{33x + 77y = 55}$$
$$68x \qquad = 69$$

or $\qquad x = \dfrac{69}{68}$

The solution of the system is $\left(\dfrac{69}{68}, \dfrac{19}{68}\right)$.

- Verify the solution $\left(\dfrac{69}{68}, \dfrac{19}{68}\right)$ using a calculator.

4. Solve $\dfrac{2}{3}x - \dfrac{4}{5}y = -\dfrac{28}{15}$
$\dfrac{5}{4}y - \dfrac{5}{4}x = \dfrac{15}{4}$

EXAMPLE 4 Solve $\dfrac{3}{2}x - \dfrac{3}{4}y = \dfrac{15}{4}$
$\dfrac{5}{3}y - \dfrac{4}{3}x = \dfrac{-19}{3}$

Solution: First multiply both sides of each equation by the LCD of the fractions in that equation, to eliminate fractions.

$$\dfrac{3}{2}x - \dfrac{3}{4}y = \dfrac{15}{4} \quad \xrightarrow[\text{LCD}\,=\,4]{(4)} \quad 4\left(\dfrac{3}{2}x - \dfrac{3}{4}y\right) = 4\left(\dfrac{15}{4}\right)$$
$$\longrightarrow \quad 6x - 3y = 15$$

$$\dfrac{5}{3}y - \dfrac{4}{3}x = \dfrac{-19}{3} \quad \xrightarrow[\text{LCD}\,=\,3]{(3)} \quad 3\left(\dfrac{5}{3}y - \dfrac{4}{3}x\right) = 3\left(\dfrac{-19}{3}\right)$$
$$\longrightarrow \quad 5y - 4x = -19$$

We will now solve the system: $6x - 3y = 15$ ...(1)
$5y - 4x = -19$ ...(2)

Rewrite the system in standard form.

- $6x - 3y = 15 \quad \longrightarrow \quad 6x - 3y = 15$ ...(1)
  $5y - 4x = -19 \quad \longrightarrow \quad -4x + 5y = -19$ ...(2)

- The LCM of the coefficients of x is 12, so multiply equation (1) by 2 and equation (2) by 3.

$$6x - 3y = 15 \xrightarrow{(2)} 12x - 6y = 30$$
$$-4x + 5y = -19 \xrightarrow{(3)} -12x + 15y = -57$$

- Add equations. $\qquad 9y = -27$

- Solve for y: $\qquad y = -3$

- Substitute -3 for y in $6x - 3y = 15$.

$$6x - 3(-3) = 15$$
$$6x + 9 = 15$$
$$6x = 6$$
$$x = 1. \quad \text{The solution of the system is } (1, -3).$$

- Verify that $(1, -3)$ satisfies the *original* system.

EXAMPLE 5   Solve the system
$$3x + .5y = 3.5$$
$$2x - 3.3y = 9.6$$

Solution:

- The equations are already in standard form, but the decimals can be eliminated by multiplying both sides of each equation by 10.

$$30x + 5y = 35 \qquad \ldots(1)$$
$$20x - 33y = 96 \qquad \ldots(2)$$

- The LCM of the coefficients of x is 60. Multiply equation (1) by 2 and equation (2) by -3.

$$30x + 5y = 35 \xrightarrow{(2)} 60x + 10y = 70$$
$$20x - 33y = 96 \xrightarrow{(-3)} -60x + 99y = -288$$

- Add the equations. $\qquad 109y = -218$

- Solve for y:
$$y = \frac{-218}{109}$$
$$= -2$$

- Substitute -2 for y in $30x + 5y = 35$.

$$30x + 5(-2) = 35$$
$$30x = 35 + 10$$
$$30x = 45$$

$$x = \frac{45}{30}$$

$$x = \mathbf{1.5}$$

The solution is $(1.5, -2)$.

- Verify that $(1.5, -2)$ is the solution.

$$3x + .5y = 3.5$$
$$3(\mathbf{1.5}) + .5(\mathbf{-2}) = 3.5$$
$$4.5 - 1.0 = 3.5 \quad \text{True}$$

$$2x - 3.3y = 9.6$$
$$2(\mathbf{1.5}) - 3.3(\mathbf{-2}) = 9.6$$
$$3.0 + 6.6 = 9.6 \quad \text{True}$$

Answers:

1. $(-4, -8)$ 2. $(2, 8)$

3. $\left(-\frac{1}{3}, \frac{2}{3}\right)$ 4. $(-4, -1)$

5. $(0.5, 1.2)$

B. IDENTIFY THE GRAPHS OF A LINEAR SYSTEM

6. Solve the system
$$4x - 5y = 21$$
$$10y - 8x + 42 = 0$$

EXAMPLE 6   Solve the system : $3x - 4y = 5$
$$8y - 6x + 10 = 0$$

Solution: $3x - 4y = 5 \longrightarrow 3x - 4y = 5$
$$8y - 6x + 10 = 0 \longrightarrow -6x + 8y = -10$$

Let us eliminate x.

$$3x - 4y = 5 \xrightarrow{(2)} 6x - 8y = 10$$
$$-6x + 8y = -10 \xrightarrow{(1)} \underline{-6x + 8y = -10}$$
$$0 = 0 \quad \text{True}$$

This is a true statement which does not contain x or y. The system is dependent and has an infinite number of solutions. The graphs of the equations in this system are **coincident lines** (the same line). Each point of the line $3x - 4y = 5$ is a solution.

7. Solve the system
$$3x - 2y = 4$$
$$9x - 6y = 13$$

EXAMPLE 7   Solve the system: $2x - 5y = 3$
$$4x - 10y = 2$$

Solution: Let us eliminate x.

$$2x - 5y = 3 \xrightarrow{(2)} 4x - 10y = 6$$
$$4x - 10y = 2 \xrightarrow{(-1)} \underline{-4x + 10y = -2}$$
$$0 = 4 \quad \text{False}$$

Answers:

6. Coincident lines

7. Parallel lines

This results in a false statement. This means that the system has no solution, and is called inconsistent. The graphs of the equations in this system are **parallel lines**.

EXERCISE 4.3

A. In exercises 1-30, solve the system of equations using elimination by addition method.

1. $x - y = 7$
$x + y = 3$

2. $x + y = 35$
$x - y = 13$

3. $x + y = 5$
$x - y = 2$

4. $4x + y = 64$
$3x + y = 59$

5. $3x + y = -8$
$5x - y = -16$

6. $2x + 3y = 5$
$x - y = 10$

7. $x + 5y = 8$
$x - 3y = -4$

8. $x - y = -6$
$y - 3x = 0$

9. $y = 3x + 2$
$6x - 2y = 5$

10. $2x + 5y = 10$
$5y = -2x + 25$

11. $6x + 10y = 8$
$-4x - 5y = -4$

12. $5x - 2y = 19$
$3x + 4y = 1$

13. $2x + 3y = 8$
$3x - 2y = -1$

14. $x - y = 12$
$2x - y = 35$

15. $4x + 9y = 8$
$6y - 2x = 3$

16. $x + y = 14$
$x - y = 6$

17. $3x + 7y = 5$
$4y = 10 - 6x$

18. $x - 2y + 11 = 0$
$2x - 3y + 18 = 0$

19. $3x + 5y = -19$
$6x + 7y = -23$

20. $3x + y - 2 = 0$
$6x + 2y = 5$

21. $3x - 2y = -13$
$9x + 5y = 16$

22. $2x - y = 7$
$4x + 3y = 9$

23. $4x + 8y = -5$
$x + 2y = 1$

24. $y + 3x = 2$
$3y + 9x = 6$

25. $3y + 11 = -2x$
$5x + 2y = 22$

26. $2x + 3y = 8$
$8x + 3y = 14$

27. $9x + 21y = 10$
$12x - 6y = 2$

28. $2x + 3y - 4 = 0$
$y - x - 3 = 0$

29. $x = \dfrac{5}{2}y + 1$
$2x - 5y = 2$

30. $3x + y + 1 = 0$
$2x - 3y + 8 = 0$

B. In exercises 31-56, solve the system of equations using elimination by addition method. Using the solution, identify whether the graph of the system consists of intersecting, parallel or coincident lines.

31. $2x = 5y + 2$
$2x - 5y = 3$

32. $x - 3y - 3 = 0$
$3x - 2 = 9y$

33. $.2x = .3y - 2$
$1.5y = x + .8$

34. $2x - 3y = 7$
$x + y = 1$

35. $0.5x + 2y = 1.15$
$-3x + 0.4y = -0.7$

36. $0.5x + 0.5y = 3$
$0.5x - 0.5y = -1$

37. $\dfrac{x}{3} + \dfrac{y}{3} = 4$
$\dfrac{x}{4} - \dfrac{y}{4} = -1$

38. $\dfrac{3x}{5} + \dfrac{5y}{3} = 2$
$\dfrac{6x}{5} - \dfrac{5y}{3} = 1$

39. $\dfrac{2}{5}x - \dfrac{1}{6}y = \dfrac{7}{10}$
$\dfrac{3}{4}x - \dfrac{2}{3}y = \dfrac{19}{8}$

40. $\dfrac{1}{2}x + \dfrac{1}{3}y = 13$
$\dfrac{1}{5}x + \dfrac{1}{8}y = 5$

41. $0.15x - 0.40y = 0.65$
$0.60x + 0.25y = -1.1$

42. $0.2x + 0.5y = 1.6$
$-0.3x + 0.4y = -0.1$

43. $2.1x - 0.6y = 8.4$
$-1.5x - 0.3y = -6$

44. $0.2x + 0.3y = 0.8$
$0.5x - 0.2y = 0.1$

45. $x = 2.5y + 1$
$2x - 5y = 3$

46. $2x - 0.5y = -0.6$
$0.3x + 0.5y = 2.21$

47. $x + y = 1$
$0.75x + 0.5y = 2.21$

48. $0.5x + 0.2y = 4$
$x = 8 - 0.4y$

49. $9x - 12y = 18$
$2y = -x + 1$

50. $11y - 4x = 3$
$2y - 3x = 12$

51. $2x - 3y = 6$
$4x - 6y = 8$

52. $4x - 3y = 1$
$3x + 4y = 1$

53. $x - 5y = 15$
$-2x + 3y = -9$

54. $3x - 2y = 5$
$-4y = -6x + 10$

55. $3x - 4y = 5$
$-9x + 12y = 7$

56. $0.2x + 0.3y = 1$
$0.1x - 0.2y = -0.2$

4.4 SOLVING SYSTEMS OF LINEAR INEQUALITIES

OBJECTIVES ■■■■

Upon completion of this section you we will be able to graph solutions of a system of linear inequalities.

Graphing the solution of a linear inequality in two variables was discussed in Section 3.5. In this section we will discuss how to solve **systems of linear inequalities** in two variables using graphing techniques.

GRAPHING A SYSTEM OF LINEAR INEQUALITIES

The solution of a system of linear inequalities is the set of all points that satisfy *both* inequalities of the system.

We will solve a system of linear inequalities by graphing each inequality on the same coordinate plane. We will use the following two steps.

> **Step 1** Graph *each* linear inequality using the same coordinate system.
>
> **Step 2** Indicate the solution by shading the common region *distinctly*.

EXAMPLE 1 Graph the solution of the linear system.

$$x + y \leq 2$$
$$2x - y > 3$$

Solution:

Step 1 Graph $x + y \leq 2$ and $2x - y > 3$ in the same coordinate plane.

The graph of $x + y \leq 2$:

i) Solve for y: $\quad y \leq -x + 2$

ii) Draw the graph of $y = -x + 2$ as a solid line since equality is included.

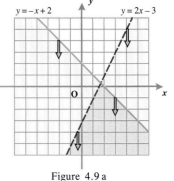

y = -x + 2   y = 2x - 3

Figure 4.9 a

x	y
-2	4
0	2
2	0

iii) Since $y \leq -x + 2$, the y-coordinates or the points satisfying the inequality are **below** (or equal to) the y-coordinates on the line. Shade the region below and on the line.

The graph of $2x - y > 3$:

i) Solve for y: $\quad y < 2x - 3$

ii) Draw the graph of $y = 2x - 3$ as a dotted line, since equality is excluded.

x	y
-1	-5
0	-3
2	1

iii)   Since $y < 2x - 3$, the y-coordinates or the points satisfying the inequality are *below* the points on the line. Shade the region below the line.

Step 2   The solution of the system is given by the overlapping region, *i.e.* the region below both lines, including the solid portion of the first line.

> *Note*   If $y > mx + b$, shade the region above the line $y = mx + b$.

🖩 We can solve systems of linear inequalities using a calculator. See examples 1-3 of Section 4.4 in appendix B.

EXAMPLE 2   Graph the solution of the system.
$$x \geq 1$$
$$y \geq x$$
$$3x + 4y < 12$$

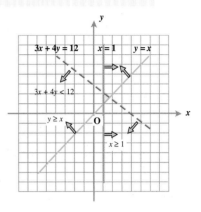

Solution:

Step 1   Graph $x \geq 1$, $y \geq x$ and $3x + 4y < 12$ in the same coordinate plane. The regions indicated by arrows in Figure 4.10 are the solutions of these three inequalities.

Step 2   The solution of the system is given by the common or the overlapping region. The solution is the shaded portion.

Points on dashed line not included
Figure 4.10

> *Note*   The graph of $x \geq 1$ is the region to the right of or on the vertical line $x = 1$.

EXERCISE 4.4

In exercises 1-40, find the graph of the solution of the system of inequalities.

1. $x + y \geq 4$
      $x - y < 1$

2. $x + y \leq 6$
      $x - y \geq 2$

3. $x \geq 1$
      $2x + y \leq 5$

4. $y - x \leq 5$
      $x \geq 2$

5. $2x - y \geq 4$
      $x + 2y \leq 1$

6. $3x + 4y \geq 12$
      $y \geq 1$

7. $4x + 3y > 6$
      $x - 2y < 4$

8. $y + 2x \geq 2$
      $y - x \leq -1$

9. $y < 3x + 2$
      $y < -2x + 3$

10. $y - x \geq -1$
      $x + 2y \leq 8$

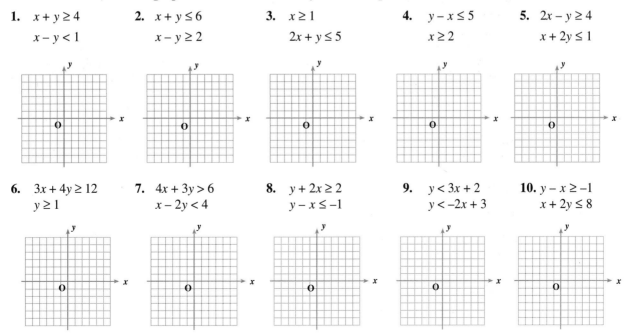

11. $y + 2 > x$
$\quad\quad y \geq 2x - 1$

12. $2x + y \geq 2$
$\quad\quad 2y - x < 8$

13. $x + 2y < 3$
$\quad\quad 2x + 4y < 12$

14. $x - 3y \geq -6$
$\quad\quad 2x + 3y \geq 6$

15. $x + 2y < 3$
$\quad\quad x + y < 1$

16. $x < 4$
$\quad\quad y - x \leq 6$

17. $2x + y \leq 4$
$\quad\quad y < 2x$
$\quad\quad x \geq 0$

18. $3x + 5y \geq 15$
$\quad\quad x + y \geq 3$

19. $x - y < 4$
$\quad\quad y \leq 0$
$\quad\quad x \geq 0$

20. $2x - y > -3$
$\quad\quad 3x - 5y > -1$

21. $y < 3x + 2$
$\quad\quad y < -2x + 3$

22. $y \leq x - 2$
$\quad\quad y \geq 2x + 1$

23. $3x + 2y > 6$
$\quad\quad x + 3y \leq 2$

24. $x + y < 2$
$\quad\quad x + y \leq 1$

25. $3x + y \leq 1$
$\quad\quad -x + 2y \geq 6$

26. $x + 2y < 3$
$\quad\quad 2x + 4y < 8$

27. $2x - y > 4$
$\quad\quad y < -x + 2$

28. $2x + 3y \leq 6$
$\quad\quad 3x + y \leq 1$
$\quad\quad x \leq 0$

29. $2x + y \leq 2$
$\quad\quad y \geq x$
$\quad\quad x \geq 0$

30. $x - y < 4$
$\quad\quad y \leq 0$
$\quad\quad x \geq 0$

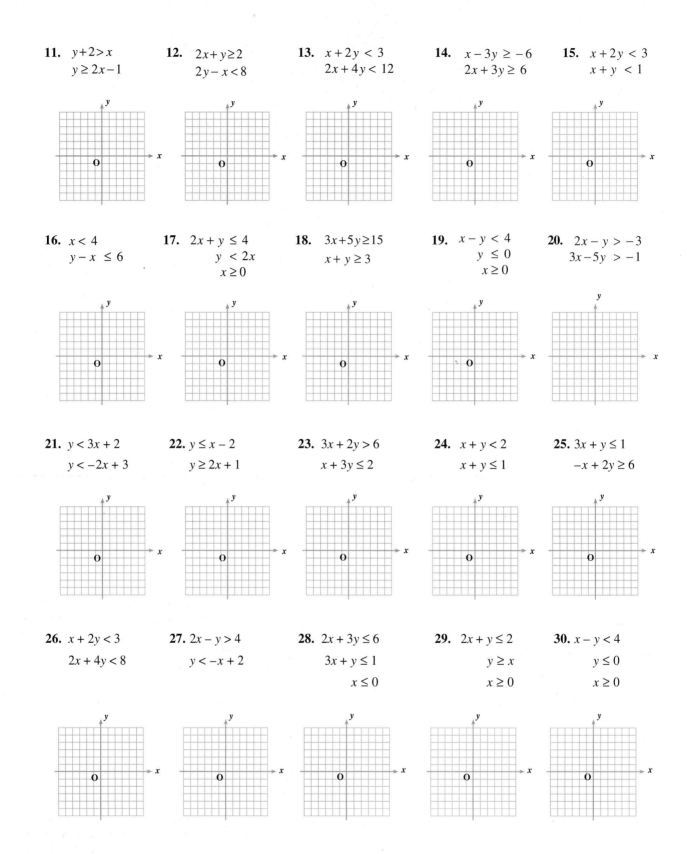

CH4 : Systems of Linear Equations and Inequalities

31. $x + y \leq 4$
$x \geq 0$
$y \geq 0$

32. $x \geq 0$
$y \geq 0$
$9x + 3y \leq 18$
$3x + 6y \leq 18$

33. $x + y \geq 1$
$x - y \leq 1$
$x - y \geq 0$
$x \leq 2$

34. $x \geq 0$
$y \geq 0$
$x + y \leq 4$

35. $x \geq 0$
$y \geq 0$
$x + y \geq 4$

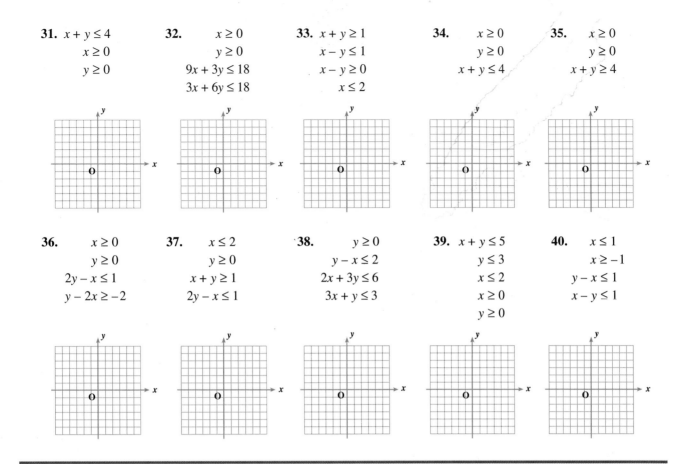

36. $x \geq 0$
$y \geq 0$
$2y - x \leq 1$
$y - 2x \geq -2$

37. $x \leq 2$
$y \geq 0$
$x + y \geq 1$
$2y - x \leq 1$

38. $y \geq 0$
$y - x \leq 2$
$2x + 3y \leq 6$
$3x + y \leq 3$

39. $x + y \leq 5$
$y \leq 3$
$x \leq 2$
$x \geq 0$
$y \geq 0$

40. $x \leq 1$
$x \geq -1$
$y - x \leq 1$
$x - y \leq 1$

4.5 APPLICATIONS

As emphasized earlier, the strategy for solving word or applied problems consists essentially of the following steps.

Objectives ■ ■ ■ ■

Upon completion of this section you will be able to set up systems of linear equations and solve word problems.

Step 1 Read the problem carefully and identify the unknowns.

Step 2 Organize the numerical information. Use diagrams, figures, or tables. Write two equations in two unknowns.

Step 3 Solve the system of equations.

Step 4 Answer the question asked in the problem.

Step 5 Verify the solution.

EXAMPLE 1 The sum of two numbers is 85. Two times the smaller number exceeds the larger number by 26. Find the numbers.

Solution:

• Let x represent the smaller number and y the larger number.

WARM-UP

1. The sum of two numbers is 15. Two times the smaller number exceeds the larger number by 6. Find the numbers.

- Since the sum of x and y is 85, we get: $x + y = 85$.
  Two times the smaller number exceeds the larger number by 26

$$2x = 26 + y$$

- Solve the system of equations.

$$
\begin{array}{ll}
x + y = 85 & (1) \\
\underline{2x - y = 26} & (2) \\
3x = 111 & \text{Add the equations} \\
x = \dfrac{111}{3} & \\
x = \mathbf{37} &
\end{array}
$$

Substitute 37 for x in equation (1).

$$
x + y = 85 \quad \longrightarrow \quad 37 + y = 85
$$
$$
y = 85 - 37
$$
$$
y = \mathbf{48}
$$

- Therefore, the two numbers are 37 and 48.

- *Verify* the solution:

$$37 + 48 = 85 \qquad \text{True}$$
$$\text{and} \qquad 2(37) = 48 + 26. \qquad \text{True}$$

Note — It is best to check by substituting the numbers into the original word statement.

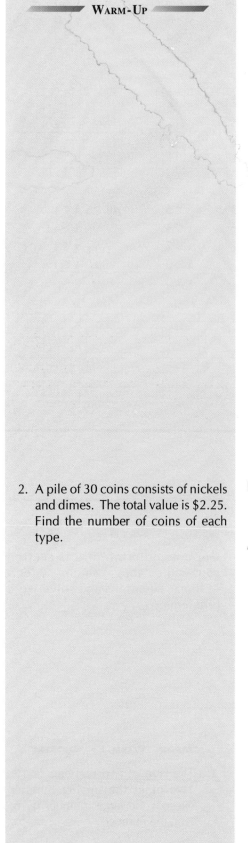

2. A pile of 30 coins consists of nickels and dimes. The total value is $2.25. Find the number of coins of each type.

EXAMPLE 2 — A pile of 40 coins consists of nickels and dimes. The total value of the coins is $3.35. Find the number of each type of coins.

Solution:

- Let number of nickels = n.

- Let number of dimes = d.

Total number of coins = $n + d \longrightarrow n + d = 40$

$$
\begin{array}{ll}
\text{Total value of nickels} & = .05n \text{ in } \textbf{dollars} \\
\text{Total value of dimes} & = .10d \text{ in } \textbf{dollars} \\
\text{Total value of the coins} & = \$3.35 \\
.05n + .10d & = \$3.35
\end{array}
$$

- Solve the system

$$
\begin{array}{l}
n + d = 40 \\
.05n + .10d = 3.35
\end{array}
\quad
\begin{array}{l}
\text{Eliminate the decimals by multiplying} \\
\text{the second equation by 100.}
\end{array}
$$

$$
\begin{array}{ll}
n + d = 40 & (1) \\
5n + 10d = 335 & (2)
\end{array}
$$

- Use the substitution method. From equation (1) we have $d = 40 - n$. Substitute $\mathbf{40 - n}$ for $\mathbf{d}$ in equation (2).

$$5n + 10(\mathbf{40} - \mathbf{n}) = 335$$
$$5n + 400 - 10n = 335$$
$$-5n + 400 = 335$$
$$-5n = 335 - 400$$
$$-5n = -65$$
$$n = 13$$

Replace n by **13** in equation (1). $\mathbf{13} + d = 40$
$$d = 27$$

- There are 13 nickels and 27 dimes.

- *Verify* the solution: 13 nickels + 27 dimes = 40 coins and also;

$$.05\,(13) = \quad .65 \qquad \text{value of nickels}$$
$$.10\,(27) = \underline{\mathbf{2.70}} \qquad \text{value of dimes}$$
$$\$3.35 \qquad \text{total value.}$$

EXAMPLE 3   A sporting goods store sells 3 fishing reels and 5 fishing rods for $309. Later, they sell 6 fishing reels and 2 fishing rods for $282. Find the price of each item.

Solution:

- Let the price of fishing reel = x dollars.

  Let the price of fishing rod = y dollars.

- **First sale:**   3 fishing reels + 5 fishing rods = 309

       or $\mathbf{3x + 5y = 309}$

- **Second sale:**   6 fishing reels + 2 fishing rods = 282

           or $\mathbf{6x + 2y = 282}$

We must solve the system: $3x + 5y = 309$ (1)

                            $6x + 2y = 282$ (2)

Use the addition method to eliminate x.

The least common multiple of 6 and 3 is 6.

Now, multiply equation (1) by -2 and add it to equation (2).

$$3x + 5y = 309 \quad \xrightarrow{(-2)} \quad -6x - 10y = -618$$
$$6x + 2y = 282 \quad \longrightarrow \quad \underline{6x + 2y = 282}$$
$$\qquad\qquad\qquad\qquad\qquad\qquad -8y = -336$$
$$\qquad\qquad\quad \longrightarrow \qquad\quad y = \mathbf{42}$$

Substitute 42 for y in equation (1).

3. A sporting goods store sells 2 fishing reels and 13 fishing rods for $280 and 1 fishing reel and 4 fishing rods for $120. Find the price for each item.

$$3x + 5y = 309$$
$$3x + 5 \cdot \mathbf{42} = 309$$
$$3x + 210 = 309 \qquad \text{Add } -210 \text{ to both sides}$$
$$3x = 99$$
$$x = \mathbf{33}$$

- Therefore, the cost of a fishing reel is $33 and the cost of a fishing rod is $42.

- *Verify* the solution.

$$3(33) + 5(42) = 99 + 210 = 309$$
$$6(33) + 2(42) = 198 + 84 = 282$$

4. A pharmacist has 40% and 60% powder mixtures on hand. How many pounds of each powder will be required to produce 6 pounds of a 50% powder mixture?

EXAMPLE 4   A pharmacist has 30% and 80% iodine solutions on hand. How many liters of each iodine solution will be required to produce 8 liters of a 50% iodine mixture?

Solution:

- Organize the information in a table.

Item	Percent iodine	amount
30% sol	.3	x
80% sol	.8	y
50% sol	.5	8

- Let the amount of 30% iodine solution = x liters.

  Let the amount of 80% iodine solution = y liters.

- The total desired is 8 liters. $\mathbf{x + y = 8}$

  30% of the x liters is iodine. $(.3x)$ ⟩ total iodine

  80% of the y liters is iodine. $(.8y)$ ⟩

  50% of the total will be iodine. $.50 \times 8 = 4$ liter

- We must solve the system

$$x + y = 8$$
$$\mathbf{.3x + .8y = 4} \text{ liters}$$

  Use the substitution method with decimals.

$$y = \mathbf{8 - x}$$
$$0.3(x) + .8(\mathbf{8 - x}) = 4 \qquad \text{Substitute } y = 8 - x.$$
$$.3x + 6.4 - .8x = 4 \qquad \text{Use Distributive Property and combine like terms.}$$
$$-.5x + 6.4 = 4 \qquad \text{Add } -6.4 \text{ to both sides.}$$
$$-.5x = -2.4 \qquad \text{Divide by } -.5.$$
$$x = \mathbf{4.8} \text{ liters}$$

Substitute x in an equation with both variables

$$4.8 + y = 8$$
$$y = 8 - 4.8$$
$$y = \mathbf{3.2}$$

- The pharmacist would require 4.8 liters of the 30% solution and 3.2 liters of 80% solution to produce 8 liters of 50% solution.

Verify that 30% of 4.8 + 80% of 3.2 = 50% of 8.

EXAMPLE 5 Swimming downstream, a swimmer can cover 2 miles in 15 minutes. It takes the swimmer 20 minutes to swim back up the stream. Find the speed of the swimmer in still water and the speed of the current.

Solution:

- Let the speed of the swimmer in still water = s miles per hour.

  Let the speed of the current = c miles per hour

- Swimming downstream, the speed of the swimmer is $(s + c)$ because the current speeds them up. Swimming upstream, the speed of the swimmer is $(s - c)$ because the current pulls against the swimmer and slows him down. Since the unit of time in the speed is hours, we convert 15 minutes and 20 minutes to hours.

  15 minutes = $\dfrac{15}{60}$ hour = $\dfrac{1}{4}$ hour.

  20 minutes = $\dfrac{20}{60}$ hour = $\dfrac{1}{3}$ hour.

  Recall: (speed) • (time) = distance

	Rate mph	Time hours	Distance miles
down	$s + c$	$\dfrac{1}{4}$	2
up	$s - c$	$\dfrac{1}{3}$	2

  Downstream: $\dfrac{1}{4}(s + c) = 2$

  Upstream: $\dfrac{1}{3}(s - c) = 2$

  Eliminate the fractions by multiplying the equations by 4 and 3 respectively to obtain the following system.

$$s + c = 8 \qquad (1)$$
$$s - c = 6 \qquad (2)$$

5. Swimming downstream, a swimmer can cover 4 miles in 20 minutes. It takes the swimmer 30 minutes to swim back. Find the speed of the current.

- To solve this system we add the two equations.

$$s + c = 8$$
$$s - c = 6$$
$$\overline{}$$
$$2s = 14 \longrightarrow s = 7$$

Substitute 7 for s in equation (1).

$$s + c = 8 \longrightarrow 7 + c = 8 \longrightarrow c = 1$$

- Therefore, the speed of the swimmer in still water is 7 miles per hour and the speed of the current is 1 mile per hour.

- *Verify* the solution.

Going downstream, $(s + c) \cdot 15$ min. $= 2$ miles

$$(7 + 1)\,\text{mph} \cdot \frac{15}{60}\ \text{hours} = 2$$

$$(8)\text{mph} \cdot \left(\frac{1}{4}\right)\text{hours} = 2\ \text{miles} \quad \text{True}$$

Going upstream: $(7 - 1)\,\text{mph} \cdot 20\,\text{min} = 2\ \text{miles}$

$$(6)\ \text{mph} \cdot \left(\frac{20}{60}\right)\text{hours} = 2\ \text{miles}$$

$$(6)\ \text{mph} \cdot \left(\frac{1}{3}\right)\text{hours} = 2\ \text{miles} \quad \text{True}$$

6. Two cars start from two towns 200 miles apart and travel towards each other. They pass each other after 2 hours. Find the speed of each car if the difference between their speeds is 10 miles per hour.

EXAMPLE 6 Two cars start from two towns 400 miles apart and travel towards each other. They pass each other after 4 hours. Find the speed of each car if the difference between their speeds is 20 miles per hour.

Solution: Consider the diagram.

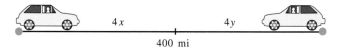

- Let the speed of the faster car $= f$ miles per hour.

  Let the speed of the slower car $= s$ miles per hour.

- The distance traveled by first car $= 4f$.

  The distance traveled by second car $= 4s$.

Car	Rate	·	Time	=	Distance
Faster	f		4		$4f$
Slower	s		4		$4s$

At the point where the two cars meet, the total distance traveled by the two cars equals the distance between the two towns.

Therefore, $4f + 4s = 400$

We also know that the difference in speeds $(f - s)$ is 20.

$$f - s = 20$$

- We need to solve the system : $4f + 4s = 400$ (1)
$f - s = 20$ (2)

We will use the addition method to eliminate s. Multiply the equation (2) by 4.

$$\begin{array}{ccc} 4f + 4s = 400 & \longrightarrow & 4f + 4s = 400 \\ f - s = 20 & \xrightarrow{(4)} & \underline{4f - 4s = 80} \\ & & 8f = 480 \\ & & f = 60 \end{array}$$

Substitute 60 for f in the equation (2)

$$f - s = 20 \longrightarrow 60 - s = 20 \longrightarrow -s = -40$$

$$\longrightarrow s = 40 \text{ miles/hr}$$

- The two cars travel at 60 miles per hour and 40 miles per hour respectively.

- *Verify* the solution:

    Distance travelled by the first car = 60 mph × 4 hours = 240 miles.
    Distance travelled by the second car = 40 mph × 4 hours = 160 miles.
    Total distance = (240) miles + (160) miles = 400 miles   True

EXERCISE 4.5

1.   The sum of two integers is 6. Two times the smaller integer is 24 less than the larger integer. Find the integers.

2   If one number is three times the other and their sum is 16, find the number.

3.   The sum of two numbers is 63. Their difference is 9. Find the numbers.

4.   The sum of the two numbers is 8 and their difference is 2. Find the numbers.

5.   The perimeter of a rectangle is 72 cm. The sum of two times the length and three times the width is 88 cm. Find the dimensions of the rectangle.

6.   A horse and two cows together cost $680. Find the cost of a cow and a horse if a horse costs $80 more than a cow.

7.   In a certain right triangle one acute angle is 15° less than two times the other acute angle. Find the difference between the two acute angles. [*Hint :* The sum of the angles of a triangle is 180°.]

8.   A pile of 80 coins consists of nickels and dimes. The total value of the coins is $7.70. Find the number of each type of coins.

9.   A theater sold $520 worth of tickets. An adult ticket costs $3.00 each and children's ticket costs $2.00 each. If total tickets sold were 190, how may tickets of **each kind** did the theater sell?

10. The total cost of 8 buckets and 5 mugs is $92, and the total cost of 5 buckets and 8 mugs is $77. Find the cost of one mug and one bucket.

11. Two pounds of rib steak and six pounds of hamburger meat cost $12.30, and three pounds of rib steak and two pounds of hamburger meat cost $9.70. Find the cost per pound of each type of meat.

12. Five books and 7 pens together cost $79, and 7 books and 5 pens together cost $77. Find the total cost of one book and 2 pens.

13. Connie invested all of her $3,000 savings, part at an annual rate of 6% and the rest at an annual rate of 9%. Her annual income from both the investments was 8% of her total investment. How much did she invest at 6%?

14. A father is three times as old as his son. After twelve years his age will be two times the age of his son. Find their present ages.

15. A hospital purchased a total of 185 bottles of glucose solution. Small bottles cost $2 each and large ones cost $3 each. The total cost was $480. How many bottles of each size were purchased?

16. Five years ago, John was three times as old as Lisa and ten years later John shall be two times as old as Lisa. What are the present ages of John and Lisa?

17. An automatic vending machine in a store provides a packet of 28 stamps containing only 10-cent and 20-cent stamps. The cost of the packet is $4. If the stamps are priced at their face value, how many stamps of each type are there?

18. A man invested $3500, part of it at yearly interest rate of 4% and the rest at 5%. He received a total annual interest of $153. How much did he invest at each rate?

19. A textbook author receives $2 royalty for each of his algebra books sold and a $3 royalty for each of his trigonometry books sold. During one royalty period, a total of 11,500 copies of the two books were sold. The author received a total of $27,800 in royalties. How many books of each kind were sold ?

20. The perimeter of a rectangular plot is 32 meters. If the length is increased by 2 meters and the width is decreased by 1 meter the area of plot remains unchanged. Find the length and width of the plot.

21. Rollins invested a part of $6,000 at 10% and the rest at 8%. His annual income from these investments is $556. How much did he invest at each rate?

22. In a parallelogram, one angle is $\frac{4}{5}$ of the adjacent angle. Determine the angles of the parallelogram.

{**Hint:** Sum of the adjacent angles $x + y = 180$ and opposite angles are equal.}

23. A pharmacist wants 1,000 oz of 12.2% alcohol solution. He has 8% and 15% alcohol solutions to mix. How many ounces of the 8% solution will be required?

24. The semi-perimeter of a rectangle is 33 cm and the difference between the length and its width is 3 cm. Find its length and width.

25. A 30% dye solution is to be mixed with an 80% dye solution to make 60 liters of 50% solution. How many liters of each solution is needed?

26. A man starts his job with a certain monthly salary and earns a fixed increment every year. If his salary was $7500 after 4 years of service and $9,000 after 10 years of service, what was his starting salary and what is the annual increment?

27. A lab technician has 15% and 40% concentrations of nitric acid. A class is conducting an experiment that requires 300 milliliters of a 25% concentration of nitric acid. How many milliliters of each concentration should be mixed to make the desired concentration?

28. A farmer sold a calf and a cow for $760, thereby, making a profit of 25% on the calf and 10% on the cow. By selling them for $767.50, he would have made a profit of 10% on the calf and 25% on the cow. Find the cost of each.

29. A supermarket mixes coffee that sells for $1.50 per pound with coffee that sells $2 per pound to obtain 25 pounds of coffee selling $1.68 per pound. How many pounds of each kind of coffee are required?

30. Two trains start from two stations 1050 miles apart and travel towards each other. They pass each other after 6 hours. Find the speed of each train if one of the trains travels 25 miles slower than the other.

31. An airplane can fly 360 miles into the wind in 3 hours. If the plane reverses the direction and the wind conditions remain the same, the return trip takes only two hours. Find the speed of the plane in still air.

32. A man rowing at the rate of 5 km an hour in still water takes three times as much time in going 40 km up the river as in going 40 km down. Find the rate at which the river flows.

33. Two cars leave a common place at the same time and travel in opposite directions. The difference in their speeds is 10 miles per hour. After two hours the cars are 200 miles apart. Find the speed of each car.

34. The population of a town is 50,000. If in a year the number of males increase by 5% and females by 3%, the population would grow to be 52,020. Find the number of males and the number of females presently living in the town.

35. A car and a plane travel 50 miles and 180 miles during the same time. The difference between their speeds is 143 miles per hour. Find the speed of the airplane.

36. A man travels 600 km to his home partly by train and partly by car. He takes 8 hours if he travels 120 km by train and the rest by car. He takes 20 minutes longer if he travels 200 km by train and the rest by car. Find the speed of the train and the car.

37. A number consists of two digits whose sum is five. When the digits are reversed, the number is increased by nine. Find the number.

38. In a two digit number the sum of the digits is 13. If the number is subtracted from the one obtained by interchanging the digits, the result is 45. Find the number.

4.6 CHAPTER SUMMARY

SOLVING A SYSTEM OF LINEAR EQUATIONS USING GRAPHING

1. The solution of a system of linear equations in two variables is the set of all ordered pairs which make all equations of the system true statements.

2. To solve a system of linear equations in two variables graphically, we graph both equations of the system in the same coordinate plane. The point of intersection, if any, is the solution of the system.

EXAMPLES

1. Solve the system using graphing

   $2x + y = 7$

   $x + 3y = 6$

   Graph the two lines

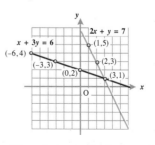

The solution is (3, 1), the point of intersection.

SOLVING SYSTEMS OF LINEAR EQUATIONS USING SUBSTITUTION

3. Solve: $2x - y = 0$
$x + y = 3$

$2x - y = 0 \quad \rightarrow \quad \mathbf{y = 2x}$

$x + y = 3 \quad \rightarrow \quad x + \mathbf{2x} = 3$
$\rightarrow \quad 3x = 3$
$\rightarrow \quad x = 1$

$2x - y = 0 \quad \rightarrow \quad 2(1) - y = 0$
$\rightarrow \quad 2 - y = 0$
$\rightarrow \quad \mathbf{y = 2}$

Solution is : $(1, 2)$

$2x - y = 0 \quad \rightarrow \quad 2(\mathbf{1}) - 2 = 0 \qquad$ True
$x + y = 3 \quad \rightarrow \quad (1) + (2) = 3 \qquad$ True

3. To solve a system of two linear equations in two variables using substitution, we use the following steps:

***Step* 1**   Solve one of the equations in terms of the other variable.

***Step* 2**   Substitute the expression for this variable into the other equation.

***Step* 3**   Solve the equation obtained in Step 2.

***Step* 4**   Substitute the value obtained in Step 3 into any equation containing both variables.

***Step* 5**   Check the solution by substituting it in the original equations.

SOLVING SYSTEMS OF LINEAR EQUATIONS USING ADDITION

4. $3x + 4y = -2$ $\qquad\qquad$ **(1)**
$2x - 3y = 4$ $\qquad\qquad$ **(2)**

Multiply equation (1) by –2 and equation (2) by 3.

$3x + 4y = -2 \quad \xrightarrow{(-2)} \quad -6x - 8y = 4$
$\underline{2x - 3y = 4 \quad \xrightarrow{(3)} \quad 6x - 9y = 12}$
$\qquad\qquad\qquad\qquad\qquad - 17y = 16$

$17y = -16 \rightarrow y = -\dfrac{16}{17}$

Multiply equation (1) by 3 and (2) by 4.

$3(3x + 4y) = 3(-2) \rightarrow 9x + 12y = -6$
$4(2x - 3y) = 4(4) \rightarrow \underline{8x - 12y = 16}$
$\qquad\qquad\qquad\qquad\qquad 17x = 10$
$\qquad\qquad\qquad\qquad\qquad x = \dfrac{17}{10}$

4. To solve a system of two linear equations in two variables using addition, we use the following steps:

***Step* 1**   Write both equations in the form $ax + by = c$. When writing the two equations in this form, align the variables.

***Step* 2**   Multiply one or both equations by suitable numbers, so that the coefficients of x (or y) in the resulting equations are negatives of each other.

***Step* 3**   Add the two equations.

***Step* 4**   Solve the equation obtained in step 3.

***Step* 5**   Substitute the value obtained in step 4 in any equation containing both variables and solve for the other variable. If this involves fractions then repeat the addition method to eliminate the other variable.

***Step* 6**   Check your answers.

SOLVING SYSTEMS OF LINEAR INEQUALITIES

5. To solve a system of linear inequalities in two variables, we use the following two steps.

    Step 1 Graph each linear inequality on the same coordinate system. Use a solid line to represent equality and a broken line if the equality does not hold.

    Step 2 The solution of the system is the region common to the solutions of individual inequalities. Indicate each region by a different type of shading. Finally, shade the overlapping region for the solution of the system in a different way.

EXAMPLES

5. Solve graphically:
    $$x - y \geq 0$$
    $$2x - y \leq 2$$

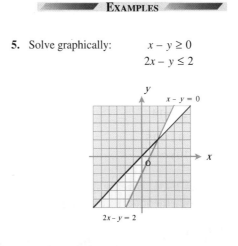

APPLICATIONS OF LINEAR SYSTEMS OF EQUATIONS

6. We use the following approach to solve application problems.

    Step 1 Read the problem carefully and identify the unknowns.

    Step 2 Organize the numerical information. Use diagrams, figures, or tables. Write two equations in two unknowns.

    Step 3 Solve the system of equations.

    Step 4 Answer the question asked in the problem.

    Step 5 Check your solution.

4.7 REVIEW EXERCISES

In exercises 1 and 2, check whether or not the given ordered pair is a solution of the system.

1. (a) $\left.\begin{array}{l} 2x+3y=4 \\ 4x+5y=6 \end{array}\right\}$ $\left(\dfrac{1}{2}, 1\right)$

    (b) $\left.\begin{array}{l} 4x-y=1 \\ 2x+3y=4 \end{array}\right\}$ $(3,2)$

2. (a) $\left.\begin{array}{l} 3x+4y=4 \\ 4x+3y=5 \end{array}\right\}$ $(0,1)$

    (b) $\left.\begin{array}{l} x+y=7 \\ 5x+12y=7 \end{array}\right\}$ $(11,-4)$

In exercises 3-12, solve the system of equations using graphing. Identify whether graphs of the system are intersecting, parallel, or coincident lines.

3. $2x = 3y$
    $2x + y = 8$

4. $2x-3y=6$
    $2x+y+10=0$

5. $2x-3y=8$
    $3x-y=-2$

6. $2x-y=1$
    $x+2y=3$

7. $y-3x+4=0$
    $6x-2y=5$

8. $y-x=0$
    $3x+3y=12$

9. $x-y=4$
    $3x=3y+12$

10. $x-y=6$
    $2x-2y-12=0$

11. $2x+3y+10=0$
    $3x-4y=19$

12. $3y-2x=0$
    $6y-4x=6$

In exercises 13-24, solve the system of equations using the method of elimination by addition. Identify whether the system represents parallel, coincident or intersecting lines.

13. $3x + 2y = 8$
$6x + 4y = 13$

14. $7x - 2y = 1$
$3x + 4y = 15$

15. $3x - y = 2$
$2x + y = 3$

16. $-6x + 5y = 2$
$-5x + 6y = 9$

17. $4x + 3y = 10$
$5y + 3x = 14$

18. $3x + 4y = 24$
$20x - 11y = 47$

19. $3x - 5y = 2$
$6x = 10y + 4$

20. $2x + 3y = 31$
$17x - 11y = 8$

21. $11x - 9y = 15$
$4x - 10y = -8$

22. $4x - 0.5 = .7$
$3x + 0.6y = 1.2$

23. $0.3x + 0.7y = 2$
$0.9x = 4 - 2.1y$

24. $x + 0.4y = 1.3$
$2x - 3y = -3.1$

In exercises 25-36, solve the system of equations using the method of substitution. Identify whether the system represents parallel, coincident or intersecting lines.

25. $y = 3x + 1$
$y = \frac{1}{2}x - 1$

26. $3y - 5x = 30$
$4x + y = 180$

27. $y = 3x + 3$
$y = 3x + 1$

28. $5x + 2y = 16$
$3x + \frac{6}{5}y = 2$

29. $x - 3y = 10$
$2x - y = 6$

30. $5x + 2y = 16$
$7.5x + 3y = 24$

31. $x - 3.5y = 0.65$
$0.6x + 0.4y = 1$

32. $3x + y = -.2$
$-3x + 2y = 1.4$

33. $y = 4x + 9$
$4x - y = 1$

34. $2y - x = -5$
$4y - 2x = -10$

35. $2x + 3y = 3$
$10x + 15y = 15$

36. $x - 2y = 6$
$2x - 4y = 8$

In exercises 37-50, solve the system of inequalities graphically.

37. $x + y < 3$
$3x - y > 6$

38. $x - 3y \geq -6$
$x - 3 \leq 0$

39. $y + 2x \leq 5$
$y + 1 > 4x$

40. $y - x < 6$
$x - 4 < 0$

41. $x - y \leq 5$
$x + y \geq -1$

42. $2x + 3 \geq 3y$
$x + y \geq 5$

43. $12x + 2y > 6$
$6x + y \leq 8$

44. $x + y \geq 0$
$2x + y \leq 4$

45. $y \geq 3x - 2$
$y + 2x < 4$

46. $2x + y \leq 4$
$y - 2 < 0$

47. $3x - 2y \leq 6$
$y \leq 2, x \geq 1$

48. $x - y \geq 0$
$x - 4 < 0$

49. $x + y \geq 4$
$x - 2 \leq 0$

50. $2x + 3y < 12$
$x - 3 \leq 0$

51. Find two numbers whose sum is 101 and difference is 37.

52. Sum of two numbers is 25 and their difference is 3. Find the numbers.

53. In a triangle ABC, $\angle C = 3 \angle B = 2(\angle A + \angle B)$. Find the three angles.
(*Hint*: Sum of the angles of a triangle = 180°)

54. The age of the father is 3 years more than three times the age of his son. Three years from now the age of the father will be 10 years more than two times the age of his son. Find their present ages.

55. An airplane flies with the wind at a speed of 550 miles per hour. When flying against the wind, the plane's speed is 470 miles per hour. Find the speed of the airplane with no wind effect.

56. If you add 1 to each of the two given numbers their ratio is $1:2$. If you subtract 5 from each of the two given numbers the ratio is $5:11$. Find the numbers.

57. How many liters of a 30% acid solution and how many liters of a 90% acid solution must be mixed to produce 300 liters of a 80% acid solution?

58. Shirley invests $10,000 in stocks and bond. The stocks return 15% a year and the bonds return 10% a year. If the total return on the investment after one year is $1100, how much did Shirley invest each in stocks and bonds?

4.8 SELF TEST

In exercises 1-4, solve the system of equations using graphing. Identify whether the graph of the system represents parallel, intersecting, or coincident lines.

1. $x - y = 3$
$2x + y = 3$

2. $2y - x = 9$
$6y - 3x = 21$

3. $2x + y = 1$
$4x + 2y = 10$

4. $3x + y = -1$
$3y - 2x - 8 = 0$

In exercises 5-10, solve the system of equations using substitution method.

5. $2x + y = 5$
$x - 2y = 10$

6. $\dfrac{x}{3} + \dfrac{y}{2} = 3$
$x - 2y = 2$

7. $3x - 5y = 7$
$9x = 15y + 21$

8. $2x + 3y - 12 = 0$
$4x - 2y - 8 = 0$

9. $4x + 3y = 8$
$6x - 5y + 7 = 0$

10. $x + 4y = 14$
$7x - 3y = 5$

In exercise 11-18, solve the system using the method of elimination by addition.

11. $5x + 4y = 3$
$7x + 5y = 3$

12. $7x = 1 + 2y$
$3x + 4y = 15$

13. $5x - 7 + 2y = 5y + 4$
$3y + 4 = x + y$

14. $3x + 4y = 24$
$20x - 11y = 47$

15. $2x + 3y = 7$
$4x + 6y = 15$

16. $2x + 3y = 31$
$17x - 11y = 8$

17. $\dfrac{3}{5}x + \dfrac{2}{3}y = 1$
$18x + 20y = 30$

18. $0.25x + 0.2y = 22$
$0.2x + 0.25y = 23$

In exercises 19-24, graph the solution of the system of inequalities:

19. $3x - 2y \leq 6$
$y > 1$

20. $x - 4 \geq 0$
$y - 2 \geq 0$

21. $2x + y > 5$
$x - y < 1$

22. $x - y > 0$
$x - 4 < 0$

23. $x - y \leq 5$
$-x - 2y \geq 4$

24. $x + y \geq 5$
$2x + 3 > 3y$

25. Sum of two numbers is 67, and their difference is 29. Find the numbers.

26. Car 1 travels from point A to point B. Car 2 leaves 2 hours later, but goes 10 miles an hour faster and passes car 1 in 11 hours. How fast does each car go?

27. Goodies Club recently ran a bake sale to raise charity. Donuts were sold for $0.50 a piece and the coffee for $0.70 per person. It is known that 120 items were sold and $68 collected. How many cups of coffee were sold?

28. Two tables and 3 chairs together cost $200 whereas 3 tables and 2 chairs together cost $250. Find the cost of one table and one chair.

Exponents and Polynomials

A0521Disc

File View Control Debug

Objective: Polynomials

Verify Skill   Discussion   Example

A polynomial in a single variable x is the sum of one or more terms of the form ax^n, where a is a real number and n is a positive whole number.

The numerical factor a is called the coefficient of the term.

The degree of a term is the value of the exponent on the variable factor.

$$ax^n \longrightarrow \text{Degree}$$
Cofficient ⟵

The term $3x^4$ has

coefficient	3
degree	4.

The degree of the polynomial is the highest of the degrees of its terms.

The polynomial $3x^4 - 2x^2 + 5$ has degree 4.   Note

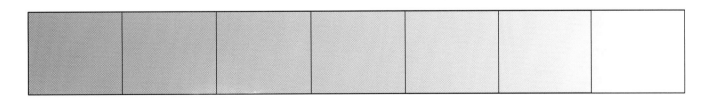

5

EXPONENTS AND POLYNOMIALS

INTRODUCTION

Polynomials play an important role in algebra. Expressions like $3x + 4$ and $4x - 1 - 2x$, which we have encountered in Chapter 2, are examples of polynomials. In this chapter we learn how to find the sum, difference, product, and quotient of two polynomials. This chapter is divided into the seven sections.

5.1 EXPONENTS

A. EXPONENTS

Exponents are used to represent repeated multiplication.

For example: $2 \cdot 2 \cdot 2 = 2^3$, $\quad x \cdot x = x^2$,

$\quad\quad\quad\quad x \cdot x \cdot x = x^3$, $\quad x \cdot x \cdot x \cdot x \cdot x = x^5$, *etc.*

For any natural number n, $x^n = \underbrace{x \cdot x \cdot \ldots \cdot x}_{n \text{ factors}}$.

In the exponential expression x^n, x is called the *base* and n is called the *exponent* or the *power*.

x^n is read as "*x raised to the nth power*" or in short, "*x to the power n*".

$$\text{Base} \longleftarrow x^n \longrightarrow \text{Exponent}$$

For any real number x, $x^1 = x$.

> **OBJECTIVES** ■■■
>
> Upon completion of this section you will be able to:
>
> A. Identify and use exponents;
>
> B. Use the product rule $a^m \cdot a^n = a^{m+n}$; and
>
> C. Use the power rules.

EXAMPLE 1 Evaluate or expand as appropriate. Indicate the base and exponent in each case.

     a. 4^3 **b.** $(-4)^3$ **c.** -4^3

     d. 4^4 **e.** $(-4)^4$ **f.** $(3x)^4$

     g. $(-5x)^3$ **h.** $-(2x)^3$

> ▬▬▬ **WARM-UP** ▬▬▬
>
> 1. Evaluate or expand as appropriate. Indicate the base and the exponent in each case.
>
>   a) 3^3

b) 2^4

c) -5^3

d) 2^5

e) $(-5)^2$

f) $(2a)^4$

g) $(-2x)^3$

h) $-(3x)^2$

Solutions:

a. 4^3 : Base $= 4$, Exponent $= 3$

$4^3 = 4 \cdot 4 \cdot 4 = 64$

b. $(-4)^3$: Base $= -4$, Exponent $= 3$

$(-4)^3 = (-4)(-4)(-4) = -64$

c. -4^3 : Base $= 4$, Exponent $= 3$

$-4^3 = -(4 \cdot 4 \cdot 4) = -64$

d. 4^4 : Base $= 4$, Exponent $= 4$

$4^4 = 4 \cdot 4 \cdot 4 \cdot 4 = 256$

e. $(-4)^4$: Base $= -4$, Exponent $= 4$

$(-4)^4 = (-4)(-4)(-4)(-4) = 256$

f. $(3x)^4$: Base $= 3x$, Exponent $= 4$

$(3x)^4 = (3x)(3x)(3x)(3x)$

$= (3 \cdot 3 \cdot 3 \cdot 3)(x \cdot x \cdot x \cdot x)$

$= 81(x \cdot x \cdot x \cdot x) = 81x^4$

g. $(-5x)^3$: Base $= -5x$, Exponent $= 3$

$(-5x)^3 = (-5x)(-5x)(-5x) = (-5 \cdot -5 \cdot -5)(x \cdot x \cdot x)$

$= -125(x \cdot x \cdot x) = -125x^3$

h. $-(2x)^3$: Base $= 2x$, Exponent $= 3$

$-[(2x) \cdot (2x) \cdot (2x)] = -(2 \cdot 2 \cdot 2)(x \cdot x \cdot x)$

$= -8(x \cdot x \cdot x) = -8x^3$

> **Note** In case of $(-x)^n$ the base is $-x$, and we repeatedly multiply $-x$. But in case of $-x^n$, the base is x and we repeatedly multiply x, and then find the opposite of x^n. $-x^n$ is the same as $-(x^n)$.

B. PRODUCT RULE

2 factors   4 factors   6 factors

$x^2 \cdot x^4 = (x \cdot x)(x \cdot x \cdot x \cdot x) = x \cdot x \cdot x \cdot x \cdot x \cdot x = x^6$. This is an example of the following product rule:

> **Product Rule** $a^m \cdot a^n = a^{m+n}$
> In a product with the same bases, the exponents are added.

WARM-UP

2. Evaluate:

a) $x^2 \cdot x^3$

b) $(2x^5)(3x^4)$

EXAMPLE 2   Evaluate: **a.** $x^3 \cdot x^5$ **b.** $(3x^2)(5x^3)$

c. $a^2 b^3 a^3 b^4$

Solutions:

a. $x^3 \cdot x^5 = x^{3+5} = x^8$

b. $(3x^2)(5x^3) = (3 \cdot 5)(x^2 \cdot x^3) = 15x^{2+3} = 15x^5$

c. $a^2 b^3 a^3 b^4 = (a^2 a^3)(b^3 b^4) = a^{2+3} b^{3+4} = a^5 b^7$

The product rule does *not* apply in either of the following situations:

1. $3^5 + 3^7 \neq 3^{12}$ **It is a sum, not a product.**   **2.** $3^5 \cdot 2^7 \neq 6^{12}$ **The bases are not the same.**

$x^n x^0 = x^{n+0} = x^n$

$x^n \cdot 1 = x^n$, so it seems reasonable to define $x^0 = 1$ for $x \neq 0$.

C. POWER RULES FOR EXPONENTS

Consider the following examples:

1. $(x^2)^4 = x^2 \cdot x^2 \cdot x^2 \cdot x^2 = x^{2 + 2 + 2 + 2} = x^{2 \cdot 4} = x^8$

Thus $(x^2)^4 = x^{2 \cdot 4}$. This is an example of the following power rule 1.

> **Power Rule 1 for powers:** $(a^m)^n = a^{mn}$, **for any real number** a, **and positive integers** m **and** n.

2. $(x \cdot y)^2 = (x \cdot y)(x \cdot y) = (x \cdot x)(y \cdot y) = x^2 \cdot y^2$.   This is an example of power rule 2.

> **Power Rule 2 for products:** $(ab)^m = a^m b^m$, **for any real numbers** a, b, **and positive integer** m.

In other words, when a product is raised to a power each factor is raised to that power.

3. $\left(\dfrac{3}{5}\right)^2 = \dfrac{3}{5} \cdot \dfrac{3}{5} = \dfrac{3 \cdot 3}{5 \cdot 5} = \dfrac{3^2}{5^2}$ This is an example of power rule 3.

> **Power Rule 3 for quotients:** $\left(\dfrac{a}{b}\right)^m = \dfrac{a^m}{b^m}$, **for real numbers** a, b $(b \neq 0)$ **and positive integer** m.

In other words, when a quotient is raised to a power, both the numerator and denominator are raised to that power.

EXAMPLE 3   Evaluate: **a.** $(2^3)^2$ **b.** $(2 \cdot 5)^3$ **c.** $\left(\dfrac{2}{3}\right)^4$

Solutions:

a. $(2^3)^2 = 2^{3 \cdot 2} = 2^6 = 64$.   Power Rule 1.

b. $(2 \cdot 5)^3 = 2^3 \cdot 5^3 = (8)(125) = 1000$.   Power Rule 2.

c. $\left(\dfrac{2}{3}\right)^4 = \dfrac{2^4}{3^4} = \dfrac{16}{81}$.   Power Rule 3.

EXAMPLE 4   Evaluate: **a.** $(3x^2)^3$ **b.** $(x^2 y^3)^4$

  c. $(4x)^3 (2x^2)^4$ **d.** $\left(\dfrac{x^2}{y^3}\right)^4$.

Solutions:

a. $(3x^2)^3 = 3^3(x^2)^3 = 3^3 x^6 = 27x^6$.

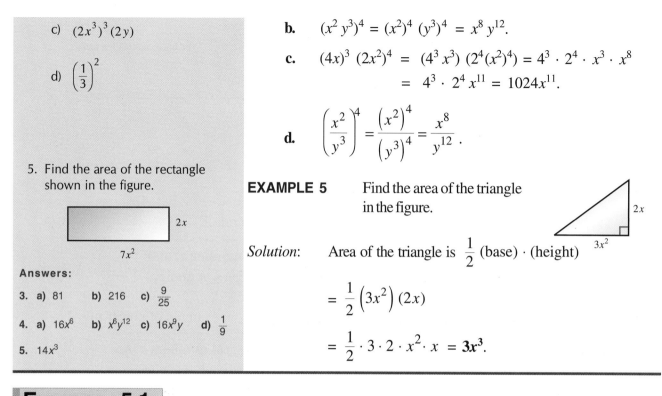

c) $(2x^3)^3 (2y)$

d) $\left(\dfrac{1}{3}\right)^2$

b. $(x^2 y^3)^4 = (x^2)^4 (y^3)^4 = x^8 y^{12}$.

c. $(4x)^3 (2x^2)^4 = (4^3 x^3)(2^4(x^2)^4) = 4^3 \cdot 2^4 \cdot x^3 \cdot x^8$
$$= 4^3 \cdot 2^4 x^{11} = 1024x^{11}.$$

d. $\left(\dfrac{x^2}{y^3}\right)^4 = \dfrac{(x^2)^4}{(y^3)^4} = \dfrac{x^8}{y^{12}}$.

5. Find the area of the rectangle shown in the figure.

$2x$

$7x^2$

EXAMPLE 5 Find the area of the triangle in the figure.

Solution: Area of the triangle is $\dfrac{1}{2}$ (base) · (height)

$2x$

$3x^2$

$$= \dfrac{1}{2}\left(3x^2\right)(2x)$$

$$= \dfrac{1}{2}\cdot 3 \cdot 2 \cdot x^2 \cdot x = 3x^3.$$

Answers:

3. **a)** 81   **b)** 216   **c)** $\dfrac{9}{25}$

4. **a)** $16x^6$ **b)** x^6y^{12} **c)** $16x^9y$ **d)** $\dfrac{1}{9}$

5. $14x^3$

EXERCISE 5.1

A. In exercises 1-12, identify the base and the exponent of the exponential expression.

1. 3^6 2. 6^3 3. -3^6 4. -6^3 5. $(-3)^6$ 6. $(-6)^2$

7. $-(-5x)^7$ 8. $-(4y)^7$ 9. $(5y)^7$ 10. $(-7y)^5$ 11. $-5y^7$ 12. $-(-7x)^5$

B. In exercises 13-36, simplify as far as possible using the product rule.

13. $x^2 \cdot x^3 \cdot y \cdot y^5$ 14. $y^2 \cdot y^3 \cdot z \cdot z^4$ 15. $(16x^2)x \cdot x$ 16. $(-5y^3)y \cdot y^2$ 17. $\dfrac{x}{y}\cdot\dfrac{x^2}{y}\cdot\dfrac{x^3}{y^2}$

18. $\dfrac{y^2}{x}\cdot\dfrac{y}{x^2}\cdot\dfrac{y^4}{x^4}$ 19. $\dfrac{x^2}{y^3}\cdot\dfrac{x^4}{y^2}\cdot\dfrac{x}{y}$ 20. $\dfrac{a}{b^2}\cdot\dfrac{a^3}{b}\cdot\dfrac{a^2}{b^3}$ 21. $(3y^2)(2y^3)$ 22. $(-2x)(-3x^3)$

23. $(7a)^2(-2a)^3$ 24. $(-3x)^2(-2x)^3$ 25. $p \cdot p^4 \cdot p^6 \cdot p^5$ 26. $4a \cdot a^3 \cdot a^4$ 27. $(6a)(-2a)^3$

28. $(-5x)(2x)^2$ 29. $(y)\cdot(3y)$ 30. $5x^2 \cdot 4x$ 31. $(-3x)\cdot(-2x)$ 32. $(-2a^2)\cdot(-3a^3)$

33. $\left(x^2y^3\right)\cdot\left(x^4y^2\right)$ 34. $\left(-3a^2\right)\cdot\left(2a^3b^2\right)$ 35. $\left(5a^3\right)\cdot\left(-2a^3\right)$ 36. $\left(x^2yz^4\right)\cdot\left(x^3z\right)$

In exercises 37-60, simplify the expression.

37. $\dfrac{2^3 \cdot 4^2}{3^2 \cdot 2^4}$ 38. $\dfrac{4^3 \cdot 2^2}{2^3 \cdot 4^2}$ 39. $5^3 - (-5)^3$ 40. $2^4 + (-2)^3$ 41. $3^2 \cdot 2^3$

42. $2^3 \cdot 3^4$ 43. $(2^3 + 3^2)\left(\dfrac{2}{3}\right)^5$ 44. $\left(3^3 + 2^2\right)\left(\dfrac{3}{2}\right)^2$ 45. $-(-2)\cdot(-2)^2$ 46. $(-3)\cdot 2^2$

47. $-(-5)^2 \cdot (-2)^3$ **48.** $2^3 \cdot 3^3 \cdot (-2)^2$ **49.** $(-2) \cdot 2^3 \cdot (-2)^2$ **50.** $3^3 \cdot (-1)^5 \cdot 4$ **51.** $\left(\dfrac{2}{3}\right)^3 \dfrac{1}{8} \cdot 3^2$

52. $\left(\dfrac{1}{5}\right)^2 \cdot (-5) \cdot 2^3$ **53.** $\left(\dfrac{2}{3}\right)^2 \cdot \left(\dfrac{9}{16}\right)$ **54.** $\left(-\dfrac{1}{2}\right)^3 \cdot \left(\dfrac{2}{3}\right)^2$ **55.** $2^3 - (-2)^2$ **56.** $4^2 + (-3)^3$

57. $-(-2)^3 - 4^3$ **58.** $(2^3 - (-2)^2) \cdot (4^2 - (-3)^2)$ **59.** $-3^3 + (-3)^3$ **60.** $(-2) \cdot (-2)^2 + 3^2 \cdot (-4)$

C. In exercises 61-70, simplify the expression using power rule.

61. $\left(xy^2\right)^2$ **62.** $\left(-3xy^2\right)^3$ **63.** $\left(5a^2 b^3\right)^2$ **64.** $\left(x^3 y^2\right)^5$ **65.** $\left(-2a^2 b^2\right)^4$

66. $(-3ab)^2 \cdot (-2ab)^2$ **67.** $\left(-2x^2y\right)^2 \cdot (2x)$ **68.** $\left(-4x^2y\right)^3$ **69.** $\left(\dfrac{2x^2}{3}\right)^3$ **70.** $\left(\dfrac{-2x^2y}{5z}\right)^2$

In exercises 71-80, determine whether the statement is true or false.

71. $(-2a)^4 = -16a^4$ **72.** $(-3x)^3 = -27x^3$ **73.** $(-3b)^3 = -(3b)^3$ **74.** $(-3b)^2 = -9b^2$ **75.** $(-2p^2)^4 = 16p^6$

76. $(-2p^2)^3 = -8p^6$ **77.** $(x^2y)^4 = x^4y^4$ **78.** $(ab^3)^2 = a^2 b^5$ **79.** $4^2(-y)^2 = 16y^2$ **80.** $-3^2(-x)^3 = -9x^3$

In exercises 81-88, simplify.

81. $(3x) \cdot (2x^2) + (4x^2)(3x)$ **82.** $2a^2b\,(ab)^2 - 4a(ab)^3$ **83.** $-2xy(x^2y)^3 - 5x^5(xy^2)^2$

84. $3x^3\left(3x^2y\right)^2 - 4x\left(x^3y\right)^2$ **85.** $(5a^7) \cdot (2a^2) - (3a^3) \cdot (7a^6)$ **86.** $4x^2(2xy)^3 - 2y^2(x^5y)$

87. $8x^3y^2 - 2x(xy)^2$ **88.** $(3ab)^3 - 2ab(ab)^2$

In exercises 89-94, find the area of the figure.

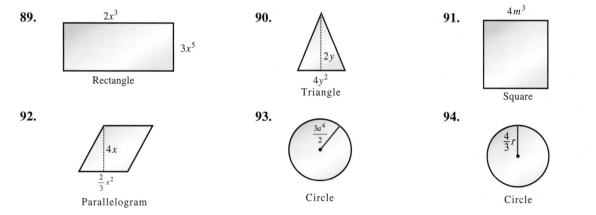

89.
$2x^3$
$3x^5$
Rectangle

90.
$2y$
$4y^2$
Triangle

91.
$4m^3$
Square

92.
$4x$
$\dfrac{2}{3}x^2$
Parallelogram

93.
$\dfrac{3a^4}{2}$
Circle

94.
$\dfrac{4}{3}r$
Circle

5.2 POLYNOMIALS

OBJECTIVES ■■■■

Upon completion of this section you will be able to:

A. Identify a polynomial, its terms, coefficients, and degree;

B. Evaluate polynomials;

C. Add polynomials; and

D. Subtract polynomials.

Recall that variables represent real numbers and therefore can be added or multiplied. Algebraic expressions in one or more variables of the form:

$$2x + 1, \quad 3t^2 - 5t + 7, \quad 3xy^2 + 7x, \quad \text{and} \quad xy^2 + 3xy - 2$$

are called polynomials.

The expressions:

$$\frac{2}{x}, \quad \frac{3x}{x^2 + 1}, \quad \text{and} \quad p^2 + 2p - 1 + \frac{4}{p} \quad \text{are not polynomials.}$$

A. POLYNOMIAL

A polynomial in a single variable x is the sum of one or more terms of the form ax^n, where a is a real number and n is a positive whole number. The number a is called the **coefficient** of the term, and n the exponent of x is called the degree of the term.

The term $3x^4$ has the coefficient 3 and degree 4.

$$\text{Coefficient} \longleftarrow 3x^4 \longrightarrow \text{degree}$$

The degree of the polynomial with two or more terms is the largest of the degrees of its terms.

The polynomial $3x^4 - 2x^2 + 5$ has degree 4.

Note A constant term such as 2 in $3x + 2$ is a special term whose degree is 0. This is due to the fact that $2 \cdot x^0 = 2 \cdot 1 = 2$. Notice that the power of x is 0; therefore, the degree is 0.

WARM-UP

1. Determine the degree, terms, and coefficients of the following polynomials.

a) $-5x^4$

b) $-2x^5 + 3x^2 - 4$

c) $3x^3 - 5x$

Answers:

1. **a.** 4; $-5x^4$; -5
    b. 5; $-2x^5, 3x^2, -4$; $-2, 3, -4$
    c. 3; $3x^3, -5x$; 3, -5

EXAMPLE 1 Determine the degree, terms, and coefficients of the following polynomials.

a. $3x^7$ **b.** $4x^2 - 3x + 1$ **c.** $2x - 3x^4$

Solutions:

a. $3x^7$, has degree 7. Its only term is $3x^7$, which has coefficient 3.

b. $4x^2 - 3x + 1$, has degree 2. Its terms are $4x^2, -3x$, and 1 with coefficients 4, -3, and 1 respectively.

c. $2x - 3x^4$, has degree 4. Its terms are $2x$ and $-3x^4$, with coefficients 2, -3, respectively.

A polynomial is said to be written in standard form if exponents of its successive terms are in descending order.

The polynomial $-3x^5 + 7x^3 + 8x^2 - 9$ is in standard form. When polynomials are written in this form, the coefficient of the leading term (-3 in this case) is called the **leading** coefficient.

- A polynomial with only *one term*, is called a **monomial**.

- A polynomial with *two terms* is called a **binomial**.

- A polynomial with *three terms* is called a **trinomial**.

- Polynomials with more than *three terms* are simply referred to as **polynomials**.

EXAMPLES

a. $3x^2$, $-\dfrac{5}{4}x$, 2, and x^7 are all examples of monomials.

b. $4x - 1$, $\dfrac{2}{3}x^2 - 3x$, and $15x^{20} - 2x^7$ are all examples of binomials.

c. $-5x^2 + 7x + \dfrac{1}{2}$, $10x^5 - 3x^2 + 2$, and $2x^{10} - \dfrac{1}{5}x^7 + 3x^2$ are all examples of trinomials.

B. EVALUATING A POLYNOMIAL

Since a polynomial is an algebraic expression, it can be evaluated by substituting specified value(s) for the variable(s).

EXAMPLE 2 Evaluate $4x^3 - 3x^2 + 7$ when $x = -3$, 0, and 4.

Solution:

For $x = -3$:

$$
\begin{aligned}
4x^3 - 3x^2 + 7 &= 4(\mathbf{-3})^3 - 3(\mathbf{-3})^2 + 7 && \text{Substitute } x = -3\\
&= 4(-27) - 3(9) + 7 && \text{Simplify}\\
&= -108 - 27 + 7\\
&= \mathbf{-128}
\end{aligned}
$$

For $x = 0$:

$$
\begin{aligned}
4x^3 - 3x^2 + 7 &= 4(\mathbf{0})^3 - 3(\mathbf{0})^2 + 7 && \text{Substitute } x = 0\\
&= 4 \cdot 0 - 3 \cdot 0 + 7 && \text{Simplify}\\
&= \mathbf{7}
\end{aligned}
$$

For $x = 4$:

$$
\begin{aligned}
4x^3 - 3x^2 + 7 &= 4(\mathbf{4})^3 - 3(\mathbf{4})^2 + 7 && \text{Substitute } x = 4\\
&= 4(64) - 3(16) + 7 && \text{Simplify}\\
&= 256 - 48 + 7\\
&= \mathbf{215}
\end{aligned}
$$

Note: Although, a polynomial is an algebraic expression, not every algebraic expression is a polynomial. For example, $\dfrac{3x+1}{4x^2+1}$ is an algebraic expression, but it is not a polynomial. It is a quotient of two polynomials.

C. ADDING POLYNOMIALS

Recall that terms of an expression that differ only in coefficients are called **like terms**. Like terms can be combined into a single term as in the following expression.

$$
\begin{aligned}
3x^2 + 4x^2 &= (3 + 4)x^2\\
&= 7x^2
\end{aligned}
$$

We use this process of combining like terms to add polynomials.

3. Add:
$5x^2 + 12x + 7$ and
$3x^2 - 11x - 12$

EXAMPLE 3   Add: $3x^2 + 4x - 7$ and $5x^2 - 7x + 9$

Solution: $(3x^2 + 4x - 7) + (5x^2 - 7x + 9)$

$= (3x^2 + 5x^2) + (4x - 7x) + (-7 + 9)$ Group together like terms.

$= (3 + 5)x^2 + (4 - 7)x + 2$ Combine like terms.

$= 8x^2 + (-3)x + 2$ Simplify.

$= \mathbf{8x^2 - 3x + 2}$

4. Add:
$7x^3 - 2x^2 + 8x - 7$ and
$14 - 9x$

EXAMPLE 4   Add: $-3x^3 + 2x^2 - 7x - 15$ and $3x - 19$

Solution: $(-3x^3 + 2x^2 - 7x - 15) + (3x - 19)$

$= -3x^3 + 2x^2 + (-7x + 3x) + (-15 - 19)$ Group together like terms.

$= -3x^3 + 2x^2 + (-7 + 3)x + (-34)$ Combine like terms.

$= \mathbf{-3x^3 + 2x^2 - 4x - 34}$

5. Add:
$12x^5 - 3x^4 + 2x^3 + 7x - 10$
and $3x^4 + 7x^3 - 2x^2 - x$

EXAMPLE 5   Add:

$6x^4 - 2x^3 + 7x^2 + 5x$ and $-3x^4 + 2x^3 + 4x^2 - 11$

Solution: $3x^2 + 4x^2 = (3 + 4)x^2 = 7x^2$

$(6x^4 - 2x^3 + 7x^2 + 5x) + (-3x^4 + 2x^3 + 4x^2 - 11)$ Group together like terms.

$= (6x^4 - 3x^4) + (-2x^3 + 2x^3) + (7x^2 + 4x^2) + (5x) + (-11)$

$= 3x^4 + 0 \cdot x^3 + 11x^2 + 5x - 11$ Combine like terms.

$= \mathbf{3x^4 + 11x^2 + 5x - 11}$ Simplify.

Answer:

3. $8x^2 + x - 5$

4. $7x^3 - 2x^2 - x + 7$

5. $12x^5 + 9x^3 - 2x^2 + 6x - 10$

D.   SUBTRACTING POLYNOMIALS

As with real numbers, subtraction of polynomials is defined in terms of addition.

> **Rule for Subtraction:**
> Change the subtraction to addition, and change the polynomial being subtracted to its opposite. (Distribute the negative.)

6. Subtract
$2x^2 + 9x - 14$ from $3x^2 - 5x - 9$

EXAMPLE 6   Subtract $3x^2 + 4x - 7$ from $2x^2 + 9x - 7$.

Solution: $(2x^2 + 9x - 7) - (3x^2 + 4x - 7)$

$= (2x^2 + 9x - 7) + (-3x^2 - 4x + 7)$ Change to addition of opposite.

$= (2x^2 - 3x^2) + (9x - 4x) + (-7 + 7)$ Group like terms.

$= (2 - 3)x^2 + (9 - 4)x + 0$ Combine like terms.

$= (-1)x^2 + 5x + 0$

$= \mathbf{-x^2 + 5x}$

EXAMPLE 7   Simplify:

$$(3x^7 - 2x^5 + 4x - 1) - (-4x^6 - 8x^5 + 2x^2 - 7)$$

Solution:

$$(3x^7 - 2x^5 + 4x - 1) - (-4x^6 - 8x^5 + 2x^2 - 7)$$

$= (3x^7 - 2x^5 + 4x - 1) + (+ 4x^6 + 8x^5 - 2x^2 + 7)$ Change to addition of the opposite.

$= 3x^7 + 4x^6 + (- 2x^5 + 8x^5) + (-2x^2) + 4x + (-1 + 7)$ Group like terms.

$= \mathbf{3x^7 + 4x^6 + 6x^5 - 2x^2 + 4x + 6}$ Simplify.

EXAMPLE 8   Simplify:

   a. $(3y^5 + 4y^3 + 7y^2 - 2y - 1) - (-3y^5 + 2y^3 + 7y + 6)$

   b. $(x^4 + 3x^3 + 4x^2 + 7x + 1) - (3x^4 + 4x^2 + 2)$

   c. $(x^3 + 2x - 1) - (4x^5 - 2x^2 + 7x + 1)$

Solutions:

   a. $(3y^5 + 4y^3 + 7y^2 - 2y - 1) - (-3y^5 + 2y^3 + 7y + 6)$

      $= (3y^5 + 4y^3 + 7y^2 - 2y - 1) + (3y^5 - 2y^3 - 7y - 6)$
                       Change subtraction to addition.

      $= [3y^5 + 3y^5] + (4y^3 - 2y^3) + 7y^2 + (-2y - 7y) + (-1 - 6)$
                       Group like terms.

      $= \mathbf{6y^5 + 2y^3 + 7y^2 - 9y - 7}$ Simplify.

   b. $(x^4 + 3x^3 + 4x^2 + 7x + 1) - (3x^4 + 4x^2 + 2)$

      $= (x^4 + 3x^3 + 4x^2 + 7x + 1) + (-3x^4 - 4x^2 - 2)$
                       Change subtraction to addition.

      $= (x^4 - 3x^4) + 3x^3 + (4x^2 - 4x^2) + 7x + (1 - 2)$
                       Group like terms.

      $= -2x^4 + 3x^3 + 0x^2 + 7x - 1$ Simplify.

      $= \mathbf{-2x^4 + 3x^3 + 7x - 1}$

   c. $(x^3 + 2x - 1) - (4x^5 - 2x^2 + 7x + 1)$

      $= (x^3 + 2x - 1) + (- 4x^5 + 2x^2 - 7x - 1)$
                       Change subtraction to addition.

      $= - 4x^5 + x^3 + 2x^2 + (2x - 7x) + [-1 + (-1)]$
                       Group like terms.

      $= \mathbf{- 4x^5 + x^3 + 2x^2 - 5x - 2}$ Simplify.

7. Simplify:

$$(x^6 + 2x^5 - 3x + 2)$$
$$- (-3x^6 + 4x - 8)$$

8. Simplify:

a) $(4y^5 + 3y^3 + 6y^2 - 3y - 4)$
    $- (- 7y^5 - 2y^3 - 6)$

b) $(8x^3 + 7x^2 + 7)$
    $- (4x^5 - 8x^4 + x^3 + 3)$

c) $(x^4 - 2x^2 + 3)$
    $- (-5x^3 + 4x^2 - 3x - 4)$

9. Find the perimeter of a square whose side is of length $3x^2 + x - 2$.

EXAMPLE 9 Find the perimeter of a triangle with sides $3x^2 + 2x$, $4x - 3$, and $x^2 - 4x$.

Solution: Perimeter of a triangle ABC

$= AB + BC + CA$

$= (4x - 3) + (3x^2 + 2x) + (x^2 - 4x)$

$= (3x^2 + x^2) + (4x + 2x - 4x) - 3$ Group like terms.

$= 4x^2 + 2x - 3$

Answers:

6. $x^2 - 14x + 5$

7. $4x^6 + 2x^5 - 7x + 10$

8. a) $11y^5 + 5y^3 + 6y^2 - 3y + 2$
   b) $-4x^5 + 8x^4 + 7x^3 + 7x^2 + 4$
   c) $x^4 + 5x^3 - 6x^2 + 3x + 7$

9. $12x^2 + 4x - 8$

EXERCISE 5.2

A. In exercises 1-10, identify the algebraic expressions which are polynomials.

1. $3x^2 + 5x - 7$
2. $-3x^3 + 5x - x$
3. $4x + 3 - 7x^2$
4. $4 - 3x + 6x^3$
5. $3x^2 + \dfrac{1}{x} + 2$

6. $3y^2 - \dfrac{1}{y} + 2y + 6$
7. $\dfrac{3x^3 - 1}{x^2}$
8. $\dfrac{4 - 2z - z^2}{z}$
9. $p(3p^2 + 4p - 1)$
10. $\dfrac{x^3}{3} - 4x^2 - 7$

In exercises 11-18, write the polynomial in descending order of powers of the variable. Also, find the degree and the constant term in each case.

11. $3x^2 + 7x - 3x^4 + 4x^3$
12. $3 + 2z^6 + 3z^2 - z^4$
13. $7x^2 + 8x^3 - 5 - 4x^5$
14. $6x^2 - 5x + 7x^3 + 2$

15. $x^4 - 3x^5 + 7x^6 - 9x^8$
16. $6 - x^6 + x^4 + x^8 + 2x^5$
17. $-6x^4 + 7x^5 - 4x^2 - 2x^3 + 1$
18. $3 - 2x^5 + 4x^6 - 5x^3$

In exercises 19-30, identify which is a monomial, binomial, trinomial, or other type of a polynomial. What is the degree of the polynomial?

19. $3x^2 - 1$
20. $1 - 2x + 3x^3$
21. $4x^3$
22. 5

23. $12x^3 + 3x$
24. $-5x^8 - 2x^4 + 5$
25. $-3x^5 + 7x^2 + 9$
26. $5x^6 + 7$

27. $15x^{10} + 16x^8 - x^4 + 2x$
28. $-6x^4 + 5x^2 + 6x - 6$
29. $x^2 + (2x + 1)$
30. $(1 - 2x) + 4x^2 - x^3$

B. In exercises 31-38, evaluate the polynomial when (i) $x = 2$ and (ii) $x = -2$.

31. $3x^2 - 7x + 5$
32. $7x + 3x^3 - 5x^4$
33. $-4x^3 + 3x^2 + 10$
34. $-3x^2 + 4x - 2(x + 2)$

35. $-x^4 + 4x^3 - 29$
36. $5x^4 - 2x - 4$
37. $11x^4 - 9x^3 + 2x^2 + 10x - 5$
38. $2x^5 + 3x^4 - x^3 + 5$

C. In exercises 39-50, add the polynomials.

39. $4x^3 + 7x^2 - 5x$, $-3x^2 + 7$
40. $x^4 - 3x^2 + 5$, $2x^2 - 4$

41. $-5x^4 + 7x^3 + 8x - 9$, $6x^4 + 9x^3 + 10x^2 + 9$
42. $5x^5 + 6x^4 - 8x^2 - 5$, $-4x^5 - 3x^4 - 9x + 10$

43. $4p^2 + 7p - 2, \quad 3p^2 - 8p + 4$

44. $3z^3 - 7z + 5, \quad 4z^3 - 5z^2 - 5$

45. $6z^3 + 7z^2 - 8z, \quad -8z^3 + 4z^2 + 10z - 2, \quad 2z^3 + 9z + 2$

46. $x^2 + x - 2, \quad x^3 + 2x^2 - x + 5, \quad x^4 + x^2 - 3$

47. $-3y^3 + 2y^2 - 8, \quad -3y^2 - 5y + 9, \quad y^3 - y^2 + 6y$

48. $5y^2 - 6y + 3, \quad -5y^3 + 9y - 13, \quad -4y^2 - 2y + 6$

49. $4y^3 - 3y^2 - 2y + 1, \quad 7y^2 - 7, \quad 3y^3 + 7y - 8$

50. $-7y^3 - 6y, \quad 3y^2 - 2y + 7, \quad 5y^3 - 11$

In exercises 51-65, simplify the given expression.

51. $(2x^2 + 3x) + (3x^2 + 4x)$

52. $(-4a^2 - 5ab) + (2a^2 + 6ab - 2b)$

53. $(4a^2 - 3a + 4) + (2a^2 + 6a + 2)$

54. $(3r^2 - 4r + 1) + (3r^3 + 6r)$

55. $(-6p^2 + 7p + 2) + (5p^2 + 3p - 1)$

56. $(7x^3 + 3x - 2) + (3x^2 - 6x + 4)$

57. $(5x^2 - 3y^2) + (3x^2 - 2xy + 6y^2)$

58. $(2x^2 + 4y + 2xy) + (-3y - 2x^2 + 4xy)$

59. $(5t^3 - 7t^2 + 8t) + (4t^3 - 6t^2 + 4t + 3)$

60. $(5y^4 - 8y + 5) + (-3y^4 + 4y + 4)$

61. $(-4r^3 + 7r + 9) + (6r^3 - 8r^2 + 10)$

62. $(x^2 + 7x) + (-3x^2 - 5x)$

63. $(2x^2 + 6x + 12) + (5x^2 - x + 4)$

64. $(3y^3 + y^2 + 1) + (-4y^3 - 6y - 3)$

65. $(-5r^3 - 6r^2 + 3r) + (r^2 - 5r - 8)$

D. **In exercises 66-75, perform the indicated operation.**

66. Subtract $5x + 3x - 8$ from $3x^2 - 4x + 8$

67. Subtract $3m^3 + 5m + 5$ from $4m^3 - 5m - 5$

68. Subtract $-6y^4 - 5y^3 + 9$ from $2y^4 - 7y^3 + 8$

69. Subtract $-4y^5 - 7y^4 + 9$ from $3y^5 - 6y^4 - 7$

70. Subtract $a^2 - 10a$ from $a^2 - 2a$

71. Subtract $x^2 + 5x - 8$ from $x^2 - 2x + 1$

72. Subtract $-2y^2 + 3y - 2$ from $4y^2 - 2y + 3$

73. Subtract $-x^3 + 3x - 2$ from $-2x^2 - x + 4$

74. Subtract $-2a^3 + 3a^2 - 7$ from $5a^2 - a + 2$

75. Subtract $-3x^3 - 4x + 1$ from $4x^3 + 5x^2 + 10$

In exercises 76-90, perform the indicated subtraction.

76. $(3t^6 + 4t + 9) - (6t^5 - 3t^2 + 5t - 9)$

77. $(-9t^4 + 7t^2 - 1) - (-9t^4 + 8t^2 + 10)$

78. $(-10t^2 - 6t - 5) - (10t^3 - 5t - 5)$

79. $(3n^5 + 4n^3 - 7n^2 + 8) - (4n^4 - 5n^3 + n^2 - 4)$

80. $(4x^2 - 3x - 5) - (x^5 - x^3 - x - 10)$

81. $(y^2 - 2xy) - (3y^2 + 4xy)$

82. $(4x^2 + x - 4) - (x^2 + 5x - 8)$

83. $(-2x^3 + x - 1) - (-x^2 + x - 4)$

84. $(5a^3 - 2a^2 + 1) - (3a^3 - 4a^2 + a)$

85. $(3y^2 - 2y - 3) - (2y^3 - 4y^2 + 4)$

86. $(2a^2 + 2a - 4) - (7a^3 + 2a + 4)$

87. $(8u^3 - 5) - (-6u^2 - 3u - 6)$

88. $(-13u^2 - 5u + 6) - (-u^3 - 16u^2 - 9)$

89. $(5u^2 - 17) - (-3u^3 + 7u^2 - 8u)$

90. $(-8u - 11) - (-2u^4 - u^3 - 12u)$

91. Determine the perimeter of the triangle whose sides are $3x^2 + 7x - 2$, $4x^2 - 5x + 1$, and $x^3 + x^2 - 2x$.

92. Determine the perimeter of the rectangle whose length is $3x^2 + 2x - 2$ and width is $3x$.

93. Find the perimeter of a square whose side is $2x^2 + 4x - 5$.

94. Find the perimeter of a right triangle having sides as given in the figure:

$x^4 + x - 1$

$x^3 + x$

$x^2 + 2$

5.3 MULTIPLICATION OF POLYNOMIALS

Upon completion of this section you will be able to:

A. Multiply a monomial and a polynomial;
B. Multiply two polynomials; and
C. Multiply binomials using the FOIL method.

Two monomials can be multiplied using the associative and commutative properties of multiplication and the rules for exponents. For example,

$$(3x^4)(2x^6) = (3 \cdot 2)(x^4 \cdot x^6) = 6x^{10}$$

The product of two monomials is a monomial whose coefficient is the product of the two coefficients, and whose variable part is the product of the variable parts.

Using the distributive property and multiplication of monomials, we can multiply two polynomials.

A. PRODUCT OF A MONOMIAL AND A POLYNOMIAL

We use the distributive property to multiply a monomial and a polynomial.

Recall : $a(b + c) = a \cdot b + a \cdot c$

EXAMPLES :

1. $3x^2(4x^3 - 7x) = (3x^2)(4x^3) - (3x^2)(7x) = 12x^5 - 21x^3$

2. $-4x^5(8x^2 + 9x - 2) = (-4x^5)(8x^2) + (-4x^5)(9x) + (-4x^5)(-2)$
    $$= -32x^7 - 36x^6 + 8x^5$$

3. $x^8(-9x^4 + 6x^2 - 7x + 1) = x^8(-9x^4) + x^8(6x^2) + x^8(-7x) + x^8(1)$
    $$= -9x^{12} + 6x^{10} - 7x^9 + x^8$$

B. PRODUCT OF TWO POLYNOMIALS

Two polynomials are multiplied by repeated applications of the distributive property. For example:

$(3x^2 + 4x)(4x^2 - 7x + 2)$

$= (3x^2 + 4x)(4x^2) + (3x^2 + 4x)(-7x) + (3x^2 + 4x)(2)$ Distributive Property.

$= (3x^2)(4x^2) + (4x)(4x^2) + (3x^2)(-7x) + (4x)(-7x) + (3x^2)(2) + (4x)(2)$ Distributive Property.

$= 12x^4 + 16x^3 - 21x^3 - 28x^2 + 6x^2 + 8x$ Multiply monomials.

$= 12x^4 + 16x^3 - 21x^3 - 28x^2 + 6x^2 + 8x$

$= 12x^4 - 5x^3 - 22x^2 + 8x$

A working rule for multiplying two polynomials is:

Rule:	**Multiplication of Two Polynomials**
Step 1	Multiply each term in the first polynomial by each term in the second polynomial. [Be careful about signs.]
Step 2	Combine the like terms.

EXAMPLE 4   Multiply $x^2 + 2x - 3$ by $4x^3 - 7x$.

Solution: There are 3 terms in the first polynomial and 2 terms in the second. Therefore, there will be $3 \cdot 2 = 6$ products in step 1.

Horizontal Method:

Step 1   Multiply each term of the first polynomial by each term in the second polynomial. The sum of the six products is :
$$4x^5 + 8x^4 + (-12x^3) + (-7x^3) + (-14x^2) + 21x$$

Step 2   Add or Combine the like terms:
$$4x^5 + 8x^4 + (-12x^3) + (-7x^3) + (-14x^2) + 21x$$
$$= 4x^5 + 8x^4 - 19x^3 - 14x^2 + 21x$$

Vertical Method:

This method of multiplying two polynomials is more convenient. It is similar to the multiplication algorithm for whole numbers.

- Write the polynomial with the fewer number of terms below the other polynomial. Both polynomials are arranged in decreasing order of powers.

- Multiply $x^2 + 2x - 3$ by $-7x$. -

- Multiply $x^2 + 2x - 3$ by $4x^3$. - - - - - - - - - - - - - - - - - - -

- Add like terms. -

- In the products write like terms underneath each other.

- Combine the like terms.

$$x^2 + 2x - 3$$
$$\times \quad\quad 4x^3 - 7x$$
$$\overline{\quad\quad\quad -7x^3 - 14x^2 + 21x}$$
$$4x^5 + 8x^4 - 12x^3$$
$$\overline{4x^5 + 8x^4 - 19x^3 - 14x^2 + 21x}$$

The Array Method :

This method is explained in the following example.

EXAMPLE 5   Multiply $2x^3 - 7x^2 + 8$ by $x^2 - 4x + 3$ using array method.

Solution: In this method the terms of the two polynomials are listed separately at the top and on the left side of the array.

	$2x^3$	$-7x^2$	8
x^2	$2x^5$	$-7x^4$	$8x^2$
$-4x$	$-8x^4$	$28x^3$	$-32x$
3	$6x^3$	$-21x^2$	24

Notice there are nine squares for the nine products. Fill in the squares with the corresponding products. Then add coefficients of like terms inside the array to get the product of the polynomials.

$$2x^5 - 15x^4 + 34x^3 - 13x^2 - 32x + 24$$

C. FOIL METHOD FOR MULTIPLYING TWO BINOMIALS

There is a special method to multiply two binomials. Since each binomial has two terms, there will be four possible terms in the product.

Consider $(2x + 3)(4x + 7)$.

We can obtain the four terms of the product as follows:

Multiply the **First** terms:	$(2x)(4x)$	$= 8x^2$
Multiply the **Outer** terms:	$(2x)(7)$	$= 14x$
Multiply the **Inner** terms:	$(3)(4x)$	$= 12x$
Multiply the **Last** terms:	$(3)(7)$	$= 21$

We add up all these terms.

Therefore

$$(2x + 3)(4x + 7) = \underbrace{(2x)(4x)}_{} \quad \underbrace{(2x)(7)}_{} \quad \underbrace{(3)(4x)}_{} \quad \underbrace{(3)(7)}_{}$$

$$\text{First} \quad + \quad \text{Outer} \quad + \quad \text{Inner} \quad + \quad \text{Last}$$
$$\text{F} \qquad\qquad \text{O} \qquad\qquad \text{I} \qquad\qquad \text{L}$$

We use the acronym **FOIL** to remember the various terms of the product of two binomials: (**F:** product of **F**irst terms, **O:** product of **O**uter terms, **I:** product of **I**nner terms, **L:** product of **L**ast terms).

> *Note*   The FOIL method essentially uses the distributive rule for multiplication of two polynomials.

---

6. Multiply $(2x - 3)(x + 1)$ using the FOIL method.

7. Multiply $(3a - 2b)$ by $(6a + 6b)$

Answers:

6. $2x^2 - x - 3$ **7.** $18a^2 + 6ab - 12b^2$

EXAMPLE 6   Multiply $(3x - 7)$ by $(4x + 5)$ using the FOIL method.

Solution:

$$\underbrace{(3x)(4x)}_{\text{First Terms}} + \underbrace{(3x)(5)}_{\text{Second Terms}} + \underbrace{(-7)(4x)}_{\text{Inner Terms}} + \underbrace{(-7)(5)}_{\text{Last Terms}}$$

$$= 12x^2 + 15x - 28x - 35$$
$$= \mathbf{12x^2 - 13x - 35}$$

EXAMPLE 7   Multiply $(7a - 3b)$ by $(4a - 5b)$ using the FOIL method.

Solution:

$$(7a - 3b)(4a - 5b) =$$

$$\underbrace{(7a)(4a)}_{\text{First Terms}} + \underbrace{(7a)(-5b)}_{\text{Second Terms}} + \underbrace{(-3b)(4a)}_{\text{Inner Terms}} + \underbrace{(-3b)(-5b)}_{\text{Last Terms}}$$

$$= 28a^2 - 35ab - 12ba + 15b^2$$
$$= \mathbf{28a^2 - 47ab + 15b^2} \qquad {\small ab = ba}$$

EXERCISE 5.3

A. In exercises 1-16, find the product of the pair of monomials.

1. $3x, 5x^4$

2. $3y^2, 6y$

3. $-4x^7, x^8$

4. $5x^6, -5x^4$

5. $-2x^5, -4x^3$

6. $-5y, -4y^6$

7. $3x^2, -7x^4$

8. $-6z, -7z^5$

9. $-5x^4, -3x$

10. $-y^6, -5y^3$

11. $(x), (3x)$

12. $(2xy), (-2x^3y^4)$

13. $(-a^2b^2), (a^3b^3)$

14. $(xy^2), (-xy)^3$

15. $(3x^2y), (-2xy^2)$

16. $(-2x^4z), (-8x^6z^5)$

B. In exercises 17-40, use the distributive law to find the product and simplify the result.

17. $x(x-4)$

18. $-y(5-y)$

19. $3a^2(a-4)$

20. $-4z^2(5+z)$

21. $2x(3x^2-3x)$

22. $2x^2(4x^2+7x)$

23. $3y^3(2y-5)$

24. $x^2(4x^4-3x^2+4)$

25. $-xy(x^2-y^2)$

26. $-3x^5(x^2-3x+2)$

27. $-2y^6(y^3+y^2-y)$

28. $-4a^2(2a^2-3a-6)$

29. $ab(3a^2-5ab-6b^2)$

30. $(x^2+3x-4)(-2x)$

31. $(6x+2)(5x^2-7x)$

32. $(3y-2)(2y^2+5)$

33. $(5x^2-3)(8x^9-3x^2)$

34. $(4y^3+5)(3y^5-5y)$

35. $(4x+3y^2)(5x^2+8xy^2)$

36. $(3x^2-5y^3)(2y-x^2y)$

37. $(-2x^2+4y)(2y+4x^2)$

38. $(9y^9-7p^2)(11p^2-4y^2)$

39. $-2(x-y^2)(3y-4x)$

40. $-3x(x^2+4y)(2y-x^2)$

In exercises 41-64, find the product and simplify.

41. $(3q-1)(4q^2-7q)$

42. $(3p+1)(2p^2-6p)$

43. $(4x-8)(3x^5-2x^2)$

44. $(3y+5)(4y^4+6y)$

45. $\left(\frac{4}{3}x^2-\frac{3}{4}\right)\left(2x-\frac{1}{5}\right)$

46. $\left(\frac{2}{3}y^3-\frac{1}{4}\right)\left(3y+\frac{1}{2}\right)$

47. $(3x^2-5x)(4x^2+7x+1)$

48. $(3y^2+5y)(3y^3-y+2)$

49. $(5x^9-3x^2+7)(x^3+x^2)$

50. $(4y^6+3y^4-6)(2y^2+y^3)$

51. $(3x+5)(3x+5)$

52. $(2x-1)(2x+1)$

53. $(y^3-7y)(y^9-10y^6+8y)$

54. $(x^4-y^4)(x^4+y^4)$

55. $(3x^5-5x^3+7)(3x^5-5x^3+7)$

56. $(3x^2+2x-1)(3x^2+2x-1)$

57. $(a^2-2a+7)(a-2)$

58. $(-x^2+3x-2)(2x-1)$

59. $(2y-2)(-5y^2+2y-1)$

60. $(a^3-2a+1)(a-2)$

61. $(2a-4)(3a^2+2a-1)$

62. $(-2y+3y+1)(3y+4)$

63. $(2y^3-3y^2+3)(y-1)$

64. $(-y^2-5y+4)(2y-3)$

C. In exercises 65-92, use the FOIL method to find the product.

65. $(4x+5)(3x-7)$

66. $(3y-2)(2y+4)$

67. $(3x^3+7x)(9x+5)$

68. $(4y^2-3y)(5y^2+5)$

69. $(-3+2s)(4+3s)$

70. $(2-5p)(6+6p)$

71. $(6t+5)(2t-3)$

72. $(3x-5)(2x+5)$

73. $(4k+5l)(4k-5l)$

74. $(2x^2-y^2)(2x^2+y^2)$

75. $(4n-3m)(3n-4m)$

76. $(3x+2y)(3x+5y)$

77. $(2y^5-3y)(3y^2-7y)$

78. $(3x^2+5x)(2x^4+3x)$

79 $(x+1)(x+5)$

80. $(a+2)(a-3)$

81. $(y-4)(y+8)$

82. $(2x-2)(x+5)$

83. $(2y-3)(2y+2)$

84. $(5a+4)(2a-3)$

85. $(x+y)(2x+y)$

86. $(2a-3b)(2a-2b)$

87. $(3x-5y)(3x+7y)$

88. $(2p+4q)(7p-3q)$

89. $(11x+3y)(2x+5y)$

90. $(2x-4y)(3x-3y)$

91. $(y-5)(y+5)$

92. $(3x-7)(3x+7)$

5.4 SPECIAL PRODUCTS

There are some special products which are used frequently. We will observe the pattern for their expansions and develop some rules from these observations.

A. SQUARES OF BINOMIALS

Recall that:

(i)   To square something means to multiply it by itself.

For example, $a^2 = a \cdot a$

$$(a + b)^2 = (a + b) \cdot (a + b)$$

$$7^2 = 7 \times 7$$

(ii)   We cannot distribute powers over the terms of the base.

For example, $(5 + 2)^2$ $\neq$ $5^2 + 2^2$

$7^2 = 49$ $25 + 4 = 29$

In general, $(a + b)^2$ $\neq$ $a^2 + b^2$

WARM-UP

1. Write $(x + 3)^2$ in expanded form.

EXAMPLE 1   Write $(x + 5)^2$ in expanded form.

Solution:

Use the FOIL method.

$$(x + 5)^2 = (x + 5)(x + 5)$$
$$= x \cdot x + x \cdot 5 + 5 \cdot x + 5 \cdot 5$$
$$\quad\quad\; \text{F} \quad\quad \text{O} \quad\quad \text{I} \quad\quad \text{L}$$
$$= x^2 + 5x + 5x + 25 \quad \text{Simplify.}$$
$$= x^2 + 2(5x) + 25 \quad \text{Combine like terms.}$$
$$= x^2 + 10x + 25$$

Observation $(x + 5)^2 =$ (square of the first term) + 2 (product of the two terms) + (square of the last term).

WARM-UP

2. Find the product $(3x - 2)^2$

EXAMPLE 2   Find the product: $(2x - 7)^2$.

Solution: Use the FOIL method

$$(2x - 7)^2 = (2x - 7)(2x - 7)$$
$$= (2x)(2x) - (2x)(7) - 7(2x) + (7)(7)$$
$$\quad\quad\; \text{F} \quad\quad\quad \text{O} \quad\quad\quad \text{I} \quad\quad\quad \text{L}$$
$$= 4x^2 - 14x - 14x + 49$$
$$= 4x^2 - 28x + 49$$

Observe the same pattern as observed in Example 1. We record this pattern as a **Rule**.

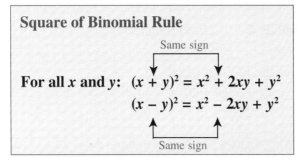

Square of Binomial Rule

Same sign

For all x and y: $(x + y)^2 = x^2 + 2xy + y^2$

$(x - y)^2 = x^2 - 2xy + y^2$

Same sign

EXAMPLE 3   Expand the following.

   a. $(3y + 4z)^2$ **b.** $(4a - 5b)^2$

   c. $\left(3m + \dfrac{4}{5}\right)^2$ **d.** $\left(\dfrac{4}{3}x - \dfrac{2}{5}\right)^2$

Solutions:

   a.

   $(3y + 4z)^2 = (\text{first term})^2 + 2(\text{product of terms}) + (\text{last term})^2$

   $\qquad\qquad\quad\downarrow\qquad\qquad\qquad\quad\downarrow\qquad\qquad\qquad\downarrow$

   $\qquad = \quad (3y)^2 \quad + \quad 2(3y)(4z) \quad + \quad (4z)^2$

   $\qquad = 9y^2 + 24yz + 16z^2$

   b.

   $(4a - 5b)^2 = (\text{first term})^2 - 2(\text{product of terms}) + (\text{last term})^2$

   $\qquad\qquad\quad\downarrow\qquad\qquad\qquad\quad\downarrow\qquad\qquad\qquad\downarrow$

   $\qquad = \quad (4a)^2 \quad - \quad 2(4a)(5b) \quad + \quad (5b)^2$

   $\qquad = 16a^2 - 40ab + 25b^2$

   c.

   $\left(3m + \dfrac{4}{5}\right)^2 = (\text{first term})^2 + 2(\text{product of terms}) + (\text{last term})^2$

   $\qquad\qquad\qquad\downarrow\qquad\qquad\qquad\quad\downarrow\qquad\qquad\qquad\downarrow$

   $\qquad = \quad (3m)^2 \quad + \quad 2(3m)\left(\dfrac{4}{5}\right) \quad + \quad \left(\dfrac{4}{5}\right)^2$

   $\qquad = 9m^2 + \dfrac{24}{5}m + \dfrac{16}{25}$

   d.

   $\left(\dfrac{4}{3}x - \dfrac{2}{5}\right)^2 = (\text{first term})^2 - 2(\text{product of terms}) + (\text{last term})^2$

   $\qquad\qquad\qquad\downarrow\qquad\qquad\qquad\quad\downarrow\qquad\qquad\qquad\downarrow$

   $\qquad = \quad \left(\dfrac{4}{3}x\right)^2 \quad - \quad 2\left(\dfrac{4}{3}x\right)\left(\dfrac{2}{5}\right) \quad + \quad \left(\dfrac{2}{5}\right)^2$

   $\qquad = \dfrac{16}{9}x^2 - \dfrac{16}{15}x + \dfrac{4}{25}$

B. PRODUCT OF SUM AND DIFFERENCE

────── WARM-UP ──────

4. Find the Product

$(x + 7)(x - 7)$

EXAMPLE 4   Find the product: $(x + 5)(x - 5)$.

Solution:

Use the FOIL method

$$(x - 5)(x + 5) = x \cdot x + x \cdot 5 + (-5) \cdot x + (5)(-5)$$

$$\qquad\qquad\qquad F \qquad O \qquad I \qquad L$$

$$= x^2 + 5x - 5x - 25$$

$$= x^2 - 25$$

We find that the product of the sum and difference of two terms equals the difference of their squares. We state this observation in the following rule. The Inner product and Outer products combine to be equal to zero.

> **Rule : Product of Sum and Difference Rule**
>
> **For all x and y : $(x + y)(x - y) = x^2 - y^2$**

────── WARM-UP ──────

5. Write the product in expanded form.

a) $(4z + 1)(4z - 1)$

b) $(3x + 4y)(3x - 4y)$

c) $\left(\dfrac{2}{5}t + 1\right)\left(\dfrac{2}{5}t - 1\right)$

Answers:

4. $x^2 - 49$

5. a) $16z^2 - 1$ b) $9x^2 - 16y^2$

c) $\dfrac{4}{25}t^2 - 1$

EXAMPLE 5   Write the product in expanded form.

a. $(3p + 4)(3p - 4)$ b. $(2x - 3y)(2x + 3y)$

c. $\left(\dfrac{2}{3}t + \dfrac{4}{5}\right)\left(\dfrac{2}{3}t - \dfrac{4}{5}\right)$

Solution:

Use the rule for the product of the sum and difference of two terms.

a. $(3p + 4)(3p - 4) = $ (first term)^2 – (last term)^2

$$= (3p)^2 - (4)^2 = 9p^2 - 16$$

b. $(2x - 3y)(2x + 3y) = $ (first term)^2 – (last term)^2

$$= (2x)^2 - (3y)^2 = 4x^2 - 9y^2$$

c. $\left(\dfrac{2}{3}t + \dfrac{4}{5}\right)\left(\dfrac{2}{3}t - \dfrac{4}{5}\right) = $ (first term)^2 – (last term)^2

$$= \left(\dfrac{2}{3}t\right)^2 - \left(\dfrac{4}{5}\right)^2 = \dfrac{4}{9}t^2 - \dfrac{16}{25}$$

C. HIGHER POWERS

For higher powers use the special product for $(a + b)^2$ and then use the rule for multiplying polynomials as needed.

EXAMPLE 6   Expand the following expression:
$(4a + b)^3$.

Solution:

$$(4a + b)^3 = (4a + b)^2 (4a + b)$$

$$= \underbrace{(4a + b)(4a + b)}(4a + b) \qquad \text{Use FOIL method.}$$

$$= (16a^2 + 8ab + b^2)(4a + b)$$

$$= \mathbf{16a^2} \cdot 4a + \mathbf{16a^2} \cdot b + \mathbf{8ab} \cdot 4a + \mathbf{8ab} \cdot b$$
$$+ \mathbf{b^2} \cdot 4a + \mathbf{b^2} \cdot b \qquad \text{Multiplication rule.}$$

$$= 64a^3 + 16a^2 b + 32a^2 b + 8ab^2 + 4ab^2 + b^3$$

$$= 64a^3 + 48a^2 b + 12ab^2 + b^3 \qquad \text{Combine like terms.}$$

EXERCISE 5.4

A. In exercises 1-22, use the rules discussed in this section to write the expression in the expanded form.

1. $(x - 2)^2$ 2. $(z + 3)^2$ 3. $(y + 4)^2$ 4. $(z - 5)^2$ 5. $(2m - 5)^2$

6. $(3x + 4)^2$ 7. $(3t + 7)^2$ 8. $(2x - 5)^2$ 9. $(5m - 3n)^2$ 10. $(3x + 2y)^2$

11. $(7r + 5s)^2$ 12. $(3x - 4y)^2$ 13. $(x + 1)^2$ 14. $(y - 3)^2$ 15. $(x + 4)^2$

16. $(3a - 5)^2$ 17. $(2x + 3y)^2$ 18. $(3a - 4b)^2$ 19. $\left(\dfrac{3}{4}x + \dfrac{2}{3}y\right)^2$ 20. $\left(3x - \dfrac{5}{3}y\right)^2$

21. $\left(\dfrac{5}{7}u - \dfrac{4}{5}v\right)^2$ 22. $\left(\dfrac{4}{3}u + \dfrac{1}{3}v\right)^2$

B. In exercises 23-50, find the product of the sum and difference of two terms.

23. $(t + 6)(t - 6)$ 24. $\left(x - \dfrac{4}{3}\right)\left(x + \dfrac{4}{3}\right)$ 25. $(4t + 5)(4t - 5)$ 26. $(2x - 3)(2x + 3)$

27. $(7x - 3y)(7x + 3y)$ 28. $(4u + 5v)(4u - 5v)$ 29. $(2x^2 - 1)(2x^2 + 1)$ 30. $(3y^3 + 1)(3y^3 - 1)$

31. $(2 - y)(2 + y)$ 32. $(3x - 2)(3x + 2)$ 33. $(4x + 5y)(4x - 5y)$ 34. $\left(\dfrac{2}{3}x - \dfrac{1}{4}y\right)\left(\dfrac{2}{3}x + \dfrac{1}{4}y\right)$

35. $(x^2 - 1)(x^2 + 1)$ 36. $(y^3 + 1)(y^3 - 1)$ 37. $(4 + r^2)(4 - r^2)$ 38. $(5 - z^3)(5 + z^3)$

39. $(3x^2 - y)(3x^2 + y)$ 40. $(4y^3 + z)(4y^3 - z)$ 41. $(3u^2 + v^2)(3u^2 - v^2)$ 42. $(5u^3 - 4)(5u^3 + 4)$

43. $\left(\dfrac{3}{2}u^2 - \dfrac{2}{3}v\right)\left(\dfrac{3}{2}u^2 + \dfrac{2}{3}v\right)$ 44. $\left(\dfrac{3}{u^2} + \dfrac{4}{v}\right)\left(\dfrac{3}{u^2} - \dfrac{4}{v}\right)$ 45. $\left(\dfrac{2}{3}u^3 + v\right)\left(\dfrac{2}{3}u^3 - v\right)$

46. $\left(\dfrac{3}{u}+\dfrac{3}{4v^3}\right)\left(\dfrac{3}{u}-\dfrac{3}{4v^3}\right)$

47. $\left(\dfrac{u}{v}+\dfrac{v}{u}\right)\left(\dfrac{u}{v}-\dfrac{v}{u}\right)$

48. $\left(\dfrac{2u}{3v}+\dfrac{3v}{2u}\right)\left(\dfrac{2u}{3v}-\dfrac{3v}{2u}\right)$

49. $\left(\dfrac{3}{4u^3}+\dfrac{1}{2v^2}\right)\left(\dfrac{3}{4u^3}-\dfrac{1}{2v^2}\right)$

50. $\left(\dfrac{2u^2}{5v}+\dfrac{5v}{2u^2}\right)\left(\dfrac{2u^2}{5v}-\dfrac{5v}{2u^2}\right)$

C. In exercises 51-60, expand cubes of the binomial.

51. $(m-3)^3$ **52.** $(x+2)^3$ **53.** $(2x+y)^3$ **54.** $(y-2z)^3$ **55.** $(4x-3y)^3$

56. $(3y-4z)^3$ **57.** $(2u-3v)^3$ **58.** $\left(\dfrac{2}{3}u-\dfrac{3}{4}v\right)^3$ **59.** $\left(\dfrac{3}{u}-\dfrac{4}{v}\right)^3$ **60.** $\left(\dfrac{2}{u^2}-\dfrac{3}{v^2}\right)^3$

5.5 INTEGER EXPONENTS

OBJECTIVES ■■■■

Upon completion of this section you will be able to:

A. Use negative numbers as exponents; and

B. Use the quotient rule for integer exponents.

In Section 5.1 we studied whole number exponents. We will now learn about negative and zero exponents and the exponents that may be variables.

A. NEGATIVE EXPONENTS

Consider, 2^n and 3^n for various integers n.

n	2^n
3	$2^3 = 8$
2	$2^2 = 4 = 8 \cdot \dfrac{1}{2}$
1	$2^1 = 2 = 4 \cdot \dfrac{1}{2}$
	Continuing this pattern will produce
0	$2^0 = 2 \cdot \dfrac{1}{2} = 1$
−1	$2^{-1} = 1 \cdot \dfrac{1}{2} = \dfrac{1}{2} = \dfrac{1}{2^1}$
−2	$2^{-2} = \dfrac{1}{2} \cdot \dfrac{1}{2} = \dfrac{1}{4} = \dfrac{1}{2^2}$
−3	$2^{-3} = \dfrac{1}{4} \cdot \dfrac{1}{2} = \dfrac{1}{8} = \dfrac{1}{2^3}$

n	3^n
3	$3^3 = 27$
2	$3^2 = 9 = 27 \cdot \dfrac{1}{3}$
1	$3^1 = 3 = 9 \cdot \dfrac{1}{3}$
	Continuing this pattern will produce
0	$3^0 = 3 \cdot \dfrac{1}{3} = 1$
−1	$3^{-1} = 1 \cdot \dfrac{1}{3} = \dfrac{1}{3} = \dfrac{1}{3^1}$
−2	$3^{-2} = \dfrac{1}{3} \cdot \dfrac{1}{3} = \dfrac{1}{9} = \dfrac{1}{3^2}$
−3	$3^{-3} = \dfrac{1}{9} \cdot \dfrac{1}{3} = \dfrac{1}{27} = \dfrac{1}{3^3}$

This pattern leads us to the following definitions.

Definitions: $a^0 = 1$, and

$a^{-n} = \dfrac{1}{a^n}$, for any non-zero real number a.

In particular $a^{-1} = \dfrac{1}{a}$, the reciprocal of a.

Note $\dfrac{1}{a^n} \cdot a^n = a^{-n} \times a^n = a^{-n+n} = a^0 = 1$, therefore $a^{-n} = \dfrac{1}{a^n}$.

EXAMPLE 1 Simplify by writing the answers with positive exponents.

    a. 2^{-3} **b.** $(2^3)^{-1}$ **c.** 4^{-4}

    d. $(5^{-1})^3$ **e.** x^{-3}, $x \neq 0$ **f.** $\dfrac{1}{x^{-4}}$, $x \neq 0$

    g. 5^0 **h.** $(2x)^0$ **i.** $\dfrac{3}{p^{-4}}$, $p \neq 0$ **j.** $\left(\dfrac{3}{4}\right)^{-3}$

Solutions:

a. $2^{-3} = \dfrac{1}{2^3} = \dfrac{1}{8}$ **b.** $(2^3)^{-1} = (8)^{-1} = \dfrac{1}{8^1} = \dfrac{1}{8}$

c. $4^{-4} = \dfrac{1}{4^4} = \dfrac{1}{256}$ **d.** $(5^{-1})^3 = \left(\dfrac{1}{5}\right)^3 = \dfrac{1^3}{5^3} = \dfrac{1}{5^3} = \dfrac{1}{125}$

e. $x^{-3} = \dfrac{1}{x^3}$ **f.** $\dfrac{1}{x^{-4}} = \dfrac{1}{\frac{1}{x^4}} = 1 \cdot \dfrac{x^4}{1} = x^4$

g. $5^0 = 1$ **h.** $(2x)^0 = 1$

i. $\dfrac{3}{p^{-4}} = 3 \cdot \dfrac{1}{p^{-4}} = 3 \cdot \dfrac{1}{\frac{1}{p^4}} = 3 \cdot \dfrac{p^4}{1} = 3p^4$

j. $\left(\dfrac{3}{4}\right)^{-3} = \dfrac{1}{\left(\frac{3}{4}\right)^3} = \dfrac{1}{\frac{3^3}{4^3}} = 1 \cdot \dfrac{4^3}{3^3} = \dfrac{4^3}{3^3} = \dfrac{64}{27}$

Note that $\left(\dfrac{3}{4}\right)^{-3} = \dfrac{1}{\left(\frac{3}{4}\right)^3} = \dfrac{1}{\frac{27}{64}} = \dfrac{64}{27} = \left(\dfrac{4}{3}\right)^3$. We can change the sign of the exponent by taking the reciprocal of the base.

1. Simplify by writing the answers with positive exponents.

a) 3^{-4}

b) $(3^{-1})^3$

c) $\dfrac{1}{x^{-5}}$

d) $\left(\dfrac{4}{3}\right)^{-2}$

e) $\dfrac{7}{e^{-3}}$

f) x^{-5}

g) $-3x^0$

h) $(-x)^0$

i) $\dfrac{4}{x^{-3}}$

j) $\left(\dfrac{2}{5}\right)^{-3}$

5.5 Integer Exponents

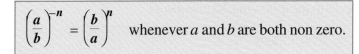

$$\left(\frac{a}{b}\right)^{-n} = \left(\frac{b}{a}\right)^{n} \quad \text{whenever } a \text{ and } b \text{ are both non zero.}$$

2. Simplify and write the answers with positive exponents.

a) $\left(\dfrac{2}{3}\right)^{-5}$

b) $\left(\dfrac{5}{y}\right)^{-1}$

c) $\left(\dfrac{1}{4}\right)^{-4}$

3. Simplify and write answers with positive exponents.

a) $\dfrac{5^{-2}}{10^{-3}}$ b) $\dfrac{x^{-3}}{y^{-2}}$

c) $\dfrac{u^{-2}\,v^{-2}}{w^{-3}}$ d) $\dfrac{x^{-2}\,y^3\,z^{-1}}{x^{-4}\,y^3\,z^2}$

e) $\left(\dfrac{x^3 y^2}{z^{-3}}\right)^{-1}$

Answers:

1. a) $\dfrac{1}{81}$ b) $\dfrac{1}{27}$ c) x^5 d) $\dfrac{9}{16}$ e) $7e^3$

   f) $\dfrac{1}{x^5}$ g) -3 h) 1 i) $4x^3$ j) $\dfrac{125}{8}$

2. a) $\dfrac{243}{32}$ b) $\dfrac{y}{5}$ c) 256

3. a) 40 b) $\dfrac{y^2}{x^3}$ c) $\dfrac{w^3}{u^2 v^2}$

   d) $\dfrac{x^2}{z^3}$ e) $\dfrac{1}{x^3 y^2 z^3}$

EXAMPLE 2 Simplify and write the answers with positive exponents.

a. $\left(\dfrac{1}{2}\right)^{-3}$ b. $\left(\dfrac{2}{x}\right)^{-5}$ c. $\left(\dfrac{3}{2}\right)^{-5}$

Solutions:

a. $\left(\dfrac{1}{2}\right)^{-3} = \left(\dfrac{2}{1}\right)^{3} = 2^3 = 8$ $\quad \left(\dfrac{a}{b}\right)^{-n} = \left(\dfrac{b}{a}\right)^{n}$

b. $\left(\dfrac{2}{x}\right)^{-5} = \left(\dfrac{x}{2}\right)^{5} = \dfrac{x^5}{2^5} = \dfrac{x^5}{32}$

c. $\left(\dfrac{3}{2}\right)^{-5} = \left(\dfrac{2}{3}\right)^{5} = \dfrac{2^5}{3^5} = \dfrac{32}{243}$

EXAMPLE 3 Simplify and write the answers with only positive exponents.

a. $\dfrac{4^{-2}}{7^{-3}}$ b. $\dfrac{x^2}{y^{-3}}$ c. $\dfrac{x^{-2}}{y^2}$

d. $\dfrac{x^{-2}\,y^2}{z^{-2}}$ e. $\left(\dfrac{x^2\,y^{-2}}{z^{-2}}\right)^{-1}$

Solutions:

a. $\dfrac{4^{-2}}{7^{-3}} = \dfrac{7^3}{4^2}$ $\quad a^{-n} = \dfrac{1}{a^n}$ b. $\dfrac{x^2}{y^{-3}} = \dfrac{x^2 y^3}{1} = x^2 y^3$

c. $\dfrac{x^{-2}}{y^2} = \left(\dfrac{1}{x^2}\right)\left(\dfrac{1}{y^2}\right) = \dfrac{1}{x^2 y^2}$

d. $\dfrac{x^{-2}\,y^2}{z^{-2}} = \dfrac{y^2\,z^2}{x^2}$

e. $\left(\dfrac{x^2 y^{-2}}{z^{-2}}\right)^{-1} = \left(\dfrac{x^2 z^2}{y^2}\right)^{-1} = \left(\dfrac{y^2}{x^2 z^2}\right)^{1} = \dfrac{y^2}{x^2 z^2}$

B. QUOTIENT RULE FOR INTEGER EXPONENTS

Consider $\dfrac{4^7}{4^3} = \dfrac{4 \cdot 4 \cdot 4 \cdot 4 \cdot \cancel{4} \cdot \cancel{4} \cdot \cancel{4}}{\cancel{4} \cdot \cancel{4} \cdot \cancel{4}} = 4^4 = 4^{7-3}$. Similarly $\dfrac{4^4}{4^6} = \dfrac{\cancel{4} \cdot \cancel{4} \cdot \cancel{4} \cdot \cancel{4}}{4 \cdot 4 \cdot \cancel{4} \cdot \cancel{4} \cdot \cancel{4} \cdot \cancel{4}}$

$$= \dfrac{1}{4^2} = \dfrac{1}{4^{6-4}}$$

For any non-zero real number a, and integers m and n

$$\dfrac{a^m}{a^n} = a^{m-n} \qquad \text{and} \qquad \dfrac{a^m}{a^n} = \dfrac{1}{a^{n-m}}.$$

EXAMPLE 4   Simplify and write the answers with positive exponents.

a. $\dfrac{3^7}{3^3}$ b. $\dfrac{5^3}{5^8}$ c. $\dfrac{6^7}{6^{-3}}$ d. $\dfrac{x^8}{x^{-4}}$

e. $\dfrac{x^2 y^8}{x^6 y^5}$ f. $\dfrac{2^4 x^5}{2^2 x^9}$ g. $\dfrac{x^6}{x^6}$

Solutions:

a. $\dfrac{3^7}{3^3} = 3^{7-3} = 3^4$ b. $\dfrac{5^3}{5^8} = \dfrac{1}{5^{8-3}} = \dfrac{1}{5^5}$

c. $\dfrac{6^7}{6^{-3}} = 6^{7-(-3)} = 6^{10}$ d. $\dfrac{x^8}{x^{-4}} = x^{8-(-4)} = x^{12}$

e. $\dfrac{x^2 y^8}{x^6 y^5} = \dfrac{y^{8-5}}{x^{6-2}} = \dfrac{y^3}{x^4}$ f. $\dfrac{2^4 x^5}{2^2 x^9} = \dfrac{2^{4-2}}{x^{9-5}} = \dfrac{2^2}{x^4} = \dfrac{4}{x^4}$

g. $\dfrac{x^6}{x^6} = x^{6-6} = x^0 = 1$

We list all the exponent laws discussed so far. Assume that all denominators and bases of the negative exponents are non-zero. Then for all integers m and n,

RULE	EXAMPLE	RULE	EXAMPLE
$a^0 = 1$	$3^0 = 1$	$a^m \cdot a^n = a^{m+n}$	$4^5 \cdot 4^6 = 4^{11}$
$a^{-n} = \dfrac{1}{a^n}$	$3^{-7} = \dfrac{1}{3^7}$	$\left(\dfrac{a}{b}\right)^{-n} = \left(\dfrac{b}{a}\right)^n$	$\left(\dfrac{2}{3}\right)^{-2} = \left(\dfrac{3}{2}\right)^2$
$(a^m)^n = a^{mn}$	$(4^2)^6 = 4^{12}$	$\dfrac{a^m}{a^n} = a^{m-n} = \dfrac{1}{a^{n-m}}$	$\dfrac{3^6}{3^8} = 3^{6-8} = 3^{-2} = \dfrac{1}{3^2} = \dfrac{1}{3^{8-6}}$
$\left(\dfrac{a}{b}\right)^m = \dfrac{a^m}{b^m}$	$\left(\dfrac{4}{7}\right)^3 = \dfrac{4^3}{7^3}$	$(ab)^m = a^m b^m$	$(3 \cdot 5)^4 = 3^4 \cdot 5^4$

5. Simplify the following:

a) $\dfrac{4^5 \cdot 4^{-3}}{(4^3)^{-1}}$

b) $(3x)^3 \, (2x)$

c) $\left(\dfrac{2x^3}{3}\right)^2$

d) $\left[\left(\dfrac{x^2 y^3}{z}\right)^2\right]^{-3}$

e) $\left[\left(\dfrac{x^{-1} y^{-3}}{z}\right)^{-1}\right]^4$

f) $\dfrac{x^4}{y^2} \cdot \dfrac{y^3}{xz^3} \cdot \dfrac{z^3}{x^2 y^2}$

6. Explain why $(3^3)^2 \neq 3^{3^2}$.

EXAMPLE 5   Simplify the following. Write the answer so that they contain only positive exponents.

a. $\dfrac{3^4 \cdot 3^9}{(3^2)^5}$ **b.** $(4x)^3 \, (8x)^2$ **c.** $\left(\dfrac{3x^5}{4}\right)^3$

d. $\left(\dfrac{x^2 y^{-3}}{z^{-2}}\right)^2$ **e.** $\left[\left(\dfrac{xy^{-2}}{z}\right)^2\right]^3$ **f.** $\dfrac{x^3}{y^2} \cdot \dfrac{y^3}{xz^2} \cdot \dfrac{z^2}{x^2 y}$

Solutions:

a. $\dfrac{3^4 \cdot 3^9}{(3^2)^5} = \dfrac{3^{13}}{3^{10}}$ $a^m \cdot a^n = a^{m+n}, \; (a^m)^n = a^{mn}$

$= 3^{13-10} = 3^3 = 27$ $\dfrac{a^m}{a^n} = a^{m-n}$

b. $(4x)^3 \, (8x)^2 = 64x^3 \cdot 64x^2$ $(ab)^m = a^m b^m$

$= 4096x^5$ $a^m \cdot a^n = a^{m+n}$

c. $\left(\dfrac{3x^5}{4}\right)^3 = \dfrac{(3x^5)^3}{4^3} = \dfrac{3^3 (x^5)^3}{4^3} = \dfrac{3^3 x^{15}}{4^3} = \dfrac{27}{64} x^{15}$

d. $\left(\dfrac{x^2 y^{-3}}{z^{-2}}\right)^2 = \left(\dfrac{x^2 z^2}{y^3}\right)^2 = \dfrac{(x^2)^2 (z^2)^2}{(y^3)^2} = \dfrac{x^4 z^4}{y^6}$ $(a^m)^n = a^{mn}$

e. $\left[\left(\dfrac{xy^{-2}}{z}\right)^2\right]^3 = \left[\left(\dfrac{x}{y^2 z}\right)^2\right]^3 = \left(\dfrac{x}{y^2 z}\right)^6 = \dfrac{x^6}{y^{12} z^6}$ $(a^m)^n = a^{mn}$

f. $\dfrac{x^3}{y^2} \cdot \dfrac{y^3}{xz^2} \cdot \dfrac{z^2}{x^2 y} = \dfrac{x^3 y^3 z^2}{x^3 y^3 z^2} = 1$

EXAMPLE 6   Explain why $(2^2)^3 \neq 2^{2^3}$.

Solution: $(2^2)^3 = 2^6 = 64$ and $2^{2^3} = 2^8 = 256$

Therefore, $(2^2)^3 \neq 2^{2^3}$.

EXERCISE 5.5

A. In exercises 1-16, evaluate the numerical expression.

1. $\left(\dfrac{1}{2}\right)^{-2}$ **2.** $\left(\dfrac{1}{3}\right)^{-3}$ **3.** $\left(\dfrac{2}{3}\right)^{3}$ **4.** $\left(\dfrac{2}{3}\right)^{-3}$ **5.** $\left(-\dfrac{4}{5}\right)^{3}$ **6.** $\left(-\dfrac{3}{2}\right)^{3}$ **7.** $\left(-\dfrac{3}{5}\right)^{-4}$ **8.** $\left(\dfrac{-3}{4}\right)^{-2}$

9. 2^{-2} **10.** 4^{-3} **11.** $\dfrac{1}{2^{-3}}$ **12.** $\dfrac{1}{3^{-2}}$ **13.** $\dfrac{5^{-2}}{5}$ **14.** $\dfrac{2^{-3}}{2^{3}}$ **15.** $\dfrac{3^{-2}}{3^{-2}}$ **16.** $\dfrac{2^{-2}}{4^{-2}}$

B. In exercises 17-54, write the expression with positive exponents. All variables are non-zero.

17. $(x^{-4})^{5}$ **18.** $\left(y^{2}\right)^{-5}$ **19.** $(x^{-3}y^{2})^{3}$ **20.** $(y^{3}z^{-5})^{2}$ **21.** $(r^{-2}sr^{3}s^{4})^{3}$

22. $(a^{3}\cdot a^{-2}b\cdot a\cdot b^{3})^{2}$ **23.** $\dfrac{k^{9}k^{-2}}{(k^{2})^{4}}$ **24.** $\dfrac{z^{-2}z^{5}}{(z^{3})^{2}}$ **25.** $\dfrac{2}{a^{-4}}$ **26.** $\dfrac{5x}{x^{-5}}$

27. $\left(\dfrac{3a^{-2}b^{4}}{5a^{2}b^{-3}}\right)^{0}$ **28.** $\dfrac{2x^{3}y^{-4}}{3x^{4}y^{4}}$ **29.** $\dfrac{pq^{3}}{pq^{5}}$ **30.** $\dfrac{a^{3}b^{5}}{a^{5}b^{7}}$ **31.** $\dfrac{2m^{6}n^{2}}{5m^{9}n^{10}}$

32. $\dfrac{5r^{3}t^{7}}{3r^{8}t^{10}}$ **33.** $\dfrac{24a^{2}b^{7}c^{8}}{36a^{7}b^{5}c^{10}}$ **34.** $\dfrac{25a^{4}b^{3}c^{7}}{20a^{5}b^{7}c^{3}}$ **35.** $\left(\dfrac{-3x^{-4}y^{2}}{5x^{2}y^{4}}\right)^{3}$ **36.** $\left[\dfrac{5a^{3}b^{2}}{6a^{-2}b^{6}}\right]^{2}$

37. $\dfrac{(4y)^{3}}{y^{3}}$ **38.** $\dfrac{(3x)^{2}}{x^{2}}$ **39.** $\dfrac{3k^{-4}l^{5}}{3^{-2}k^{-6}l^{-2}}$ **40.** $\dfrac{5x^{4}y^{-5}}{5^{-3}x^{5}y^{7}}$ **41.** $\left(\dfrac{a^{3}}{b^{2}}\right)^{6}$

42. $\left[\dfrac{x^{2}}{y^{3}}\right]^{3}$ **43.** $(3x^{-1}y^{-2})^{2}$ **44.** $(-2x^{-4})x^{2}$ **45.** $(-2x^{2})(x^{-5})^{2}$ **46.** $(2a^{-2})(a^{6}b^{-1})$

47. $(-4x^{2})^{-1}(2x^{2})^{2}$ **48.** $(3a^{-2})(4a^{2}b^{-4})$ **49.** $\dfrac{x^{6}(x^{4})^{-2}}{(x^{-2})^{2}}$ **50.** $\dfrac{y^{7}(y^{-3})^{2}}{(y^{3})^{-3}}$ **51.** $\dfrac{2x^{-2}y^{3}}{(4xy^{-3})^{2}}$

52. $\dfrac{2y^{-2}z^{4}}{(3y^{2}z^{-2})^{2}}$ **53.** $\dfrac{2^{-5}x^{2}y^{-3}}{2^{-8}x^{-3}y^{2}}$ **54.** $\dfrac{3^{-4}a^{2}b^{-4}}{3^{-5}a^{4}b^{-2}}$

In exercises 55-60, evaluate the expression for $x = 2$, and $y = -3$.

55. $\dfrac{x^{3}}{y^{-2}}$ **56.** $\dfrac{x^{-3}}{y^{4}}$ **57.** $\left(\dfrac{x}{y^{2}}\right)^{-2}$ **58.** $\left(\dfrac{x}{y^{2}}\right)^{3}$ **59.** $(-x^{-1}y)^{3}$ **60.** $\left(-2yx^{-2}\right)^{2}$

In exercises 61-70, simplify the numerical expression.

61. $2^{2}\cdot 3^{-2}+3^{2}\cdot 2^{-3}$ **62.** $3^{2}\cdot 2^{-3}+2^{2}\cdot 3^{-3}$ **63.** $5\cdot 4^{-2}-3\cdot 2^{-3}$ **64.** $3\cdot 3^{-3}-2\cdot 9^{-2}$ **65.** $2\cdot 5^{-2}-3^{-1}\cdot 3^{-2}$

66. $3\cdot 2^{-2}-3^{-2}\cdot 3^{3}$ **67.** $2^{-2}+3^{-2}$ **68.** $8^{-2}+5^{-5}$ **69.** $9^{-2}+3^{-3}$ **70.** $4^{-2}+2^{-2}$

In exercises 71-74, simplify the expression and write the answer in terms of positive exponents.

71. $\left(2x^{-2}y^{2}\right)^{-2}$ **72.** $\left(3x^{-3}y^{-2}\right)^{2}$ **73.** $\left(-2x^{2}y\right)^{-3}$ **74.** $\left(-x^{2}y^{-1}\right)^{-2}$

In exercises 75-80, simplify the expression and write the answer in terms of positive exponent.

75. $\left(\dfrac{5}{x}\right)^{-2}$ **76.** $\left(\dfrac{2x}{y}\right)^{-3}$ **77.** $\left(\dfrac{x}{y^{2}}\right)^{-2}\cdot\left(\dfrac{y}{x^{2}}\right)$ **78.** $\left[\dfrac{y}{x^{2}}\right]^{-3}\cdot\left[\dfrac{x}{y^{2}}\right]$ **79.** $x^{2^{3}}$ **80.** $y^{3^{2}}$

5.6 QUOTIENT OF TWO POLYNOMIALS

Dividing a polynomial by a monomial is rather simple. It can be done by using the distributive law and the rules of exponents. The method of long division, for finding the quotient of two polynomials, is similar to the process for dividing numbers studied in arithmetic.

A. DIVIDING A POLYNOMIAL BY A MONOMIAL

Dividing a polynomial by a monomial is the same as multiplying a polynomial by the reciprocal of the monomial. We can use the distributive law.

$$\frac{a+b}{c} = \frac{1}{c} \cdot (a+b) = \frac{1}{c} \cdot a + \frac{1}{c} \cdot b = \frac{a}{c} + \frac{b}{c} .$$

Thus, $\frac{a+b}{c} = \frac{a}{c} + \frac{b}{c}$.

Note that this is nothing more than adding two fractions with a common denominator in "reverse".

To divide a polynomial by a monomial, divide each term of the polynomial by the monomial.

WARM-UP

1. Simplify the following

a) $\dfrac{27x^4 - 18x^2 + 9x}{3x^3}$

b) $\dfrac{20y^6 - 4y^3 + 4y}{4y^4}$

c) $\dfrac{45y^5 + 25y^4 + 10y^3}{5y^3}$

EXAMPLE 1   Simplify the following.

a. $\dfrac{16x^4 - 8x^2 + 12x}{4x^2}$ b. $\dfrac{6y^{10} - 3y^6 + 4y^3 + 8y}{3y^3}$

c. $\dfrac{16m^4 - 12m^3 + 4m^2 + 8m - 9}{4m^2}$

Solutions:

a. $\dfrac{16x^4 - 8x^2 + 12x}{4x^2} = \dfrac{16x^4}{4x^2} - \dfrac{8x^2}{4x^2} + \dfrac{12x}{4x^2} = 4x^2 - 2 + \dfrac{3}{x}$

b. $\dfrac{6y^{10} - 3y^6 + 4y^3 + 8y}{3y^3} = \dfrac{6y^{10}}{3y^3} - \dfrac{3y^6}{3y^3} + \dfrac{4y^3}{3y^3} + \dfrac{8y}{3y^3}$

$= 2y^7 - y^3 + \dfrac{4}{3} + \dfrac{8}{3y^2}$

c. $\dfrac{16m^4 - 12m^3 + 4m^2 + 8m - 9}{4m^2}$

$= \dfrac{16m^4}{4m^2} - \dfrac{12m^3}{4m^2} + \dfrac{4m^2}{4m^2} + \dfrac{8m}{4m^2} - \dfrac{9}{4m^2}$

$= 4m^2 - 3m + 1 + \dfrac{2}{m} - \dfrac{9}{4m^2}$

EXAMPLE 2 Find the polynomial, which when divided by $3x^2$, yields $4x^3 - 5x^2 - 7$ as a quotient.

Solution:

$$\frac{\text{Polynomial}}{3x^2} = 4x^3 - 5x^2 - 7.$$

$$\left(\frac{\text{Polynomial}}{3x^2}\right)3x^2 = (4x^3 - 5x^2 - 7)(3x^2) \quad \text{\footnotesize Multiply both sides by } 3x^2$$

$$\text{Polynomial} = (4x^3)(3x^2) - (5x^2)(3x^2) - (7)(3x^2)$$

$$= 12x^5 - 15x^4 - 21x^2.$$

B. QUOTIENT OF TWO POLYNOMIALS

Let us divide 873 by 21 using long division.

$$\begin{array}{r} \mathbf{???} \longrightarrow \text{\footnotesize Quotient} \end{array}$$

Divisor $\longleftarrow$ $21\overline{)873}$ $\longrightarrow$ Dividend   **Step 1:** Write the division in the long division format.

$$\mathbf{???} \longrightarrow \text{\footnotesize Remainder}$$

Dividing 873 by 21 means finding the quotient and the remainder.

$$\begin{array}{r} 4 \\ 21\overline{)873} \end{array}$$

Step 2: First find the largest multiple of 21 less than 87.
$21 \times 4 = 84 < 87$

$$\begin{array}{r} 4 \\ 21\overline{)873} \\ -84 \\ \hline 3 \end{array}$$

Step 3: Multiply 21 by 4 and write the product below 87. Subtract 84 from 87.

$$\begin{array}{r} 4 \\ 21\overline{)873} \\ -84\downarrow \\ \hline 33 \end{array}$$

Step 4: Bring down the next digit 3.

Quotient $\longleftarrow$
Divisor $\longleftarrow$ $21\overline{)873}$

$$\begin{array}{r} 41 \\ -84\downarrow \\ \hline 33 \\ -21 \\ \hline \end{array}$$
Remainder $\longleftarrow$ 12

Step 5: Repeat step 2 and step 3 with 33 as the new dividend, and continue the process until the remainder is less than the divisor and there is no more digit in the quotient to drop down.

Therefore, $873 \div 21 = 41$ R 12

or $\dfrac{873}{21} = 41 + \dfrac{12}{21} = 41\dfrac{12}{21} = 41\dfrac{4}{7}$

Divisor (21) × Quotient (41) + Remainder (12) = Dividend (873)

Long division for polynomials is carried out in a similar manner as division for whole numbers. However, before carrying out the long division for polynomials, make sure that:

1. the dividend and the divisor are both written with *descending powers* of the variable in its terms.
   For example: $7x^2 - 3x + 4x^3$ is written as $4x^3 + 7x^2 - 3x$.

2. missing terms in the dividend and the divisor are inserted with the coefficient of 0.
   For example: $5x^4 - 7x^2 + 8$ is written as $5x^4 + 0\,x^3 - 7x^2 + 0\,x + 8$.

The division algorithm is explained in the following example.

WARM-UP

3. Divide $3x^2 + 10x + 6$ by $x + 2$.

EXAMPLE 3   Divide $x^2 + 11x + 30$ by $x + 5$.

Solution:

Notice that both the dividend [$x^2 + 11x + 30$] and the divisor [$x + 5$] are written in terms of descending powers of x, and the dividend and divisor have no missing exponents in x. We can now use the division algorithm (long division).

Divide $x^2 + 11x + 30$ by $x + 5$

Step 1   Write the division in long division format, with the polynomial written in descending powers and with missing terms in the dividend shown with 0 coefficients.

$$x + 5 \overline{\smash{)}\, x^2 + 11x + 30}$$

Step 2   Divide the first term of the dividend by the first term of the divisor ($x^2 \div x = x$). Place the quotient directly above the first term of the dividend.

$$x + 5 \overline{\smash{)}\, x^2 + 11x + 30}\ .1$$

with x above

Step 3   As with long division of numbers, we multiply next. We multiply the monomial we got in step 2, by the entire divisor. We may need to use distributive law if the divisor has two or more terms as in this case.

$$x(x + 5) = \underline{x^2 + 5x}$$

$$x + 5 \overline{\smash{)}\, x^2 + 11x + 30}$$
$$\underline{x^2 + 5x}$$

Step 4   As with long division of numbers, we subtract next. However in algebra it is often easier to add the opposite. Recall, this is exactly how we learned to subtract polynomials.

$$-(x^2 + 5x) = -x^2 - 5x$$

$$
\begin{array}{r}
x \\
x+5 \overline{\smash{)} x^2 + 11x + 30} \\
-x^2 - 5x \\
\hline
6x + 30
\end{array}
$$

Step 5   Repeat steps 3 and 4 until the remainder is 0 or the degree of the remainder is less than the degree of the divisor.

$$
\begin{array}{r}
x + \mathbf{6} \\
x+5 \overline{\smash{)} x^2 + 11x + 30} \\
x^2 + 5x \\
\hline
6x + 30 \\
6(x+5) = \mathbf{6x \pm 30} \\
\hline
0
\end{array}
$$

$\dfrac{6x}{x} = \mathbf{6}$

Step 6   Write the division in the form

$$\text{quotient} + \frac{\text{remainder}}{\text{divisor}}$$

$$\frac{x^2 + 11x + 30}{x + 5} = x + 6 + \frac{0}{x+5} \longrightarrow \text{the remainder} \\ \longrightarrow \text{divisor}$$

$$= x + 6$$

Note | The division process terminates when the remainder is either zero or the degree of the remainder is less than the degree of the divisor.

EXERCISE 5.6

A. In exercises 1-30, find the quotient.

1. $\dfrac{21x^4}{3x^2}$ 2. $\dfrac{32y^5}{8y^3}$ 3. $\dfrac{16x^7 y}{2x^5 y}$ 4. $\dfrac{15a^5 b^2}{5a^2 b}$ 5. $\dfrac{(-2y)^3 z^2}{2y^2 z}$

6. $\dfrac{(-6x)^2 y^3}{3x y^2}$ 7. $\dfrac{15s^2 t^3}{-5st^2}$ 8. $\dfrac{14a^3 b^2}{7ab}$ 9. $\dfrac{4x+6}{2}$ 10. $\dfrac{3x^2 + 4x}{x}$

11. $\dfrac{10y^2 - 8y}{2y}$ 12. $\dfrac{5a^2 + 10a}{-5a}$ 13. $\dfrac{9y^2 - 27y}{-3y}$ 14. $\dfrac{15x^2 - 10xy}{5x}$ 15. $\dfrac{34x^3 + 4x^2}{2x^2}$

16. $\dfrac{4x^2 y + 12xy^2}{4xy}$

17. $\dfrac{25a^3 b^2 - 50a^2 b^3}{25ab^2}$

18. $\dfrac{12ab^3 - 6a^3 b}{-3\,ab}$

19. $\dfrac{15xy^2 + 20}{5x}$

20. $\dfrac{22\,mn - 23}{-11n}$

21. $\dfrac{-16x^2 yz^2 - 4xy^2 z}{-8xyz}$

22. $\dfrac{4m^3 - 3m^2 + 5}{2m}$

23. $\dfrac{3x^4 - 5x^2 + 6}{6x}$

24. $\dfrac{6k^5 - k^4 + 3k^2 + 9k + 10}{3k^2}$

25. $\dfrac{3a^4 - 5a^3 + 6a^2 - 5a + 5}{5a^2}$

26. $\dfrac{24x^6 y^7 - 12x^5 y^{12} + 36xy}{48x^2 y^3}$

27. $\dfrac{15y^3 z^3 + 10y^4 z^6 - 20yz}{25yz^2}$

28. $\dfrac{22a^2 b + 11ab - 44ab^2}{11ab}$

29. $\dfrac{9p^2 q + 6pq - 3pq^2}{pq}$

30. $\dfrac{35x^2 y^2 + 7xy + 63x^3 y^3}{7xy}$

B. In exercises 31-34, identify the divisor, dividend, quotient, and remainder.

31. $(8k^4 - 12k^3 - 2k^2 + 7k - 6) \div (2k - 3) = 4k^3 - k + 2$

32. $(x^3 + 3x^2 + 3x + 1) \div (x + 1) = x^2 + 2x + 1$

33. $\dfrac{-6m - m^2 + m^4}{m^2 - 2} = m^2 + 1 + \dfrac{-6m + 2}{m^2 - 2}$

34. $\dfrac{x^5 + x^3 - 5x}{x^2 - 2} = x^3 + 3x + \dfrac{x}{x^2 - 2}$

In exercises 35-64, use long division to find the quotient and remainder.

35. $\dfrac{x^2 + 7x + 12}{x + 4}$

36. $\dfrac{x^3 + 5x + 6}{x - 4}$

37. $\dfrac{x^2 - 6x + 9}{x - 3}$

38. $\dfrac{x^3 + 6x - 8}{x + 2}$

39. $\dfrac{6y^2 - y - 12}{2y - 3}$

40. $\dfrac{10y^2 - 5y - 7}{2y - 5}$

41. $\dfrac{9t^2 + 2t^3 + 5t - 6}{2t + 3}$

42. $\dfrac{6x - 12x^2 + 8x^3 - 1}{2x - 1}$

43. $(x^2 - 14x + 49) \div (x - 7)$

44. $(y^2 - y - 6) \div (y - 3)$

45. $(4a^2 - 16) \div (2a + 4)$

46. $(6x^2 - 7x) \div (3x - 2)$

47. $(2a^2 - 9a + 8) \div (2a + 3)$

48. $(24 + 6x^2 + 25x) \div (3x - 1)$

49. $(5 - 23y + 12y^2) \div (4y - 1)$

50. $10y^2 + 5y + 1 \div (2y + 1)$

51. $\dfrac{3x^2 + 13x + 16x^4 + 3}{4x + 3}$

52. $\dfrac{8x^4 - 7x^2 + 6x^3 + x + 12}{2x - 1}$

53. $\dfrac{27a^3 + 8}{3a + 2}$

54. $\dfrac{8 - 27x^3}{2 - 3x}$

55. $\dfrac{x^4 - 1}{x^2 + 1}$

56. $\dfrac{1 - y^4}{1 - y^2}$

57. $\dfrac{t^5 - 32}{t - 2}$

58. $\dfrac{x^6 - 1}{x - 1}$

59. $2x + 3\overline{)6x^3 + 23x^2 + 27x + 9}$

60. $3y - 2\overline{)9y^3 + 6y^2 + 4y - 8}$

61. $2x + 5\overline{)16x^2 - 10x + 16x^3 - 5}$

62. $3x - 5\overline{)11x + 9x^3 - 9x^2 - 6}$

63. $\dfrac{2y^2 - 5y - 3}{2y + 4}$

64. $\dfrac{4 + 5y + 2y^2}{2y - 1}$

65. Find the polynomial, which when divided by $4x - 2$, yields the quotient $3x^2 - 7x + 5$?

66. Find the polynomial, which when divided by $x + 1$, yields the quotient $x^2 - x + 1$.

67. A polynomial, when divided by $4 - x^2$, yields $4x^3 - 7x + 2$ as the quotient and $2x - 3$ as the remainder. Find the polynomial.

68. What polynomial, when divided by $x^3 + 3$, yields the quotient $2x - 1$ and $3x + 4$ as the remainder?

5.7 SCIENTIFIC NOTATION

Scientific notation is a convenient way of expressing very large or very small numbers. In scientific notation numbers are written in the form $a \times 10^n$ where $1 \le |a| < 10$ and a is written in decimal form. Hence 4.32×10^{15} is the scientific notation for 4,320,000,000,000,000. Numbers in the form $1 \le |a| < 10$ have exactly one place to the left of the decimal point.

A. EXPRESS NUMBERS IN SCIENTIFIC NOTATION

Observe that:

a) $53.9 = 5.39 \times 10$

b) $539.72 = 5.3972 \times 10^2$

c) $.053 = 5.3 \times 10^{-2}$

d) $5.39 = 5.39 \times 10^0$

In each case the number on the right side of the equal sign is the scientific notation version of the number on the left side of the equal sign. These observations lead us to the following rule.

Rule: **To convert a number from standard notation to scientific notation,** *Step* **1** Move the decimal to the right of the first non zero digit. *Step* **2 a)** If the decimal was moved n places to the left then multiply by 10^n.   **b)** If the decimal was moved n places to the right then multiply by 10^{-n}.

EXAMPLE 1 Convert the following to scientific notation.

a. 37.54   **b.** 375.4   **c.** −3754

d. .3754   **e.** .03754   **f.** −.003754

Solutions:

a. 37.54: Move the decimal **to the left 1** digit and **multiply by 10^1.** Thus, $37.54 = 3.754 \times 10^1$

b. 375.4: Move the decimal **to the left 2** digits and **multiply by 10^2.** Thus, $375.4 = 3.754 \times 10^2$.

c. −3754.0: Move the decimal **to the left 3** digits and **multiply by 10^3.** Thus, $-3754 = -3.754 \times 10^3$.

d. .3754: Move the decimal **to the right 1** digit and **multiply by 10^{-1}.** Thus, $.3754 = 3.754 \times 10^{-1}$.

e. .03754: Move the decimal **to the right 2** places and **multiply by 10^{-2}.** Thus, $.03754 = 3.754 \times 10^{-2}$.

f. $-.003754$:   Move the decimal **to the right 3** places and **multiply by 10^{-3}.**

Thus, $-.003754 = -3.754 \times 10^{-3}$.

We may verify the answers with a calculator.
See also example 1 of section 5.7 in Appendix B.

B. CONVERTING FROM SCIENTIFIC NOTATION TO STANDARD NOTATION

To convert a number from scientific to standard notation, move the decimal point to the left if the exponent of 10 is negative and to right if the exponent of 10 is positive. The number of places moved corresponds to the absolute value of n, the power of 10.

$-4.6 \, E \, 8$ is the usual form found on a calculator display and represents the number -4.6×10^8 in scientific notation. This represents the number $-460,000,000$. Similarly $-4.6 \, E - 8$ represents -4.6×10^{-8}, which is equal to $-.000000046$.

WARM-UP

2. Convert into standard form.

   a. 3.5×10^{-3}

   b. 2.8×10^4

Answers:

2. a) 0.0035   b) 28000

EXAMPLE 2   Convert the following into standard notation.

a. 2.75×10^3 b. -4.03×10^{-4}

Solutions:

a. 2.75×10^3 :   Move the decimal in 2.75 three digits to the right.

$2.75 \times 10^3 = 2750$

b. -4.03×10^{-4}:   Move the decimal in -4.03 four digits to the left.

$-4.03 \times 10^{-4} = -.000403$

Notes

1. Multiplying by 10^{-4} is the same as multiplying by $\dfrac{1}{10^4}$ or dividing by 10,000.   This is the reason the decimal point moves to left.

2. If a is in standard form;
   $N = a \times 10^k$ for k positive implies $N > 10$
   $N = a \times 10^0$ implies $1 \le N < 10$
   $N = a \times 10^{-k}$ for k positive implies $0 < N < 1$

C.   APPLICATIONS

WARM-UP

3. A plane travels at 3,000 miles per hour. Express this value in scientific notation.

EXAMPLE 3   Light travels 300,000,000 meters per second. A light year is the distance that light travels in one year. Use scientific notation to express the number of meters traveled in one light year.

Solution:

$300,000,000 = 3.0 \times 10^8$

Number of seconds in one year $= 365 \times 24 \times 60 \times 60$

$= 31536000 = 3.1536 \times 10^7$ Express in scientific notation.

Number of meters traveled in one light year:

= (Number of meters traveled in one second)
  × (Number of seconds in one year)

= $(3 \times 10^8) \times (3.1536 \times 10^7)$

= $(3 \times 3.1536)10^{15}$ = $\mathbf{9.4608 \times 10^{15}}$ **meters**

Answer:

3. 3×10^3 mi/hr

EXERCISE 5.7

A. In exercises 1-26, write the given number in scientific notation.

1. 4501
2. 230.6
3. 95.37
4. 9.573
5. − 847.509
6. − 83.759

7. 400.09
8. 305.09
9. 0.034
10. 0.0027
11. 0.00809
12. 0.0207

13. 2,456,000
14. −75,000
15. 0.000043
16. 0.000076

17. −819,000,000
18. 0.00000093
19. 0.0529×10^5
20. 0.0238×10^4

21. 775×10^5
22. 17.23×10^4
23. 0.0037×10^{-3}
24. 0.027×10^{-2}

25. 0.000000678
26. 0.000625

B. In exercises 27-47, write the given number in standard notation.

27. 7.86×10^2
28. 58.6×10^3
29. 3.59×10^5
30. 32.9×10^4

31. 4.9705×10^4
32. 42.925×10^3
33. 5.2349×10^{-1}
34. 52.2596×10^{-2}

35. $- 3.457 \times 10^2$
36. $- 24.57 \times 10^3$
37. $- 3.456 \times 10^{-3}$
38. $- 2.234 \times 10^{-4}$

39. 5.7095×10^{-8}
40. 2.609×10^{-3}
41. 9.725×10^{-4}
42. 3.225×10^{-2}

43. 2.3×10^2
44. 4.56×10^3
45. 2.5×10^7
46. 6.71×10^{-8}
47. 7.13×10^{-10}

C. In exercises 48-51, use scientific notation to express the answer.

48. In chemistry, the molar mass = atomic mass × Avogadro's constant. Suppose the atomic mass of an element is 2.3244×10^{-26} kg and Avogardo's constant is $\dfrac{6.023 \times 10^{23}}{mol}$. Find the molar mass in terms of $\dfrac{kg}{mol}$.

49. Light travels 300,000,000 meters per second. Find the number of kilometers traveled in one hour.

    Hint: Change $\dfrac{3 \times 10^8 \text{ m}}{sec}$ to $\dfrac{kilometers}{hour}$.

50. If E = energy emitted by an oscillation and V = frequency of oscillation, then $E = kV$ where k is Planck's constant 6.626×10^{-24} J. Find E if $V = 1.25$ E 15/s in J (Joules).

51. The density of an object is $\dfrac{weight}{volume}$. If the density of an object is $3.25 \times 10^{-7} \dfrac{oz}{ft^3}$, and the volume is 2.2×10^3 ft^3, then find the weight.

5.8 CHAPTER SUMMARY

1.
$$2^5 \cdot 2^3 \;=\; 2^{5+3} = 2^8$$
$$(2^5)^4 \;=\; 2^{20}$$
$$(2x)^4 \;=\; 2^4\,x^4$$
$$\left(\frac{3}{p}\right)^4 \;=\; \frac{3^4}{p^4}$$

1. Assume that no denominator is zero. Then for integers m and n:

Rule
$$a^m \cdot a^n \;=\; a^{m+n}$$
$$(a^m)^n \;=\; a^{mn}$$
$$(ab)^m \;=\; a^m b^m$$
$$\left(\frac{a}{b}\right)^m \;=\; \frac{a^m}{b^m}$$

2. The degree of $4x^3 - 5x + 2$ is 3.

2. **The degree of a polynomial** is the maximum of the exponents in each term.

3.
$$(3x + 5x^2 + 3x - 7) + (x^3 + 5x - 4)$$
$$(3x^3 + 5x^2 + 3x - 7) + (x^3 + 5x - 4)$$
$$= (3 + 1)\,x^3 + 5x^2 + (3 + 5)\,x + (-7 - 4)$$
$$= 4x^3 + 5x^2 + 8x - 11$$

3. **Addition of polynomials:** Polynomials are added by combining their like terms.

4.
$$(2x^2 - 3x + 5) - (x^2 + 4x - 7)$$
$$(2x^2 - 3x + 5) - (x^2 + 4x - 7)$$
$$= 2x^2 - 3x + 5 + (-x^2 - 4x + 7)$$
$$= x^2 - 7x + 12$$

4. **Subtraction of polynomials:** Change the signs of the terms in the second polynomial (the one to be subtracted), and add the resulting polynomial and the first polynomial.

5. Evaluate $2x^2 + 5x - 7$ for $x = 2$
$$2(2)^2 + 5(2) - 7 = 8 + 10 - 7 = 11$$

5. **Evaluating a polynomial:** Evaluate a polynomial for a given value of the variable by direct substitution of the value for the variable.

6.
$$(x^2 + 2x + 3)\,(x + 5)$$
$$= x^2 \cdot x + x^2 \cdot 5 + 2x \cdot x + 2x \cdot 5 + 3 \cdot x + 3 \cdot 5$$
$$= x^3 + 5x^2 + 2x^2 + 10x + 3x + 15$$
$$= x^3 + 7x^2 + 13x + 15$$

6. **Multiplying two polynomials:**
Multiply each monomial in the first polynomial by each monomial in the second polynomial, and simplify by combining like terms.

7.
$$(3x + 5)(4x - 3)$$
$$= (3x)(4x) + (3x)(-3) \;+\; (5)(4x) \quad + (5)(-3)$$
First Terms Outer Terms Inner Terms Last Terms
$$= 12x^2 - 9x + 20x - 15 = 12x^2 + 11x - 15$$

7. **Multiplying two binomials:** Use the FOIL method to multiply the two binomials.

8. Special Products:

$$(a + b)^2 = a^2 + 2ab + b^2$$
$$(a - b)^2 = a^2 - 2ab + b^2$$
$$(a + b)(a - b) = a^2 - b^2$$

9. Integer Exponents: Assume $a \neq 0$, $b \neq 0$, and m and n are integers.

Rules:

$$a^{-n} = \frac{1}{a^n}$$
$$a^0 = 1$$
$$\frac{a^m}{a^n} = a^{m-n} = \frac{1}{a^{m-n}}$$
$$\left(\frac{a}{b}\right)^{-n} = \left(\frac{b}{a}\right)^n$$

10. Quotient of a polynomial and a monomial:

Divide each term of the polynomial by the monomial and simplify.

11. Quotient of a polynomial and a polynomial:

Perform division with polynomials similarly to long division with whole numbers.

$$\overset{\text{Quotient}}{\text{Divisor} \,)\, \overline{\text{Dividend}}}$$
$$\underline{\quad \cdots \cdots \quad}$$
$$\text{Remainder}$$

12. Writing in scientific notation:

Use a two step method

Step 1 Move the decimal to the right of the first non-zero digit.

Step 2 If the decimal is moved n digits to the left, multiply by 10^n. If the decimal is moved n places to the right multiply by 10^{-n}.

13.
To change scientific notation to standard notation: move the decimal point to the left if exponent of 10 is negative and to the right if the exponent is positive. The number of places moved corresponds to $|n|$ where n is the exponent of 10.

EXAMPLES

8.
$$(4x + 3y)^2 = (4x)^2 + 2(4x)(3y) + (3y)^2$$
$$= 16x^2 + 24xy + 9y^2$$
$$(3p - 5)^2 = (3p)^2 - 2(3p)(5) + (5)^2$$
$$= 9p^2 - 30p + 25$$
$$(3x + 5y)(3x - 5y) = (3x)^2 - (5y)^2$$
$$= 9x^2 - 25y^2$$

9.
$$3^{-5} = \frac{1}{3^5} = \frac{1}{243}$$
$$(-13)^0 = 1$$
$$\frac{5^7}{5^3} = 5^{7-3} = 5^4$$
$$\left(\frac{2}{3}\right)^{-2} = \left(\frac{3}{2}\right)^2 = \frac{3^2}{2^2} = \frac{9}{4}$$

10.
$$\frac{4x^3 - 6x^2 + 8x - 2}{2x}$$
$$= \frac{4x^3}{2x} - \frac{6x^2}{2x} + \frac{8x}{2x} - \frac{2}{2x}$$
$$= 2x^2 - 3x + 4 - \frac{1}{x}$$

11. Divisor × Quotient + Remainder = Dividend
$$\frac{\text{Dividend}}{\text{Divisor}} = \text{Quotient} + \frac{\text{Remainder}}{\text{Divisor}}$$

12. 0.00035 : Move the decimal to the right by 4 places and multiply by 10^{-4}

$$0.00035 = 3.5 \times 10^{-4}$$

456.9 : Move the decimal to the left by two places and multiply by 10^2

$$456.9 = 4.569 \times 10^2$$

13. $1.25 \times 10^4 = 12500$

$$1.25 \times 10^{-3} = .00125$$

5.9 REVIEW EXERCISES

In exercises 1-8, evaluate the numerical expression.

1. $\dfrac{2^3 \cdot 3^4}{4^2}$

2. $\dfrac{4^2 \cdot 3^3}{2^3}$

3. $\dfrac{-2^2 \cdot 5^3}{10^2}$

4. $\dfrac{-3^4 \cdot 5^4}{15^3}$

5. $\dfrac{(-2)^2 (-3)^3}{6^2}$

6. $\dfrac{(-4)^2 (-2)^3}{8^3}$

7. $(-5^3)^2 \left(\dfrac{2}{5}\right)^3$

8. $(3^2)^3 \left(-\dfrac{1}{3}\right)^3$

In exercises 9-16, write the expression in exponent form.

9. $(27x^2)(2xy)(3y)$

10. $(9b^3)(3bc^2)(2c^3)$

11. $3(2x^2)(2x)^2$

12. $5(3x)^2(3x^2)^2$

13. $\dfrac{x^3}{y^2} \cdot \dfrac{y^6}{x^9}$

14. $\dfrac{a^6}{b^5} \cdot \dfrac{b^3}{a^{-10}}$

15. $\dfrac{x}{y^2} \cdot \dfrac{y^4}{z^2} \cdot \dfrac{z}{x^3 z}$

16. $\dfrac{a^2}{b} \cdot \dfrac{b^2}{c^3} \cdot \dfrac{c^3}{ca^3}$

In exercises 17-20, evaluate the polynomial for the given value of x.

17. $5x^4 - 7x + 1$ for $x = 2$

18. $6x^5 - 7x^2 - 7x + 2$ for $x = -2$

19. $2x^3 - 4x^2 + 5$ for $x = -1$

20. $3y^3 + 2y - 6$ for $x = 3$

In exercises 21-24, write the polynomial in descending powers, and find its degree.

21. $4x^3 - 7x - 5x^7 + 3x^2 - 2$

22. $5x^4 - 4x^2 - 3x^3 - 5 - x$

23. $5x^5 - 7x + 5x^2 - 5 + 3x^4$

24. $6x^3 + 2x - 3x^2 + 4x^5 + 7$

In exercises 25-36, perform the indicated operations.

25. **Add** $3p^2 - 5p + 3$ and $4p^3 - 3p^2 + 2$

26. **Add** $2x^2 + 5x - 4$ and $3x^3 - 4x^2 + 5$

27. **Subtract** $3x^3 + 5x^2 + 4x$ from $4x^4 - 3x^2 + 7x$

28. **Subtract** $5z^3 - 6z^2 + 3z$ from $3z^5 - 2z^3 + 3z - 4$

29. **Subtract** $4p^3 - 3p^2 + 2p$ from $3p^2 - 5p + 3$

30. **Subtract** $5x^4 + 4x^3 - 2x$ from $x^5 + 5x^4 + 2x + 2$

31. **Multiply** $2x$ and $-7x^3$

32. **Multiply** $-3y$ and $-5y^6$

33. **Multiply** $4x^3$ and $(3x^2 - 5x + 2)$

34. **Multiply** $3a^2(5a^4 - 2a - 6)$

35. **Multiply** $(3x^3 + 5x + 1)(7x^2 - 2x)$

36. **Multiply** $(2y^4 - 3y - 1)$ and $(2y^3 + 5y)$

In exercises 37-40, use FOIL Method to find the product.

37. $(5y^2 - 3y)(3y - 2)$

38. $(3x^3 - x)(2x + 1)$

39. $(4x^2 + 3x)(3x - 5)$

40. $(4y^3 - 4y^2)(2y + 3)$

In exercises 41-48, simplify using special products.

41. $\left(\dfrac{4}{5}x + 3y^2\right)^2$ **42.** $\left(\dfrac{2}{3}y - 4x^2\right)^2$ **43.** $\left(\dfrac{3}{2}x^2 - 7\right)^2$ **44.** $\left(5a - \dfrac{2}{3}b^3\right)^2$

45. $(5x + 3y^2)(5x - 3y^2)$ **46.** $(2y - 5x^2)(2y + 5x^2)$

In exercises 47-54, simplify and write the answer with positive exponents.

47. $\dfrac{x^3 \cdot x^{-2}}{x^4}$ **48.** $\dfrac{a^{-5} \cdot a^4}{a^3}$ **49.** $\dfrac{a^{-2} \cdot b^3}{a^5 b^{-5}}$ **50.** $\dfrac{x^{-3} \cdot y^2}{x^2 y^3}$

51. $\dfrac{(2a^{-1})^2 \cdot (3a^{-2})}{b^{-4}b^2}$ **52.** $\dfrac{(3x^{-1})^3 \cdot (2x^{-1})^2}{y^2 y^{-3}}$ **53.** $\dfrac{(6p^{-2})(2q^{-5})^2}{p^{-3}(q^2)^4}$ **54.** $\dfrac{(3x^{-3})(2y^{-2})^3}{x^{-2}(y^{-3})^2}$

55. Write as the sum of three terms $\dfrac{4t^3 - 6t^2 + 8t}{6t^2}$.   **56.** Write as the sum of three terms $\dfrac{3t^5 - 5t^3 - 7}{7t^3}$.

In exercises 57-62, find the quotient and the remainder.

57. $\dfrac{4a^2 - 5a + 7}{2a - 3}$ **58.** $\dfrac{2x^2 - x - 3}{2x - 3}$ **59.** $\dfrac{5x^3 + 4x - 3}{x^2 - x - 1}$

60. $\dfrac{x^3 - 9x^2 + 17x - 4}{x - 2}$ **61.** $\dfrac{y^4 + 4y^3 + 6y^2 + 7}{y^2 + 2}$ **62.** $\dfrac{y^3 - 6y^2 + 13y - 9}{y^2 - 5y + 6}$

63. **Write in scientific notation.**   **(a)** 1,357,000   **(b)** 0.00357   **(c)** 12,345,600   **(d)** 0.0456

64. **Write without exponents.**   **(a)** $(3 \times 10^{-5})(2.7 \times 10^7)$ **(b)** $\dfrac{4 \times 10^5}{8 \times 10^8}$ **(c)** $(5 \times 10^3)(2.3 \times 10^{-5})$

5.10 SELF TEST

1. Simplify: $\dfrac{3^{-2} \cdot 5^3}{3 \cdot 5}$ **2.** Simplify: $\dfrac{4^3 \cdot 2^{-2}}{4 \cdot 2}$

3. Find the value of the polynomial $3x^3 + 2x^2 - x - 2$ for $x = -1$.

4. Find the value of the polynomial $3x^4 - 5x^2 - 2$ for $x = 2$.

5. Write in scientific notation: **(a)** 9784   **(b)** 0.000235   **(c)** 34.85   **(d)** 0.00321

6. Write in standard notation: **(a)** 2.7×10^5 **(b)** 9.8×10^{-3} **(c)** 2.9×10^{-4} **(d)** 8.7×10^2

In exercises 7-12, identify the resulting polynomial as monomial, binomial, trinomial, or a polynomial? Find the degree of each.

7. $(3x^2 + 5x - 7) + (4x^2 + 1)$ **8.** $(4y^3 + 2y + 7) + (3y - 7)$ **9.** $(2x + 1)(2x - 1)$

10. $(3y + 5)(3y + 4)$ **11.** $(3x^2)(5x^3)$ **12.** $(4a^3)(-5x^3)$

13. Add: $4x^3 + 7x - 1$ and $5x^4 + 9x^2 + 8x + 4$ **14. Add:** $3x^3 + 6x^2 + 6$ and $2x^4 + 3x^3 + 7x - 6$

15. Subtract: $5x^3 - 7x^2 + 2$ and $3x^2 + 5x - 1$ **16. Subtract:** $9x^4 - 7x^3 - 4$ and $9x^3 + x^2 - 4$

17. Simplify: $(5x^3 + 2x^2 - 3x) - (2x^4 + 4x^2 - 2x + 1) + (x^4 + 2x + 2)$

18. Simplify: $(x^4 - x^3 - x^2 - 1) + (x^4 + x^3 + x^2 - 1) - (2x^4 - x^3 - 2x^2 + 1)$

19. Multiply: $5x^3(-3x^4 + 2x^2 - 3)$ **20. Multiply:** $6y^2(y^3 - 2y^2 - y + 6)$

21. Multiply: $(3x^2 + 5x - 7)(4x^3 + 6x + 1)$ **22. Multiply:** $(4 + x^2 + 2x)$ by $(x - 2)$

23. Write as a sum of four terms $\dfrac{-6x^3 + 8x^2 + 8x - 2}{2x^2}$.

24. Divide $3x^3 + 5x^2 + 6x + 3$ by $5x$ and find the quotient and remainder.

25. Find the quotient and remainder $(15x^5 - 7x^3 + 8x^2 + 9) \div (x^2 + x + 1)$.

26. Divide $31x - 12x^2 - 35 + 8x^4 + 8x^3$ by $3x + 2x^2 - 5$.

Factoring and Quadratic Equations

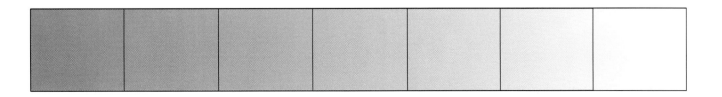

The window shown contains:

A0622Disc

File View Control Debug

Objective: Factoring Trinomials of the Type $ax^2 + bx + c$, where $a \neq 0$ and $a \neq 1$

Verify Skill   Discussion   Example

After adequate practice one can factor trinomials of the type $ax^2 + bx + c$ directly using mental calculations. The thought process is demonstrated in the following illustrations.

Factor of a

$ax^2 + bx + c = (\Box x + \Box)(\Box x + \Box)$

Factor of c

For example   Factors of 6

$6x^2 + 7x + 2 = (3x + 2)(2x + 1)$

Factor of 2

Inner product

$ax^2 + bx + c = (\Box x + \Box)(\Box x + \Box)$

Outer product

Inner product + outer product = bx

Inner product = $4x$

$6x^2 + 7x + 2 = (3x + 2)(2x + 1)$

Outer product = $3x$

Inner product + outer product = $7x$

Note: The objective is to find a combination of factors of a and c such that the outer and inner products add up to the middle term **bx**.

Note

Copyright © 2005 Educo International, Inc.

6.1 **Factors, Greatest Common Factor (GCF)**

6.2 **Factoring Trinomials**

6.3 **Special Factorization**

6.4 **Solving Quadratic Equations by Factoring**

6.5 **Applications of Quadratic Equations**

6.6 **Chapter Summary**

6.7 **Review Exercises**

6.8 **Self Test**

FACTORING AND QUADRATIC EQUATIONS

INTRODUCTION

In Chapters 1, 2, and 3 we learned about algebraic expressions and the difference between algebraic expressions and equations. In this chapter, we will discuss procedures for expressing polynomials of degree two or three as products of simple polynomials. This process is generally referred to as *factoring*. We will then use these factoring procedures to solve equations of degree two, a process which is called solving quadratic equations by factoring.

This chapter is divided into the following sections.

    6.1 *Factors, Greatest Common Factor (GCF);*

    6.2 *Factoring Trinomials;*

    6.3 *Special Factorization;*

    6.4 *Solving Quadratic Equations by Factoring; and*

    6.5 *Applications of Quadratic Equations.*

6.1 FACTORS, GREATEST COMMON FACTOR (GCF)

Recall that when two or more numbers, variables or algebraic expressions are multiplied, each is called a **factor**.

$$7 \cdot 11 \qquad 4y^3 \cdot 13x^5 \qquad (5x - 5)(3x - 8)$$

   ↑   ↑   ↑   ↑   ↑   ↑
factor factor   factor factor   factor factor

OBJECTIVES ■■■■

Upon completion of this section you will be able to:

A. Find the Greatest Common Factor of the terms of a polynomial;

B. Factor out the Greatest Common Factor; and

C. Factor a polynomial by grouping.

When we are asked to factor a number or an algebraic expression, we are being asked, "What factors, when multiplied, will give that number or expression?" For example, we can factor 77 as $7 \cdot 11$ since $7 \cdot 11 = 77$.

We can factor $21x^7$ as $3x^3 \cdot 7x^4$ since $3x^3 \cdot 7x^4 = 21x^7$.

Factoring is simply the reverse of multiplying.

The factors of $2x^2 + 6xy + 12xy^2$ are not so easy to recognize. In this chapter, we will be learning techniques for finding the factors of a polynomial. We will begin with greatest common factors.

A. GREATEST COMMON FACTOR

A **common factor** of two or more integers is an integer which is a factor of each of the given integers.

The largest of all common factors of a set of numbers is called their **greatest common factor (GCF).**

1. Find the greatest common factor of 22, 165, and 33.

2. Find the greatest common factor of:

   a) 12, 36

   b) 28, 20

   c) 15, 45, and 60

3. Find the greatest common factor of:

   a) $3x^3, 12x, 18x^4$

EXAMPLE 1   Find the greatest common factor of 12, 32, and 40.

Solution:

The factors of 12 are   **1, 2**, 3, **4**, 6, 12.

The factors of 32 are   **1, 2, 4**, 8, 16, 32.

The factors of 40 are   **1, 2, 4**, 5, 8, 10, 20, 40.

4 is the largest number that divides evenly the three given numbers.

Thus, the greatest common factor of 12, 32, and 40 is 4.

If there is no common prime factor, we say GCF is 1.

EXAMPLE 2   Find the greatest common factor of:

   a. 18, 35   **b.** 48, 40   **c.** 20, 16, 24

Solutions:

   a. $\mathbf{18} = 2 \cdot 3 \cdot 3,$ $\mathbf{35} = 5 \cdot 7$

   There are no common prime factors.

   Therefore, the GCF of 18 and 35 is **1**.

   b. $\mathbf{48} = 2 \cdot 2 \cdot 2 \cdot 2 \cdot 3,$ $\mathbf{40} = 2 \cdot 2 \cdot 2 \cdot 5$

   $= \mathbf{8} \cdot 6$ $= \mathbf{8} \cdot 5$

   The GCF of 48 and 40 is **8**.

   c. $\mathbf{20} = \mathbf{2 \cdot 2} \cdot 5,$ $\mathbf{16} = \mathbf{2 \cdot 2} \cdot 2 \cdot 2,$ $\mathbf{24} = \mathbf{2 \cdot 2} \cdot 2 \cdot 3$

   $= \mathbf{4} \cdot 5$ $= \mathbf{4} \cdot 4$ $= \mathbf{4} \cdot 6$

   The greatest common factor of 20, 16, and 24 is **4**.

EXAMPLE 3   Find the greatest common factor of:

   a. $12x^3, 45x^8, -9x^2$

   b. x^3y^2, x^4y^5, xy^6

   c. $6x^2y^3, 8x^2, 24x^3y$

Solutions:

   a.   Factor out each term completely.

   $12x^3 = 2 \cdot 2 \cdot 3 \cdot x \cdot x \cdot x = \mathbf{3x^2} \cdot 4x$

   $45x^8 = \mathbf{3} \cdot 3 \cdot 5 \cdot \mathbf{x} \cdot \mathbf{x} \cdot x \cdot x \cdot x \cdot x \cdot x \cdot x = \mathbf{3x^2} \cdot 15x^6$

   $-9x^2 = -3 \cdot \mathbf{3} \cdot \mathbf{x} \cdot \mathbf{x} = \mathbf{3x^2}(-3)$

   The greatest common factor of $12x^3, 45x^8,$ and $-9x^2$ is $\mathbf{3x^2}$.

   Before working on b) and c) parts, we list the steps for finding the greatest common factor of monomials.

Step 1　Find the greatest common factor of the numerical coefficients of the monomials.

Step 2　Find the smallest exponent on each variable. Write the product of the variables raised to its respective minimum exponent.

Step 3　The greatest common factor is the product of the quantities determined in steps 1 and 2.

b. **Monomials:** $x^3 y^2$, $x^4 y^5$, xy^6.

    Step 1　Coefficients: 1, 1, 1

             Greatest common factor of coefficients is 1.

    Step 2　The minimum exponent on x is 1 and on y is 2.

             Hence, the common variable part is $x^1 y^2$.

             The greatest common factor is $1 \cdot xy^2$ or $\boldsymbol{xy^2}$.

c. **Monomials:** $6x^2y^3$, $8x^2$, and $24x^3y$.

    Step 1　Find the greatest common factor of coefficients 6, 8, and 24:

$$6 = \mathbf{2} \cdot 3$$
$$8 = \mathbf{2} \cdot 4$$
$$24 = \mathbf{2} \cdot 12$$

             The GCF of 6, 8, and 12 is 2.

    Step 2　The minimum exponent of x is 2. The variable y is not present in each monomial, therefore, y is not a factor in GCF.

    Step 3　The greatest common factor is $\boldsymbol{2x^2}$.

B. FACTORING OUT THE GREATEST COMMON FACTOR

The greatest common factor for a polynomial is the largest monomial that divides (is a factor of) each term of the polynomial.

The greatest common factor of the terms of a polynomial can be used to write the polynomial in factored form. To accomplish this, we use the distributive property "backwards".

For example, consider the polynomial $8x^3 - 12x^2$. The greatest common factor of its terms, $8x^3$ and $-12x^2$, is $\boldsymbol{4x^2}$.

Thus,　　$8x^3 - 12x^2 = (\boldsymbol{4x^2})\,(2x) - (\boldsymbol{4x^2})\,(3)$

                    $= \boldsymbol{4x^2}\,(2x - 3)$　　　Distributive Property.

To factor out the greatest common factor of a polynomial:

> **Step 1**   Find the greatest common factor of the terms of the polynomial.
>
> **Step 2**   Write each term with the greatest common factor, obtained in Step 1, as a factor and use the distributive property backwards.

4. Factor out the greatest common factor.

a) $2x^3 + 12x^2 - 6x^4$

b) $35x^3y + 14xy^2$

c) $3a(a^2 + 4) - 2(a^2 + 4)$

d) $15a^2 + 105b + 35d$

EXAMPLE 4   Factor out the greatest common factor.

     a. $15x^5 + 25x^3 - 45x^2$ **b.** $25r^3s + 15rs^3$

     c. $2a(a + 4) - (a + 4)$ **d.** $10a^2 + 12b + 14$

Solutions:

a. $15x^5 + 25x^3 - 45x^2$

Step 1   The terms of the polynomial are $15x^5, 25x^3, -45x^2$.

The greatest common factor of 15, 25, and 45 is **5**.

The minimum of the exponents of x is **2**.

Therefore, the greatest common factor of the terms is $\mathbf{5x^2}$.

Step 2 $15x^5 + 25x^3 - 45x^2$

$= \mathbf{(5x^2)}(3x^3) + \mathbf{(5x^2)}(5x) - \mathbf{(5x^2)}(9)$ Factor out G.C.F.

$= \mathbf{(5x^2)}(3x^3 + 5x - 9)$ Distributive property.

b. $\mathbf{25r^3s + 15rs^3}$

Step 1   The two terms of the polynomial are $25r^3s$ and $15rs^3$.

The greatest common factor of the two terms is $\mathbf{5rs}$.

Step 2 $25r^3s + 15rs^3$

$= \mathbf{(5rs)}(5r^2) + \mathbf{(5rs)}(3s^2)$ Factor out G.C.F.

$= \mathbf{5rs}(5r^2 + 3s^2)$ Distributive property.

c. $\mathbf{2a(a + 4) - (a + 4) = 2a(a + 4) - 1(a + 4)}$

$\mathbf{a + 4}$ is the greatest common factor of $2a(a + 4)$ and $1(a + 4)$.

Thus, $2a(a + 4) - 1(a + 4) = (a + 4)(2a - 1)$

d. $\mathbf{10a^2 + 12b + 14}$

The three terms are $10a^2$, $12b$, and 14.

The greatest common factor is **2**.

$$10a^2 + 12b + 14 = \mathbf{2}(5a^2) + \mathbf{2}(6b) + \mathbf{2} \cdot (7)$$

$$= \mathbf{2}(5a^2 + 6b + 7)$$

- It is important to understand the importance of "factoring out a minus sign". This will help us avoid making errors later in some complicated situations.

$$-a - b = -1(a + b) = -(a + b)$$

$$-a + b = -1(a - b) = -(a - b)$$

Change each sign when factoring out a minus sign.

EXAMPLE 5   Factor out the minus sign.

   a. $-x - 5$ **b.** $-x + 5$ **c.** $-5p + 20$

Solutions:

a. $-x - 5 = -1(x + 5) = -(x + 5)$

b. $-x + 5 = -1(x - 5) = -(x - 5)$

c. $-5p + 20 = (-5)p + (-5)(-4)$
$$= -5(p + (-4)) = -5(p - 4)$$

C. FACTOR BY GROUPING

Let us examine the expression $3a(a^2 + 4) - 2(a^2 + 4)$.

We can multiply, using distributive property, to obtain:

$$3a(a^2 + 4) - 2(a^2 + 4) = 3a^3 - 2a^2 + 12a - 8$$

We cannot factor the polynomial on right side by factoring out the greatest common factor. However, we know that it can be factored as $(a^2 + 4)(3a - 2)$. How do we get this factorization if we start with the polynomial $3a^3 - 2a^2 + 12a - 8$ instead? We can *rewrite* the polynomial as

$$3a^3 - 2a^2 + 12a - 8 = (3a^3 - 2a^2) + (12a - 8)$$
$$= a^2(3a - 2) + 4(3a - 2)$$
$$= (a^2 + 4)(3a - 2)$$

Factor each of the two groups.

This process of factoring an expression in groups of terms is called **factoring by grouping.**

Notes

1. There is no hard and fast rule for factoring by grouping. The terms should be so grouped that the different groups have a factor in common.

2. There are many polynomials which cannot be factored at all. A polynomial that cannot be factored is called a *prime polynomial*.

EXAMPLE 6   Factor the following by grouping.

   a. $3x + 5 + 9ax + 15a$

   b. $y^2 + 4y + 8y + 32$

   c. $3ab - 8a - 6b + 16$

WARM-UP

Solutions:

Method 1	Method 2

a. $3x + 5 + 9ax + 15a$

$= (3x+5) + (9ax + 15a)$

$= 1 \cdot (\mathbf{3x + 5}) + 3a(\mathbf{3x + 5})$

$= (1 + 3a)(\mathbf{3x + 5})$

a. $3x + 5 + 9ax + 15a$

$= (3x + 9ax) + (5 + 15a)$

$= 3x(\mathbf{1 + 3a}) + 5(\mathbf{1 + 3a})$

$= (3x + 5)(\mathbf{1 + 3a})$

Method 1	Method 2

b) $x^2 + 6x + x + 6$

b. $y^2 + 4y + 8y + 32$

$= (y^2 + 4y) + (8y + 32)$

$= y(\mathbf{y + 4}) + 8(\mathbf{y + 4})$

$= (y + 8)(\mathbf{y + 4})$

b. $y^2 + 4y + 8y + 32$

$= (y^2 + 8y) + (4y + 32)$

$= y(\mathbf{y + 8}) + 4(\mathbf{y + 8})$

$= (y + 4)(\mathbf{y + 8})$

c) $x^3 + 2x^2 + x + 2$

c. $3ab - 8a - 6b + 16$

$= (3ab - 8a) - (6b - 16)$*

$= a(\mathbf{3b - 8}) - 2(\mathbf{3b - 8})$

$= (a - 2)(\mathbf{3b - 8})$

c. $3ab - 8a - 6b + 16$

$= 3ab - 6b - 8a + 16$

$= (3ab - 6b) - (8a - 16)$

$= 3b(\mathbf{a - 2}) - 8(\mathbf{a - 2})$

$= (3b - 8)(\mathbf{a - 2})$

Answers:

6. a) $(2a + 1)(5x + 3)$

   b) $(x + 1)(x + 6)$

   c) $(x^2 + 1)(x + 2)$

* **Note** that: $-6b + 16 = -1(6b - 16)$

$= -(6b - 16)$

Reverse distributive property.

EXERCISE 6.1

A. In exercises 1-12, find the greatest common factor.

1. $4, 30, 42$ **2.** $15, 30, 65$ **3.** $30, 45, 75$ **4.** $6, 9, 72$

5. $36, 48m, 60m^2$ **6.** $15, 45x^2, 75x^3$ **7.** $15m, 12n^2, 30p$ **8.** $4x, 24y^2, 30z$

9. $16m^2n^3, 36m^3n^5, 24mn^2$ **10.** $20ab^2, 30a^2b, 60a^2b^2$ **11.** $28x^4y^3, 42x^3y^2, 63xy^5$ **12.** $18y^2z^2, 24yz, 30y^4z^4$

In exercises 13-20, identify the missing factor.

13. $36 = 4(\ )$ **14.** $45 = 9(\ )$ **15.** $5x^2 = x(\ )$ **16.** $15y^4 = y^2(\ )$

17. $3x^4y^5 = 3x^2(\ )$ **18.** $3yz^4 = z^2(\ )$ **19.** $24p^4q^5 = 3p^3q^2(\ )$ **20.** $15x^3y^2 = 5xy(\ )$

In exercises 21-28, determine whether or not the expression is completely factored.

21. $3a^2 + 4a$

22. $5x^2 - 7x^3$

23. $4(3x^2y - 2x)$

24. $3(4a^2b - 6a)$

25. $(3p - q)(p + q)$

26. $(2x + y)(x - 2y)$

27. $2(m - 1) + mn(m - 1)$

28. $3(x + 2y) + 5m(x + 2y)$

B. In exercises 29-66, factor out the greatest common factor and write the expression in factored form. Use the distributive property to verify your answer.

29. $4x + 6x^3$

30. $6x^3 + 9x$

31. $28x^2 + 42x^3$

32. $24x - 36x^4$

33. $8y^3 - 4y^5$

34. $10z^4 - 25z^6$

35. $11y^2 - 12z^3$

36. $9x^3 + 12y^3$

37. $2a + 2$

38. $3b - 3$

39. $16 - 4y$

40. $12 + 12x^2$

41. $7x^2 - 21x$

42. $2x^4 - 4x$

43. $3a^4 - 9a^2$

44. $2x^2y - 3x^3y^2$

45. $5x^2y - 7ab^3$

46. $6a^2b^3 - 12b$

47. $18x^2y^2 - 9a^2b^2$

48. $3x^3 + 6x^2 + 9x$

49. $5y^3 - 20y^2 + 10y$

50. $3a^4 - 9a^3 - 6a^2$

51. $2x^5 - 3x^4 + 2x^3$

52. $4x^5y^5 - 8x^4y^4 + x^3y^3$

53. $25m^5 - 50m^4 + 100m^3$

54. $9x^3 - 12x^5 + 24x^6$

55. $45m^2n^3 - 36mn^2 + 63m^3n$

56. $12x^3y^2 + 15xy^2 - 21x^2y$

57. $3a(1 - 5b) - 4b(1 - 5b)$

58. $3x(y - 5) - 5y(y - 5)$

59. $r(r - 2s) - s(2s - r)$

60. $a(a - 2b) + b(2b - a)$

61. $a(x - 4) - b(x - 4)$

62. $b(y + 2) - 3a(y + 2)$

63. $c(a - 2) - b(2 - a)$

64. $a(x - y) + 2b(y - x)$

65. $4x(2 + c) - 3y(c + 2)$

66. $6y(a + 4b) - 2x(4b + a)$

In exercises 67-72, factor out the "minus sign" and any other common factor.

67. $x - 3$

68. $-y - 5$

69. $-x^2 - 5x$

70. $-3y + 3$

71. $-10x + 15$

72. $-5x - 10$

C. In exercises 73-90, factor by grouping.

73. $x^2 + 5y - xy - 5x$

74. $y^2 - 3y + xy - 3x$

75. $ar + br - a - b$

76. $xy - xb + y - b$

77. $x^2 + 2xy + 3x + 6y$

78. $x^3 + x^2 + x + 1$

79. $x^2y - x^2 - 3y + 3$

80. $y^3 - y^2 + y - 1$

81. $x^4 - 2x^3 + x^2 + x - 1$
   [Split $-2x^3 = -x^3 - x^3$]

82. $2y^2 + 6y + 5y + 15$

83. $3a^2 + 3ab - ab - b^2$

84. $2a^2 - 2ab - 3ab + 3b^2$

85. $2y^2 + 5y + 6y + 15$

86. $3p - pq + 3pq - q^2$

87. $2x^2 - 3xy - 2xy + 3y^2$

88. $a^2 + b^2 + 2ab + 2bc + 2ca$

89. $m^4 + 4m^3 + 4m^2 + 2m + 4$
   [Split $4m^3 = 2m^3 + 2m^3$]

90. $a^3 + a - 3a^2 - 3$

6.2 FACTORING TRINOMIALS

Upon completion of this section you will be able to:

A. Factoring trinomials of the type $x^2 + bx + c$;

B. Factoring trinomials of the type $ax^2 + bx + c$; and

C. Factoring those trinomials which can be reduced to the above forms.

In this section, you will learn how to factor trinomials of the form $ax^2 + bx + c$, where a, b, and c are integers.

From section 5.3, we know the product of two binomials is often a trinomial. Recall, the process in the following illustrations.

Two Binomials	By the FOIL Method	Trinomial
$(x + 1)(x - 5)$ =	$x^2 - 5x + 1x - 5$ =	$x^2 - 4x - 5$
$(x - 6)(x - 6)$ =	$x^2 - 6x - 6x + 36$ =	$x^2 - 12x + 36$
$(x - 1)(x + 5)$ =	$x^2 + 5x - 1x - 5$ =	$x^2 + 4x - 5$
$(x - 9)(x - 3)$ =	$x^2 - 3x - 9x + 27$ =	$x^2 - 12x + 27$
$(x + p)(x + q)$ =	$x^2 + px + qx + pq$ =	$x^2 + \underbrace{(p + q)}_{\text{sum}}x + \underbrace{pq}_{\text{product}}$

In these illustrations, we start from two binomials of the type $(x + p)$ and $(x + q)$ and we have seen, by using FOIL method, that their product is a trinomial $x^2 + (p + q)x + pq$. In this section, we shall do the reverse operations given the trinomial to find the factors.

A. FACTORING TRINOMIALS OF THE TYPE $x^2 + bx + c$.

Recall: $(x + p)(x + q) = x^2 + (p + q)x + pq$

If we shift sides of this equation we obtain:

$$x^2 + (p + q)x + pq = (x + p)(x + q)$$
$$\downarrow \qquad \downarrow \qquad \downarrow \qquad \downarrow$$
$$x^2 + bx + c = (x + ?)(x + ?)$$

The factors on the right are determined if we know two numbers p and q whose **product is** c, the constant term, and **sum is** b, the coefficient of x. This process is illustrated in the following examples.

1. Factor:

   a) $x^2 - 3x - 4$

EXAMPLE 1   Factor: **a.** $x^2 - 5x + 4$ **b.** $x^2 + 8x + 12$

                   c. $x^2 - 12x - 28$

Solutions:

   a. $x^2 - 5x + 4$

You need to find two numbers whose product is 4 and whose sum is -5. The list of all possible two factor products is:

$$4 \cdot 1 = 4 \ , \qquad (-2)(-2) = 4$$
$$2 \cdot 2 = 4 \ , \qquad \mathbf{(-4)(-1) = 4}$$

Verify that the factors -4 and -1 satisfy both the requirements.

$$(-4) \cdot (-1) = 4 \text{ (the last term)}$$

and $(-4) + (-1) = -5$ (the coefficient of middle term).

Therefore, $x^2 - 5x + 4 = (x - 4)(x - 1)$

Always pay special attention to the sign of your numbers. Remember to use the FOIL Method to check your factors.

b. $x^2 + 8x + 12$

You need to find two numbers whose *product* is 12 and whose *sum* is 8. Let's first look at some factors of 12.

$$1 \cdot 12 = 12, \quad \text{and} \quad 1 + 12 = 13$$
$$\mathbf{2 \cdot 6 \ = 12} \quad \text{and} \quad \mathbf{2 + 6 \ = 8}$$
$$3 \cdot 4 \ = 12 \quad \text{and} \quad 3 + 4 \ = 7$$

Factors 6 and 2 satisfy both the requirements.

Therefore, $x^2 + 8x + 12 = (x + 6)(x + 2)$

Remember to always check your factors using the FOIL Method.

c. $x^2 - 12x - 28$

Since the second and third terms are negative, special attention to signs is needed when factoring.

You need two numbers whose product is -28 (last term) and whose sum is -12 (coefficient of the middle term). Let us list some factors of -28.

$$1 \cdot (-28) = -28 \quad \text{and} \quad 1 + (-28) = -27$$
$$\mathbf{2 \cdot (-14) = -28} \quad \text{and} \quad \mathbf{2 + (-14) \ = -12}$$

Factors 2 and -14 satisfy both the requirements.

Therefore, $x^2 - 12x - 28 = (x + 2)(x - 14)$

WARM-UP

b) $x^2 + 7x + 6$

c) $x^2 - 5x + 6$

With practice, you will be able to narrow the list of possible factors whose sum can be tested to determine the correct factorization. The following observations will, however, help facilitate the process.

Observation   **1.**   To factor $x^2 + bx + c$, you need to find two numbers whose product is **c** and whose sum is **b**.

- If c is positive, the two factors must have like signs. This sign will be the same sign as the sign of b.
- If c is negative, then the two factors will have different signs.
- Always check your answer using the distributive property or by using the FOIL Method.

Often, all the terms of trinomials have common factors. You should always factor out whatever is common in all the terms and then factor the remaining trinomial. This two stage process is called *factoring completely*. For example, the trinomial $3y^2 + 6y - 45$ has a common factor of 3.

Therefore, $3y^2 + 6y - 45 = \mathbf{3}y^2 + \mathbf{3} \cdot 2y - \mathbf{3} \cdot 15 = \mathbf{3}(y^2 + 2y - 15)$ Factor the trinomial.

$$= 3(y + 5)(y - 3)$$ $5(-3) = -15$ and $5 + (-3) = 2$

EXAMPLE 2   Factor the following trinomials completely.

     a. $9x^2 + 27x + 18$ **b.** $6 - 2x^2 - 4x$

Solutions:

   a.   In $9x^2 + 27x + 18$, each term has a common factor of 9.

$$9x^2 + 27x + 18 = \mathbf{9}x^2 + \mathbf{9} \cdot 3x + \mathbf{9} \cdot 2$$

$$= \mathbf{9}(x^2 + 3x + 2)$$ Factor the trinomial.

$$= 9(x + 2)(x + 1)$$ $2 \cdot 1 = 2$ and $2 + 1 = 3$.

- If the terms of the trinomial are not written in standard form, then the terms should be rearranged in the descending order of exponents. If the coefficient of the quadratic term (the x^2 term) is negative, then factor out a negative factor.

   b. $6 - 2x^2 - 4x$ Rearrange with exponents in descending order.

$$= -2x^2 - 4x + 6$$ Factor out -2.

$$= -2(x^2 + 2x - 3)$$ Factor the trinomial.

$$= -2(x + 3)(x - 1)$$ $3 \cdot (-1) = -3$ and $3 + (-1) = 2$.

B.   **FACTORING TRINOMIALS OF THE TYPE** $ax^2 + bx + c$, **WHERE** $a \neq 0$ **AND** $a \neq 1$.

Let us consider, again, the process of multiplying two binomials using FOIL Method.

$$\begin{array}{cccc} \text{F} & \text{O} & \text{I} & \text{L} \end{array}$$
$$(2x + 1)(3x + 2) = \ \ 6x^2 + 4x + 3x + 2$$

Switching the sides of this equation, we get:

$$6x^2 + 7x + 2 = (6x^2 + 4x + 3x + 2) = (2x + 1)(3x + 2)$$

$$(6x^2 + 4x) + (3x + 2)$$

$$2x(3x + 2) + 1(3x + 2)$$

$$(2x + 1)(3x + 2)$$

Observe that the trinomial $6x^2 + 7x + 2$ can be re-written by splitting the middle term into two parts,

$$6x^2 + \boxed{7x} + 2$$

$$= 6x^2 + (4x + 3x) + 2$$

giving us four terms. These four terms can be regrouped, as shown in the illustrations, so that we may factor the trinomial by grouping.

The primary objective here is to understand how to rewrite the *middle term bx*. In general, to factor a trinomial of the form $ax^2 + bx + c$, *choose factors of the product ac* that *add up to b*, then use these factors to rewrite the middle term **bx**, as explained in the following example.

EXAMPLE 3   Factor the following polynomials.

    a. $3x^2 + 7x + 4$ **b.** $4a^2 + 4a - 3$

    c. $25x + 10x^2 - 15$

Solutions:

a. $3x^2 + 7x + 4$: Compare it with $ax^2 + bx + c$.

In this trinomial $a = 3$ and $c = 4$, so $ac = (3)(4) = 12$. What two factors of **12** will add up to be 7, the coefficient of the middle term ? **STOP and THINK.**

The factors are **3** and **4**. To factor by grouping, the middle term must be rewritten using these numbers.

$$
\begin{aligned}
3x^2 + 7x + 4 &= 3x^2 + 3x + 4x + 4 && \text{Rewrite middle term.}\\
&= (3x^2 + 3x) + (4x + 4) && \text{Group terms.}\\
&= 3x(x + 1) + 4(x + 1) && \text{Distributive property.}\\
&= (x + 1)(3x + 4) && \text{Distributive property.}
\end{aligned}
$$

So, the trinomial $3x^2 + 7x + 4 = (x + 1)(3x + 4)$. Use the FOIL Method to verify that the product is equal to the given trinomial.

b. $4a^2 + 4a - 3$: Compare it with $ax^2 + bx + c$.

In this trinomial $ac = (4)(-3) = -12$. What two factors of -12 add up to **4**, the coefficient of the middle term ?

STOP and THINK.

The factors are **6** and -2.

Rewrite the middle term using **6** and **−2.**

$$
\begin{aligned}
4a^2 + 4a - 3 &= 4a^2 + 6a - 2a - 3 && \text{Rewrite middle term.}\\
&= (4a^2 + 6a) + (-2a - 3) && \text{Group terms.}\\
&= 2a(2a + 3) - 1(2a + 3) && \text{Distributive property.}\\
&= (2a - 1)(2a + 3) && \text{Distributive property.}
\end{aligned}
$$

Hence, the factored form of

    $4a^2 + 4a - 3$ is $(2a + 3)(2a - 1)$

c) $15x + 9x^2 - 6$

Use the FOIL Method to verify that the product is equal to the given trinomial.

c. **$25x + 10x^2 - 15$:**

First, let's rewrite this trinomial so the exponents are in descending order.

$25x + 10x^2 - 15 = 10x^2 + 25x - 15$

Observe that all the terms of this trinomial have **5** as a common factor.

$5(2x^2 + 5x - 3)$ Factor out the common factor 5.

Compare: $2x^2 + 5x - 3$ with $ax^2 + bx - c$

$$ac = -6, \text{ and } b = 5$$

What two factors of -6 add up to 5?   **Stop and Think**

The factors are $+6$ and -1. Rewrite the middle term using 6 and -1.

$$2x^2 + 5x - 3 = 2x^2 + 6x - x - 3$$
$$= 2x(x + 3) - 1(x + 3)$$
$$= (x + 3)(2x - 1)$$

Hence, the factored form of $10x^2 + 25x - 15$

$$= 5(2x^2 + 5x - 3)$$
$$= 5(x + 3)(2x - 1)$$

Answers:

3. **a)** $(2x + 3)(x - 5)$
   b) $(2a + 3)(3a - 1)$
   c) $3(x + 2)(3x - 1)$

Direct Method of factoring $ax^2 + bx + c$

After adequate practice one can factor trinomials of the type $ax^2 + bx + c$ directly using mental calculations. The thought process is demonstrated in the following illustrations.

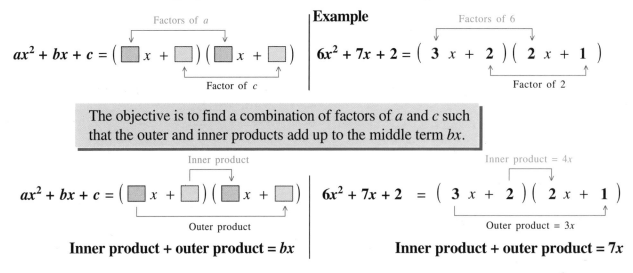

> The objective is to find a combination of factors of a and c such that the outer and inner products add up to the middle term bx.

Inner product + outer product = bx   **Inner product + outer product = $7x$**

Note: Most people often make more than one guess before they come up with the correct combination.

C. MISCELLANEOUS EXAMPLES [HIGHER DEGREE]

EXAMPLE 4   Factor the following.

     a. $x^3 - 6x^2 + 5x$ **b.** $2a^4 + 4a^3 - 30a^2$

     c. $2x^3 - 3x^2 + 2x - 3$

Solutions:

a. $x^3 - 6x^2 + 5x = x(x^2 - 6x + 5)$

     Now we factor $x^2 - 6x + 5$. $(-5)(-1) = 5$, $(-5) + (-1) = -6$

$$= (x - 1)(x - 5)$$

     Therefore, $x^3 - 6x^2 + 5x = x(x^2 - 6x + 5)$

$$= x(x - 1)(x - 5)$$

b. $2a^4 + 4a^3 - 30a^2 = 2a^2(a^2 + 2a - 15)$ Factor out $2a^2$.

     Now we factor $a^2 + 2a - 15$. $5(-3) = -15$, $5 + (-3) = 2$

     Therefore, $a^2 + 2a - 15 = (a + 5)(a - 3)$

     Hence, $2a^4 + 4a^3 - 30a^2 = 2a^2(a^2 + 2a - 15)$

$$= 2a^2(a - 3)(a + 5)$$

c. $2x^3 - 3x^2 + 2x - 3 = (2x^3 - 3x^2) + (2x - 3)$

$$= x^2(2x - 3) + 1(2x - 3)$$

$$= (x^2 + 1)(2x - 3)$$

EXERCISE 6.2

A. In exercises 1-12, complete the factoring.

1. $x^2 + 8x + 15 = (x + 3)(\quad)$ 2. $z^2 + 9z + 18 = (z + 6)(\quad)$ 3. $x^2 + 15x + 56 = (x + 8)(\quad)$

4. $x^2 + 16x + 63 = (x + 9)(\quad)$ 5. $t^2 - 2t - 15 = (\quad)(t - 5)$ 6. $p^2 - 14p + 45 = (\quad)(p - 5)$

7. $3r^2 - 8r - 3 = (r - 3)(\quad)$ 8. $4x^2 - 16x + 15 = (\quad)(2x - 5)$ 9. $4y^3 - 10y^2 - 6y = 2y(2y\quad)(\quad -3)$

10. $6x^3 + 7x^2 - 3x = x(2x + \quad)(3x - 1)$ 11. $2x^4 - 14x^3 + 24x^2 = 2x^2(x - 3)(\quad - 4)$

12. $20y^2a - 26ay - 6a = 2a(5y\quad)(\quad - 3)$

In exercises 13-48, factor the trinomial.

13. $x^2 - 9x - 22$ 14. $x^2 + 8x + 7$ 15. $x^2 - 10x + 25$ 16. $a^2 - 7a + 12$

17. $z^2 - z - 30$ 18. $y^2 + y - 56$ 19. $x^2 - x - 6$ 20. $x^2 - 8x - 65$

21. $x^2 + x - 6$ **22.** $x^2 + 12x + 27$ **23.** $x^2 - 5x + 6$ **24.** $x^2 + 21x + 108$

25. $x^2 - 5x + 4$ **26.** $x^2 + 22x + 85$ **27.** $x^2 - 3x - 4$ **28.** $x^2 - 11x - 42$

29. $x^2 + 3x - 4$ **30.** $x^2 - 4x - 77$ **31.** $x^2 - 4x - 5$ **32.** $x^2 - 6x - 135$

33. $x^2 + 4x - 5$ **34.** $x^2 + 12x - 133$ **35.** $x^2 - 6x + 5$ **36.** $y^2 + y - 132$

37. $x^2 - 5x - 14$ **38.** $y^2 + 5y - 104$ **39.** $x^2 + 5x - 14$ **40.** $z^2 + 7z - 144$

41. $x^2 - 9x + 14$ **42.** $a^2 + 19a - 150$ **43.** $x^2 + 4x - 21$ **44.** $y^2 + y - 72$

45. $x^2 - 4x - 21$ **46.** $x^2 - x - 156$ **47.** $x^2 - 10x + 21$ **48.** $20 + 12x + x^2$

B. In exercises 49-96, factor the trinomial completely over the integers.

49. $2x^2 + 6x + 4$ **50.** $3b^2 + 15b + 18$ **51.** $3x^2 + 3x - 18$ **52.** $xy^2 + 7xy - 8x$

53. $2p^3 + 6p^2 + 4p$ **54.** $6z^2 + 12z - 90$ **55.** $3x^3 + 3x^2 - 36x$ **56.** $5y^3 - 50y^2 - 120y$

57. $2x^2 + 5x - 3$ **58.** $2x^2 + 9x + 10$ **59.** $2x^2 - 5x - 3$ **60.** $6x^2 + 7x - 3$

61. $3x^2 - 5x - 2$ **62.** $6x^2 + x - 2$ **63.** $3x^2 + 5x - 2$ **64.** $3y^2 - 4y - 4$

65. $4x^2 - 7x - 15$ **66.** $14x^2 - x - 3$ **67.** $4x^2 + 7x - 15$ **68.** $14x^2 + 19x - 3$

69. $6x^2 + 7x - 3$ **70.** $4x^2 - 16x + 7$ **71.** $6x^2 - 7x - 3$ **72.** $12x^2 - 23x + 10$

73. $6x^2 - 11x + 3$ **74.** $5x^2 - 22x + 21$ **75.** $6x^2 + 11x + 3$ **76.** $2x^2 + x - 45$

77. $6x^2 - 5x + 1$ **78.** $12x^2 - x - 35$ **79.** $6x^2 - x - 1$ **80.** $2x^2 - 17x - 30$

81. $6x^2 + x - 1$ **82.** $3x^2 - 10x + 8$ **83.** $6x^2 + 5x + 1$ **84.** $9x^2 - 22x + 8$

85. $10x^2 + 11x - 6$ **86.** $7x^2 + 13x + 6$ **87.** $10x^2 - 11x - 6$ **88.** $13x^2 - 5x - 8$

89. $10x^2 + 19x + 6$ **90.** $9y^2 - y - 8$ **91.** $10x^2 - 19x + 6$ **92.** $5x^2 + x - 4$

93. $-r^2 + 4r + 32$ **94.** $24 + 2r - r^2$ **95.** $-40t - 75 - 5t^2$ **96.** $-x^2 + 16x + 17$

6.3 SPECIAL FACTORIZATION

Recall that a number is called a *perfect square* if it is the square of an integer. For example, 4 is a perfect square since $4 = 2^2$. Similarly, a number is called a *perfect cube* if it is a cube (third power) of an integer. Thus, -8 is a perfect cube since $-8 = (-2)^3$.

Perfect squares less than 200 are:

> 1, 4, 9, 16, 25, 36, 49, 64, 81, 100, 121, 144, 169, 196.

> *Perfect squares are never negative.*

Perfect cubes between 1 and 1000 are:

> 1, 8, 27, 64, 125, 216, 343, 512, 729, 1000.

Perfect cubes between -1000 and -1 are:

> $-1000, -729, -512, -343, -216,$
> $-125, -64, -27, -8, -1.$

> *Perfect cubes can be positive or negative.*

OBJECTIVES ■■■■

Upon completion of this section you will be able to:

A. Factor the Difference of Two Squares;

B. Factor a Perfect Square Trinomial;

C. Factor the Sum of Two Cubes; and

D. Factor the Difference of Two Cubes.

Expressions containing variables with even exponents are perfect squares, for example $x^8 y^6 = (x^4 y^3)^2$. Again, an expression of the type $x^6 y^3$ is a perfect cube since $x^6 y^3 = (x^2 y)^3$.

Recall, the following special products.

$$
\begin{aligned}
(a - b)(a + b) &= a^2 - b^2 \\
(a + b)^2 &= a^2 + 2ab + b^2 \\
(a - b)^2 &= a^2 - 2ab + b^2 \\
(a + b)(a^2 - ab + b^2) &= a(a^2 - ab + b^2) + b(a^2 - ab + b^2) \\
&= a^3 - a^2b + ab^2 + ba^2 - ab^2 + b^3 \\
&= a^3 + b^3 \\
(a - b)(a^2 + ab + b^2) &= a(a^2 + ab + b^2) - b(a^2 + ab + b^2) \\
&= a^3 + a^2b + ab^2 - ba^2 - ab^2 - b^3 \\
&= a^3 - b^3
\end{aligned}
$$

We will use these products to perform special factorizations.

A. DIFFERENCE OF TWO SQUARES

$$(a - b)(a + b) = a^2 - b^2 \longrightarrow a^2 - b^2 = (a - b)(a + b)$$

EXAMPLE 1   Factor the following terms:

a. $x^2 - 36$ **b.** $y^2 - \dfrac{9}{4}$

c. $9z^2 - 25$ **d.** $16x^2 - 25y^2$

e. $16x^4 - 25y^2$

━━━ WARM-UP ━━━

1. Factor the following terms:

   a) $9y^2 - 4$

   b) $z^2 - \dfrac{16}{9}$

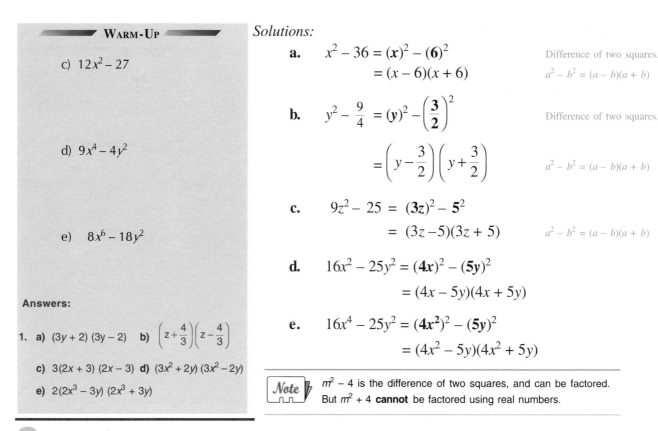

c) $12x^2 - 27$

d) $9x^4 - 4y^2$

e) $8x^6 - 18y^2$

Answers:

1. a) $(3y + 2)(3y - 2)$ b) $\left(z + \dfrac{4}{3}\right)\left(z - \dfrac{4}{3}\right)$

c) $3(2x + 3)(2x - 3)$ d) $(3x^2 + 2y)(3x^2 - 2y)$

e) $2(2x^3 - 3y)(2x^3 + 3y)$

Solutions:

a. $x^2 - 36 = (x)^2 - (6)^2$ Difference of two squares.
     $\qquad\ = (x - 6)(x + 6)$ $a^2 - b^2 = (a - b)(a + b)$

b. $y^2 - \dfrac{9}{4} = (y)^2 - \left(\dfrac{3}{2}\right)^2$ Difference of two squares.

     $\qquad\ = \left(y - \dfrac{3}{2}\right)\left(y + \dfrac{3}{2}\right)$ $a^2 - b^2 = (a - b)(a + b)$

c. $9z^2 - 25 = (3z)^2 - 5^2$
     $\qquad\ = (3z - 5)(3z + 5)$ $a^2 - b^2 = (a - b)(a + b)$

d. $16x^2 - 25y^2 = (4x)^2 - (5y)^2$
     $\qquad\qquad = (4x - 5y)(4x + 5y)$

e. $16x^4 - 25y^2 = (4x^2)^2 - (5y)^2$
     $\qquad\qquad = (4x^2 - 5y)(4x^2 + 5y)$

Note: $m^2 - 4$ is the difference of two squares, and can be factored. But $m^2 + 4$ **cannot** be factored using real numbers.

B.   PERFECT SQUARE TRINOMIALS

Perfect square trinomials can be factored according to the following rules.

same sign
$$a^2 + 2ab + b^2 = (a + b)^2$$

same sign
$$a^2 - 2ab + b^2 = (a - b)^2.$$

Notice that, in $a^2 + 2ab + b^2$, two of the terms are perfect squares, and the middle term is twice the product of these numbers.

For example, to factor $9a^2 + 30\,ab + 25b^2$, we have

$$\underbrace{(3a)^2}_{\substack{\textbf{Perfect Square} \\ \textbf{of 3a}}} + \underbrace{2(3a)(5b)}_{\substack{\textbf{Two times the product} \\ \textbf{of 3a and 5b}}} + \underbrace{(5b)^2}_{\substack{\textbf{Perfect Square} \\ \textbf{of 5b}}}$$

$$= (3a + 5b)^2$$

Likewise $$\underbrace{16x^2}_{\substack{\textbf{Perfect Square} \\ \textbf{(4x)}^2}} + \underbrace{40x}_{\substack{\textbf{Twice the product} \\ \textbf{2(4x) (5)}}} + \underbrace{25}_{\substack{\textbf{Perfect Square} \\ \textbf{5}^2}}$$

$$= (4x + 5)^2$$

same sign

A similar observation can be made about $a^2 - 2ab + b^2$. Here, $a^2 - 2ab + b^2 = (a - b)^2$.

EXAMPLE 2   Factor the trinomials.

    a. $x^2 - 6x + 9$ **b.** $x^2 + 6x + 9$

    c. $4x^2 - 28x + 49$ **d.** $9a^2 + 30ab + 25b^2$

Solutions:

  a. $x^2 - 6x + 9 \ =$

$$x^2 \qquad - \qquad \underbrace{6x} \qquad + \qquad 9$$

Perfect Square   –   Two times the   +   Perfect Square
of x product of x and 3   of 3

$$= (x - 3)^2$$

  b. $x^2 + 6x + 9 \ =$

$$x^2 \qquad + \qquad \underbrace{6x} \qquad + \qquad 9$$

Perfect Square   Twice the Product   Perfect Square
x^2 + $2(x)\,(3)$ + 3^2

$$= (x + 3)^2$$

Observation   The sign of the middle term of the perfect square trinomial is the same as the sign between the two terms under the square.

same sign

$$x^2 + 4x + 4 = x^2 + 2 \cdot (2 \cdot x) + (2)^2 = (x + 2)^2$$

$$x^2 - 4x + 4 = x^2 - 2 \cdot (2 \cdot x) + (2)^2 = (x - 2)^2$$

same sign

---

  c. $4x^2 - 28x + 49 \ =$

$$4x^2 \qquad - \qquad \underbrace{28x} \qquad + \qquad 49$$

Perfect Square   –   Two times the   +   Perfect Square
of $2x$ product of $2x$ and 7   of 7

$$= (2x - 7)^2$$

  d. $9a^2 + 30ab + 25b^2 =$

$$9a^2 \qquad + \qquad \underbrace{30ab} \qquad + \qquad 25b^2$$

Perfect Square   Two times the product   Perfect Square
$(3a)^2$ + $2(3a)(5b)$ + $(5b)^2$

$$= (3a + 5b)^2$$

2.   Factor the trinomials.

  a) $x^2 - 8x + 16$

  b) $x^2 + 12x + 36$

  c) $9x^2 - 42x + 49$

  d) $25y^2 + 90y + 81$

Answers:

2. **a)** $(x - 4)^2$ **b)** $(x + 6)^2$

   c) $(3x - 7)^2$ **d)** $(5y + 9)^2$

C. SUM OF TWO CUBES

The sum of two cubes can be factored with the help of the following formula.

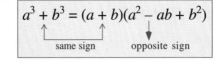

This result may be verified by expanding the product on the right.

> **Note** Recall that the sum of two squares cannot be factored.

WARM-UP

3. Factor each of the following expressions.

   a) $x^3 + 27$

   b) $27x^3 + 64$

   c) $8p^6 + 1$

   d) $64x^6 + 125y^6$

Answers:

3. a) $(x + 3)(x^2 - 3x + 9)$

   b) $(3x + 4)(9x^2 - 12x + 16)$

   c) $(2p^2 + 1)(4p^4 - 2p^2 + 1)$

   d) $(4x^2 + 5y^2)(16x^4 - 20x^2y^2 + 25y^4)$

EXAMPLE 3 Factor each of the following expressions.

   a. $x^3 + 8$ **b.** $8x^3 + 27$

   c. $64p^6 + 27q^3$ **d.** $8m^6 + 125n^6$

Solutions:

a. $x^3 + 8 = x^3 + 2^3 = (x + 2)(x^2 - 2x + 2^2)$ $a^3 + b^3 = (a + b)(a^2 - ab + b^2)$

               $= (x + 2)(x^2 - 2x + 4)$

> **Note** $x^2 - 2x + 4$ is not factorable.

b. $8x^3 + 27 = (2x)^3 + 3^3$ Sum of two cubes.

          $= (2x + 3)[(2x)^2 - (2x)(3) + 3^2]$

          $= (2x + 3)(4x^2 - 6x + 9)$ $a^3 + b^3 = (a + b)(a^2 - ab + b^2)$

c. $64p^6 + 27q^3 = (4p^2)^3 + (3q)^3$ Sum of two cubes.

            $= (4p^2 + 3q)[(4p^2)^2 - (4p^2)(3q) + (3q)^2]$

            $= (4p^2 + 3q)[16p^4 - 12p^2q + 9q^2]$

d. $8m^6 + 125n^6 = (2m^2)^3 + (5n^2)^3$ Sum of two cubes.

            $= (2m^2 + 5n^2)[(2m^2)^2 - (2m^2)(5n^2) + (5n^2)^2]$

            $= (2m^2 + 5n^2)(4m^4 - 10m^2n^2 + 25n^4)$

> **Note** $4a^2 + 9b^2$ is a sum of two squares, namely $(2a)^2 + (3b)^2$. It cannot be factored.

D. DIFFERENCE OF TWO CUBES

The difference of two cubes can be factored with the help of the following formula.

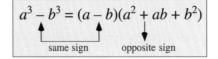

The result may be verified by expanding the product on the right.

EXAMPLE 4   Factor each of the following expressions.

  a. $x^3 - 8$ b. $8x^3 - 27$

  c. $64p^6 - 27q^3$ d. $8m^6 - 125n^6$

Solutions:

a. $x^3 - 8 = (x)^3 - 2^3$ Difference of two cubes.

   $= (x - 2)[(x)^2 + 2(x) + (2)^2]$

   $= (x - 2)(x^2 + 2x + 4)$

b. $8x^3 - 27 = (2x)^3 - 3^3$ Difference of two cubes.

   $= (2x - 3)[(2x)^2 + (2x)(3) + 3^2]$

   $= (2x - 3)(4x^2 + 6x + 9)$

c. $64p^6 - 27q^3 = (4p^2)^3 - (3q)^3$ Difference of two cubes.

   $= (4p^2 - 3q)[(4p^2)^2 + (4p^2)(3q) + (3q)^2]$

   $= (4p^2 - 3q)(16p^4 + 12p^2q + 9q^2)$

d. $8m^6 - 125n^6 = (2m^2)^3 - (5n^2)^3$ Difference of two cubes.

   $= (2m^2 - 5n^2)[(2m^2)^2 + (2m^2)(5n^2) + (5n^2)^2]$

   $= (2m^2 - 5n^2)[4m^4 + 10m^2n^2 + 25n^4]$

Note $2m^2 - 5n^2$ is not a difference of squares since 2 and 5 are not perfect squares.

GENERAL STRATEGY FOR FACTORING A POLYNOMIAL

Step 1   Look for the greatest common factor (GCF) of all the terms, other than 1. If the GCF is **1** then proceed to Step 2 with the given polynomial. If the GCF is other than **1**, then factor it out and proceed with the reduced polynomial to Step 2.

given polynomial = (GCF)(reduced polynomial)

Step 2   If the given polynomial or the reduced polynomial has only two terms then determine if it is one of the following:

   a. Difference of two squares   **b.** Difference of two cubes

   c. Sum of two cubes   **d.** None of the above three. In this case factoring is complete.

Step 3   If the expression has only three terms then check if it is one of the following forms.

   a. Perfect Square: $a^2 + 2ab + b^2$ or $a^2 - 2ab + b^2$

   b. Trinomial with leading coefficient 1: $x^2 + bx + c$

   c. Trinomial with leading coefficient not equal to 1: $ax^2 + bx + c$

   And try to factor the trinomial.

Step 4   If the expression has more than three terms then try to factor using the grouping method.

Step 5   Check if each factor can be factored further. Factoring always means factoring completely.

EXERCISE 6.3

A. In exercises 1-42, factor the binomial completely wherever possible.

1. $x^2 - 9$
2. $y^2 - 16$
3. $4x^2 - 25$
4. $9y^2 - 36$
5. $16a^2 + b^2$

6. $25y^2 + 15$
7. $81a^2 - 25b^2$
8. $25x^2 - 16y^2$
9. $2a^2 - 8b^2$
10. $4x^2 - 16y^2$

11. $3x^2 - 12y^2$
12. $12y^2 - 75z$
13. $2 - 8t^2$
14. $18x^2 - 2$
15. $18 - 50a^2$

16. $32 - 72x^2$
17. $xy^2 - x^3$
18. $a^2b^2 - b^2$
19. $2a^2b - 18b^3$
20. $27x^3 - 12xy^2$

21. $5a^3 - 20ab^2$
22. $5xy^2 - 80x^3$
23. $3t^2 - 27$
24. $125 - 5y^2$
25. $a^2bc - b^3c$

26. $y^3z - x^2yz$
27. $m^4 - 81$
28. $16 - x^4$
29. $9p^2 + 4q^2$
30. $16x^2 - 9y^2$

31. $r^4 - 49$
32. $81 + y^4$
33. $a^2 - 64$
34. $49 - y^2$
35. $4y^2 - 1$

36. $25x^2 - 1$
37. $9y^2 - 1$
38. $x^4 - y^4$
39. $x^2 + 64$
40. $y^4 - 16x^4$

41. $16 - a^2b^2$
42. $81 - z^4$

B. In exercises 43-78, factor the expression completely.

43. $x^2 - 6x + 9$
44. $y^2 + 6y + 9$
45. $x^2 + 8x + 16$
46. $z^2 - 10z + 25$

47. $a^2 + 10a + 25$
48. $36 - 12x + x^2$
49. $r^2 - 14r + 49$
50. $x^2 + 12x + 36$

51. $y^2 - 7y + \dfrac{49}{4}$
52. $x^2 + 9x + \dfrac{81}{4}$
53. $t^2 + 5t + \dfrac{25}{4}$
54. $\dfrac{x^2}{25} - \dfrac{xy}{15} + \dfrac{y^2}{36}$

55. $2x^2 - 8x + 8$
56. $3x^2 + 12x + 12$
57. $3a^2 + 18a + 27$
58. $4x^2 - 32x + 64$

59. $a^2b - 2ab^2 + b^3$
60. $x^2z + zy^2 + 2xyz$
61. $4x^2 + 28x + 49$
62. $49a^2 + 28ab + 4b^2$

63. $4p^2 - 36pq + 81q^2$
64. $9x^2b^2 - 6xb + 1$
65. $9 + 24x + 16x^2$
66. $4a^3 + 20a^2 + 25a$

67. $2x^3 - 8x^2y + 8xy^2$
68. $27a^2b - 18ab + 3b$
69. $32ab^2 - 48ab + 18a$
70. $128a^3b + 64a^2b^2 + 8ab^3$

71. $16a^2 + 24ab + 9b^2$
72. $81x^2 + 64y^2 - 144xy$
73. $49z^2 - 28zt + 4t^2$
74. $36x^2 + 60xy + 25y^2$

75. $9x^2 + 48x^2y + 64x^2y^2$
76. $49x^4 + 9y^4 - 42x^2y^2$
77. $a^2b^2x^2 - 20a^2b^2x + 100a^2b^2$
78. $a^4b^2 + b^4a^2 - 2a^3b^3$

C. In exercises 79-85, factor using formulas for the sum of two cubes.

79. $x^3 + 27$
80. $1 + a^3$
81. $64r^3 + 125s^3$
82. $128x^3 + 54y^3$

83. $125x^3 + 8y^3$
84. $(x + y)^3 + (x - y)^3$
85. $8x^6 + 64y^6$

D. In exercises 86-94, factor using formulas for difference of two cubes.

86. $z^3 - 64$
87. $x^3 - 1$
88. $y^3 - 125z^3$
89. $27a^3 - b^3$
90. $8x^3 - 125y^3$

91. $729p^3 - 1000q^3$
92. $x - 8xy^3$
93. $x^6 - y^6$
94. $\dfrac{1}{216} - 729y^3$

6.4 SOLVING QUADRATIC EQUATIONS BY FACTORING

An equation is called a **quadratic equation** or a **second degree equation** if it can be written in the form $ax^2 + bx + c = 0$, where a, b, and c, are real numbers, and $a \neq 0$. If $a = 0$, the equation reduces to a linear equation $bx + c = 0$.

As with linear equations, solving a quadratic equation means finding numbers which make the equation true upon substitution. For example, $x = -1$ is a solution of $4x^2 + 3x - 1 = 0$ because $4(-1)^2 + 3(-1) - 1 = 0$ is a true statement, since $4 - 3 - 1 = 0$.

In this section, we will see how factoring can be used to solve quadratic equations.

A. ZERO-FACTOR PROPERTY

If a and b are real numbers, and $ab = 0$, then $a = 0$ or $b = 0$.

This property can be stated differently. If the product of two factors is zero then at least one of these factors must be zero.

EXAMPLE 1   Given $(x - 4)(3x + 2) = 0$, find the value(s) of x which satisfy the equation.

Solution:

$(x - 4)(3x + 2) = 0 \longrightarrow x - 4 = 0$ or $3x + 2 = 0$.

Zero factor property.

Notice $x - 4 = 0$ and $3x + 2 = 0$ are linear equations.

$$x - 4 = 0 \quad \text{or} \quad 3x + 2 = 0$$
$$x = 4 \quad \text{or} \quad 3x = -2$$
$$x = -\frac{2}{3}$$

So, the solutions to $(x - 4)(3x + 2) = 0$ are $x = 4$ and $x = -\frac{2}{3}$.

B. SOLVING QUADRATIC EQUATIONS

We use a four-step approach for solving quadratic equations by factoring.

Step 1   Write the equation in the *standard form*: $ax^2 + bx + c = 0$.

Step 2   Factor the trinomial $ax^2 + bx + c$ and replace $ax^2 + bx + c$ by the factored form in the equation.

Step 3   Using the zero-factor property, equate each factor to zero and solve for the unknown x.

Step 4   Check the solutions by substituting the solutions in the *original* equation.

Notes

1. There are always two solutions to a quadratic equation. (Sometimes repeated)

2. Since some trinomials cannot be factored, we will not be able to solve all quadratic equations by factoring.

WARM-UP

2. Write the following equations in standard form.

a) $2x^2 - x = 3$

b) $4x^2 = 3(x - 2)$

c) $x^2 = x + 5$

d) $2x = x^2 + 1$

3. Solve the following equations.

a) $2x^2 - x - 3 = 0$

EXAMPLE 2   Write the following equations in the standard form.

a. $3x^2 - 5x = 7$ b. $2x^2 = 4(x - 5)$

c. $3x = x^2 - 2$ d. $x^2 = -5$

Solutions:

a.
$$3x^2 - 5x = 7$$
$$3x^2 - 5x + (-7) = 7 + (-7) \qquad \text{Add } -7 \text{ to both sides.}$$
$$3x^2 - 5x - 7 = 0$$

b.
$$2x^2 = 4(x - 5)$$
$$2x^2 = 4x - 20 \qquad \text{Distributive Property.}$$
$$2x^2 - 4x = -20 \qquad \text{Add } -4x \text{ on both sides.}$$
$$2x^2 - 4x + 20 = 0 \qquad \text{Add 20 on both sides.}$$

c.
$$3x = x^2 - 2$$
$$-x^2 + 3x = -2 \qquad \text{Add } -x^2 \text{ to both sides.}$$
$$-x^2 + 3x + 2 = 0 \qquad \text{Add 2 to both sides.}$$
$$x^2 - 3x - 2 = 0 \qquad \text{Multiply both sides by } -1.$$

d.
$$x^2 = -5$$
$$x^2 + 5 = 0 \qquad \text{Transfer } -5 \text{ to left side.}$$

EXAMPLE 3   Solve the following equations.

a. $x^2 - 3x - 4 = 0$ b. $x^2 + 5x = 14$

c. $3y^2 - 48 = 0$ d. $9p^2 = 25$

e. $3z^2 = 5z$ f. $2x^2 - x - 10 = 0$

g. $x^2 + 4x + 4 = 0$

Solutions:

a. $x^2 - 3x - 4 = 0$

Step 1   Not needed. The equation is already in the standard form $x^2 - 3x - 4 = 0$.

Step 2 $(x - 4)(x + 1) = 0$ \qquad Factor.

Step 3 $(x - 4)(x + 1) = 0$

$\longrightarrow \qquad x - 4 = 0$ or $x + 1 = 0$ \qquad Zero-factor property.

$\longrightarrow \qquad x = 4$ or $x = -1$

The solutions are **4** and **−1**.

Step 4   ***Check*** the solutions: $x^2 - 3x - 4 = 0$

$x = 4$: $\quad (4)^2 - 3(4) - 4 = 0 \qquad x = -1$: $\ (-1)^2 - 3(-1) - 4 = 0$

$\qquad\qquad 16 - 12 - 4 = 0 \qquad\qquad\qquad\qquad 1 + 3 - 4 = 0$

$\qquad\qquad\quad 4 - 4 = 0$ True $\qquad\qquad\qquad\qquad 4 - 4 = 0$ True

b. $x^2 + 5x = 14$

- $x^2 + 5x - 14 = 0$
- $(x + 7)(x - 2) = 0$ Factor.

$\longrightarrow$ $x + 7 = 0$ or $x - 2 = 0$ Zero-factor property.

$\longrightarrow$ $x = -7$ or $x = \mathbf{2}$

The solutions are -7 and 2.

- ***Check*** the solutions: $x^2 + 5x - 14 = 0$

$x = -7$: $(-7)^2 + 5(-7) - 14 = 0$
                   $49 - 35 - 14 = 0$ True

$x = 2$: $(2)^2 + 5(2) - 14 = 0$
                   $4 + 10 - 14 = 0$ True

c. $3y^2 - 48 = 0$

$3y^2 - 48 = 0$

- Factor $3y^2 - 48$ as $3(y - 4)(y + 4)$.
- $3y^2 - 48 = 0$

$3(y - 4)(y + 4) = 0$

$\longrightarrow$ $y - 4 = 0$ or $y + 4 = 0$

$\longrightarrow$ $y = 4$ or $y = -4$

The solutions are 4 and -4.

- ***Check*** the solutions: $3y^2 - 48 = 0$

$y = 4$: $3(4)^2 - 48 = 0$
            $48 - 48 = 0$
                 $0 = 0$ True

$y = -4$: $3(-4)^2 - 48 = 0$
             $48 - 48 = 0$
                 $0 = 0$ True

d. $9p^2 = 25$

- $9p^2 - 25 = 0$
- $(3p - 5)(3p + 5) = 0$ Since $9p^2 - 25 = (3p - 5)(3p + 5)$

$\longrightarrow$ $3p - 5 = 0$ or $3p + 5 = 0$

$\longrightarrow$ $p = \dfrac{5}{3}$ or $p = -\dfrac{5}{3}$

The solutions are $\dfrac{5}{3}$ and $-\dfrac{5}{3}$.

- ***Check*** the solutions: $9p^2 - 25 = 0$

$p = \dfrac{5}{3}$: $9\left(\dfrac{5}{3}\right)^2 - 25 = 0 \rightarrow 25 - 25 = 0$
                             $0 = 0$ True

$p = -\dfrac{5}{3}$: $9\left(-\dfrac{5}{3}\right)^2 - 25 = 0 \rightarrow 25 - 25 = 0$
                              $0 = 0$ True

b) $x^2 - 2x + 1 = 0$

c) $9z^2 = 16$

d) $x^2 + 8x + 16 = 0$

e) $4z^2 = 8z$

e. $3z^2 = 5z$

- $3z^2 - 5z = 0$

- $z(3z - 5) = 0$ [Since $3z^2 - 5z = z(3z - 5)$].

$\longrightarrow$ $z = 0$ or $3z - 5 = 0$

$\longrightarrow$ $z = 0$ or $z = \dfrac{5}{3}$

The solutions are **0** and $\dfrac{5}{3}$.

- **Check** the solutions: $3z^2 - 5z = 0$

$z = \mathbf{0}$: $3(\mathbf{0})^2 = 5(\mathbf{0})$ $\longrightarrow$ $0 = 0$ True

$z = \dfrac{\mathbf{5}}{\mathbf{3}}$: $3\left(\dfrac{\mathbf{5}}{\mathbf{3}}\right)^2 = 5\left(\dfrac{\mathbf{5}}{\mathbf{3}}\right)$ $\longrightarrow$ $3\left(\dfrac{25}{9}\right) = 5\left(\dfrac{5}{3}\right)$

                        $\longrightarrow$ $\dfrac{25}{3} = \dfrac{25}{3}$ True

f) $2x^2 + 3x - 5 = 0$

f. $2x^2 - x - 10 = 0$

$2x^2 - x - 10 = 0$

- $(2x - 5)(x + 2) = 0$ Replace $2x^2 - x - 10$ by $(2x - 5)(x + 2)$.

$\longrightarrow$ $2x - 5 = 0$ or $x + 2 = 0$

$\longrightarrow$ $2x = 5$ or $x = -2$

$\longrightarrow$ $x = \dfrac{5}{2}$ or $x = -2$

The solutions are $\dfrac{5}{2}$ and **−2.**

- **Check** the solutions: $2x^2 - x - 10 = 0$

$x = \dfrac{\mathbf{5}}{\mathbf{2}}$: $2\left(\dfrac{\mathbf{5}}{\mathbf{2}}\right)^2 - \left(\dfrac{\mathbf{5}}{\mathbf{2}}\right) - 10 = 0$

          $2 \cdot \dfrac{25}{4} - \dfrac{5}{2} - 10 = 0$

             $\dfrac{20}{2} - 10 = 0$

             $10 - 10 = 0$ True

$x = -\mathbf{2}$: $2(-\mathbf{2})^2 - (-\mathbf{2}) - 10 = 0$

            $2 \cdot 4 + 2 - 10 = 0$

             $10 - 10 = 0$ True

g) $y^2 - 6y + 9 = 0$

g. $x^2 + 4x + 4 = 0$

$x^2 + 4x + 4 = 0$ Replace $x^2 + 4x + 4$ by $(x + 2)(x + 2)$ on the left side of the equation.

- $(x + 2)(x + 2) = 0$

$$\longrightarrow \qquad x + 2 = 0 \qquad \text{or} \qquad x + 2 = 0$$
$$\longrightarrow \qquad x = -2 \qquad \text{or} \qquad x = -2$$

The solutions are -2 and -2 (repeated).

- **Check** the solutions: $\qquad x^2 + 4x + 4 = 0$

$$x = -2: \quad (-2)^2 + 4(-2) + 4 = 0$$
$$4 + (-8) + 4 = 0 \quad \longrightarrow \quad 0 = 0 \qquad \text{True}$$

C. ZERO-FACTOR PROPERTY FOR MORE THAN TWO FACTORS

The zero-factor property can be extended to more than two factors. For example, if $a \cdot b \cdot c = 0$, then $a = 0$ or $b = 0$ or $c = 0$.

EXAMPLE 4   Solve the following equations.

   a. $(2x + 5)(x^2 - x - 12) = 0$ **b.** $4y^3 - y = 0$

   c. $(z^2 - 4)(z^2 - 9) = 0$

Solutions:

a.   **$(2x + 5)(x^2 - x - 12) = 0$.**

Since $\qquad x^2 - x - 12 = (x - 4)(x + 3)$

$(2x + 5)(x^2 - x - 12) = 0 \longrightarrow (2x + 5)(x - 4)(x + 3) = 0$

The zero-factor property gives us:

$$2x + 5 = 0 \qquad \text{or} \qquad x - 4 = 0 \qquad \text{or} \qquad x + 3 = 0$$
$$\longrightarrow \qquad 2x = -5 \qquad \text{or} \qquad x = 4 \qquad \text{or} \qquad x = -3$$
$$\longrightarrow \qquad x = -\frac{5}{2} \qquad \text{or} \qquad x = 4 \qquad \text{or} \qquad x = -3$$

Hence, the solutions of $(2x + 5)(x^2 - x - 12) = 0$ are

$$-\frac{5}{2}, \textbf{ 4, } \text{ and } \textbf{-3.}$$

We leave the verification of the solutions as an exercise.

b.   **$4y^3 - y = 0$**

Observe that $4y^3 - y = y(4y^2 - 1) = y(2y - 1)(2y + 1)$.

The given equation becomes $y(2y - 1)(2y + 1) = 0$.

The zero-factor property gives us:

$$y = 0 \qquad \text{or} \qquad 2y - 1 = 0 \qquad \text{or} \qquad 2y + 1 = 0$$
$$\longrightarrow \qquad y = 0 \qquad \text{or} \qquad 2y = 1 \qquad \text{or} \qquad 2y = -1$$
$$\longrightarrow \qquad y = 0 \qquad \text{or} \qquad y = \frac{1}{2} \qquad \text{or} \qquad y = -\frac{1}{2}$$

Hence, the solutions of $4y^3 - y = 0$ are $\textbf{0, } \dfrac{1}{2}, \textbf{ and } -\dfrac{1}{2}$.

Checking of the solutions is left as an exercise.

c) $(x^2 - 16)(x^2 - 81) = 0$

c. $(z^2 - 4)(z^2 - 9) = 0$

Observe that :

$(z^2 - 4)(z^2 - 9) = (z^2 - 2^2)(z^2 - 3^2)$
$$= (z - 2)(z + 2)(z - 3)(z + 3)$$

Hence, the given equation becomes $(z - 2)(z + 2)(z - 3)(z + 3) = 0$

The zero factor property gives us :

$z - 2 = 0$ or $z + 2 = 0$ or $z - 3 = 0$ or $z + 3 = 0$

$\longrightarrow$ $z = 2$ or $z = -2$ or $z = 3$ or $z = -3$

Hence, the solutions of $(z^2 - 4)(z^2 - 9) = 0$ are $2, -2, 3,$ and -3.

Answers:

4. a) $-4, 3, -\dfrac{7}{3}$ b) $0, -2, 2$

   c) $-4, 4, -9, 9$

EXERCISE 6.4

A. In exercises 1-16, solve the equation using zero-factor property.

1. $(x - 5)(3x + 4) = 0$ 2. $(y - 4)(2y - 3) = 0$ 3. $(2x + 3)(3x + 5) = 0$ 4. $(3y - 4)(2y - 3) = 0$

5. $t(t - 2) = 0$ 6. $x(x + 2) = 0$ 7. $(t + 1)(2t - 3) = 0$ 8. $(x - 1)(3x - 4) = 0$

9. $2x(x - 5)(x - 7) = 0$ 10. $3y(y - 3)(y - 4) = 0$ 11. $(x + 3)(x + 2) = 0$ 12. $(y - 3)(y - 4) = 0$

13. $(z - 4)(z + 5) = 0$ 14. $x(x - 4) = 0$ 15. $t(t + 4) = 0$ 16. $a(a + 4)(a - 3) = 0$

In exercises 17-22, solve the equation.

17. $y^2 - 7y = 0$ 18. $t^2 - 4 = 0$ 19. $x^2 - 9 = 0$

20. $2x^2 - 18 = 0$ 21. $3x^2 - 12 = 0$ 22. $9x^2 - 1 = 0$

B. In exercises 23-62, solve the equation.

23. $x^2 - 7x + 10 = 0$ 24. $x^2 + 9x + 20 = 0$ 25. $x^2 + 10x + 24 = 0$ 26. $x^2 + 5x - 6 = 0$

27. $y^2 = 6y + 7$ 28. $x^2 = 7x - 12$ 29. $t^2 + 2 = -3t$ 30. $x^2 - 36 = -5x$

31. $9m^2 = 64$ 32. $4y^2 = 100$ 33. $25p^2 - 20p + 4 = 0$ 34. $10x^2 - 7x - 12 = 0$

35. $a^2 - 8a + 15 = 0$ 36. $y^2 - 3y - 10 = 0$ 37. $a^2 + 4a - 21 = 0$ 38. $y^2 - 7y = 8$

39. $2x^2 + 7x = 4$ 40. $3y^2 + y = 10$ 41. $x(x - 12) = -27$ 42. $a(a + 4) = 45$

43. $y(y + 3) = 28$ 44. $(x + 4)(x - 1) = 14$ 45. $(y + 8)(y - 3) = -30$ 46. $(t - 5)(t + 4) = 52$

47. $(z - 4)(z + 7) = -18$ 48. $(x + 5)(3x - 2) = -14$ 49. $2z^2 - z = 10$ 50. $12y^2 - y = 6$

51. $15x^2 = 7x$ 52. $9y^2 = -2y$ 53. $x(x - 9) = 22$ 54. $7y^2 + 49y = -84$

55. $\dfrac{5}{2}x - 1 - x^2 = 0$ 56. $6 - x - x^2 = 0$ 57. $z^2 = \dfrac{1}{2}(z + 1)$ 58. $x^2 = \dfrac{1}{5}(32x - 12)$

59. $10 = r(6r - 7)$ 60. $14 = x(x + 5)$ 61. $2x(x - 1) = 5(x + 3)$ 62. $y(y - 1) = 1 - \dfrac{y}{6}$

C. In exercises 63-80, solve the equations using zero factor property for more than two factors.

63. $2x^2 + x^3 = 0$ 64. $12y^3 + y^2 = 0$ 65. $4t^3 - 25t = 0$ 66. $16x^3 - 9x = 0$

67. $t^3 - 8t^2 - 9t = 0$ **68.** $x^3 + 2x^2 - 3x = 0$ **69.** $7x^4 = 2x^2\left(x + \dfrac{5}{2}\right)$ **70.** $2x^3 = 2x(7x - 12)$

71. $3x = -4x^2(3x + 5)$ **72.** $19y^2 = 3y - 14y^3$ **73.** $x^4 - 5x^2 + 4 = 0$ **74.** $2y^3 - 16y - 2y = 0$

75. $x(x^2 - 1) = 0$ **76.** $y(y - 1)(y^2 - 4) = 0$ **77.** $3y^3 - 27y = 0$ **78.** $4x^3 - 36x = 0$

79. $5p^4 - 80p^2 = 0$ **80.** $4p(p^2 - 1)(p^2 - 4) = 0$

6.5 APPLICATIONS OF QUADRATIC EQUATIONS

In this section, we will consider some simple application problems and show how the solution of quadratic equations helps in solving some practical problems.

The overall strategy for solving these problems is the same as the strategy used in solving applications with linear equations.

1. **Read** the problem carefully.

2. **Draw** a diagram, set up a table or a chart, or identify a pertinent formula.

3. **Identify** and name the unknowns.

4. **Translate** the sentences to mathematical equations.

5. **Solve** the equations.

6. **Interpret** your answer.

7. **Check** the solution.

OBJECTIVES ■■■■

Upon completion of this section you will be able to:

A. Apply quadratic equations to number problems; and

B. Apply quadratic equations to problems in Geometry.

A. APPLICATION TO NUMBER PROBLEMS

EXAMPLE 1   The product of two consecutive integers is 156. Find the integers.

Solution:

- If the *smaller* of the two integers is n, then the *next consecutive* integer is $n + 1$.

- The product of n and $n + 1$ is $n(n + 1)$.

- It is given that $n(n + 1) = 156$.

- Therefore, the solution of the problem depends on solving the equation **$n(n + 1) = 156$.**

  $n^2 + n = 156$

WARM-UP

1. The product of two consecutive integers is 6. Find the integers.

$$n^2 + n - 156 = 0$$
$$(n - 12)(n + 13) = 0$$
$$\longrightarrow \quad n - 12 = 0 \quad \text{or} \quad n + 13 = 0 \quad \text{Zero-factor property.}$$
$$\longrightarrow \quad n = \mathbf{12} \quad \text{or} \quad n = \mathbf{-13} \quad \text{Solutions of the equation.}$$

The two integers are n and $n + 1$. When $n = 12$, $n + 1 = 13$, so the two integers are 12 and 13. When $n = -13$, $n + 1 = -12$, so the two integers are **−13** and **−12**. Therefore, there are two solutions to the problem.

Verify that in each case the product is 156.

B. APPLICATION TO GEOMETRY

▼ WARM-UP ◤

2. The length of a rectangle is twice its width. The area of the rectangle is 8 square cm. Find the dimensions of the rectangle.

EXAMPLE 2 The length of a rectangle is three times its width. The area of the rectangle is 147 square centimeters. Find the dimensions of the rectangle.

Solution:

Draw a rectangle. Recall the formula $A = l \cdot w$

Suppose the width of the rectangle is x cm.

Then the length of the rectangle is $3x$ cm.

The area of the rectangle is $(\mathbf{3x})\mathbf{x}$ sq.cm.

The area is given to be 147 square centimeters.

Therefore,

$$(3x)x = 147 \quad \longrightarrow \quad 3x^2 = 147$$
$$\longrightarrow \quad 3x^2 - 147 = 0$$
$$\longrightarrow \quad 3(x^2 - 49) = 0$$
$$\longrightarrow \quad 3(x - 7)(x + 7) = 0$$
$$\longrightarrow \quad x - 7 = 0 \quad \text{or} \quad x + 7 = 0 \quad \text{Zero-factor property.}$$
$$\longrightarrow \quad x = \mathbf{7} \quad \text{or} \quad x = \mathbf{-7} \quad \text{Solutions of the equation.}$$

The width cannot be negative. Therefore, the only choice is $x = 7$. Hence, the dimensions of the rectangle are

Width $= x = \mathbf{7}$ cm   Length $= 3x = 3(7) = \mathbf{21}$ cm.

Verify that your solution is correct:

$$\text{Area} = (\text{width})(\text{length}) = 7\text{cm} \cdot 21 \text{ cm}$$
$$= 147 \text{ cm}^2 \quad \text{True}$$

- In our next problem, we will use the *Pythagorean formula*. Recall that for a right triangle:

$$(\text{Hypotenuse})^2 = (\text{Base})^2 + (\text{Height})^2$$
$$c^2 = a^2 + b^2$$

EXAMPLE 3   One side of a rectangle is 7 cm more than the other. If the diagonal of the rectangle is 13 cm, find the dimensions of the rectangle.

Solution:

Draw the figure to visualize the problem.
Suppose the smaller side is x cm.
Then, the longer side is $x + 7$ cm.

By the Pythagorean formula:

(Diagonal)^2 = (Length)^2 + (Width)^2

$$(13)^2 = (x + 7)^2 + x^2$$
$$x^2 + (x + 7)^2 = 13^2$$
$$x^2 + (x^2 + 14x + 49) = 169$$
$$2x^2 + 14x + 49 - 169 = 0$$
$$2x^2 + 14x - 120 = 0$$
$$2(x - 5)(x + 12) = 0$$
$$\longrightarrow \quad x - 5 = 0 \quad \text{or} \quad x + 12 = 0$$
$$\longrightarrow \quad x = 5 \quad \text{or} \quad x = -12$$

$x = -12$ is not a possible solution, because side of a rectangle can never be negative. Therefore, $x = 5$ is the only solution.

Thus, the smaller side = **5 cm**.
and the longer side   = 5 cm + 7 cm = **12 cm.**

EXAMPLE 4   The height of a triangle is 4 times its base. The area of the triangle is 288 square centimeters. Find the base and the height of the triangle.

Solution:

Suppose the base is x *cm*. Then, the height is **4x** *cm*.
Draw a triangle, show the base and the height.

Area of triangle = $\dfrac{1}{2}$ (base)(height)

$$= \frac{1}{2} x(\mathbf{4x}) = 2x^2$$

It is given that the area is 288 square centimeters. Therefore,

$$2x^2 = 288 \longrightarrow \qquad x^2 = 144$$
$$\longrightarrow \qquad x^2 - 144 = 0$$
$$\longrightarrow \qquad (x - 12)(x + 12) = 0$$
$$\longrightarrow \quad x - 12 = 0 \quad \text{or} \quad x + 12 = 0$$
$$\longrightarrow \qquad x = 12 \quad \text{or} \quad x = -12$$

$x = -12$ is not a feasible solution.

Hence, Base = x = **12** *cm*   Height = 4x = **48** *cm*

Check :   Area = $\dfrac{1}{2}$ (12 *cm*) (48 *cm*) = 288 sq cm.

3.   The width of a rectangle is 4 cm less than the length. If the diagonal of the rectangle is $4\sqrt{5}$ cm, find the dimensions of the rectangle.

4.   The height of a triangle is 2 times its base. The area of the triangle is 196 cm^2. Find the base and height of the triangle.

5. The product of the measures of two complementary angles is 1800°. Find the measure of the greater angle.

EXAMPLE 5 The product of the measures of two complementary angles is 1400°. Find the measure of the greater angle.

Solution:

Draw two complementary angles, so the sum of the measures of the angles is 90°.

angles are complementary.

Let the measure of the greater angle $= x$

Then, the measure of the smaller angle $= 90 - x$

The product of the two measures $= (90 - x)x$

The product of the two measures $= 1400°$ Given.

Therefore,

$(90 - x)x = 1400 \longrightarrow 90x - x^2 = 1400$

$\longrightarrow x^2 - 90x + 1400 = 0$

$\longrightarrow (x - 70)(x - 20) = 0$

$\longrightarrow x - 70 = 0$ or $x - 20 = 0$

$\longrightarrow x = 70$ or $x = 20$

The two angles are 20° and 70°. Therefore, the measure of the greater angle $= 70°$.

6. If a stone is dropped from a certain height and is allowed to fall freely then the distance (d) covered by the stone in time t is given by $d = 16 t^2$. Find the distances covered by the stone in time t if:

a) $t = 2$ sec   b) $t = 1.5$ sec

EXAMPLE 6 If an apple falls freely from a tree, the distance (d) covered by the apple in time t is given by $d = 16t^2$. Determine the distances covered by the apple in time t if: **a.** $t = 0.5$ sec   **b.** 0.8 sec

Solutions: $d = 16t^2$

a. $d = 16(0.5)^2 = 4$ **ft**   Substitute 0.5 for t.

b. $d = 16(0.8)^2 \approx 10.24$ **ft**   Substitute 0.8 for t.

Answers:

2. 2 cm , 4 cm
3. 4 cm ; 8 cm
4. base = 14 cm , height = 28 cm
5. 60°   6. a) 64 ft   b) 36 ft

EXERCISE 6.5

A. Solve the following word problems

1. The product of two consecutive even integers is 168. Find the integers.

2. The product of two consecutive integers is 72. Find the integers.

3. The product of two consecutive odd integers is 323. Find the integers.

4. Find two consecutive positive odd integers whose squares have the sum of 290.

5. If the sum of the squares of three consecutive integers is 194, find the integers.

6. If a stone is dropped from a certain height and is allowed to fall freely then the distance (d) covered by the stone in time t is given by $d = 16t^2$. Find the distances covered by the stone in time t if :
   (a) $t = 2$ sec   **(b)** $t = 1.5$ sec

7. Refer to the above exercise (# 6). In how much time the stone will cover a distance of 144 ft?

8. The sum of a number and its reciprocal is $\dfrac{-25}{12}$. Find the numbers.

9. The product of two consecutive integers is 132. Find the integers.

10. Find two consecutive positive even integers whose squares have the sum 340.

11. A natural number added to the square of its preceding number equals 73. What is the number?

12. The age of the father and his son together is 60 years. The product of the numbers representing their ages is 576. Find their ages.

13. The product of two successive multiples of 5 is 300. Determine the multiples.

14. The sum of the squares of three consecutive natural numbers is 110. Determine the numbers.

B. 15. One side of a rectangle is 5 meters longer than the other. If the area of the rectangle is 126 square meters, determine the length of the longer side.

16. The length of a rectangle is 7 units more than width and the area of rectangle is 540 square units. Find the length of the rectangle.

17. A rectangle with an area of 112 square yards has length 6 yards more than its width. Find the perimeter of the rectangle.

18. The area of rectangular field is 1620 square yards. Its length exceeds its width by 9 yards. Find its length.

19. The area of a square is numerically equal to two times its perimeter. Determine the length of a side of the square.

20. The length of a rectangle is 5 ft longer than its width, and the area of this rectangle is 36 square feet. Find its dimensions.

21. The width of a rectangular floor is 3 feet less than its length. If the area of the floor is 108 square feet, determine the dimensions of the floor.

22. The length of a rectangular park is 8 meters more than its width and the area of the park is 240 square meters. Find the dimensions of the park.

23. The base of a triangle is 2 feet more than twice its height. If the area of the triangle is 12 square feet, determine its base and height.

24. The area of right triangle is 63 square units. The base of the triangle exceeds that of its height by 5 units. Find the altitude of the triangle.

25. A rectangular lawn is 60 feet by 80 feet. A strip has been mowed inside the lawn along its boundary and half the lawn remains to be mowed. Find the width of the strip.

26. The sides of a right triangle are $(x - 1)$, x, the $(x + 1)$ meters. Find the length of the sides of this right triangle.

27. The width of a rectangle is 5 cm and its length is one less than its diagonal. Find the area of the rectangle.

28. The area of a right triangle is 30 square units. Determine its base and the altitude, if the altitude exceeds the base by 7 units.

29. A lot has the shape of a right triangle. The difference between the two sides is 2 meters. The hypotenuse is 6 meters less than twice the length of the longer side. Find the length of the shorter side.

30. Product of the measures of two supplementary angles is 7931°. Find the measures of the two angles.

31. Product of the measures of two complementary angles is 2016°. What is the measure of the greater angle ?

32. The sides (in meters) of a right triangular plot containing the right angle are $5x$ and $(3x - 1)$. If the area of the triangle is 60 square meters, find the sides of the triangle.

6.6 CHAPTER SUMMARY

EXAMPLES

FACTORS

1. Find the greatest common factor of

   $24x^3y^2z$, $36x^2y^4$, $60x^2yz^2$

   Coefficients: 24, 36, 60
   Greatest Common Factor of coefficients = **12**.

   Exponents of x : 3, 2, 2;
   Exponents of y : 2, 4, 1;
   Exponents of z : 1, 0, 2.

   Minimum exponent of $x = 2 \;\rightarrow\; x^2$
   Minimum exponent of $y = 1 \;\rightarrow\; y$
   Minimum exponent of $z = 0 \;\rightarrow\; z^0$

   Greatest Common Factor $= 12x^2\,y^1z^0 = \mathbf{12x^2y}$

2. Factor: $15x^3 + 2y^2 - 6x^2y - 5xy$

   $= (15x^3 - 6x^2y) + (2y^2 - 5xy)$

   $= 3x^2(5x - 2y) + y(2y - 5x)$

   $= 3x^2(5x - 2y) - y(5x - 2y)$

   $= \mathbf{(5x - 2y)}\,(3x^2 - y)$

3. Factor: $x^2 + 7x + 6$

   Here, $b = 7$, $c = 6$

   Use 6 and 1: $\mathbf{6 \cdot 1 = 6}$ and $\mathbf{6 + 1 = 7}$

   $x^2 + \mathbf{6x} + x + 6$
   $(x^2 + \mathbf{6x}) + (x + 6) = x\,(\mathbf{x + 6}) + 1\,(\mathbf{x + 6})$
   $\qquad\qquad\qquad = (x + 1)\,(x + 6)$

FACTORS

1. **Finding the greatest common factor of monomials.**

   Step 1 Find the greatest common factor of the coefficients of monomials.

   Step 2 Determine exponents of various variables in each monomial.

   Step 3 Take the minimum of the exponents of each variable. Write each variable raised to the respective minimum exponent.

   Step 4 The greatest common factor is the product of all quantities determined in the three steps above.

2. **Factoring by Grouping**

   Step 1 Group the terms in such a way that each group has a common factor.

   Step 2 Use the distributive property to factor each group of terms.

   Step 3 If all the groups share a common factor, then use the distributive property to factor out this common factor.

   Step 4 If the groups do not share a common factor, try regrouping and repeat the steps 1 to 3 again.

FACTORING TRINOMIALS

3. **Factoring $x^2 + bx + c$:**

   Step 1 Write the expression in *standard form*.

   Step 2 Find two numbers whose sum is b and product is c.

   Step 3 If the numbers are p and q, then
   $x^2 + bx + c = (x + p)(x + q)$

4. Factoring $ax^2 + bx + c$, $a \neq 1$

Step 1 Factor out the GCF, if any.

Step 2 Find two numbers such that their sum is **b** and their product is **ac**.

Step 3 Split the middle term using the integers found in Step 2.

Step 4 Factor by grouping.

SPECIAL FACTORIZATIONS

5. $a^2 - b^2 = (a - b)(a + b)$

6. $a^2 + 2ab + b^2 = (a + b)^2$

7. $a^2 - 2ab + b^2 = (a - b)^2$

8. $a^3 + b^3 = (a + b)(a^2 - ab + b^2)$

9. $a^3 - b^3 = (a - b)(a^2 + ab + b^2)$

10. General Strategy For Factoring a Polynomial

Step 1 Look for the greatest common factor (GCF) of all the terms, other than 1. If the GCF is **1**, then proceed to Step 2 with the given polynomial. If the GCF is other than **1**, then factor it out and proceed with the reduced polynomial to Step 2.

given polynomial = (GCF) (reduced polynomial)

Step 2 If the given polynomial or the reduced polynomial has only two terms then determine if it is one of the following:

   a. Difference of two squares.

   b. Difference of two cubes.

   c. Sum of two cubes.

   d. None of the above three. In this case, factoring is complete.

Step 3 If the expression has only three terms, then check if it is one of the following forms.

4. Factor: $12x^2 - 17x - 5$
$a = 12$, $b = -17$, $c = -5$

The numbers are -20 and 3.
$b = -17$, $a \cdot c = -60$

$-20 + 3 = -17$ and $(-20)(3) = -60$.
$12x^2 - \mathbf{17x} - 5 = 12x^2 - \mathbf{20x + 3x} - 5$

$= 4x(3x - 5) + 1(3x - 5)$
$= (3x - 5)(4x + 1)$

5. $9x^2 - 49 = (3x)^2 - 7^2 = (3x - 7)(3x + 7)$

6. $4x^2 + 4x + 1 = (2x)^2 + 2(2x)(1) + 1^2 = (2x + 1)^2$

7. $4x^2 - 4x + 1 = (2x)^2 - (2x)(1) + 1^2 = (2x - 1)^2$

8. $8p^3 + 27 = (2p)^3 + 3^3$
$= (2p + 3)[(2p)^2 - (2p)(3) + 3^2]$
$= (2p + 3)(4p^2 - 6p + 9)$

9. $27r^3 - 1 = (3r)^3 - 1^3$
$= (3r - 1)[(3r)^2 + (3r)(1) + 1^2]$
$= (3r - 1)(9r^2 + 3r + 1)$

10. (a) $4ax^2 - 36a$
$= 4a(x^2 - 9) = 4a(x - 3)(x + 3)$

(b) $xy^3 - 27x$
$= x(y^3 - 27) = x(y - 3)(y^2 + 3y + 9)$

(c) $xy^2 - 5xy + 6x$
$= x(y^2 - 5y + 6) = x(y - 2)(y - 3)$

(d) $3x^2 - 6x + 3$
$= 3(x^2 - 2x + 1) = 3(x - 1)^2$

(e) $14x^2 - 35x - 21$

$= 7(2x^2 - 5x - 3)$

$= 7(x - 3)(2x + 1)$

(f) $x^2 - 4x + 4 + xy - 2y$

$= (x - 2)^2 + y(x - 2)$

$= (x - 2)(x - 2 + y)$

$= (x - 2)(x + y - 2)$

a. Perfect Square:
$a^2 + 2ab + b^2$ or $a^2 - 2ab + b^2$

b. Trinomial with leading coefficient 1:
$x^2 + bx + c$

c. Trinomial with leading coefficient not 1:
$ax^2 + bx + c$
And try to factor the trinomial.

Step 4 If the expression has more than three terms then try to factor using the grouping method.

Step 5 Check if each factor can be factored further. Factoring always means factoring completely.

APPLICATIONS OF FACTORING

11. If $(2x - 3)(3x + 1) = 0$,
then $2x - 3 = 0$ or $3x + 1 = 0$

11. Zero-factor property

If a and b are real numbers such that
$ab = 0$, then either $a = 0$ or $b = 0$.

12. Solve: $6x^2 - x = 1$

$6x^2 - x - 1 = 0$

$(2x - 1)(3x + 1) = 0$

since $6x^2 - x - 1 = (2x - 1)(3x + 1)$

$\rightarrow \quad 2x - 1 = 0 \quad$ or $\quad 3x + 1 = 0$

$\rightarrow \quad 2x = 1 \quad$ or $\quad 3x = -1$

$\rightarrow \quad x = \dfrac{1}{2} \quad$ or $\quad x = -\dfrac{1}{3}$

12. Three-step approach to solve quadratic equations by factoring.

Step 1 Write the equation in the standard form $ax^2 - bx + c = 0$.

Step 2 Factor $ax^2 + bx + c$ into *linear factors* and replace $ax^2 + bx + c$ by its factored form.

Step 3 Equate each factor to zero and solve.

6.7 REVIEW EXERCISES

In exercises 1-8, find the greatest common factor of the monomials.

1. 9, 75, 90

2. 20, 55, 85

3. 16, 25, 49

4. 4, 9, 25

5. $12p^3q,\ 16p^2q^2,\ 28p^4qr^2, 36p^5q^3s$

6. $8a^2b,\ 12a^2b^3,\ 16a^3b^2, 32a^4b^2$

7. $15x^2y,\ 25xz^2,\ 9y^2z^2$

8. $10xy^2,\ 15x^2z,\ 20yz$

In exercises 9-16, factor out the greatest common factor.

9. $27x^3 - 36x^2$

10. $12x^4 - 18x^3$

11. $63y^2 - 14z^2$

12. $6x^2 - 22y^2$

13. $30p^2q^3 + 45p^4q^2 - 75pq^4$

14. $12x^2y^2 + 18x^3y^2 - 24x^4y^2$

15. $4s(3s - 5t) - 5t^2(5t - 3s)$

16. $2x(y - z) - y(z - y)$

In exercises 17-24, factor by grouping.

17. $12x^2 - 15x - 20y + 16xy$ **18.** $a^2 - b + ab - a$ **19.** $12x^3 - 4x^2y + 3xy - y^2$

20. $x^2 + y - xy - x$ **21.** $r^4 + 3r^3 + 3r^2 + 7r - 6$ **22.** $xy - ab + bx - ay$

23. $3x^5 - 3x^3y - 2x^2y^2 + 2y^3 + x^2 - y$ **24.** $6ab - b^2 + 12ac - 2bc$

In exercises 25-28, complete the blanks.

25. $x^2 + 2x - 15 = (x + 5)\,(\quad)$ **26.** $y^2 + y - 56 = (y + 8)\,(\quad)$

27. $12x^2 + 13x - 14 = (\ +7)\,(\ -2)$ **28.** $3y^2 - 4y - 4 = (y - 2)\,(\ + 2)$

In exercises 29-76, factor completely.

29. $x^2 + 6x - 16$ **30.** $x^2 + 27x + 176$ **31.** $x^2 - 6x + 8$ **32.** $x^2 - 12x - 45$

33. $36x^2 - 1$ **34.** $4y^2 - 36$ **35.** $16t^2 + 8t + 1$ **36.** $3x^2 - 10x + 8$

37. $8y^2 - 6y - 2$ **38.** $2x^2 - 17x - 30$ **39.** $3p^2 - 10p - 8$ **40.** $12x^2 - x - 35$

41. $2x^3 - 5x^2 - 3x$ **42.** $x^2 - 24x + 143$ **43.** $(x-1)^2 + 5(x-1) + 6$ **44.** $x^4 - 10x^2 + 9$

45. $x^4 + x^2 - 6$ **46.** $z^4 - 26z^2 + 25$ **47.** $2x^4 - 7x^2 - 4$ **48.** $z^4 - 13z^2 + 36$

49. $x^2 + 3x + 6$ **50.** $y^2 + 2x + 5$ **51.** $3x^2 + 5x + 8$ **52.** $2x^2 - 5x + 5$

53. $p^2 - 16$ **54.** $25 - z^2$ **55.** $4a^2 - 49$ **56.** $36 - 25x^2$

57. $4p^2 + 25$ **58.** $3x^2 - 27$ **59.** $x^4 - 36$ **60.** $25 - y^4$

61. $16x^4 - 81$ **62.** $36 - 4x^2$ **63.** $y^2 - 8y + 16$ **64.** $2x^2 - 8x + 8$

65. $2z^2 + 12z + 18$ **66.** $4x^2 + 12x + 9$ **67.** $x^2 - 5x + \dfrac{25}{4}$ **68.** $y^2 - \dfrac{3}{2}y + \dfrac{9}{16}$

69. $9x^2 + 30xy + 25y^2$ **70.** $4a^2 - 12ab + 9b^2$ **71.** $27x^3 - 125y^3$ **72.** $3x^3 - 24$

73. $8r^3s^3 + 27t^3$ **74.** $x - 8xy^3$ **75.** $216a^3b^6 - 125c^6$ **76.** $54a^6b + 2a^3b^4$

In exercises 77-100, solve the equation.

77. $(x + 4)(3x - 5) = 0$ **78.** $(4x + 5)(x - 4) = 0$ **79.** $(2x + 3)(x^2 + 1) = 0$

80. $(3x + 4)(x^2 + 3) = 0$ **81.** $p^2 + 15p + 50 = 0$ **82.** $x^2 + 3x - 18 = 0$

83. $p^2 - 15p + 50 = 0$ **84.** $x^2 - 3x - 10 = 0$ **85.** $x^2 - 15x = 100$

86. $6x^2 - x = 2$ **87.** $2m^2 + m = 0$ **88.** $2x + 3x^2 = 0$

89. $4x^2 + 4x + 1 = 0$ **90.** $9y^2 - 6y + 1 = 0$ **91.** $x^2 = 12 - x$

92. $y^2 = 11y - 28$ **93.** $2x^2 + 5x + 3 = 0$ **94.** $2x^2 + 9x = 5$

95. $2 + y = 6y^2$ **96.** $4 + 8x = 5x^2$ **97.** $x^4 + 8x^2 + 15 = 0$

98. $z^4 - 26z^2 + 25 = 0$ **99.** $x^4 - 13x^2 + 36 = 0$ **100.** $x^4 - 37x^2 + 36 = 0$

101. The product of two consecutive odd integers is 143. Find the integers.

102. The product of two successive multiples of 3 is 180. Find the multiples.

103. The sum of the squares of two consecutive numbers is 221. Find the numbers.

104. The length of a room is 3 meters more than its width. The area of the room is 70 square meters. Determine its length and width.

105. When the square of a whole number is added to 4 times the next number the result is 81. Find the number.

106. Diagonal of a rectangle is two cms more than its length and its width is 10 cm. Find the area of the rectangle.

107. The area of a rectangular window is 154 square feet. If the width is 3 feet less than the length, find the dimensions.

108. The sides of a right-angled triangle containing the right angle are x and $(x - 2)$ units. If the area of the triangle is 60 square units, calculate the length of the base and height of the triangle.

109. A piece of wire is 12 feet in length. It is to be cut into two pieces. Each of these pieces will then be bent into squares such that the sum of their areas is 5 square feet. How long will the two pieces be?

110. Find two numbers whose sum is 29 and the sum of the squares of the numbers is 425.

111. The hypotenuse of a right triangle is 1 inch longer than the longer side. The shorter side is 8 inches shorter than the hypotenuse. Find the length of the three sides of the triangle.

112. The length of a hall is 3 meters more than its width. If the area of the hall is 108 m², find its length and breadth.

113. Two cars leave at the same time. One car travels north and the other car travels west. When the car traveling west has gone 24 miles, the distance between the two cars was 4 miles more than three times the distance covered by the car traveling north. Find the distance traveled by the car heading north.

114. The hypotenuse of a right triangle is 1 inch less than twice the shortest side. If the third side is 1 inch more than the shortest side, find the sides of the triangle.

115. The product of the measures of two supplementary angles is 5,600°. Find the measure of the greater angle.

116. The square of a number is 15 times that number. Find the number.

6.8 SELF TEST

In exercises 1-4, factor out the greatest common factor.

1. $24x^3y^4 + 40x^2y - 64xy^2$

2. $2a(x + y) - 3b(x + y)$

3. $3a(4b - a) + 5b(a - 4b)$

4. $15x^2y^3 - 20xy^2 + 25x^3y^3$

In exercises 5-10, factor by grouping.

5. $12x^2 + 20x - 15y - 9xy$

6. $x^3 + x^2 + x + 1$

7. $12x^3 - 4x^2y + 9xy - 3y^2 - 6x + 2y$

8. $a^3 + a - 3a^2 - 3$

9. $8p^2 - 2pq - 3q^2 - 20p + 15q$

10. $6(3x - 4y) - 8(4y - 3x)^2$

In exercises 11-12, complete the factorization.

11. $6x^2 - 7x - 20 = (2x\quad)(\quad)$

12. $9x^2 + 30x + 25 = (3x + \quad)(\quad + 5)$

In exercises 13-26, factor the polynomial completely.

13. $25a^2 - 10a + 1$ **14.** $6x^2 - 24$ **15.** $3x^2 + 4$ **16.** $2z^2 + 3$ **17.** $x^3 - 3x^2 - 18x$

18. $x^3 + 4x^2 - 21x$ **19.** $8x^2 - 2x - 15$ **20.** $12x^2 - 23x + 10$ **21.** $12p^2 - 27q^2$ **22.** $18x^2 - 50y^2$

23. $x^2 + x + 1$ **24.** $y^2 - y + 1$ **25.** $8m^3 + n^6$ **26.** $8x^3 - y^3$

In exercises 27-34, solve the equation.

27. $x^2 - 3x = 18$ **28.** $2x^2 - 3x + 1 = 0$ **29.** $6x^2 + 10x - 4 = 0$ **30.** $2y^2 + y - 1 = 0$

31. $x^4 = 4x^2 + 45$ **32.** $x^4 + 9 = 10x^2$ **33.** $6x^3 + 7x^2 = 10x$ **34.** $48y^3 - 13y^2 = y$

35. The difference of two whole numbers is 2. If two times the square of the smaller number added to three times the square of the larger number equals 140, find the numbers.

36. Find two natural numbers which differ by 3, such that the sum of their squares is 117.

37. The triangular sail of a schooner has an area of 30 square meters. The base of the sail is 4 meters less than the height of the sail. Find the height of the sail.

38. The sum of two numbers is 9 and the sum of their squares is 41. Find the numbers.

39. A ladder is leaning against a wall. The distance of the bottom of the ladder from the wall is 4 feet less than the length of the ladder. The top of the ladder from the floor is 2 feet less than the length of the ladder. Determine the length of the ladder.

40. The hypotenuse of a right triangle is 13 cm and the difference between other two sides is 7 cm, Find the two unknown sides.

41. Explain why $(4x^2 - 9)(3x + 5)$ is not a complete factorization of $12x^3 + 20x^2 - 27x - 45$.

42. Explain why $(a^2 + 1)(a^2 - 1)$ is not a complete factorization of $a^4 - 1$.

Rational Expressions

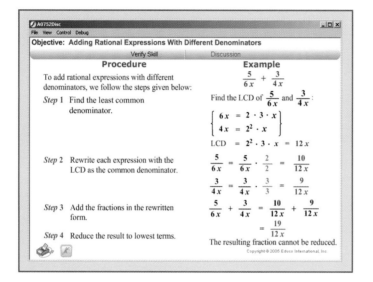

A0752Disc
File View Control Debug

Objective: Adding Rational Expressions With Different Denominators

Verify Skill   Discussion

Procedure

To add rational expressions with different denominators, we follow the steps given below:

Step 1 Find the least common denominator.

Step 2 Rewrite each expression with the LCD as the common denominator.

Step 3 Add the fractions in the rewritten form.

Step 4 Reduce the result to lowest terms.

Example

$$\frac{5}{6x} + \frac{3}{4x}$$

Find the LCD of $\frac{5}{6x}$ and $\frac{3}{4x}$:

$$\left\{ \begin{array}{l} 6x = 2 \cdot 3 \cdot x \\ 4x = 2^2 \cdot x \end{array} \right\}$$

$$\text{LCD} = 2^2 \cdot 3 \cdot x = 12x$$

$$\frac{5}{6x} = \frac{5}{6x} \cdot \frac{2}{2} = \frac{10}{12x}$$

$$\frac{3}{4x} = \frac{3}{4x} \cdot \frac{3}{3} = \frac{9}{12x}$$

$$\frac{5}{6x} + \frac{3}{4x} = \frac{10}{12x} + \frac{9}{12x}$$

$$= \frac{19}{12x}$$

The resulting fraction cannot be reduced.

Copyright © 2005 Educo International, Inc.

7 RATIONAL EXPRESSIONS

We know that arithmetic fractions such as $\frac{3}{7}, \frac{6}{4}, -\frac{2}{5}$ are *quotients of two integers*, with the denominator not equal to zero. These are also called *rational numbers*. In the same way *rational expressions* are *quotients of two polynomials*. Rational expressions can be added, subtracted, multiplied, and divided in much the same way as arithmetic fractions. In this chapter we study rational expressions.

This chapter is divided into eight sections.

7.1 EVALUATING RATIONAL EXPRESSIONS

Recall that a *rational number* can be written as a ratio of two integers such as $\frac{18}{71}$. In algebra, the ratio of two polynomials is called a **rational expression**.

For example:

$\dfrac{2x^2+1}{3x^2+4x-7}$ is a rational expression.

$\dfrac{2\sqrt{2}-3}{\sqrt{x^2+5}}$ is **not** a rational expression, because the denominator is not a polynomial.

> **OBJECTIVES** ■■■■
>
> Upon completion of this section you will be able to:
>
> A. Find the values of the variable(s) for which a rational expression is not defined; and
>
> B. Evaluate rational expressions.

A. WHEN A RATIONAL EXPRESSION IS NOT DEFINED

Since division by zero is not defined, we must be careful not to use a value of the variable that gives a denominator of zero. Therefore a rational expression is said to be *undefined* or *not defined* for the real number "*a*" if on substituting "*a*" for the variable, the denominator of the rational expression becomes zero.

To determine the values of the variable for which a rational expression is not defined, we proceed as follows:

> ***Step* 1**   Set the denominator of the rational expression to zero.
>
> ***Step* 2**   Solve the equation obtained in step 1.

The solutions of this equation are the values for which the rational expression is not defined.

1. Determine the values for which the expressions are not defined.

a) $\dfrac{4x+5}{x-6}$

b) $\dfrac{4y}{2y-3}$

c) $\dfrac{t^2+4}{t^2-16}$

d) $\dfrac{5z-1}{z^2-3z-4}$

EXAMPLE 1 For each of the following rational expressions determine the values for which the expressions are not defined.

a. $\dfrac{x^2-1}{x+7}$ b. $\dfrac{2y}{3y-2}$ c. $\dfrac{t^2+1}{t^2-9}$

d. $\dfrac{5z}{z^2-6z+8}$ e. $\dfrac{3x}{x^2+5}$

Solutions:

a. $\dfrac{x^2-1}{x+7}$: $x+7=0$

$x=-7$

Therefore, the rational expression $\dfrac{x^2-1}{x+7}$ is not defined for $x=-7$.

b. $\dfrac{2y}{3y-2}$: $3y-2=0$

$3y=2$

$y=\dfrac{2}{3}$

Therefore, the rational expression $\dfrac{2y}{3y-2}$ is not defined for $y=\dfrac{2}{3}$.

c. $\dfrac{t^2+1}{t^2-9}$: $t^2-9=0$

$(t-3)(t+3)=0$

$t-3=0$ or $t+3=0$

$t=3$ or $t=-3$

Therefore, the rational expression $\dfrac{t^2+1}{t^2-9}$ is not defined for $t=3$ and $t=-3$.

d. $\dfrac{5z}{z^2-6z+8}$: $z^2-6z+8=0$

$(z-2)(z-4)=0$

$\longrightarrow$ $z-2=0$ or $z-4=0$

$\longrightarrow$ $z=2$ or $z=4$

Therefore, the rational expression $\dfrac{5z}{z^2-6z+8}$ is not defined for $z=2$ and $z=4$.

e. $\dfrac{3x}{x^2+5}$: $x^2 + 5 = 0$ Set the denominator to zero.

The equation $x^2 + 5 = 0$ has no real solution, since $x^2 \geq 0$ for all x, so $x^2 + 5 \geq 5$ for all x and can never be 0.

Therefore, the rational expression is *defined for all* values of x.

There are no points at which this rational expression is not defined.

B. EVALUATING A RATIONAL EXPRESSION

To evaluate a rational expression for a given value of the variable, substitute the value for the variable in the expression and simplify. For example, the value of $\dfrac{2x}{x^2-4}$ for $x = 1$ is:

$$\frac{2(1)}{(1)^2-4} = \frac{2}{1-4} = \frac{2}{-3} = -\frac{2}{3}.$$

EXAMPLE 2   Find the numerical value of each of the following rational expressions for the given value of the variable.

     a. $\dfrac{5x-7}{2x^2+3x-1}$; $x = 2$

     b. $\dfrac{3p^2-7}{p^3+p^2+p+4}$; $p = -1$

Solutions:

a.   **Substitute 2 for x in** $\dfrac{5x-7}{2x^2+3x-1}$,

$$\frac{5(2)-7}{2(2^2)+3(2)-1} = \frac{10-7}{2(4)+6-1} = \frac{3}{8+6-1}$$

$$= \frac{3}{13}$$

b.   **Substitute -1 for p in** $\dfrac{3p^2-7}{p^3+p^2+p+4}$,

$$\frac{3(-1)^2-7}{(-1)^3+(-1)^2+(-1)+4} = \frac{3(1)-7}{-1+1-1+4} = \left(\frac{-4}{3}\right)$$

$$= -\frac{4}{3}$$

A. In exercises 1-32, find the value(s) of the variable for which the rational expression is not defined.

1. $\dfrac{4}{5x}$

2. $\dfrac{5}{6z+1}$

3. $\dfrac{3x^2+1}{5x-2}$

4. $\dfrac{3y^2-1}{3y+4}$

5. $\dfrac{5x-7}{x+3}$

6. $\dfrac{5z+2}{z-2}$

7. $\dfrac{5x+3}{1-4x^2}$

8. $\dfrac{3x+2}{4x^2-9}$

9. $\dfrac{4x+1}{x^2-4}$

10. $\dfrac{x+1}{x^3-1}$

11. $\dfrac{3x+1}{x^3+1}$

12. $\dfrac{2x+3}{4x^2-36}$

13. $\dfrac{2t}{t^2-1}$

14. $\dfrac{3x}{x^2-4}$

15. $\dfrac{2x}{9x^2-1}$

16. $\dfrac{13x}{x^4-81}$

17. $\dfrac{1}{y^2-5y+6}$

18. $\dfrac{1}{x^2-2x-8}$

19. $\dfrac{5y}{y^2-6y+8}$

20. $\dfrac{7y}{2y^2-3y-2}$

21. $\dfrac{y+1}{6y^2-y-1}$

22. $\dfrac{2y+1}{(2y+5)\,(y-2)}$

23. $\dfrac{13p}{p^2+36}$

24. $\dfrac{3x}{2x^2+1}$

25. $\dfrac{5y}{3y^2+1}$

26. $\dfrac{5z-3}{z^2+11z+30}$

27. $\dfrac{3x+5}{x^2+9x+18}$

28. $\dfrac{3x}{75x-27x^2}$

29. $\dfrac{2x+1}{-48+12x+6x^2}$

30. $\dfrac{4}{b^2-9b^2}$

31. $\dfrac{3x-1}{18x^3+24x^2+8x}$

32. $\dfrac{5}{a^4-16}$

B. In exercises 33-60, evaluate the rational expression for the indicated value.

33. $\dfrac{3x-5}{2x}$; $x=5$

34. $\dfrac{2y+5}{3y}$; $y=2$

35. $\dfrac{5x^2-6x}{2x}$; $x=-4$

36. $\dfrac{3z^2-5z}{4z}$; $z=-2$

37. $\dfrac{y^2+1}{y^2-1}$; $y=2$

38. $\dfrac{z^2-4}{z^2+3}$; $z=-3$

39. $\dfrac{z^3-2}{2z^2+1}$; $z=-3$

40. $\dfrac{2z^2+z-1}{z^2-5z}$; $z=4$

41. $\dfrac{t-9}{t^2-4t+4}$; $t=-5$

42. $\dfrac{2-3t}{-4+4t+3t^2}$; $t=3$

43. $\dfrac{2x+3}{x^2-7x+8}$; $x=-5$

44. $\dfrac{2x^2-1}{4x^2-12x+9}$; $x=-2$

45. $\dfrac{t+8}{t^2-4t+3}$; $t=-1$

46. $\dfrac{x+4}{x^2-5x-6}$; $x=3$

47. $\dfrac{2p-1}{3p^2+4p-5}$; $p=0$

48. $\dfrac{3x-1}{2x^2+11x+5}$; $x=-1$

49. $\dfrac{-4a+6}{3-5a+7a^2}$; $a=1$

50. $\dfrac{2x-3}{2+3x-x^2}$; $x=0$

51. $\dfrac{4x^2+3x-1}{2x^2+5x+9}$; $x=-2$

52. $\dfrac{3x^2-2x+1}{2x^2+3x-1}$; $x=1$

53. $\dfrac{2x^2-1}{x^3+4x^2+1}$; $x=3$

54. $\dfrac{2y^2+1}{2y^3+y-1}$; $y=-3$

55. $\dfrac{3x-1}{2x^2+11x+5}$; $x=-1$

56. $\dfrac{4x^2-13}{2x^4-2x^3+9}$; $x=-2$

57. $\dfrac{3t^2+3}{3t^3+t^2-5}$; $t=-2$

58. $\dfrac{2-5t}{2t^2-t-6}$; $t=5$

59. $\dfrac{5u^3+9u-6}{3u^4-4u^3+8}$; $u=-3$

60. $\dfrac{18u^3-13u+9}{30u^4+6u^2+11}$; $u=0$

7.2 SIMPLIFYING RATIONAL EXPRESSIONS

Recall that a fraction is said to be in lowest terms if the numerator and the denominator have no common factors other than 1 or –1. In other words, a fraction is in lowest terms if the greatest common factor of the numerator and the denominator is 1. For example: $\frac{3}{5}$ and $-\frac{15}{7}$ are in lowest terms but $\frac{2}{4}$ is not, because 2 is a common factor between 2 and 4. In exactly the same way, we say:

A rational expression $\frac{P}{Q}$ $(Q \neq 0)$ is in **lowest terms** if *P* and *Q* have no common factors, other than 1.

A. THE FUNDAMENTAL PROPERTY OF RATIONAL EXPRESSIONS

The value of a rational expression is a real number for each permissible value of the variable. Hence all properties of real numbers also apply to rational expressions. Recall an important property of rational numbers: $\frac{ak}{bk} = \frac{a}{b}$ *for all non-zero numbers k.* This property when applied to rational expressions gives us the following:

> **Fundamental Property of Rational Expressions:**
>
> $\frac{PK}{QK} = \frac{P}{Q}$ for all rational expressions $\frac{PK}{QK}$, and for any non-zero number or expression *K*.

B. WRITING A RATIONAL EXPRESSION IN LOWEST TERMS

Recall the steps used in writing a numeric fraction in lowest terms. For example, to write $\frac{16}{24}$ in lowest term:

1. Factor the numerator and factor the denominator.

2. Cancel common factors.

   Thus $\frac{16}{24} = \frac{2 \cdot 8}{3 \cdot 8} = \frac{2}{3}$.   Fundamental property.

 Note   The critical step is to find the greatest common factor of the denominator and the numerator.

We follow the same steps to write a rational expression in lowest terms.

> **Step 1**   Determine the greatest common factor of the numerator and the denominator.
>
> **Step 2**   Divide the numerator and the denominator by the greatest common factor.

Notes

1. Simplifying a rational expression also means writing the rational expression in lowest terms.
2. In step 2 we are really applying the fundamental property of rational expressions.

WARM-UP

1. Write the following in lowest terms.

a) $\dfrac{63}{90}$

b) $\dfrac{9x^7}{15x^3}$

c) $\dfrac{6x+42}{5x+35}$

d) $\dfrac{9-18x}{4x-2}$

EXAMPLE 1   Write the following in lowest terms.

a. $\dfrac{36}{63}$ b. $\dfrac{12x^5}{18x^3}$ c. $\dfrac{4x-20}{7x-35}$ d. $\dfrac{2-x}{2x-4}$

Solutions:

a. $\dfrac{36}{63}$:

- The greatest common factor of 36 and 63 is 9.

- $\dfrac{36}{63} = \dfrac{9\cdot 4}{9\cdot 7} = \dfrac{4}{7}$ Divide the numerator and the denominator by the GCF.

b. $\dfrac{12x^5}{18x^3}$:   Recall, to find the greatest common factor of the x-terms, take x raised to the lowest of the two exponents.

- The greatest common factor of $12x^5$ and $18x^3$ is $6x^3$.

- $\dfrac{12x^5}{18x^3} = \dfrac{(6x^3)(2x^2)}{(6x^3)(3)}$ Divide the numerator and denominator by the GCF.

  $= \dfrac{2x^2}{3}$

c. $\dfrac{4x-20}{7x-35}$:

- $4x-20 = 4(x-5)$ and $7x-35 = 7(x-5)$, so the greatest common factor is $x-5$.

  $\dfrac{4x-20}{7x-35} = \dfrac{4(x-5)}{7(x-5)}$ Divide the numerator and the denominator by the GCF.

- $= \dfrac{4}{7}$

d. $\dfrac{2-x}{2x-4} = \dfrac{-1(x-2)}{2(x-2)} = -\dfrac{1}{2}$

CH-7:   Rational Expressions

302

EXAMPLE 2 Simplify each of the following rational expressions:

    a. $\dfrac{2x-5}{2x-5}$ b. $\dfrac{2x-5}{2x+5}$

    c. $\dfrac{2x-5}{5-2x}$ d. $\dfrac{7x-3}{6-14x}$

Solutions:

a. $\dfrac{2x-5}{2x-5} = 1$

b. $\dfrac{2x-5}{2x+5}$ cannot be reduced. The binomials have no common factors.

c. $\dfrac{2x-5}{5-2x}$ Rewrite the denominator with descending powers.

  $= \dfrac{2x-5}{-2x+5}$ Commutative Property of Addition: $5-2x = -2x+5$

  $= \dfrac{1(2x-5)}{-1(2x-5)}$ Factor numerator and denominator. $-2x+5 = -1(2x-5)$

  $= \dfrac{1}{-1}$ Divide the numerator and denominator by the GCF: $(2x-5)$

  $= -1$

> **Note** A ratio of opposite binomials always simplifies to –1.

d. $\dfrac{7x-3}{6-14x}$ Rewrite the denominator with descending powers.

  $= \dfrac{7x-3}{-14x+6}$ Commutative property of addition: $6-14x = -14x+6$

  $= \dfrac{1(7x-3)}{-2(7x-3)}$ Factor the denominator: $-14x+6 = -2(7x-3)$

  $= -\dfrac{1}{2}$ Divide the numerator and the denominator by the GCF: $(7x-3)$

EXAMPLE 3 Simplify each of the following rational expressions:

    a. $\dfrac{t^2-9}{t-3}$ b. $\dfrac{2z^2+11z+12}{3z^2+11z-4}$ c. $\dfrac{x^3+5x^2+6x}{x^2-2x-8}$

WARM-UP

2. Simplify each of the following rational expressions.

  a) $\dfrac{3x-5}{3x+5}$

  b) $\dfrac{3x-5}{3x-5}$

  c) $\dfrac{3x-5}{5-3x}$

  d) $\dfrac{3x-5}{9x-15}$

3. Simplify each of the following rational expressions.

  a) $\dfrac{t^2-4}{t+2}$

b) $\dfrac{2x^2+3x-5}{2x^2+7x+5}$

c) $\dfrac{x^4+6x^3-7x^2}{x^2-2x+1}$

Answers:

1. a) $\dfrac{7}{10}$ b) $\dfrac{3}{5}x^4$ c) $\dfrac{6}{5}$ d) $-\dfrac{9}{2}$

2. a) $\dfrac{3x-5}{3x+5}$ b) 1 c) -1 d) $\dfrac{1}{3}$

3. a) $t-2$ b) $\dfrac{x-1}{x+1}$ c) $\dfrac{x^2(x+7)}{x-1}$

Solutions:

a. $\dfrac{t^2-9}{t-3}$:

- $t^2-9=(t-3)(t+3)$ Factor the numerator.

  $t-3=1(t-3)$ Factor the denominator.

So, the greatest common factor is $t-3$.

- $\dfrac{t^2-9}{t-3}=\dfrac{(t-3)(t+3)}{1\cdot(t-3)}=t+3$ Divide the numerator and the denominator by the GCF.

b. $\dfrac{2z^2+11z+12}{3z^2+11z-4}$:

- You need to factor the numerator and the denominator by grouping. To factor the numerator by grouping, find two numbers whose product is $2\cdot12$ or 24 and whose sum is 11, $(8+3)$. Hence,

$$2z^2+11z+12=2z^2+8z+3z+12$$
$$=2z(z+4)+3(z+4)$$
$$=(2z+3)(z+4)$$

To factor the denominator by grouping, find two numbers whose product is $3(-4)$ or -12 and whose sum is 11, $(-1+12)$. Hence,

$$3z^2+11z-4=3z^2-z+12z-4$$
$$=z(3z-1)+4(3z-1)$$
$$=(z+4)(3z-1)$$

The greatest common factor is $(z+4)$.

- $\dfrac{2z^2+11z+12}{3z^2+11z-4}=\dfrac{(2z+3)(z+4)}{(z+4)(3z-1)}=\dfrac{2z+3}{3z-1}$.

c. $\dfrac{x^3+5x^2+6x}{x^2-2x-8}=\dfrac{x(x^2+5x+6)}{(x+2)(x-4)}$

$$=\dfrac{x(x+2)(x+3)}{(x+2)(x-4)}$$

$$=\dfrac{x(x+3)}{x-4}$$

EXERCISE 7.2

B. In exercises 1-28, write the rational expression in lowest terms.

1. $\dfrac{12}{18}$
2. $\dfrac{16}{22}$
3. $\dfrac{15x^4}{3x^2}$
4. $\dfrac{32y^3}{4y}$
5. $\dfrac{-26p^3 q^5}{39p^4 q}$
6. $\dfrac{36u^4 v^5}{45u^3 v^6}$

7. $\dfrac{-24u^2 v}{60uv^3}$
8. $\dfrac{44a^3 b^4}{-33a^2 b^3}$
9. $\dfrac{\left(2x^3\right)^3}{5x^4}$
10. $\dfrac{\left(3x^2\right)^2}{5x^3}$
11. $\dfrac{24t-30}{12}$
12. $\dfrac{3x+15}{27}$

13. $\dfrac{7a\,(a-b)}{21(a-b)}$
14. $\dfrac{3x\,(x+y)}{9(x+y)}$
15. $-\dfrac{3p\,(p-4)}{8-2p}$
16. $\dfrac{3x\,(6-x)}{3x-18}$
17. $\dfrac{9t^2\,(s-t)}{12t\,(t-s)^2}$
18. $\dfrac{5x^3\,(x-y)}{15x\,(y-x)^2}$

19. $\dfrac{3\,(a+4)}{(a+4)\,(2a-1)}$
20. $\dfrac{3(x-5)}{6(x-5)(x+2)}$
21. $\dfrac{x^2-y^2}{x-y}$
22. $\dfrac{x^2-16}{x+4}$
23. $\dfrac{6y\,(y-z)}{15y^2\,(y-z)^2}$
24. $\dfrac{3x-6}{x^2-4x+4}$

25. $\dfrac{2x+2y}{4x^2-4y^2}$
26. $\dfrac{-3x^2+12}{x^2-x-2}$
27. $\dfrac{x^2+2x-15}{x^2-25}$
28. $\dfrac{x^2-x-2}{x^2-4x+4}$

In exercises 29-68, simplify the rational expression.

29. $\dfrac{3x-6}{x^2-4x+4}$
30. $\dfrac{2x+4}{x^2+4x+4}$
31. $\dfrac{3y^2-6y}{-9y+18}$
32. $\dfrac{2x+2}{2x^2+x-1}$

33. $\dfrac{x^2-2x+1}{3x^2-2x-1}$
34. $\dfrac{x^2+x-6}{x^2+6x+9}$
35. $\dfrac{x^2-4}{x^3-8}$
36. $\dfrac{4x^2-4y^2}{x^2+2y+2x+xy}$

37. $\dfrac{x^2-9y^2}{x^2+3y+3x+xy}$
38. $\dfrac{bx+cy+by+cx}{b^2-c^2}$
39. $\dfrac{2t^3+19t^2-21t}{2t^2+21t}$
40. $\dfrac{4x^2-13x+3}{4x-1}$

41. $\dfrac{x^3+1}{x^3+a}$, $a\neq 1$
42. $\dfrac{x^3+8}{x^2-2x+4}$
43. $\dfrac{x^3+27}{x^2-6x+9}$
44. $\dfrac{x^3-8}{x^2+2x+4}$

45. $\dfrac{(a+b)^3}{a^2+2ab+b^2}$
46. $\dfrac{x^3-y^3}{x^2+2xy+y^2}$
47. $\dfrac{x^2-4xy+4y^2}{x^3-8y^3}$
48. $\dfrac{x^3+27}{2x^2-18}$

49. $\dfrac{(a-b)^3}{a^2-2ab+b^2}$
50. $\dfrac{(x+y)^3}{x^2+2xy+y^2}$
51. $\dfrac{2x^2-2y^2}{x^2+2y+2x+xy}$
52. $\dfrac{x^3-3x^2+2x}{x^2y-2xy}$

53. $\dfrac{p^2-3p+9}{p^3+27}$
54. $\dfrac{3x^3-24}{2x^2-15x+22}$
55. $\dfrac{16p^2-25q^2}{16p^2-40pq+25q^2}$
56. $\dfrac{5x^2-15x^3}{1-9x^2}$

57. $\dfrac{16p^2-25q^2}{16p^2+40pq+25q^2}$
58. $\dfrac{9x^2-16}{3x^2+x-4}$
59. $\dfrac{4x^2+8x+3}{6+x-2x^2}$
60. $\dfrac{2x^2-x-10}{2x^2-11x+15}$

61. $\dfrac{6t^2-7t-5}{2t^2+5t+2}$
62. $\dfrac{x^2+5x-50}{x^2-13x+40}$
63. $\dfrac{14a^2(7-3a)}{21a(3a-7)}$
64. $\dfrac{x^2-3x+2}{x^2-4x+3}$

65. $\dfrac{y^2+8y+16}{y^2-2y-24}$
66. $\dfrac{2z^2-9z+4}{2z^2-5z-12}$
67. $\dfrac{2-7y+6y^2}{6y^2+5y-6}$
68. $\dfrac{z^2+7z-8}{z^2+6z-7}$

7.3 MULTIPLYING AND DIVIDING RATIONAL EXPRESSIONS

Multiplication and division of rational expressions is performed in the same way as multiplication and division of numeric fractions. The major difference is that in rational expressions we have to use techniques of factoring algebraic expressions as discussed in the last chapter.

A. MULTIPLICATION OF RATIONAL EXPRESSIONS

Recall how we multiply two numeric fractions.

$$\frac{10}{9} \cdot \frac{21}{25} = \frac{10 \cdot 21}{9 \cdot 25} = \frac{(2 \cdot 5)(3 \cdot 7)}{(3 \cdot 3)(5 \cdot 5)} = \frac{2 \cdot 3 \cdot 5 \cdot 7}{3 \cdot 3 \cdot 5 \cdot 5} = \frac{14}{15}$$

To multiply two rational expressions we follow the same steps:

Step 1	Multiply the numerators, showing the new numerator as a product of the given numerators.
Step 2	Multiply the denominators, showing the new denominator as a product of the given denominators.
Step 3	Factor all the expressions in the numerator and the denominator.
Step 4	Reduce to lowest terms.

WARM-UP

1. Multiply and write your answers in lowest terms.

   a) $\dfrac{(2x+5)(x-1)}{(x-1)(x+3)} \cdot \dfrac{(x+3)(x+1)}{(2x+5)}$

EXAMPLE 1 Multiply and write your answer in lowest terms.

a. $\dfrac{(x+3)(2x-1)}{x+4} \cdot \dfrac{x+4}{(2x-1)}$

b. $\dfrac{x(2x+3)}{\left(x^2+4\right)(x-3)} \cdot \dfrac{(x-3)\left(x^2+4\right)(x-5)}{(2x-1)}$

Solutions:

a. $\dfrac{(x+3)(2x-1)}{x+4} \cdot \dfrac{x+4}{(2x-1)}$

Step 1 The product of numerators $= (x+3)(2x-1)(x+4)$.

Step 2 The product of denominators $= (x+4)(2x-1)$.

Step 3 Not needed, because the new numerator and the denominator is already factored.

$Step\ 4$ $\quad \dfrac{(x+3)\,(2x-1)}{x+4} \cdot \dfrac{x+4}{(2x-1)} = \dfrac{(x+3)\,(2x-1)\,(x+4)}{(x+4)\,(2x-1)}$

$$= \dfrac{x+3}{1} = x+3$$

b. $\quad \dfrac{x\,(2x+3)}{\left(x^2+4\right)(x-3)} \cdot \dfrac{(x-3)\left(x^2+4\right)(x-5)}{(2x-1)}$

b) $\dfrac{(3x+1)\,(2x-1)}{(x+2)\,(2x+1)} \cdot \dfrac{(x+2)\,(2x+1)}{(x-2)(3x+1)}$

- The product of the numerators:
$$= x(2x+3)\,(x-3)\,(x^2+4)\,(x-5).$$

- The product of the denominators $= (x^2+4)\,(x-3)\,(2x-1)$

- $\dfrac{x(2x+3)}{\left(x^2+4\right)(x-3)} \cdot \dfrac{(x-3)\left(x^2+4\right)(x-5)}{(2x-1)}$

$$= \dfrac{x\,(2x+3)\,(x-3)\left(x^2+4\right)(x-5)}{\left(x^2+4\right)(x-3)(2x-1)} = \dfrac{x\,(2x+3)\,(x-5)}{2x-1}$$

Note Observe that multiplication of rational expressions is really quite easy when the expressions are already factored. The hard part of multiplication process is to factor the expressions correctly.

EXAMPLE 2 Multiply and write your answer in lowest terms.

a. $\dfrac{x^2-7x+12}{x} \cdot \dfrac{x^2}{x-3}$ **b.** $\dfrac{a-b}{3b} \cdot \dfrac{b^3}{(a-b)^2}$

2. Multiply and write your answers in lowest terms.

a) $\dfrac{4x^2+16x+15}{3x} \cdot \dfrac{9x^2}{2x+5}$

Solutions:

a. $\dfrac{x^2-7x+12}{x} \cdot \dfrac{x^2}{x-3}$

- The product of numerators $= (x^2-7x+12)\,(x^2).$

- The product of denominator $= x(x-3).$

- $\dfrac{x^2-7x+12}{x} \cdot \dfrac{x^2}{x-3} = \dfrac{(x^2-7x+12)\,(x^2)}{x\,(x-3)}$ Factor the numerator.

$$= \dfrac{(x-3)\,(x-4)\,x\cdot x}{x\,(x-3)}$$

$$= x(x-4)$$ Reduce to lowest terms.

b) $\dfrac{(x+y)^3 \cdot y^2}{y \cdot (x+y)}$

b. $\dfrac{a-b}{3b} \cdot \dfrac{b^3}{(a-b)^2} = \dfrac{(a-b)(b^3)}{(3b)(a-b)^2}$

$= \dfrac{(a-b)\,b \cdot b \cdot b}{(3b)(a-b)(a-b)}$ Factor the numerator and the denominator.

$= \dfrac{b \cdot b}{3(a-b)} = \dfrac{b^2}{3(a-b)}$ Reduce to lowest terms.

3. Multiply and simplify.

$\dfrac{4x+12}{6x^3+24x^2} \cdot \dfrac{4x^2+16x}{x+3}$

EXAMPLE 3 Multiply and simplify.

$\dfrac{3x^2-12}{6-3x} \cdot \dfrac{2x^2-4x}{x+2}$

Solution:

$\dfrac{3x^2-12}{6-3x} \cdot \dfrac{2x^2-4x}{x+2} = \dfrac{\left(3x^2-12\right)\left(2x^2-4x\right)}{(-3x+6)\,(x+2)}$

$= \dfrac{\left[3\left(x^2-4\right)\right]\left[2x(x-2)\right]}{-3(x-2)\,(x+2)}$

$= \dfrac{3 \cdot 2x\,(x-2)\,(x+2)\,(x-2)}{-3\,(x-2)\,(x+2)}$

$= \dfrac{2x\,(x-2)}{-1}$

$= -2x(x-2) = -2x^2+4x$

$= 4x - 2x^2$

Answers:

1. a) $x+1$ **b)** $\dfrac{2x-1}{x-2}$

2. a) $3x(2x+3)$ **b)** $y(x+y)^2$

3. $\dfrac{8}{3x}$

Note ▷ When multiplying the numerators and denominators of the two rational expressions we *do not expand* the products. They need to be factored for simplification.

B. DIVISION OF RATIONAL EXPRESSIONS

Recall that in order to divide two fractions, for example, $\dfrac{2}{3}$ by $\dfrac{5}{12}$, we multiply $\dfrac{2}{3}$ by the reciprocal

of $\dfrac{5}{12}$. Thus, $\dfrac{2}{3} \div \dfrac{5}{12} = \dfrac{2}{3} \cdot \dfrac{12}{5}$ Reciprocal of $\frac{5}{12}$ is $\frac{12}{5}$.

$= \dfrac{2 \cdot 12}{3 \cdot 5} = \dfrac{2 \cdot 3 \cdot 4}{3 \cdot 5} = \dfrac{8}{5}$

Recall that the reciprocal of a fraction is obtained by swapping the numerator and the denominator of the fraction. We use the same definition for the reciprocal of a rational expression.

If $\dfrac{R}{S}$ is a non-zero rational expression, then the **reciprocal** of $\dfrac{R}{S}$ is defined to be $\dfrac{S}{R}$.

To divide a rational expression $\dfrac{P}{Q}$ by a non-zero expression $\dfrac{R}{S}$, or to simplify $\dfrac{P}{Q} \div \dfrac{R}{S}$, we use the following operation.

$$\frac{P}{Q} \div \frac{R}{S} = \frac{P}{Q} \cdot \frac{S}{R}$$

EXAMPLE 4 Simplify and write the answer in lowest terms.

$$\textbf{a.} \quad \frac{7a\,x}{5ab\,x} \div \frac{7y}{5b}$$

$$\textbf{b.} \quad \frac{4(2x+1)\,(x+3)}{9x\,(3x-4)} \div \frac{8\,(x+3)}{6x\,(x+2)}$$

Solutions:

a.
$$\frac{7a\,x}{5\,a\,b\,x} \div \frac{7y}{5b}$$

$$= \frac{7a\,x}{5ab\,x} \cdot \frac{5b}{7y}$$

• Change the division to multiplication and then multiply.

$$= \frac{7a\,x \cdot 5b}{5ab\,x \cdot 7y} = \frac{1}{y}$$

b.
$$\frac{4(2x+1)\,(x+3)}{9x\,(3x-4)} \div \frac{8\,(x+3)}{6x\,(x+2)}$$

$$= \frac{4(2x+1)\,(x+3)}{9x\,(3x-4)} \cdot \frac{6x\,(x+2)}{8\,(x+3)}$$

• Change the division to multiplication and then multiply.

$$= \frac{4(2x+1)\,(x+3)\,6x\,(x+2)}{9x\,(3x-4)\cdot 8\,(x+3)}$$

• Multiply

$$= \frac{\overset{}{24}(2x+1)\,(x+3)\,x\,(x+2)}{x\cdot \underset{3}{72}(3x-4)\,(x+3)}$$

$$= \frac{(2x+1)\,(x+2)}{3(3x-4)}$$

EXAMPLE 5 Simplify and write the answer in lowest terms.

$$\textbf{a.} \quad \frac{4p^2}{15pq^3} \div \frac{8pq^2}{21p^2q^3} \qquad \textbf{b.} \quad \frac{x^2-4}{x} \div (x+2)$$

Solutions:

a.
$$\frac{4p^2}{15pq^3} \div \frac{8pq^2}{21p^2q^3}$$

Step 1
$$\frac{4p^2}{15pq^3} \div \frac{8pq^2}{21p^2q^3} = \frac{4p^2}{15pq^3} \cdot \frac{21p^2q^3}{8pq^2}$$

Divide   Multiply

Step 2
$$\frac{(4p^2)(21p^2q^3)}{(15pq^3)(8pq^2)} = \frac{(4 \cdot 21)(p^2p^2q^3)}{(15 \cdot 8)\, pq^3\, pq^2}$$

$$= \frac{2 \cdot 2 \cdot 3 \cdot 7\, p^2 \cdot p^2 \cdot q^3}{3 \cdot 5 \cdot 2 \cdot 2 \cdot 2\, p^2 \cdot q^3 \cdot q^2} = \frac{7p^2}{10q^2}$$

b) $\dfrac{3x^2 - 27}{x} \div (x+3)$

b.
$$\frac{x^2 - 4}{x} \div (x+2)$$

Step 1
$$\frac{x^2-4}{x} \div (x+2) = \frac{x^2-4}{x} \cdot \frac{1}{x+2}$$

Divide   Multiply

Step 2
$$\frac{x^2-4}{x(x+2)} = \frac{(x-2)(x+2)}{x(x+2)} = \frac{x-2}{x}$$

6. Simplify and write your expression in lowest terms.

a) $\dfrac{x^2 - 36}{x^2 + 2x - 8} \div \dfrac{x^2 + 5x - 6}{x^2 - 4x + 4}$

EXAMPLE 6 Simplify and write the answer in lowest terms.

a. $\dfrac{x^2 - 9}{x^2 - 8x + 12} \div \dfrac{x^2 - 6x + 9}{x^2 - 4}$

b. $(4t^2 - 9) \div \dfrac{2t^2 + 5t + 3}{t + 2}$

Solutions:

a.
$$\frac{x^2-9}{x^2-8x+12} \div \frac{x^2-6x+9}{x^2-4} = \frac{x^2-9}{x^2-8x+12} \cdot \frac{x^2-4}{x^2-6x+9}$$

Divide   Multiply

$$= \frac{(x^2-9)(x^2-4)}{(x^2-8x+12)(x^2-6x+9)}$$

$$= \frac{(x-3)(x+3)(x-2)(x+2)}{(x-2)(x-6)(x-3)(x-3)}$$

$$= \frac{(x+3)(x+2)}{(x-6)(x-3)}$$

b. $(4t^2 - 9) \div \dfrac{2t^2 + 5t + 3}{t + 2} = \dfrac{4t^2 - 9}{1} \cdot \dfrac{t + 2}{2t^2 + 5t + 3}$

$\Big\downarrow$ Divide $\qquad\qquad\qquad$ $\Big\downarrow$ Multiply

$$= \frac{(2t - 3)\,(2t + 3)}{1} \cdot \frac{(t + 2)}{(2t + 3)\,(t + 1)}$$

$$= \frac{(2t - 3)\,(t + 2)}{(t + 1)}$$

EXAMPLE 7 Perform the indicated operations and simplify.

a. $\dfrac{2a^2 + 5a - 3}{a^2 + 2a - 3} \div \left(\dfrac{a^2 + 2a - 35}{a^2 - 6a + 5} \div \dfrac{a^2 - 9a + 14}{2a^2 - 5a + 2} \right)$

b. $\dfrac{z^2 + z - 12}{z^2 - 4} \div \left(\dfrac{z - 3}{z + 2} \cdot \dfrac{z + 4}{z - 2} \right)$

Solutions: Recall that we must first simplify the expressions within the grouping symbols.

a. $\dfrac{2a^2 + 5a - 3}{a^2 + 2a - 3} \div \left(\dfrac{a^2 + 2a - 35}{a^2 - 6a + 5} \div \dfrac{a^2 - 9a + 14}{2a^2 - 5a + 2} \right)$

$$= \frac{2a^2 + 5a - 3}{a^2 + 2a - 3} \div \left(\frac{a^2 + 2a - 35}{a^2 - 6a + 5} \cdot \frac{2a^2 - 5a + 2}{a^2 - 9a + 14} \right)$$

$$= \frac{2a^2 + 5a - 3}{a^2 + 2a - 3} \div \frac{(a^2 + 2a - 35)\,(2a^2 - 5a + 2)}{(a^2 - 6a + 5)\,(a^2 - 9a + 14)}$$

$$= \frac{2a^2 + 5a - 3}{a^2 + 2a - 3} \cdot \frac{(a^2 - 6a + 5)\,(a^2 - 9a + 14)}{(a^2 + 2a - 35)\,(2a^2 - 5a + 2)}$$

$$= \frac{(2a^2 + 5a - 3)\,(a^2 - 6a + 5)\,(a^2 - 9a + 14)}{(a^2 + 2a - 3)\,(a^2 + 2a - 35)\,(2a^2 - 5a + 2)} \quad \text{Multiply.}$$

$$= \frac{(2a - 1)\,(a + 3)\,(a - 5)\,(a - 1)\,(a - 2)\,(a - 7)}{(a - 1)\,(a + 3)\,(a + 7)\,(a - 5)\,(2a - 1)\,(a - 2)} \quad \text{Factorize.}$$

$$= \frac{(a - 1)\,(a - 2)\,(a + 3)\,(a - 5)\,(2a - 1)\,(a - 7)}{(a - 1)\,(a - 2)\,(a + 3)\,(a - 5)\,(2a - 1)\,(a + 7)} \quad \begin{array}{l}\text{Rearrange}\\\text{the factors.}\end{array}$$

$$= \frac{(a - 7)}{(a + 7)}$$

b) $(4t^2 - 9) \div \dfrac{2t^2 - t - 3}{t - 3}$

7. Perform the indicated operations and simplify.

a) $\left[\dfrac{4x^2 + 4x + 1}{3x + 5} \div \dfrac{2x^2 + 3x + 1}{3x^2 + 8x + 5} \right]$

$\div \dfrac{(2x + 1)(x + 3)}{2x + 3}$

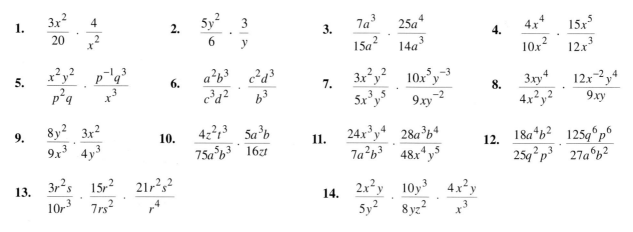

b) $\dfrac{x^2+x-6}{x^2-1} \div \left(\dfrac{x+3}{x-1} \cdot \dfrac{x-3}{x+2} \right)$

b. $\dfrac{z^2+z-12}{z^2-4} \div \left(\dfrac{z-3}{z+2} \cdot \dfrac{z+4}{z-2} \right)$

$= \dfrac{z^2+z-12}{z^2-4} \div \left(\dfrac{(z-3)(z+4)}{(z+2)(z-2)} \right)$ • Multiply inside parenthesis.

$= \dfrac{z^2+z-12}{z^2-4} \cdot \dfrac{(z+2)(z-2)}{(z-3)(z+4)}$ • Change division to multiplication.

$= \dfrac{(z+4)(z-3)}{(z-2)(z+2)} \cdot \dfrac{(z+2)(z-2)}{(z-3)(z+4)}$ • Factorize.

$= 1$ • Cancel common factors.

Answers:

4. a) y b) $\dfrac{1}{x-9}$

5. a) $20x^2y$ b) $\dfrac{3(x-3)}{x}$

6. a) $\dfrac{(x-6)(x-2)}{(x+4)(x-1)}$ b) $\dfrac{(2t+3)(t-3)}{t+1}$

7. a) $\dfrac{2x+3}{x+3}$ b) $\dfrac{(x-2)(x+2)}{(x+1)(x-3)}$

EXERCISE 7.3

A. In exercises 1-14, perform the multiplication and write the answer in lowest terms.

1. $\dfrac{3x^2}{20} \cdot \dfrac{4}{x^2}$

2. $\dfrac{5y^2}{6} \cdot \dfrac{3}{y}$

3. $\dfrac{7a^3}{15a^2} \cdot \dfrac{25a^4}{14a^3}$

4. $\dfrac{4x^4}{10x^2} \cdot \dfrac{15x^5}{12x^3}$

5. $\dfrac{x^2y^2}{p^2q} \cdot \dfrac{p^{-1}q^3}{x^3}$

6. $\dfrac{a^2b^3}{c^3d^2} \cdot \dfrac{c^2d^3}{b^3}$

7. $\dfrac{3x^2y^2}{5x^3y^5} \cdot \dfrac{10x^5y^{-3}}{9xy^{-2}}$

8. $\dfrac{3xy^4}{4x^2y^2} \cdot \dfrac{12x^{-2}y^4}{9xy}$

9. $\dfrac{8y^2}{9x^3} \cdot \dfrac{3x^2}{4y^3}$

10. $\dfrac{4z^2t^3}{75a^5b^3} \cdot \dfrac{5a^3b}{16zt}$

11. $\dfrac{24x^3y^4}{7a^2b^3} \cdot \dfrac{28a^3b^4}{48x^4y^5}$

12. $\dfrac{18a^4b^2}{25q^2p^3} \cdot \dfrac{125q^6p^6}{27a^6b^2}$

13. $\dfrac{3r^2s}{10r^3} \cdot \dfrac{15r^2}{7rs^2} \cdot \dfrac{21r^2s^2}{r^4}$

14. $\dfrac{2x^2y}{5y^2} \cdot \dfrac{10y^3}{8yz^2} \cdot \dfrac{4x^2y}{x^3}$

B. In exercises 15-20, perform the division and simplify.

15. $\dfrac{3p^2}{8p^4} \div \dfrac{6p^3}{24p^4}$

16. $\dfrac{2x^3}{3x^2} \div \dfrac{5x^4}{15x^6}$

17. $\dfrac{25x^8}{9x^4} \div \dfrac{15x^5}{10x^2}$

18. $\dfrac{15x^4}{10x^2} \div \dfrac{10x^3}{25x}$

19. $\dfrac{5a^3}{\left(4a^2\right)^2} \div \dfrac{15a^2}{8a^4}$

20. $\dfrac{5x^4}{(3x)^3} \div \dfrac{15x^2}{9x^4}$

In exercises 21-80, perform the indicated operation(s) and simplify.

21. $\dfrac{x+6}{x^2-4} \cdot \dfrac{2x-4}{2x+12}$

22. $\dfrac{x+8}{x^2-9} \cdot \dfrac{2x-6}{2x+16}$

23. $\dfrac{x^2+2x+1}{2x} \cdot \dfrac{x^2-x}{x^2-1}$

24. $\dfrac{x^2-4x+4}{3x} \cdot \dfrac{x^2+2x}{x^2-4}$

25. $\dfrac{a^2-4}{a^2-1} \cdot \dfrac{a+1}{a+2}$

26. $\dfrac{a^2-9}{a^2-16} \cdot \dfrac{a-4}{a-3}$

27. $(x+1) \cdot \dfrac{1}{x^2+2x+1}$

28. $\left(x^2-4x+4\right) \cdot \dfrac{1}{(x-2)}$

29. $\dfrac{x+4}{x^2-9} \cdot \dfrac{4(x-3)}{3x+12}$

30. $\dfrac{x-y}{4y} \cdot \dfrac{y^3}{(x-y)^3}$

31. $\dfrac{a^2+2a+1}{a} \cdot \dfrac{a^2+a}{a^2-1}$

32. $\dfrac{x^2-9}{x+2} \cdot \dfrac{x^2-4}{x-3}$

33. $\dfrac{6(x+2)}{3(x-1)^2} \cdot \dfrac{9(x-1)}{(x+2)}$

34. $\dfrac{3(x-2)}{9(x+1)} \cdot \dfrac{27(x+1)^2}{9(x-2)}$

35. $\dfrac{2a-5}{3} \div \dfrac{5-2a}{9}$

36. $\dfrac{3x-7}{5} \div \dfrac{7-3x}{10}$

37. $\dfrac{t^2-36}{t-3} \cdot \dfrac{t^2-9}{t+6}$

38. $\dfrac{x^2-9}{x+3} \cdot \dfrac{x^2-8}{x-3}$

39. $\dfrac{3y-6}{5y-20} \cdot \dfrac{10y-40}{27y-54}$

40. $\dfrac{8z-12}{14z+7} \cdot \dfrac{42z+21}{32z-48}$

41. $\dfrac{3a^2+2a}{2ab-3b} \cdot \dfrac{2ab^3-3b^3}{3a^3+2a^2}$

42. $\dfrac{y^2+y-2}{yx^2} \cdot \dfrac{xy^3}{y^2+5y+6}$

43. $\dfrac{x^6 y^6}{x^2+13x+30} \cdot \dfrac{x^2+2x-3}{x^7 y^2}$

44. $\dfrac{6-a-2a^2}{4a^2+3a-10} \cdot \dfrac{3a^2+7a-20}{2a^2+5a-12}$

45. $\dfrac{x^2-36}{x^2-25} \div \dfrac{x+6}{x+5}$

46. $\dfrac{25x^2+10x+1}{x^2-8x+16} \div \dfrac{5x+1}{x-4}$

47. $\dfrac{x^2-9}{4x^2} \div \dfrac{x+3}{2x}$

48. $\dfrac{a^2+2a-35}{12x} \div \dfrac{9x-3x}{a^2+4a-21}$

49. $\dfrac{x^2-4}{2a-ax} \div \dfrac{x^2+4x+4}{2a+ax}$

50. $\left(2x^2-9x-5\right) \div \dfrac{2x^2+x}{x}$

51. $\dfrac{x^2-x-6}{x^2-4} \div \dfrac{9-x^2}{x^2-x-2}$

52. $\dfrac{2x^2-7x-4}{20-x-x^2} \div \dfrac{2x^2-9x-5}{x^2-5}$

53. $\dfrac{x^2-4}{2a-ax} \div \dfrac{x^2+4x+4}{-2a-ax}$

54. $\dfrac{a^3-b^3}{b^2-a^2} \cdot \dfrac{b^2+ab}{a^3+a^2b+ab^2}$

55. $\dfrac{x^2-4}{2a-ax} \div \dfrac{x^2+4x+4}{a(2+x)}$

56. $\dfrac{x^2-7x+12}{x^2-16} \div \dfrac{x^2-2x-3}{x^2-2x-24}$

57. $(2a^2-9a-5) \div \dfrac{2a^2+a}{a}$

58. $(4x^2+4x+1) \div \dfrac{2x^2+x}{x}$

59. $\dfrac{3t^2-5t-2}{4t^2-3t-1} \div \dfrac{3t^2+7t+2}{5t^2-3t-2}$

60. $\dfrac{3x^2-x-4}{9x^2-16} \div \dfrac{4x^2-4}{3x^2-2x-1}$

61. $\dfrac{2x+3}{2x+4} \cdot \dfrac{x^2-4}{x+1}$

62. $\dfrac{(x+1)}{x+2} \cdot \dfrac{(2x+4)}{x-3}$

63. $\dfrac{6y^2}{y^2-y-6} \cdot \dfrac{y+2}{3y}$

64. $\dfrac{15x^3}{x^2+4x+4} \cdot \dfrac{x+2}{5x^2}$

65. $\dfrac{z^2+2z-15}{z^2-z-2} \div \dfrac{z^2+3z-10}{z^2+4z+3}$

66. $\dfrac{x^2-7x+12}{x^2-16} \div \dfrac{x^2-2x-3}{x^2-2x-24}$

67. $\dfrac{3a^2-2a}{3a+2} \div (2-3a) \div \dfrac{3a}{3a-3}$

68. $\dfrac{x^2+4x+3}{x^2 y} \div \dfrac{x^2+2x+1}{xy^2}$

69. $\dfrac{a^3 y^2}{a^2-3a-10} \div \dfrac{ay^4}{a^2-a-20}$

70. $\dfrac{3a^2b-9ab}{y^2 x} \div \dfrac{3a^2-a^3}{yx^2}$

71. $\dfrac{x^2 + 3x - 40}{x^2 + 2x - 35} \div \dfrac{x^2 + 2x - 48}{x^2 - 3x - 18}$

72. $\dfrac{x^2 - 1}{x^2 + x - 2} \times \dfrac{x^3 + 8}{x^4 + 4x^2 + 16} \div \dfrac{x^2 + x}{x^3 + 2x^2 + 4x}$

73. $\dfrac{x^2 - 9}{6x^2 + x - 1} \cdot \dfrac{2x^2 + 5x + 2}{x^2 + 4x + 3} \div \dfrac{x^2 - 3x}{x^2 - x - 2}$

74. $\dfrac{8x^2 - 26x + 15}{3x^2 - x - 4} \cdot \dfrac{3x^2 - 7x + 4}{2x^2 - 7x + 5} \div \dfrac{4x^2 + x - 3}{x^2 - 1}$

75. $\dfrac{t^2 + 10t + 25}{t^2 + 10t} \div \dfrac{t + 5}{t + 10} \cdot \dfrac{10t}{t^2 + 15t + 30}$

76. $\left(\dfrac{x^2 + 7x + 10}{x^2 - 3x - 10} \div \dfrac{x^2 + 3x - 10}{x - 4} \right) \div \dfrac{x - 4}{x^2 - 7x + 10}$

77. $\dfrac{4z^2 - 10z + 6}{z^3 - 3z^2} \div \dfrac{2z - 3}{z^2} \cdot \dfrac{z - 3}{2z - 2}$

78. $\left(\dfrac{2x^2 + 3x - 2}{x + 3} \right) \div \left(\dfrac{3x^2 + 7x + 2}{4x^2 + 15x + 9} \right)$

79. $\dfrac{p^2 - 4}{p^2 - p^6} \div \left(\dfrac{p^2 - 3p - 10}{p^2 - 8p + 15} \cdot \dfrac{p^2 - p - 2}{p^2 + 3p + 2} \right)$

80. $\left(\dfrac{3x^2 + 14x - 5}{x^2 - 3x + 2} \cdot \dfrac{2x^2 - 3x - 2}{3x^2 + 2x - 1} \right) \div \dfrac{2x^2 + 11x + 5}{2\left(x^2 - 1\right)}$

7.4 LEAST COMMON DENOMINATOR OF RATIONAL EXPRESSIONS

OBJECTIVES ▪▪▪▪

Upon completion of this section you will be able to:

A. Find the least common denominator (LCD) of rational expressions; and

B. Rewrite a rational expression with a given new denominator.

Our next goal is to define addition and subtraction of rational expressions. This is done in the same way as is done for numeric fractions. Recall that we needed the *least common denominator* to add or subtract two fractions with different denominators. In this section we will learn how to find the *least common denominator* of rational expressions.

A. LEAST COMMON DENOMINATOR

As in the case of numeric fractions, the **least common denominator** of two rational expressions is simply the *least common multiple of their denominators*. The least common multiple of two polynomials is the smallest of the common multiples of the polynomials.

To find the least common multiple of two or more polynomials, we follow the steps given below :

> *Step* **1**   Factor each polynomial completely.
>
> *Step* **2**   For each polynomial, determine the different factors and the maximum of their exponents.
>
> *Step* **3**   The least common multiple (LCM) of the polynomials is the product of different factors each raised to its maximum exponent, as determined in Step 2.

───── WARM-UP ─────

1. Find the least common multiple of:

EXAMPLE 1   Find the least common multiple of :

a. $2x - 2$ and $x - 3$

b. $x^3 - x^2$ and $x^2 - 2x + 1$

c. $x^2 - x,\ x - 1,\ x^2 - 1$

Solutions:

a. $2x - 2$ and $x - 3$

Step 1   Factor the polynomials.

$$2x - 2 = 2(x - 1)$$
$$x - 3 = (x - 3)$$

Step 2

Factors	2	$x - 1$	$x - 3$
Highest power	1	1	1

Step 3   Least common multiple $= 2^1(x - 1)^1 (x - 3)^1$

$$= 2(x - 1)(x - 3)$$

b. $x^3 - x^2$ and $x^2 - 2x + 1$

Step 1   Factor the polynomials. $x^3 - x^2 = x^2(x - 1)$

$$x^2 - 2x + 1 = (x - 1)(x - 1)$$
$$= (x - 1)^2$$

Step 2

Factors	x	$x - 1$
Highest power	2	2

Step 3   Least common multiple $= x^2 (x - 1)^2$

c. $x^2 - x,\ x - 1,\ x^2 - 1$

Step 1   Factor the polynomials.

$$x^2 - x = x(x - 1)$$
$$x - 1 = (x - 1)$$
$$x^2 - 1 = (x - 1)(x + 1)$$

Step 2

Factors	x	$x - 1$	$x + 1$
Highest exponent	1	1	1

Step 3   Least common multiple $= x^1(x - 1)^1 (x + 1)^1$

$$= x(x - 1)(x + 1)$$

EXAMPLE 2   Find the least common denominator of:

a. $\dfrac{4}{a - 4}$ and $\dfrac{7}{a - 6}$ **b.** $\dfrac{t}{t - 3}$ and $\dfrac{2}{3 - t}$

Solutions:

a.   The denominators are : $a - 4$ and $a - 6$

- Factor the denominators.

$$a - 4 = a - 4, \qquad a - 6 = a - 6$$

Factors	$a - 4$	$a - 6$
Highest exponent	1	1

- $\ \text{L C D} \ = (a - 4)(a - 6)$

a) $x + 1$ and $x^3 - x$

b) $(x - 2)$, $x^2 + 2x - 8$, and
$x^2 + 6x + 8$

2. Find the least common denominator.

a) $\dfrac{1}{a + 3}$ and $\dfrac{1}{a - 3}$

b) $\dfrac{3}{x-1}$ and $\dfrac{5}{1-x}$

> **Note** — If the denominators are co-prime, that is, there is no common factor, then the LCD is the product of the denominators.

b. The denominators are: $t-3$ and $3-t$

- Factor the denominators.

$$t-3 = t-3,$$
$$3-t = -1(-3+t) = -1(t-3)$$

-
Factors	$t-3$	-1
Highest exponent	1	1

- $LCD = -1(t-3)$

3. Find the least common denominator of the following rational expressions.

a) $\dfrac{1}{x-2}, \dfrac{x+4}{x^2-4x+4}, \dfrac{5x}{x^2-4}$

EXAMPLE 3 Find the least common denominator of the following rational expressions.

a. $\dfrac{1}{x-1}, \dfrac{x+2}{x^2-2x+1}$ and $\dfrac{4x}{x^2-1}$

b. $\dfrac{2x-1}{x^2+8x+12}, \dfrac{x}{x^2-36}$ and $\dfrac{3-5x}{x^3+12x^2+36x}$

Solutions:

a. The denominators are: $x-1$, x^2-2x+1 and x^2-1

- Factor the denominators.

$$x-1 = x-1$$
$$x^2-2x+1 = (x-1)^2$$
$$x^2-1 = (x-1)(x+1)$$

-
Factors	$x-1$	$x+1$
Highest exponent	2	1

- Least Common Denominator $= (x-1)^2(x+1)^1$

  $= (x+1)(x-1)^2$

b) $\dfrac{1}{x^2+6x+8}, \dfrac{x}{x^2-16}, \dfrac{4x+3}{x^3+8x^2+16x}$

b. The denominators are:

$$x^2+8x+12, \quad x^2-36 \text{ and } x^3+12x^2+36x$$

- Factor the denominators.

$$x^2+8x+12 = (x+2)(x+6)$$
$$x^2-36 = (x-6)(x+6)$$
$$x^3+12x^2+36x = x(x^2+12x+36) = x(x+6)^2$$

-
Factors	x	$x+2$	$x-6$	$x+6$
Highest exponent	1	1	1	2

- $LCD = x(x+2)(x-6)(x+6)^2$

Answers:

1. **a)** $x(x-1)(x+1)$ **b)** $(x+4)(x+2)(x-2)$

2. **a)** $(a+3)(a-3)$ **b)** $-1(x-1)$

3. **a)** $(x+2)(x-2)^2$ **b)** $x(x+2)(x-4)(x+4)^2$

B. REWRITING RATIONAL EXPRESSIONS WITH A GIVEN DENOMINATOR

The fundamental property of rational expressions can be used to rewrite a rational expression with a **new denominator,** so that the original rational expression equals the new rational expression.

The formula $\dfrac{P}{Q} = \dfrac{P \cdot K}{Q \cdot K}$ is the key to the process. We show this with the help of some examples.

EXAMPLE 4   Rewrite each of the following rational expressions with a new denominator as indicated.

a. $\dfrac{4}{15}$; 90 b. $\dfrac{3y}{4z}$; $8xz^2$

c. $\dfrac{p-3}{p+4}$; $p^2 - 16$

d. $\dfrac{15t}{t^2 - 7t}$; $t^3 - 10t^2 + 21t$

──── **WARM-UP** ────

4. Rewrite each of the following rational expressions with a new denominator as indicated.

a) $\dfrac{3}{5}$; 30

b) $\dfrac{2z}{5y}$; $10x^2y$

c) $\dfrac{p-5}{p+3}$; $p^2 - 9$

Use the following steps:

Step 1   Find the quotient : $\dfrac{\text{new denominator}}{\text{old denominator}} = K$.

Step 2   Multiply the given fraction by $\dfrac{K}{K}$.

Solutions:

a. $\dfrac{4}{15}$; 90 • $\dfrac{\text{new denominator}}{\text{old denominator}} = \dfrac{90}{15} = 6$

       • $\dfrac{4}{15} = \dfrac{4}{15} \cdot \dfrac{6}{6} = \dfrac{24}{90}$

b. $\dfrac{3y}{4z}$; $8xz^2$ • $\dfrac{\text{new denominator}}{\text{old denominator}} = \dfrac{8xz^2}{4z} = 2xz$

       • $\dfrac{3y}{4z} = \dfrac{3y}{4z} \cdot \dfrac{2xz}{2xz} = \dfrac{6xyz}{8xz^2}$

c. $\dfrac{p-3}{p+4}$; $p^2 - 16$ • $\dfrac{p^2 - 16}{p+4} = \dfrac{(p-4)(p+4)}{p+4} = p-4$

       • $\dfrac{p-3}{p+4} = \dfrac{p-3}{p+4} \cdot \dfrac{p-4}{p-4}$

       $= \dfrac{p^2 - 7p + 12}{p^2 - 16}$

d) $\dfrac{11}{x^2 + 2x}$; $x^3 + 6x^2 + 8x$

d. $\dfrac{15}{t^2 - 7t}$; $t^3 - 10t^2 + 21t$

• $\dfrac{t^3 - 10t^2 + 21t}{t^2 - 7t} = \dfrac{t(t-7)(t-3)}{t(t-7)} = \mathbf{t - 3}$

• $\dfrac{15}{t^2 - 7t} = \dfrac{15}{t^2 - 7t} \cdot \dfrac{t - 3}{t - 3}$

$= \dfrac{15(t-3)}{(t^2 - 7t)(t-3)} = \dfrac{15t - 45}{t^3 - 10t^2 + 21t}$

5. Find the least common denominator of the following rational expressions and rewrite them with the LCD as the new denominator.

$\dfrac{1}{3s^2\, t^3}$, $\dfrac{3}{5st^5}$, and $\dfrac{6}{9s^3 t}$

EXAMPLE 5   Find the least common denominator of the following rational expressions and rewrite them with the least common denominator as the new denominator.

$\dfrac{1}{2x^2 y}$, $\dfrac{3}{4x^3 y^2}$, and $\dfrac{4}{3xy^5}$

Solution: The least common multiple of 2, 4, and 3 is 12.

The highest exponent on x is 3.

The highest exponent on y is 5.

Hence, the least common multiple = $\mathbf{12x^3 y^5}$.

$\dfrac{\text{New denominator}}{\text{Old denominator}}$

$\downarrow$

$\dfrac{1}{2x^2 y} = \dfrac{1}{2x^2 y} \cdot \dfrac{\mathbf{6xy^4}}{\mathbf{6xy^4}} = \dfrac{\mathbf{6xy^4}}{\mathbf{12x^3 y^5}}$ $\dfrac{12x^3 y^5}{2x^2 y} = 6xy^4$

$\dfrac{3}{4x^3 y^2} = \dfrac{3}{4x^3 y^2} \cdot \dfrac{\mathbf{3y^3}}{\mathbf{3y^3}} = \dfrac{\mathbf{9y^3}}{\mathbf{12x^3 y^5}}$ $\dfrac{12x^3 y^5}{4x^3 y^2} = 3y^3$

$\dfrac{4}{3xy^5} = \dfrac{4}{3xy^5} \cdot \dfrac{\mathbf{4x^2}}{\mathbf{4x^2}} = \dfrac{\mathbf{16x^2}}{\mathbf{12x^3 y^5}}$ $\dfrac{12x^3 y^5}{3xy^5} = 4x^2$

Note   When writing a rational expression as an equivalent fraction with a specified denominator, do not cancel common factors in the final answer.

Answers:

4. a) $\dfrac{18}{30}$ b) $\dfrac{4x^2 z}{10x^2 y}$

c) $\dfrac{p^2 - 8p + 15}{p^2 - 9}$ d) $\dfrac{11x + 44}{x^3 + 6x^2 + 8x}$

5. $45s^3\, t^5$; $\dfrac{15st^2}{45s^3 t^5}$, $\dfrac{27s^2}{45s^3 t^5}$, $\dfrac{30t^4}{45s^3 t^5}$

EXERCISE 7.4

A. In exercises 1-20, find the least common denominator.

1. $\dfrac{3}{a}, \dfrac{2}{b}$

2. $\dfrac{2}{x}, \dfrac{3}{y}$

3. $\dfrac{x+4}{x^2}, \dfrac{x-2}{x}$

4. $\dfrac{a-3}{b}, \dfrac{a+4}{b^3}$

5. $\dfrac{2x^2}{x-1}, \dfrac{3}{x^2-5x+4}$

6. $\dfrac{5x}{x-1}, \dfrac{4}{x^2-3x+2}$

7. $\dfrac{1}{p-4}, \dfrac{2}{4-p}$

8. $\dfrac{3}{x-2}, \dfrac{4}{2-x}$

9. $\dfrac{3x}{x^2+5x-6}, \dfrac{x+2}{x-1}$

10. $\dfrac{2x+1}{3x+4}, \dfrac{x-1}{3x-4}$

11. $\dfrac{5}{x+3}, \dfrac{x-1}{x+6}$

12. $\dfrac{3}{x+4}, \dfrac{5x}{x^2-16}$

13. $\dfrac{x+4}{x-3}, \dfrac{x+2}{3-x}$

14. $\dfrac{2x}{x^2+6x+8}, \dfrac{x}{x^2-16}$

15. $\dfrac{3}{x^2+x-2}; \dfrac{x}{x+2}$

16. $\dfrac{5}{2x^2-9x+10}; \dfrac{x-2}{2x-5}$

17. $\dfrac{1}{6x^2-7x+2}; \dfrac{2}{6x^2+5x-6}$

18. $\dfrac{2}{2a^3+2a^2-4a}; \dfrac{3}{a^3+2a^2-3a}$

19. $\dfrac{1}{t^2+4t-12}, \dfrac{-2}{t^2+t-30}, \dfrac{4t}{t^2+2t-24}$

20. $\dfrac{3}{x^2-x-2}, \dfrac{4}{x^2+x-6}, \dfrac{-5}{x^2+4x+3}$

B. In exercises 21-56, find the least common denominator and rewrite the rational expressions with the LCD as the new denominator.

21. $\dfrac{2}{3x-6}, \dfrac{1}{2x-4}$

22. $\dfrac{3}{2x-4}, \dfrac{1}{3x-6}$

23. $\dfrac{1}{8x+16}, \dfrac{2}{x^2+x-2}$

24. $\dfrac{1}{x^2-3x+2}, \dfrac{1}{2x-4}$

25. $\dfrac{3+t}{t^2-4}, \dfrac{1}{t-2}$

26. $\dfrac{x+3}{x^2-9}, \dfrac{1}{x-3}$

27. $\dfrac{2p}{p^2-3p-4}, \dfrac{1}{p+1}$

28. $\dfrac{3x}{3x^2+2x-1}, \dfrac{1}{3x-1}$

29. $\dfrac{2a+1}{a^2+3a}, \dfrac{1}{a^2-9}$

30. $\dfrac{x+2}{x^2-2x}, \dfrac{1}{x^2-4}$

31. $\dfrac{5}{x+3}, \dfrac{2x}{x^2+6x+9}$

32. $\dfrac{x}{x-4}, \dfrac{x-1}{x^2-8x+16}$

33. $\dfrac{4}{x-3}, \dfrac{5}{x+5}$

34. $\dfrac{3x+2}{x-1}, \dfrac{3x+1}{x+1}$

35. $\dfrac{x-1}{x-3}, \dfrac{x-2}{x+3}$

36. $\dfrac{3x}{x+1}, \dfrac{2x}{x+2}$

37. $\dfrac{3a}{4a+5b}, \dfrac{2b}{4a-5b}$

38. $\dfrac{a-1}{2a-3b}, \dfrac{b+1}{2a+3b}$

39. $\dfrac{c}{3c-d}, \dfrac{d}{3c+d}$

40. $\dfrac{2x}{x-y}, \dfrac{y}{x+y}$

41. $\dfrac{5}{2x+3}, \dfrac{4}{x+2}$

42. $\dfrac{5x+1}{x-3}, \dfrac{2x-1}{3x-9}$

43. $\dfrac{x-1}{x-4}, \dfrac{x+1}{ax-4a}$

44. $\dfrac{4}{(x-1)(x-2)}, \dfrac{2}{(x-2)(x-3)}$

45. $\dfrac{4}{5x^2}, \dfrac{3}{4x^3}$

46. $\dfrac{4}{x}, \dfrac{5}{y}$

47. $\dfrac{x-1}{x-3}, \dfrac{x+1}{x+3}, \dfrac{x}{x^2-9}$

48. $\dfrac{1}{x+1}, \dfrac{x}{x-2}, \dfrac{x^2+2}{x^2-x-2}$

49. $\dfrac{x}{x^3+27}, \dfrac{-2}{x^2+6x+9}$

50. $\dfrac{a}{a^3-8}, \dfrac{5}{a^2-a-2}$

51. $\dfrac{3}{x+2}, \dfrac{1}{x-4}$

52. $\dfrac{5}{x-2}, \dfrac{2}{x+3}$

53. $z, \dfrac{1}{z}$

54. $x^2, \dfrac{1}{x^2}$

55. $\dfrac{3}{t+1}, \dfrac{2}{t^2}, \dfrac{t}{t-1}$

56. $\dfrac{2}{x-1}, \dfrac{3}{x^3}, \dfrac{x}{x+1}$

Upon completion of this section you will be able to:

A. Add rational expressions with like denominators;

B. Add rational expressions with different denominators; and

C. Subtract rational expressions.

Recall that in chapter 1 we examined how to add or subtract two numeric fractions. To add two fractions with the same denominator we simply add the numerators and place the sum over the common denominator. For example,

$$\frac{3}{5} + \frac{4}{5} = \frac{3+4}{5} = \frac{7}{5}$$

To add two fractions with different denominators, we first find the LCD of the two fractions, then rewrite the two fractions with the LCD as the new denominator, and finally add the fractions. For example,

$$\frac{5}{6} + \frac{1}{8} = \frac{5}{6} \cdot \frac{4}{4} + \frac{1}{8} \cdot \frac{3}{3} \qquad \text{LCD} = 24$$

$$= \frac{20}{24} + \frac{3}{24} = \frac{20+3}{24} = \frac{23}{24}$$

Addition and subtraction of rational expressions are performed in the same way.

A. ADDING TWO RATIONAL EXPRESSIONS WITH THE SAME DENOMINATOR

To add two rational expressions $\frac{P}{Q}$ and $\frac{R}{Q}$ with the same denominator, add the numerators, place the sum over the common denominator and, if possible, reduce the resulting rational expression $\frac{P+R}{Q}$ to lowest terms.

WARM-UP

1. Add as indicated:

a) $\dfrac{3}{x+2} + \dfrac{2x}{x+2}$

b) $\dfrac{2t}{(t+3)^2} + \dfrac{6}{(t+3)^2}$

Answers:

1. a) $\dfrac{2x+3}{x+2}$ b) $\dfrac{2}{t+3}$

EXAMPLE 1   Add as indicated:

a. $\dfrac{4}{x+1} + \dfrac{5x}{x+1}$ b. $\dfrac{4t}{(t+1)^2} + \dfrac{4}{(t+1)^2}$

Solutions:

a. $\dfrac{4}{x+1} + \dfrac{5x}{x+1} = \dfrac{4+5x}{x+1}$ Same denominator.

$= \dfrac{5x+4}{x+1}$

b. $\dfrac{4t}{(t+1)^2} + \dfrac{4}{(t+1)^2} = \dfrac{4t+4}{(t+1)^2}$

$= \dfrac{4(t+1)}{(t+1)^2}$ Reduce to lowest terms.

$= \dfrac{4}{t+1}$

B. ADDING RATIONAL EXPRESSIONS WITH DIFFERENT DENOMINATORS

To add rational expressions with different denominators, we follow the steps given below:

> **Step 1** Find the least common denominator.
>
> **Step 2** Rewrite each expression with the LCD as the common denominator.
>
> **Step 3** Add the fractions in the rewritten form.
>
> **Step 4** Reduce the result to lowest terms.

EXAMPLE 2 Add the following rational expressions.

a. $\dfrac{5}{4x} + \dfrac{2}{3x}$ **b.** $\dfrac{2}{x} + \dfrac{3}{y}$

c. $\dfrac{4x}{x+3} + \dfrac{-5x}{x-3}$ **d.** $\dfrac{x}{(x-1)(x-1)} + \dfrac{3}{(x-1)(x+1)}$

e. $\dfrac{2}{3y(y+3)} + \dfrac{y-1}{y^2(y-4)}$

f. $t+2+\dfrac{1}{t-2}$

Solutions:

a. $\dfrac{5}{4x} + \dfrac{2}{3x}$

Step 1 Find the LCD of $\dfrac{5}{4x}$ and $\dfrac{2}{3x}$:

$$\left\{\begin{array}{l} 4x = 2^2 \cdot x \\ 3x = 3x \end{array}\right\}$$

$$LCD = 2^2 \cdot 3 \cdot x = \mathbf{12x}.$$

Step 2 $\dfrac{5}{4x} = \dfrac{5}{4x} \cdot \dfrac{\mathbf{3}}{\mathbf{3}} = \dfrac{15}{12x}$ $\dfrac{12x}{4x} = 3$

$\dfrac{2}{3x} = \dfrac{2}{3x} \cdot \dfrac{\mathbf{4}}{\mathbf{4}} = \dfrac{8}{12x}$ $\dfrac{12x}{3x} = 4$

Step 3 $\dfrac{5}{4x} + \dfrac{2}{3x} = \dfrac{15}{\mathbf{12x}} + \dfrac{8}{\mathbf{12x}} = \dfrac{\mathbf{15+8}}{12x} = \dfrac{23}{12x}$

Step 4 The resulting fraction cannot be reduced.

Note The work shown in step 3 is a complete solution of the problem.

WARM-UP

2. Add the following rational expressions.

a) $\dfrac{3}{2x} + \dfrac{1}{6x}$

---

b) $\dfrac{4}{r} + \dfrac{5}{s}$

c) $\dfrac{2}{x-4} + \dfrac{5x}{x+4}$

d) $\dfrac{2x}{x^2-4x+4} + \dfrac{3}{x^2-4}$

b. $\dfrac{2}{x} + \dfrac{3}{y}$

Step 1 The LCD of $\dfrac{2}{x}$ and $\dfrac{3}{y}$ is xy.

Step 2 $\dfrac{2}{x} = \dfrac{2}{x} \cdot \dfrac{y}{y} = \dfrac{2y}{xy}$ $\qquad \dfrac{xy}{x} = y$

$\dfrac{3}{y} = \dfrac{3}{y} \cdot \dfrac{x}{x} = \dfrac{3x}{xy}$ $\qquad \dfrac{xy}{y} = x$

Step 3 $\dfrac{2}{x} + \dfrac{3}{y} = \dfrac{2y}{xy} + \dfrac{3x}{xy} = \dfrac{2y+3x}{xy}$

Step 4 The resulting fraction cannot be reduced.

Note: Step 3 shows a complete solution.

c. $\dfrac{4x}{x+3} + \dfrac{-5x}{x-3}$

Step 1 The LCD of $\dfrac{4x}{x+3}$ and $\dfrac{-5x}{x-3}$ is $(x+3)(x-3)$.

Step 2 $\dfrac{4x}{x+3} = \dfrac{4x}{x+3} \cdot \dfrac{x-3}{x-3} = \dfrac{4x(x-3)}{(x+3)(x-3)}$ $\qquad \dfrac{\text{LCD}}{x+3} = x-3$

$\dfrac{-5x}{x-3} = \dfrac{-5x}{x-3} \cdot \dfrac{x+3}{x+3} = \dfrac{-5x(x+3)}{(x-3)(x+3)}$ $\qquad \dfrac{\text{LCD}}{x-3} = x+3$

Step 3 $\dfrac{4x}{x+3} + \dfrac{-5x}{x-3} = \dfrac{4x(x-3)}{(x+3)(x-3)} + \dfrac{-5x(x+3)}{(x+3)(x-3)}$

$= \dfrac{4x(x-3) + [-5x(x+3)]}{(x+3)(x-3)}$

$= \dfrac{(4x^2 - 12x) + (-5x^2 - 15x)}{x^2 - 9}$

$= \dfrac{-x^2 - 27x}{x^2 - 9}$

Step 4 The resulting fraction cannot be reduced.

Note: Step 3 gives a complete solution.

d. $\dfrac{x}{(x-1)(x-1)} + \dfrac{3}{(x-1)(x+1)}$

Step 1 Find LCD of the two fractions.

$$(x-1)(x-1) = (x-1)^2$$

LCD of $(x-1)^2$ and $(x-1)(x+1) = (x+1)(x-1)^2$

Step 2 $\quad \dfrac{x}{(x-1)(x-1)} = \dfrac{x}{(x-1)^2} \cdot \dfrac{x+1}{x+1} \qquad \dfrac{(x+1)(x-1)^2}{(x-1)(x-1)} = x+1$

$$= \dfrac{x(x+1)}{(x-1)^2(x+1)}$$

$$\dfrac{3}{(x-1)(x+1)} = \dfrac{3}{(x-1)(x+1)} \cdot \dfrac{x-1}{x-1} \qquad \dfrac{(x+1)(x-1)^2}{(x-1)(x+1)} = x-1$$

$$= \dfrac{3(x-1)}{(x+1)(x-1)(x-1)}$$

$$= \dfrac{3(x-1)}{(x+1)(x-1)^2}$$

Step 3 $\quad \dfrac{x}{(x-1)(x-1)} + \dfrac{3}{(x-1)(x+1)}$

$$= \dfrac{x(x+1)}{(x-1)^2(x+1)} + \dfrac{3(x-1)}{(x-1)^2(x+1)}$$

$$= \dfrac{x(x+1)+3(x-1)}{(x-1)^2(x+1)}$$

$$= \dfrac{x^2+x+3x-3}{(x-1)^2(x+1)} = \dfrac{x^2+4x-3}{(x-1)^2(x+1)}$$

Step 4 $\quad$ The resulting fraction cannot be reduced.

e. $\quad \dfrac{2}{3y(y+3)} + \dfrac{y-1}{y^2(y-4)} :$

e) $\quad \dfrac{2}{y(y+2)} + \dfrac{y+1}{y^3(y-3)}$

Step 1 $\quad$ Find LCD of the two fractions.

$$3y(y+3) = 3y(y+3)$$
$$y^2(y-4) = y^2(y-4)$$
$$\text{LCD} = 3y^2(y-4)(y+3)$$

Step 2 $\quad \dfrac{2}{3y(y+3)} = \dfrac{2}{3y(y+3)} \cdot \dfrac{y(y-4)}{y(y-4)} \qquad \dfrac{\text{LCD}}{3y(y+3)} = y(y-4)$

$$= \dfrac{2y(y-4)}{3y^2(y+3)(y-4)}$$

$$\dfrac{y-1}{y^2(y-4)} = \dfrac{y-1}{y^2(y-4)} \cdot \dfrac{3(y+3)}{3(y+3)} \qquad \dfrac{\text{LCD}}{y^2(y-4)} = 3(y+3)$$

$$= \dfrac{3(y-1)(y+3)}{3y^2(y+3)(y-4)}$$

Step 3 $\dfrac{2}{3y(y+3)} + \dfrac{y-1}{y^2(y-4)}$

$$= \dfrac{2y(y-4)}{3y^2(y+3)(y-4)} + \dfrac{3(y-1)(y+3)}{3y^2(y+3)(y-4)}$$

$$= \dfrac{2y(y-4) + 3(y-1)(y+3)}{3y^2(y+3)(y-4)}$$

$$= \dfrac{2y^2 - 8y + 3y^2 + 6y - 9}{3y^2(y+3)(y-4)} = \dfrac{5y^2 - 2y - 9}{3y^2(y+3)(y-4)}$$

Step 4 The resulting fraction cannot be reduced.

f) $t+3+\dfrac{1}{t-3}$

f. $t+2+\dfrac{1}{t-2} = \dfrac{t+2}{1} + \dfrac{1}{t-2}$ $\qquad$ LCD $= t-2$

$$= \dfrac{t+2}{1} \cdot \dfrac{t-2}{t-2} + \dfrac{1}{t-2} \cdot \dfrac{1}{1} = \dfrac{(t+2)(t-2)}{t-2} + \dfrac{1}{t-2}$$

$$= \dfrac{(t+2)(t-2)+1}{t-2}$$

$$= \dfrac{t^2-4+1}{t-2} = \dfrac{t^2-3}{t-2}$$

- For some problems it is necessary to "factor out a minus sign" in order to find the least common denominator, as shown in the following example.

3. Add.

a) $\dfrac{3x}{x^2-4} + \dfrac{4}{4-x^2}$

EXAMPLE 3   Add the following rational expressions.

a. $\dfrac{x}{x^2-9} + \dfrac{3}{9-x^2}$ $\qquad$ **b.** $\dfrac{1}{x+1} + \dfrac{2x}{1-x^2}$

c. $\dfrac{2x}{x^2-9} + \dfrac{3}{x^2-6x+9}$

d. $\dfrac{3a}{2a-1} + \dfrac{a-1}{a^2+3a} + \dfrac{a}{2a^2+5a-3}$

Solutions:

a. $\dfrac{x}{x^2-9} + \dfrac{3}{9-x^2}$

The LCD of the two fractions is $x^2 - 9$. $x^2-9 = x^2-9,$

$\qquad\qquad\qquad\qquad\qquad\qquad\qquad\qquad 9 - x^2 = -1(x^2-9)$

Therefore, $\dfrac{x}{x^2-9} + \dfrac{3}{9-x^2} = \dfrac{x}{x^2-9} + \dfrac{3}{9-x^2} \cdot \dfrac{-1}{-1}$

$$= \frac{x}{x^2 - 9} + \frac{-3}{x^2 - 9}$$

$$= \frac{x - 3}{x^2 - 9} \qquad \text{Reduce.}$$

$$= \frac{x - 3}{(x - 3)(x + 3)} = \frac{1}{x + 3}$$

b. $\dfrac{1}{x+1} + \dfrac{2x}{1-x^2}$

b) $\dfrac{1}{x+3} + \dfrac{2x}{9-x^2}$

- Find the L C D of the two fractions.

  $x + 1 = 1 + x$,

  $1 - x^2 = -1(x^2 - 1) = -1\,(x - 1)\,(x + 1)$,

  $\qquad \text{LCD} = -1\,(x - 1)\,(x + 1)$

- We rewrite the fractions with LCD as the common denominator, and add.

$$\frac{1}{x+1} + \frac{2x}{1-x^2} = \frac{-1(x-1)}{-(x+1)(x-1)} + \frac{2x}{(1-x^2)}$$

$$= \frac{-x+1}{-(x^2-1)} + \frac{2x}{-(x^2-1)} = \frac{-x+1+2x}{-(x^2-1)}$$

$$= \frac{x+1}{-(x^2-1)} = \frac{(x+1)}{-(x+1)(x-1)}$$

$$= \frac{-1}{x-1}$$

c. $\dfrac{2x}{x^2 - 9} + \dfrac{3}{x^2 - 6x + 9}$

c) $\dfrac{x}{x^2 - 4} + \dfrac{7}{x^2 + 4x + 4}$

- Find the LCD of the two fractions.

  $x^2 - 9 = (x - 3)\,(x + 3)$

  $x^2 - 6x + 9 = (x - 3)\,(x - 3) = (x - 3)^2$

  $\qquad \text{LCD} = (x - 3)(x - 3)\,(x + 3)$

  $\qquad\qquad = (x^2 - 9)\,(x - 3)$

  $\qquad\qquad \text{OR}$

  $\qquad \text{LCD} = (x - 3)^2\,(x + 3).$

- We rewrite the fractions with LCD as the common denominator, and add.

d) $\dfrac{5x}{3x+4}+\dfrac{x-4}{x^2+4x}+\dfrac{2x}{3x^2+16x+16}$

$$\frac{2x}{x^2-9}+\frac{3}{x^2-6x+9}=\frac{2x}{\left(x^2-9\right)}\cdot\frac{(x-3)}{(x-3)}+\frac{3}{(x-3)^2}\cdot\frac{(x+3)}{(x+3)}$$

$$=\frac{2x(x-3)+3(x+3)}{(x-3)^2(x+3)}$$

$$=\frac{2x^2-6x+3x+9}{(x-3)^2(x+3)}=\frac{\mathbf{2x^2-3x+9}}{\mathbf{(x-3)^2(x+3)}}$$

d. $\quad\dfrac{3a}{2a-1}+\dfrac{a-1}{a^2+3a}+\dfrac{a}{2a^2+5a-3}$

Find the LCD of the fractions.

$$2a-1=2a-1$$

$$a^2+3a=a(a+3)$$

$$2a^2+5a-3=(2a-1)(a+3)$$

Therefore, the LCD $=\mathbf{a(2a-1)(a+3)}$.

Now we rewrite the fractions with the LCD as the common denominator and add.

$$\frac{3a}{2a-1}+\frac{a-1}{a^2+3a}+\frac{a}{2a^2+5a-3}$$

$$=\frac{3a}{2a-1}\cdot\frac{\mathbf{a(a+3)}}{\mathbf{a(a+3)}}+\frac{a-1}{a(a+3)}\cdot\frac{\mathbf{2a-1}}{\mathbf{2a-1}}+\frac{a}{(2a-1)(a+3)}\cdot\frac{\mathbf{a}}{\mathbf{a}}$$

$$\frac{a(2a-1)(a+3)}{2a-1}=a(a+3)\qquad\frac{a(2a-1)(a+3)}{a(a+3)}=2a-1\qquad\frac{a(2a-1)(a+3)}{(2a-1)(a+3)}=a$$

$$=\frac{3a^2\,(a+3)}{a(2a-1)(a+3)}+\frac{(a-1)(2a-1)}{a(2a-1)(a+3)}+\frac{a^2}{a(2a-1)(a+3)}$$

$$=\frac{3a^2\,(a+3)+(a-1)(2a-1)+a^2}{a(2a-1)(a+3)}$$

$$=\frac{3a^3+9a^2+2a^2-3a+1+a^2}{a(2a-1)(a+3)}$$

$$=\frac{3a^3+12a^2-3a+1}{a(2a-1)(a+3)}$$

Answers:

2. a) $\dfrac{5}{3x}$ **b)** $\dfrac{4s+5r}{rs}$

c) $\dfrac{5x^2-18x+8}{x^2-16}$ **d)** $\dfrac{2x^2+7x-6}{(x+2)(x-2)^2}$

e) $\dfrac{2y^3-5y^2+3y+2}{y^3(y+2)(y-3)}$ **f)** $\dfrac{t^2-8}{t-3}$

3. a) $\dfrac{3x-4}{x^2-4}$ **b)** $\dfrac{-1}{x-3}$

c) $\dfrac{x^2+9x-14}{(x-2)(x+2)^2}$

d) $\dfrac{5x^3+25x^2-8x-16}{x(x+4)(3x+4)}$

C. Subtracting Rational Expressions

Recall the definition of subtraction for two numeric fractions. For example $\frac{3}{5} - \frac{1}{3}$ is defined to be the sum of $\frac{3}{5}$ and the additive inverse of $\frac{1}{3}$, that is $\frac{3}{5} + \left(-\frac{1}{3}\right)$. The same definition for subtracting two rational expressions can be stated as:

$$\frac{P}{Q} - \frac{R}{Q} = \frac{P}{Q} + \frac{(-R)}{Q} = \frac{P - R}{Q}$$

$$\frac{P}{Q} - \frac{R}{S} = \frac{P}{Q} + \frac{(-R)}{S} = \frac{P \cdot S}{Q \cdot S} + \frac{-R \cdot Q}{S \cdot Q} = \frac{PS + (-RQ)}{QS}$$

Unlike denominators.
Recall, $QS = SQ$.

EXAMPLE 4   Perform the indicated operations and simplify.

a. $\dfrac{4}{2q} - \dfrac{5}{2q}$

b. $\dfrac{3}{10x} - \dfrac{4}{15y}$

c. $\dfrac{x+6}{x-3} - \dfrac{x-12}{3-x}$

d. $\dfrac{3}{t+2} + \dfrac{2}{t-2} - \dfrac{t-1}{t^2-4}$

e. $\dfrac{4}{3x(x+3)} - \dfrac{x-1}{x^2(x-2)}$

Solutions:

a. $\dfrac{4}{2q} - \dfrac{5}{2q}$:

Therefore, $\dfrac{4}{2q} - \dfrac{5}{2q} = \dfrac{4-5}{2q}$ Common denominator.

b. $\dfrac{3}{10x} - \dfrac{4}{15y} = \dfrac{3}{10x} \cdot \dfrac{3y}{3y} - \dfrac{4}{15y} \cdot \dfrac{2x}{2x}$ LCD $= 30xy$.

$= \dfrac{9y}{30xy} - \dfrac{8x}{30xy} = \dfrac{9y - 8x}{30xy}$

c. $\dfrac{x+6}{x-3} - \dfrac{x-12}{3-x} = \dfrac{x+6}{x-3} - \dfrac{(x-12)}{3-x}$

$= \dfrac{x+6}{x-3} - \dfrac{(x-12)(-1)}{x-3}$

$= \dfrac{x+6+x-12}{x-3}$ $\dfrac{1}{3-x} = \dfrac{-1}{x-3}$

$= \dfrac{2x-6}{x-3} = \dfrac{2(x-3)}{x-3} = 2$

WARM-UP

4. Subtract.

a) $\dfrac{4}{q} - \dfrac{5}{q}$

b) $\dfrac{3}{5x} - \dfrac{2}{20y}$

c) $\dfrac{x+5}{x-5} - \dfrac{x-10}{5-x}$

d) $\dfrac{4}{t+3} + \dfrac{3}{t-3} - \dfrac{t+2}{t^2-9}$

d. $\dfrac{3}{t+2} + \dfrac{2}{t-2} - \dfrac{t-1}{t^2-4} = \dfrac{3}{t+2} + \dfrac{2}{t-2} - \dfrac{(t-1)}{t^2-4}$

LCD $= t^2 - 4 = (t-2)(t+2)$

$= \dfrac{3}{t+2} \cdot \dfrac{t-2}{t-2} + \dfrac{2}{t-2} \cdot \dfrac{t+2}{t+2} - \dfrac{(t-1)}{t^2-4}$

$= \dfrac{3(t-2)}{(t+2)(t-2)} + \dfrac{2(t+2)}{(t-2)(t+2)} - \dfrac{t-1}{t^2-4}$

$= \dfrac{3t-6}{t^2-4} + \dfrac{2t+4}{t^2-4} - \dfrac{t-1}{t^2-4}$

$= \dfrac{3t-6+2t+4-t+1}{t^2-4} = \dfrac{4t-1}{t^2-4}$

e) $\dfrac{3}{2x(x+2)} - \dfrac{x-3}{x^3(x+4)}$

e. $\dfrac{4}{3x(x+3)} - \dfrac{x-1}{x^2(x-2)} = \dfrac{4}{3x(x+3)} - \dfrac{(x-1)}{x^2(x-2)}$

LCD $= 3x^2(x-2)(x+3)$

$= \dfrac{4}{3x(x+3)} \cdot \dfrac{x(x-2)}{x(x-2)} - \dfrac{(x-1)}{x^2(x-2)} \cdot \dfrac{3(x+3)}{3(x+3)}$

$= \dfrac{4x(x-2)}{3x^2(x-2)(x+3)} - \dfrac{3(x-1)(x+3)}{3x^2(x-2)(x+3)}$

$= \dfrac{4x(x-2) - 3(x-1)(x+3)}{3x^2(x-2)(x+3)}$

$= \dfrac{4(x^2-2x) - 3(x^2+2x-3)}{3x^2(x-2)(x+3)}$

$= \dfrac{4x^2-8x-3x^2-6x+9}{3x^2(x-2)(x+3)} = \dfrac{x^2-14x+9}{3x^2(x-2)(x+3)}$

Answers:

4. **a)** $-\dfrac{1}{q}$ **b)** $\dfrac{6y-x}{10xy}$ **c)** 2

   d) $\dfrac{6t-5}{t^2-9}$ **e)** $\dfrac{3x^3+10x^2+2x+12}{2x^3(x+2)(x+4)}$

Exercise 7.5

A. In exercises 1-10, add the rational expressions with like denominators. Write your answer in lowest terms.

1. $\dfrac{2}{x} + \dfrac{3}{x}$ 2. $\dfrac{3}{y} + \dfrac{4}{y}$ 3. $\dfrac{3}{x^2} + \dfrac{4x+1}{x^2}$ 4. $\dfrac{x}{x^3} + \dfrac{2+3x}{x^3}$ 5. $\dfrac{2}{y+1} + \dfrac{2y}{y+1}$

6. $\dfrac{3}{x+1} + \dfrac{2x}{x+1}$ 7. $\dfrac{3}{x^2} + \dfrac{5}{x^2}$ 8. $\dfrac{4x+3}{2x-7} + \dfrac{3x-8}{2x-7}$ 9. $\dfrac{t^2+4t}{t+2} + \dfrac{4}{t+2}$ 10. $\dfrac{x^2+2x}{x-2} + \dfrac{3}{x-2}$

B. In exercises 11-29, add the rational expressions with different denominators.

11. $\dfrac{x}{8} + \dfrac{5}{12}$ 12. $\dfrac{x}{10} + \dfrac{2}{15}$ 13. $\dfrac{x-3}{x} + \dfrac{2x-1}{2x}$ 14. $\dfrac{y-2}{y} + \dfrac{3y-1}{3y}$ 15. $\dfrac{1}{y} + \dfrac{3}{y^2}$

16. $\dfrac{1}{x^3} + \dfrac{2}{x}$ 17. $\dfrac{x-5}{4x^2} + \dfrac{x+1}{4x}$ 18. $\dfrac{x+1}{3x^2} + \dfrac{2x+2}{2x}$ 19. $y + \dfrac{8}{3y}$ 20. $\dfrac{4}{x+4} + x$

21. $\dfrac{2a}{a-7}+\dfrac{5}{7-a}$ **22.** $\dfrac{4x}{6-x}+\dfrac{5}{x-6}$ **23.** $\dfrac{2x}{3-y}+\dfrac{5}{y-3}$ **24.** $\dfrac{3x}{x-4}+\dfrac{2}{x+6}$ **25.** $\dfrac{1}{x+1}+2(x-1)$

26. $\dfrac{6}{5b+10}+\dfrac{2b}{(b-5)(b+2)}$ **27.** $\dfrac{2-t}{9t+6}+\dfrac{t-2}{6t+4}$ **28.** $\dfrac{2a}{4a^2-9b^2}+\dfrac{1}{2a-3b}$ **29.** $\dfrac{x-2}{2x+4}+\dfrac{2-x}{3x+6}$

C. In exercises 30-55, subtract the rational expressions.

30. $\dfrac{4}{ab}-\dfrac{2}{ab}$ **31.** $\dfrac{4}{3}-\dfrac{2}{x}$ **32.** $\dfrac{5}{2}-\dfrac{3}{x}$ **33.** $\dfrac{4}{x}-\dfrac{7}{x}$ **34.** $\dfrac{2}{x}-\dfrac{5}{x}$

35. $\dfrac{3}{x+2}-\dfrac{10}{x+2}$ **36.** $\dfrac{y^2}{y^4+1}-\dfrac{1}{y^4+1}$ **37.** $\dfrac{x^2}{x^3-1}-\dfrac{1}{x^3-1}$ **38.** $\dfrac{3x}{(x+2)^2}-\dfrac{5}{(x+2)^2}$

39. $\dfrac{4x}{(x-3)^2}-\dfrac{12}{(x-3)^2}$ **40.** $\dfrac{x}{x-y}+\dfrac{3y}{(y-x)(x+y)}$ **41.** $\dfrac{4x}{(x-3)^2}-\dfrac{(9-x)(x-1)}{(x-3)^2}$

42. $\dfrac{5x}{(x+4)^2}-\dfrac{5x^2-1}{(x+4)^2}$ **43.** $\dfrac{2x-1}{6x^2}-\dfrac{x+4}{9x}$ **44.** $\dfrac{2}{3-x}-\dfrac{4}{x-3}$ **45.** $\dfrac{4}{x-2}-\dfrac{5}{2-x}$

46. $\dfrac{2}{x-7}-\dfrac{5}{7-x}$ **47.** $\dfrac{6}{2a+2}-\dfrac{a+4}{4a-4}$ **48.** $\dfrac{3}{(a-6)(a+6)}-\dfrac{2}{6-a}$

49. $\dfrac{3a}{(a-2)(a+1)}-\dfrac{10a}{(a+3)(a-2)}$ **50.** $\dfrac{1}{a-b}-\dfrac{2a}{a^2-b^2}$ **51.** $\dfrac{3a}{9a^2-4b^2}-\dfrac{1}{3a+2b}$

52. $\dfrac{3}{x-2}-\dfrac{x-2}{x^2-4}$ **53.** $\dfrac{2}{z-4}-\dfrac{z+12}{z^2-16}$ **54.** $\dfrac{1}{x-y}-\dfrac{2y}{(x-y)(x+y)}$ **55.** $\dfrac{4x}{x^2+2x-3}-\dfrac{5x}{x^2+5x+6}$

D. In exercises 56-81, perform the indicated operations.

56. $\dfrac{3x}{x^2+3x+2}+\dfrac{2x}{x^2-x-2}$ **57.** $\dfrac{m}{m-1}-\dfrac{1}{m}+1$ **58.** $\dfrac{x}{1-x}+\dfrac{1}{x}-1$

59. $\dfrac{16}{r^2s}+\dfrac{1}{rs}-\dfrac{6}{rs^2}$ **60.** $\dfrac{15}{x^2y^2}-\dfrac{1}{xy}+\dfrac{3}{x^2}$ **61.** $\dfrac{2x+3}{5x}-\dfrac{2x-1}{10x}+\dfrac{4}{x}$

62. $\dfrac{x+2}{3x}+\dfrac{x-5}{6x}-\dfrac{2}{x}$ **63.** $\dfrac{5}{a+1}-\dfrac{1}{a^2-1}+\dfrac{2}{a-1}$ **64.** $\dfrac{3}{x-1}+\dfrac{4}{x^2-1}-\dfrac{5}{1+x}$

65. $\dfrac{16x-x^2}{x^2-4}+\dfrac{2x+3}{2-x}+\dfrac{3x-2}{x+2}$ **66.** $\dfrac{3x}{9x+2}-\dfrac{5x}{2-9x}+\dfrac{x}{81x^2-4}$ **67.** $\dfrac{5}{x}-\dfrac{3}{x-1}-\dfrac{7}{2\left(x^2-1\right)}$

68. $\dfrac{4}{2x-4}+\dfrac{3}{3x-6}-\dfrac{4}{2x^2-8}$ **69.** $\dfrac{2x}{x^2-2x+1}-\dfrac{4}{x^2-1}+\dfrac{3x}{x+1}$ **70.** $\dfrac{2}{3x}+\dfrac{3}{x^2-1}-\dfrac{5x}{x+1}$

71. $-\dfrac{5}{2x}+\dfrac{4}{x-4}-\dfrac{3}{x^2-16}$ **72.** $\dfrac{4}{x^2-9}+\dfrac{3}{x+3}-\dfrac{5}{x}$ **73.** $\dfrac{x+1}{x^2+3x}-\dfrac{x-1}{x^2-3x}+\dfrac{2}{x^2-9}$

74. $\dfrac{4}{x^2-4}+\dfrac{5}{2x^2-8x+8}+3$ **75.** $\dfrac{3}{x^2-25}+\dfrac{4}{x^2+4x-5}-\dfrac{1}{x-1}$ **76.** $\dfrac{2x}{3x-1}+\dfrac{x+1}{2x+1}-\dfrac{7x}{6x^2-x-1}$

77. $\dfrac{-2x-x^2}{x^2-4}+\dfrac{2x}{2+x}-\dfrac{5}{2-x}$ **78.** $\dfrac{3x+x^2}{9-x^2}-\dfrac{x}{3+x}-\dfrac{3}{x-3}$ **79.** $\dfrac{1}{x+1}-\left(\dfrac{1}{x-1}-\dfrac{1}{x^2-1}\right)$

80. $\dfrac{1}{a-b}-\left(\dfrac{1}{a+b}-\dfrac{1}{a^2-b^2}\right)$ **81.** $\dfrac{1}{x-2}-\left(\dfrac{1}{x+2}-\dfrac{1}{x^2-4}\right)$

7.6 COMPLEX FRACTIONS

A rational expression with fractions in the numerator or in the denominator is called a **complex fraction**.

OBJECTIVES ■■■■

Upon completion of this section you will be able to simplify complex fractions using two different methods.

For example: $\dfrac{\frac{3}{5}}{\frac{4}{7}}$, $\dfrac{3+\frac{4}{5}}{1\frac{2}{3}-\frac{5}{2}}$, and $\dfrac{2-\frac{3}{x}}{\frac{3}{x^2}+\frac{5}{x}}$

are all complex fractions.

We will show how to simplify complex fractions using two different methods.

Procedure for simplification of Complex Fractions:

Method 1:

Step 1 Find the LCD of all fractions appearing in the numerator and the denominator.

Step 2 Multiply the numerator and the denominator by the LCD. Simplify the numerator and denominator.

Step 3 Write the answer in lowest terms.

Note Step 2 is allowed by the fundamental property of Rational expressions $\dfrac{P}{Q}=\dfrac{PK}{QK}$ for all non-zero K.

WARM-UP

1. Simplify by Method 1.

    a) $\dfrac{2\frac{1}{5}}{\frac{3}{10}}$

EXAMPLE 1 Simplify: **a.** $\dfrac{1\frac{2}{7}}{\frac{6}{11}}$ **b.** $\dfrac{\frac{xy}{z^2}}{\frac{x^3}{y^2z}}$ **c.** $\dfrac{x-\frac{1}{x}}{2+\frac{1}{x}}$

Solutions:

a. $\dfrac{1\frac{2}{7}}{\frac{6}{11}}=\dfrac{\frac{9}{7}}{\frac{6}{11}}$

Step 1 The LCD of the fractions $\dfrac{9}{7}$ and $\dfrac{6}{11}$ is 77.

Step 2 Multiply the numerator and the denominator by LCD.

$$\dfrac{\frac{9}{7}}{\frac{6}{11}}=\dfrac{\left(\frac{9}{7}\right)(77)}{\left(\frac{6}{11}\right)(77)}$$

$$=\dfrac{9\cdot 11}{6\cdot 7}=\dfrac{99}{42}$$

Step 3 Express in lowest terms $\dfrac{99}{42}=\dfrac{3\cdot 3\cdot 11}{2\cdot 3\cdot 7}=\dfrac{33}{14}$

b. $\dfrac{\dfrac{xy}{z^2}}{\dfrac{x^3}{y^2z}}$ The LCD of $\dfrac{xy}{z^2}$ and $\dfrac{x^3}{y^2z}$ is y^2z^2.

Multiply the numerator and the denominator by the LCD.

$$\dfrac{\dfrac{xy}{z^2}}{\dfrac{x^3}{y^2z}} = \dfrac{\left(\dfrac{xy}{z^2}\right)(y^2z^2)}{\dfrac{x^3}{y^2z}(y^2z^2)} = \dfrac{xy^3}{x^3z} = \dfrac{y^3}{x^2z}$$

c. $\dfrac{x-\dfrac{1}{x}}{2+\dfrac{1}{x}}$:   The LCD of the fractions in the numerator and the denominator is x.

Multiply the numerator and the denominator by the LCD.

$$\dfrac{x-\dfrac{1}{x}}{2+\dfrac{1}{x}} = \dfrac{\left(x-\dfrac{1}{x}\right)x}{\left(2+\dfrac{1}{x}\right)x} = \dfrac{x\cdot x-\dfrac{1}{x}\cdot x}{2\cdot x+\dfrac{1}{x}\cdot x} = \dfrac{x^2-1}{2x+1}$$

Simplification of Complex Fractions:

Method 2:

Step 1   Simplify the numerator.

Step 2   Simplify the denominator.

Step 3   Multiply the numerator by the reciprocal of the denominator.

For example: $\dfrac{\dfrac{4}{7}}{\dfrac{2}{3}} = \dfrac{4}{7} \div \dfrac{2}{3} = \dfrac{4}{7}\cdot\dfrac{3}{2}$

Simplify and write in lowest terms. $\dfrac{\overset{2}{\cancel{4}}}{7}\cdot\dfrac{3}{\underset{1}{\cancel{2}}} = \dfrac{2\cdot 3}{7} = \dfrac{6}{7}$

Now we simplify expressions in example 1 by method 2.

EXAMPLE 2   Simplify the complex fractions by method 2.

a. $\dfrac{1\frac{2}{7}}{\dfrac{6}{11}}$ **b.** $\dfrac{\dfrac{xy}{z^2}}{\dfrac{x^3}{y^2z}}$ **c.** $\dfrac{x-\dfrac{1}{x}}{2+\dfrac{1}{x}}$

2. Simplify the complex fractions by Method 2.

a) $\dfrac{2\frac{1}{5}}{\frac{3}{10}}$

b) $\dfrac{\frac{z^2}{xy}}{\frac{y^2z}{x^3y}}$

c) $\dfrac{x^2-\frac{1}{x}}{3+\frac{1}{x}}$

Solutions:

a. $\dfrac{1\frac{2}{7}}{\frac{6}{11}} = \dfrac{\frac{9}{7}}{\frac{6}{11}}$

Step 1   Not needed.

Step 2   Not needed.

Step 3 $\dfrac{\frac{9}{7}}{\frac{6}{11}} = \dfrac{9}{7} \div \dfrac{6}{11}$ Divide numerator by denominator.

$= \dfrac{9}{7} \cdot \dfrac{11}{6} = \dfrac{9 \cdot 11}{7 \cdot 6} = \dfrac{3 \cdot 3 \cdot 11}{7 \cdot 2 \cdot 3} = \dfrac{33}{14}$.   Compare with example 1 *a*.

b. $\dfrac{\frac{xy}{z^2}}{\frac{x^3}{y^2z}} = \dfrac{xy}{z^2} \div \dfrac{x^3}{y^2z}$

$= \dfrac{xy}{z^2} \cdot \dfrac{y^2z}{x^3} = \dfrac{xy^3z}{z^2x^3} = \dfrac{y^3}{zx^2}$ Compare with example 1 *b*.

c. $\dfrac{x-\frac{1}{x}}{2+\frac{1}{x}}$

Step 1   Simplify the numerator,

$$x - \frac{1}{x} = x \cdot \frac{x}{x} - \frac{1}{x} = \frac{x^2}{x} - \frac{1}{x} = \frac{x^2-1}{x}$$

Step 2   Simplify the denominator,

$$2 + \frac{1}{x} = 2 \cdot \frac{x}{x} + \frac{1}{x} = \frac{2x}{x} + \frac{1}{x} = \frac{2x+1}{x}$$

Step 3   Divide the numerator by the denominator.

$$\frac{x-\frac{1}{x}}{2+\frac{1}{x}} = \frac{x^2-1}{x} \div \frac{2x+1}{x} = \frac{x^2-1}{x} \cdot \frac{x}{2x+1}$$

$$= \frac{x^2-1}{2x+1}$$ Compare with example 1 *c* .

EXAMPLE 3   Simplify the following complex fraction.

$$\frac{\dfrac{x}{x-y} - \dfrac{y}{x+y}}{x^2 - y^2}$$

Solution:

Method 1:

Step 1   The LCD of the numerator and the denominator is:

$$(x-y)(x+y)$$

Step 2   Multiply the numerator and the denominator by the LCD.

$$\frac{\dfrac{x}{x-y} - \dfrac{y}{x+y}}{(x^2 - y^2)} = \frac{\left(\dfrac{x}{x-y} - \dfrac{y}{x+y}\right)(x-y)(x+y)}{(x^2 - y^2)(x-y)(x+y)}$$

$$= \frac{\dfrac{x}{x-y}(x-y)(x+y) - \dfrac{y}{x+y}(x-y)(x+y)}{(x^2 - y^2)(x-y)(x+y)}$$

$$= \frac{x(x+y) - y(x-y)}{(x^2 - y^2)^2}$$

$$= \frac{x^2 + xy - yx + y^2}{(x^2 - y^2)^2} = \frac{x^2 + y^2}{(x^2 - y^2)^2}$$

EXERCISE 7.6

In exercises 1-12, simplify the complex fraction.

1. $\dfrac{\dfrac{1}{5}}{\dfrac{2}{9}}$ 2. $\dfrac{\dfrac{2}{3}}{\dfrac{4}{5}}$ 3. $\dfrac{\dfrac{1}{4} - \dfrac{1}{5}}{\dfrac{3}{6}}$ 4. $\dfrac{\dfrac{1}{3} - \dfrac{1}{4}}{\dfrac{3}{4}}$ 5. $\dfrac{\dfrac{2}{3} + \dfrac{4}{5}}{\dfrac{1}{3}}$ 6. $\dfrac{\dfrac{1}{2} + \dfrac{2}{3}}{\dfrac{1}{3}}$

7. $\dfrac{\dfrac{5}{6}}{-\dfrac{5}{4}}$ 8. $\dfrac{-\dfrac{3}{4}}{\dfrac{3}{8}}$ 9. $\dfrac{\dfrac{1}{6} - \dfrac{2}{7}}{\dfrac{1}{7}}$ 10. $\dfrac{\dfrac{2}{5} - \dfrac{1}{3}}{\dfrac{1}{5}}$ 11. $\dfrac{-\dfrac{5}{8} + \dfrac{3}{4}}{\dfrac{7}{8}}$ 12. $\dfrac{\dfrac{5}{6} - \dfrac{3}{4}}{\dfrac{7}{8}}$

In exercises 13-60, use any method to simplify the complex fraction.

13. $\dfrac{\dfrac{p^2}{q}}{5\dfrac{p}{q^2}}$ 14. $\dfrac{\dfrac{x^2}{y^2}}{3\dfrac{x}{y}}$ 15. $\dfrac{\dfrac{t+3}{t}}{\dfrac{t-4}{2}}$ 16. $\dfrac{\dfrac{x-2}{x}}{\dfrac{x+3}{2}}$ 17. $\dfrac{\dfrac{6}{x}}{\dfrac{1+x}{4x^5}}$ 18. $\dfrac{\dfrac{5}{x^2}}{\dfrac{1-x}{3x}}$

7.6   Complex Fractions

19. $\dfrac{\frac{1}{x}-x}{\frac{x^2-1}{3}}$ **20.** $\dfrac{x+\frac{1}{x}}{\frac{1+x^2}{2}}$ **21.** $\dfrac{\frac{y+4}{y}}{\frac{1}{y}+\frac{1}{5}}$ **22.** $\dfrac{\frac{x-3}{x}}{\frac{1}{x}-2}$ **23.** $\dfrac{\frac{1}{a}-\frac{1}{b}}{\frac{a}{b}-\frac{b}{a}}$ **24.** $\dfrac{\frac{1}{x}+\frac{1}{y}}{\frac{1}{y^2}-\frac{1}{x^2}}$

25. $\dfrac{t-1-\frac{2}{t}}{\frac{2t^2}{3}}$ **26.** $\dfrac{x+1-\frac{3}{x}}{\frac{3x^2}{4}}$ **27.** $\dfrac{1-a-\frac{2}{a}}{\frac{6}{a^2}+\frac{1}{a}-1}$ **28.** $\dfrac{x-1-\frac{4}{x}}{\frac{2}{x^2}-\frac{1}{x}+1}$ **29.** $\dfrac{x^2-16}{\frac{1}{4}-\frac{1}{x}}$ **30.** $\dfrac{x^2-9}{\frac{1}{x}+\frac{1}{3}}$

31. $\dfrac{81-x^2}{\frac{1}{9}-\frac{1}{x}}$ **32.** $\dfrac{25-x^2}{\frac{1}{5}+\frac{1}{x}}$ **33.** $\dfrac{2+\frac{1}{x}}{1-\frac{2}{x}}$ **34.** $\dfrac{\frac{1}{x}-3}{1+\frac{3}{x}}$ **35.** $\dfrac{\frac{a}{b}+\frac{1}{a}}{\frac{a}{b}-\frac{1}{a}}$ **36.** $\dfrac{\frac{x}{y}+\frac{2}{x}}{\frac{x}{y}-\frac{1}{x}}$

37. $\dfrac{1+\frac{3}{y}}{1-\frac{9}{y^2}}$ **38.** $\dfrac{2+\frac{4}{y}}{4-\frac{16}{y^2}}$ **39.** $\dfrac{3+\frac{6}{y}}{5-\frac{20}{y^2}}$ **40.** $\dfrac{2+\frac{10}{t-5}}{3-\frac{4}{t-5}}$ **41.** $\dfrac{5-\frac{25}{t+5}}{1-\frac{3}{t+5}}$ **42.** $\dfrac{4-\frac{2}{t+7}}{5+\frac{9}{t+7}}$

43. $\dfrac{\frac{3}{2x+1}-3}{2-\frac{4x}{2x+1}}$ **44.** $\dfrac{2+\frac{5}{y}-\frac{12}{y^2}}{4-\frac{4}{y}-\frac{3}{y^2}}$ **45.** $\dfrac{1-\frac{7}{b}+\frac{12}{b^2}}{1+\frac{1}{b}-\frac{20}{b^2}}$ **46.** $\dfrac{1-\frac{x}{2x+1}}{x-\frac{1}{2x+1}}$ **47.** $\dfrac{x-7+\frac{5}{x-1}}{x-3+\frac{1}{x-1}}$

48. $\dfrac{y-6+\frac{22}{2y+3}}{y-5+\frac{11}{2y+3}}$ **49.** $\dfrac{\frac{1}{y}-\frac{2}{y-1}}{\frac{3}{y}+\frac{1}{y-1}}$ **50.** $\dfrac{\frac{3}{t+1}+\frac{1}{t}}{\frac{2}{t+1}+\frac{3}{t}}$ **51.** $\dfrac{\frac{8}{t}-\frac{1}{8}}{\frac{1}{4}-\frac{1}{t}}$ **52.** $\dfrac{\frac{1}{2}-\frac{1}{t}}{\frac{1}{4}-\frac{1}{t^2}}$

53. $\dfrac{\frac{1}{t+4}-\frac{1}{4}}{\frac{1}{t^2-16}}$ **54.** $\dfrac{\frac{t}{t+2}-\frac{3}{t}}{\frac{4}{t^2+4t+4}}$ **55.** $\dfrac{\frac{7}{t}-\frac{2t}{t-3}}{\frac{3}{t^2-6t+9}}$ **56.** $\dfrac{\frac{4}{6-t}-1}{\frac{t-2}{t^2-36}}$ **57.** $\dfrac{\frac{x}{(x+4)^2}-3}{5-\frac{2}{x+4}}$

58. $\dfrac{\frac{2x^2-7x}{3-x}}{\frac{2x^2}{x^3-3x^2}}$ **59.** $\dfrac{\frac{3}{x^2}-\frac{9}{x^3}}{\frac{x^2-4x+3}{x^4-x^3}}$ **60.** $\dfrac{\frac{x}{x-2}-\frac{4}{x+1}}{\frac{10-2x}{x^2-x-2}+1}$

The statements $\dfrac{3}{x-1} + \dfrac{2x}{x+1} = 2$,

and $\dfrac{2}{y^2-9} + \dfrac{1}{y+3} = \dfrac{y}{y-3}$ are examples of equations

containing rational expressions.

A. SOLVING EQUATIONS CONTAINING RATIONAL EXPRESSIONS

An equation containing rational expression(s) is called a Rational equation. In order to solve a rational equation, we first clear the equation of all fractions. The best way to do this is to multiply both sides of the equation by the LCD of the rational expressions which appear in the equation.

> *Note*
>
> We can do this because we are dealing with an **equation**. This could not be done in the previous sections because in 7.1-7.6 we were dealing with expressions, **not** equations.

Steps to solve a Rational equation involving rational expressions:

> **Step 1** Find the LCD of all rational expressions appearing in the equation.
>
> **Step 2** Multiply both sides of the equation by the LCD and simplify so that the resulting equation does not contain any fractions.
>
> **Step 3** Solve the resulting equation.
>
> **Step 4** Verify the answer obtained in step 3 by substituting the solution in the original equation. Reject any solution that makes any denominator zero.

EXAMPLE 1 Solve $\dfrac{3}{x-1} + \dfrac{2x}{x+1} = 2$.

Solution:

Step 1 The LCD of the rational terms in the given equation is: $(x-1)(x+1)$.

Step 2 $\left(\dfrac{3}{x-1} + \dfrac{2x}{x+1}\right)(x-1)(x+1) = 2(x-1)(x+1)$

Multiply both sides by the LCD.

$\dfrac{3(x-1)(x+1)}{x-1} + \dfrac{2x(x-1)(x+1)}{x+1} = 2(x-1)(x+1)$

$3(x+1) + 2x(x-1) = 2(x-1)(x+1)$

Step 3 $3x + 3 + 2x^2 - 2x = 2(x^2-1)$

$2x^2 + x + 3 = 2x^2 - 2$

$-2x^2 + 2x^2 + x = -2 - 3$

$x = -5$

Thus $x = -5$ is a possible solution of the equation.

Step 4 *Verification:* Substitute -5 for x in the original equation.

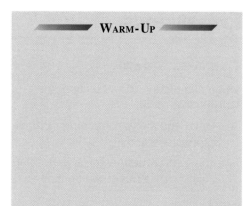
$$\frac{3}{x-1} + \frac{2x}{x+1} = 2$$

$$\frac{3}{-5-1} + \frac{2(-5)}{-5+1} = 2$$

$$-\frac{3}{6} + \frac{-10}{-4} = 2$$

$$-\frac{1}{2} + \frac{5}{2} = 2$$

$$\frac{4}{2} = 2 \qquad \text{True}$$

Thus $x = -5$ is a solution.

2. Solve the following equations.

a) $\dfrac{2a}{a-3} = \dfrac{3}{a-3} - 1$

EXAMPLE 2   Solve the following equations.

a. $2 - \dfrac{4}{x} = \dfrac{x+1}{5}$ b. $-\dfrac{2a}{a+1} = 1 + \dfrac{2}{a+1}$

c. $\dfrac{2}{t^2 - 1} - \dfrac{1}{2} = \dfrac{1}{t-1}$

Solutions:

a. $2 - \dfrac{4}{x} = \dfrac{x+1}{5}$

Step 1   The LCD of the rational expressions is **5x**.

Step 2 $\left(2 - \dfrac{4}{x}\right)5x = \left(\dfrac{x+1}{5}\right)5x$ Multiply both sides by the LCD.

$$10x - \left(\dfrac{4}{x}\right)5x = (x+1)x$$

$$10x - 20 = x^2 + x$$

Step 3 $10x - 20 = x^2 + x$

$$-x^2 + 10x - 20 - x = 0$$

$$-x^2 + 9x - 20 = 0$$

$$x^2 - 9x + 20 = 0 \qquad \text{Multiply both sides by } -1.$$

$$(x - 4)(x - 5) = 0 \qquad \text{Factor}$$

$$x - 4 = 0 \qquad \text{or} \qquad x - 5 = 0$$

$$x = 4 \qquad ; \qquad x = 5$$

Thus the possible solutions are $x = \mathbf{4}$ and $x = \mathbf{5}$.

Step 4   **Check** the solutions: $2 - \dfrac{4}{x} = \dfrac{x+1}{5}$

$x = \mathbf{4}:$ Substitute 4 for x in the original equation.

$$2 - \dfrac{4}{4} = \dfrac{4+1}{5} \longrightarrow 1 = 1 \qquad \text{True}$$

$x = \mathbf{5}:$ Substitute 5 for x in the original equation.

$$2 - \dfrac{4}{5} = \dfrac{5+1}{5} \longrightarrow \dfrac{6}{5} = \dfrac{6}{5} \qquad \text{True}$$

Thus $x = 4$ and $x = 5$ are both solutions.

b. $-\dfrac{2a}{a+1} = 1 + \dfrac{2}{a+1}$

Step 1   The L C D of the rational expressions is $a + 1$.

Step 2 $-\dfrac{2a}{a+1}(a+1) = \left(1 + \dfrac{2}{a+1}\right)(a+1)$ Multiply both sides by the L C D.

$$-2a = (a+1) + \left(\dfrac{2}{a+1}\right)(a+1)$$

$$-2a = a + 1 + 2$$

Step 3 $-2a = a + 3$

$-2a - a = 3$

$-3a = 3$

$$a = \dfrac{3}{-3} = -1$$

Step 4   *Check* the solutions: Substitute -1 for a in the original equation.

$$-\dfrac{2a}{a+1} = 1 + \dfrac{2}{a+1}$$

$$\dfrac{-2(-1)}{-1+1} = 1 + \dfrac{2}{-1+1}$$

Notice that upon substitution, $a = -1$ makes the denominator zero. Therefore -1 is an extraneous solution. Since -1 was the only candidate for a solution, the given equation has **no solution**.

c. $\dfrac{2}{t^2 - 1} - \dfrac{1}{2} = \dfrac{1}{t-1}$

Step 1   The LCD of the rational expressions is $2(t^2 - 1)$.

Step 2 $\left(\dfrac{2}{t^2-1} - \dfrac{1}{2}\right)[\,2(t^2-1)\,] = \left(\dfrac{1}{t-1}\right)[\,2(t^2-1)\,]$

Multiply both sides by the L C D.

$$\left(\dfrac{2}{t^2-1}\right)[\,2(t^2-1)\,] - \dfrac{1}{2}[\,2(t^2-1)\,] = \dfrac{2(t^2-1)}{t-1}$$

$$4 - (t^2 - 1) = 2(t+1)$$

$$5 - t^2 = 2t + 2$$

$$-t^2 - 2t + 3 = 0$$

$$t^2 + 2t - 3 = 0$$

Step 3 $t^2 + 2t - 3 = 0$

$(t-1)(t+3) = 0$ Factor

$t - 1 = 0$ or $t + 3 = 0$

$t = 1$ or $t = -3$

---

b) $3 - \dfrac{4}{x} = \dfrac{x}{2}$

c) $\dfrac{2}{a+1} + \dfrac{1}{a-1} = 1$

Step 4   *Check* the solutions:

$t = 1$:   Substituting 1 for t makes the denominator 0 on both sides.

Therefore, $t = 1$ is an **extraneous solution**.

$t = -3$:   Substituting -3 for t in the original equation.

$$\frac{2}{(-3)^2 - 1} - \frac{1}{2} = \frac{1}{-3-1}$$

$$-\frac{1}{4} = -\frac{1}{4} \qquad \text{True}$$

Thus $t = -3$ is the only solution of the equation.

B. Solving an Equation for a Particular Unknown in Terms of Another Unknown

So far, in this chapter, we solved equations containing only one variable. In real life situations we deal with equations that may involve several unknown quantities and we may be interested in just one of those unknown, at a time. Some of these situations are described below:

1.   Relationship between the **speed (s)** of a car, when it covers a **distance (d)** in **time (t)** is given by

$$s = \frac{d}{t}.$$

From this equation, we can find the distance d in terms of s and t. We call this, solving for d in terms of s and t. Similarly, we can solve this equation for the time (t) in terms of the speed and the distance.

$$t = \frac{d}{s} \qquad (1).$$

2.   Relationship between the **height (h)** of a stone thrown vertically up with the **speed (u)** after the **time (t)** seconds in the air is given by:

$$h = ut - 16t^2.$$

From this equation, we can find the **speed (u)** in terms of the height (h) and **time (t)**. We call this, solving for u in terms of h and t.

$$u = \frac{h}{t} + 16t \qquad (2).$$

In general we can solve the equations containing several variables for a particular variable in terms of the others by using the following step by step approach.

Step 1   Simplify both sides of the equation by using multiplication or distributive properties to clear all grouping symbols, fractions or decimals.

Step 2   Isolate the terms containing the target variable, for which the equation is to be solved, on the left side by using addition properties.

Step 3   Factor out the target variable from terms on the left side and divide both sides by the factor of the target variable.

The process is illustrated in the following examples.

EXAMPLE 3   Solve the equation for b. $\dfrac{2}{c} = \dfrac{1}{a} + \dfrac{1}{b}$

Solution:

    Step 1   The LCD of the rational expressions is $\boldsymbol{abc}$.

             Multiply both sides of the equation by abc.

$$\left(\dfrac{2}{c}\right)abc = \left(\dfrac{1}{a} + \dfrac{1}{b}\right)abc$$

$$\dfrac{2\,abc}{c} = \dfrac{abc}{a} + \dfrac{abc}{b} \longrightarrow 2ab = bc + ac$$

    Step 2 $2ab - bc = ac$ Collect all terms containing b on one side.

    Step 3 $(2a - c)b = ac$ Factor out b.

$$b = \dfrac{ac}{2a - c} \quad \text{Solve for } b.$$

EXAMPLE 4   Solve for F : $C = \dfrac{5}{9}(F - 32)$.

Solution:

$$9C = 9\left[\dfrac{5}{9}(F - 32)\right]$$

$$9C = 5(F - 32)$$

$$= 5F - 160$$

$$9C + 160 = 5F \quad \text{or} \quad 5F = 9C + 160$$

$$F = \dfrac{9}{5}C + 32$$

EXERCISE 7.7

A. **In exercises 1–46, solve the equation for the given unknown.**

1. $2x - \dfrac{1}{3} = \dfrac{2}{5}$

2. $\dfrac{5x}{6} - 4 = \dfrac{2}{3}$

3. $\dfrac{x}{2} - \dfrac{1}{3} = \dfrac{5}{6}$

4. $\dfrac{2x}{5} - \dfrac{3}{4} = \dfrac{7}{10}$

5. $\dfrac{2x - 3}{4} - \dfrac{x}{3} = \dfrac{5x}{6}$

6. $\dfrac{2}{5} - \dfrac{4x - 3}{2} = \dfrac{7x}{10}$

7. $\dfrac{3x - 5}{4} + \dfrac{2x - 3}{5} = \dfrac{9}{10}$

8. $\dfrac{7}{4} - \dfrac{2x - 5}{7} = \dfrac{3x - 2}{7}$

9. $\dfrac{1}{4} + \dfrac{9}{x} = 1$

10. $\dfrac{1}{3} - \dfrac{5}{x} = 2$

11. $\dfrac{2}{y} + \dfrac{1}{2} = \dfrac{7}{2y}$

12. $\dfrac{3}{x} - \dfrac{1}{5} = \dfrac{2}{5x}$

13. $\dfrac{p}{p + 3} = \dfrac{3}{5}$

14. $\dfrac{x}{x - 5} = \dfrac{2}{3}$

15. $\dfrac{12}{3a - 2} = 3$

16. $\dfrac{6}{4 - 3z} = 3$

17. $3 + \dfrac{8}{x} = 5$ **18.** $3 - \dfrac{12}{a} = 7$ **19.** $\dfrac{6}{t} + 3 = 11$ **20.** $x + 1 - \dfrac{2}{x} = 0$

21. $\dfrac{-3}{2a+5} = \dfrac{2}{a-1}$ **22.** $\dfrac{4}{5x-1} = \dfrac{2}{2x-1}$ **23.** $\dfrac{5a}{a-4} = \dfrac{4a}{a-4} + 5$ **24.** $\dfrac{1}{y+5} = \dfrac{y}{y+12}$

25. $\dfrac{z}{z-2} = \dfrac{5}{3z-8}$ **26.** $\dfrac{2t}{t-3} = t - \dfrac{6}{t-3}$ **27.** $\dfrac{3}{t+2} - \dfrac{2}{t^2-4} = \dfrac{2}{t-2}$

28. $\dfrac{2}{x-3} + \dfrac{3}{x^2-9} = \dfrac{4}{x+3}$ **29.** $\dfrac{2}{x-1} + \dfrac{x-2}{3} = \dfrac{4}{x-1}$ **30.** $\dfrac{3}{x+2} - \dfrac{x+3}{2} = \dfrac{3}{x+2}$

31. $\dfrac{y+4}{y+7} - \dfrac{3}{8} = \dfrac{y}{y+3}$ **32.** $\dfrac{x-3}{x-1} - \dfrac{3}{4} = \dfrac{x}{x+2}$ **33.** $\dfrac{4}{t} - \dfrac{1}{t+3} = \dfrac{3t+2}{t^2+2t-3}$

34. $\dfrac{2}{x} + \dfrac{1}{x+1} = \dfrac{3x^2-2x}{x^2+x}$ **35.** $\dfrac{5}{a-2} + \dfrac{10}{a+2} = 7$ **36.** $\dfrac{3}{x+3} - \dfrac{5}{x-3} = 4$

37. $\dfrac{x}{x-2} + 4 = \dfrac{2}{x-2}$ **38.** $\dfrac{p}{p+2} - 5 = \dfrac{3}{p+2}$ **39.** $\dfrac{t-1}{t} - \dfrac{t+1}{t} = 0$

40. $\dfrac{x-2}{x} - \dfrac{x+2}{x} = 0$ **41.** $\dfrac{a-3}{a-1} = \dfrac{2a-4}{a-1}$ **42.** $\dfrac{x-2}{x-1} = \dfrac{2x-3}{x-1}$

43. $\dfrac{2}{x-3} - \dfrac{3}{x+3} = \dfrac{12}{x^2-9}$ **44.** $\dfrac{3}{x+4} - \dfrac{2}{x-4} = \dfrac{5}{x^2-16}$ **45.** $\dfrac{x-4}{x-3} + \dfrac{x-2}{x-3} = x-3$

46. $\dfrac{x+1}{x+2} - \dfrac{x+3}{x+2} = x+2$

B. In exercises 47-66, solve the equation for the specified variable.

47. $T = \dfrac{VP}{R}$; for P **48.** $A = \dfrac{BC}{a}$; for B **49.** $I = \dfrac{E}{R+r}$; for R **50.** $X = \dfrac{Y}{Z+a}$; for Z

51. $\dfrac{3}{r} = \dfrac{1}{p} + \dfrac{1}{q}$; for p **52.** $\dfrac{2}{X} = \dfrac{1}{Y} - \dfrac{1}{Z}$; for Z **53.** $V = u + at$; for a **54.** $S = u + \dfrac{1}{2}at^2$; for a

55. $V = lwh$; for h **56.** $S = a + (n-1)d$; for d **57.** $F = \dfrac{w(R-r)}{2r}$; for r **58.** $V = \dfrac{1}{3}\pi r^2 h$; for h

59. $y = mx + b$; for m **60.** $W = RI^2 t$; for R **61.** $I = Prt$; for r **62.** $S = ut + \dfrac{1}{2}gt^2$; for u

63. $A = \dfrac{1}{2}h(b_1 + b_2)$; for b_1 **64.** $s = \dfrac{1}{2}(a + b + c)$; for c **65.** $V = \pi r^2 h$; for h **66.** $S = \pi r(r + 2h)$; for h

7.8 APPLICATIONS

Many applications, such as shared-work problems, distance speed problems, and other types of problems involve equations containing rational expressions. In this section we will discuss how to convert these types of problems into mathematical models.

Recall the procedure for solving application problems discussed earlier in the text.

OBJECTIVES ■ ■ ■ ■

Upon completion of this section you will be able to solve:

A. Application problems involving unknown numbers;

B. Application problems involving distances; and

C. Application problems involving variation.

Procedures for solving application problems.

Step 1 Read the problem carefully, and identify what is to be found *(the unknown)*. Choose a variable to represent the numerical value of the unknown quantity.

Step 2 Write down mathematical expressions for any other unknown quantities using the assigned variable. If possible, draw figures or diagrams. *Diagrams help us understand the problem better.*

Step 3 Translate the problem into an equation.

Step 4 Solve the equation.

Step 5 Answer the question asked. *Be sure that the answer makes sense and follows the logic of the question.*

Step 6 Verify your answer by using the *original* statement of the problem.

A. APPLICATION PROBLEMS INVOLVING NUMBERS

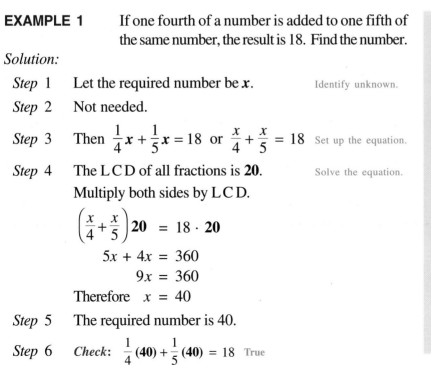

EXAMPLE 1 If one fourth of a number is added to one fifth of the same number, the result is 18. Find the number.

Solution:

Step 1   Let the required number be x.   Identify unknown.

Step 2   Not needed.

Step 3   Then $\frac{1}{4}x + \frac{1}{5}x = 18$ or $\frac{x}{4} + \frac{x}{5} = 18$ Set up the equation.

Step 4   The LCD of all fractions is **20**.   Solve the equation.
Multiply both sides by LCD.

$$\left(\frac{x}{4} + \frac{x}{5}\right)20 = 18 \cdot 20$$
$$5x + 4x = 360$$
$$9x = 360$$
Therefore $x = 40$

Step 5   The required number is 40.

Step 6   *Check*: $\frac{1}{4}(40) + \frac{1}{5}(40) = 18$ True

WARM-UP

1. If two-thirds of a number is added to one-half of the same number, the result is seven. Find the number.

2. Three times the reciprocal of a certain number subtracted from two times that number is five. Find the number.

EXAMPLE 2 Three times a number is subtracted from four times its reciprocal. The result is 11. Find the number.

Solution:

- Let the number be x.

- Then from the given condition we get:

$$4\left(\frac{1}{x}\right) - 3x = 11 \quad \text{or} \quad \frac{4}{x} - 3x = 11. \quad \text{The L C D} = x$$

- $$\left(\frac{4}{x} - 3x\right)x = 11x$$

$$\frac{4}{x} \cdot x - 3x^2 = 11x$$

$$4 - 3x^2 = 11x$$

$$0 = 3x^2 + 11x - 4$$

$$3x^2 + 11x - 4 = 0$$

$$(x + 4)(3x - 1) = 0$$

$$x + 4 = 0 \quad \text{or} \quad 3x - 1 = 0$$

$$x = -4 \quad \text{or} \quad x = \frac{1}{3}$$

- Therefore the number is -4 or $\frac{1}{3}$.

- *Check* the solution for :

$$x = -4: \quad \frac{4}{x} - 3x = 11 \quad \longrightarrow \quad \frac{4}{-4} - 3(-4) = 11$$

$$\longrightarrow \quad -1 + 12 = 11 \quad \text{True}$$

Answers:

1. 6.   **2.** 3 and $-\frac{1}{2}$

$$x = \frac{1}{3}: \quad \frac{4}{x} - 3x = 11 \quad \longrightarrow \quad \frac{4}{\frac{1}{3}} - 3\left(\frac{1}{3}\right) = 11$$

$$\longrightarrow \quad 12 - 1 = 11 \quad \text{True}$$

B. APPLICATION PROBLEMS INVOLVING DISTANCE

3. A boat moving downstream with the current travels 250 miles in the same time that it can travel 200 miles against the current. If the current is 5 miles per hour, what is the speed of the boat in still water?

EXAMPLE 3 An airplane flying against the wind travels 175 miles in the same time that it can travel 200 miles with the wind. If the wind speed is 10 miles per hour, what is the speed of the airplane in still air?

Solution:

- Let the speed of the airplane $= x$ miles per hour
  Wind speed = 10 miles per hour.

- *Formula for the distance travelled:*
  Distance = Rate · Time

  Hence use Time = $\dfrac{\text{Distance}}{\text{Rate}}$

Flight	Rate	Distance	Time
With Wind	$x + 10$	200	$\dfrac{200}{x+10}$
Against Wind	$x - 10$	175	$\dfrac{175}{x-10}$

Since the time taken in both cases is same, we have

$$\frac{200}{x+10} = \frac{175}{x-10}$$

- We will solve this equation for x. It is an equation containing rational expressions.

  The L C D of the fractions is $(x + 10)(x - 10)$.

  Multiply both sides of the equation by $(x + 10)(x - 10)$ and simplify.

  $$\frac{200}{x+10}\,(x-10)(x+10) = \frac{175}{x-10}\,(x-10)(x+10)$$

  $$200(x - 10) = 175(x + 10)$$
  $$200x - 2000 = 175x + 1750$$
  $$-175x + 200x = 1750 + 2000$$
  $$25x = 3750 \quad\longrightarrow\quad x = 150$$

- Therefore, the speed of the airplane in still air is 150 miles per hour.

- ### APPLICATION PROBLEMS INVOLVING WORK

  The key to problems involving work is to *find the fraction of the job done in a unit of time,* where the unit of time can be an hour, a day, a week, or something else.

  For example, if a job can be completed in **n** days, then the fraction of the work done per day equals "nth part of the job", and is given by $\dfrac{1}{n}$. You can also think that if a job can be completed in x hours then the rate of work is $\dfrac{1}{x}$ of the job per hour.

EXAMPLE 4   A drain can empty a swimming pool in 4 days. A second drain can empty this pool in 2 days. In how much time will the two drains working together empty the pool?

Solution:

Find the rate of work for each drain and use the formula:

rate × time = work done

Suppose the two drains together empty the pool in x days.

Drain	Time alone	Rate · Time = Work done	
First	4 days	$\frac{1}{4}$ · x	$\frac{x}{4}$
Second	2 days	$\frac{1}{2}$ · x	$\frac{x}{2}$

Now,

Work done by first drain	+	Work done by second drain	= 1 (complete job)
$\frac{x}{4}$	+	$\frac{x}{2}$	= 1

We solve the equation : $\dfrac{x}{4} + \dfrac{x}{2} = 1$

The L C D is 4. Multiply both sides of the equation by 4.

$$\left(\frac{x}{4} + \frac{x}{2}\right)(4) = 1 \cdot 4$$

$$\frac{x}{4} \cdot 4 + \frac{x}{2} \cdot 4 = 4$$

$$x + 2x = 4$$

$$3x = 4$$

$$x = \frac{4}{3}$$

Therefore, the two drains together empty the pool in

$\frac{4}{3}$ days or **1 day and 8 hours.**

5. A train operating with one engine covers a distance in 4 hours. If a second engine is added to the same train, it covers the same distance in 2.5 hours. How long will it take to cover the same distance if the second engine was to do it alone?

EXAMPLE 5 A mechanic helped by his assistant can repair an engine in 4 hours. Working alone, the mechanic would have taken 6 hours to repair the engine. How long will it take the assistant to repair the engine all by himself?

Solution:

Suppose that the assistant can repair the engine in x hours.

Repair	Time	Rate fraction of job done
Mechanic	6 hours	$\frac{1}{6}$
Assistant	x hours	$\frac{1}{x}$
Together	4 hours	$\frac{1}{4}$

In one hour,

Work done by mechanic	+	Work done by assistant	=	Work done by two together
↓		↓		↓
$\dfrac{1}{6}$	+	$\dfrac{1}{x}$	=	$\dfrac{1}{4}$

Therefore, we must solve the equation: $\dfrac{1}{6} + \dfrac{1}{x} = \dfrac{1}{4}$.

Here $\qquad LCD = 12x$

$$12x\left(\frac{1}{6} + \frac{1}{x}\right) = 12x\left(\frac{1}{4}\right) \longrightarrow 2x + 12 = 3x$$

$$\longrightarrow 12 = x \ \text{ or } \ x = 12$$

Therefore, the assistant will need 12 hours to repair the engine when working alone.

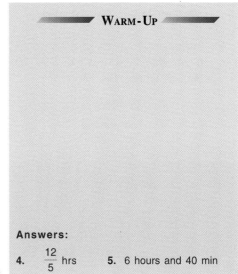
C. APPLICATION PROBLEMS INVOLVING VARIATIONS

If we say that y varies directly as x, then it means that the ratio $\dfrac{y}{x}$ is a constant. If this constant is k, we get

$\dfrac{y}{x} = k$. Therefore, the expression y *varies directly* as x results in the equation $y = kx$, where k is the *constant of variation*. The constant of variation can be different from case to case. For example, John can walk *twice* as fast as Michael; Thomas can walk one and one-half times faster than *Michael*.

$$\frac{\text{Speed of John}}{\text{Speed of Michael}} = \frac{2x}{1x} = 2 \,(\text{constant})$$

$$\frac{\text{Speed of Thomas}}{\text{Speed of Michael}} = \frac{\frac{3}{2}x}{1x} = \frac{3}{2} = 1.5 \,(\text{constant})$$

A few more examples of variation :

Variation	Ratio (k)	Equation
y varies directly as x	$\dfrac{y}{x}$	$y = kx$
y varies directly as square of x	y/x^2	$y = kx^2$
y varies inversely as x	$\dfrac{y}{\left(\dfrac{1}{x}\right)}$	$y = \dfrac{k}{x}$
y varies inversely as square of x	$\dfrac{y}{\left(\dfrac{1}{x^2}\right)}$	$y = \dfrac{k}{x^2}$
z varies jointly as x and y	z/xy	$z = kxy$

6. Suppose A varies directly as B. Given that $A = 5$ when $B = 20$. Find B, when A is 12.

EXAMPLE 6   Suppose A varies directly as B. Given that $A = 4$ when B is 10, find B when A is 18.

Solution:

The relationship A varies directly as B results in the equation $A = kB$ where k is the constant of variation. The given condition "$A = 4$ when $B = 10$" allow us to determine the constant of variation. Substitute $A = 4$ and $B = 10$ in $A = kB$.

$$4 = 10\,k \quad \text{or} \quad k = \frac{4}{10} = \frac{2}{5}.$$

Therefore, the equation of variation becomes $A = \frac{2}{5}B$.

Now to find the value of B, when $A = 18$, substitute 18 for A in the equation $A = \frac{2}{5}B$.

$$18 = \frac{2}{5}B \longrightarrow B = \frac{90}{2} = 45$$

We see that $\quad k = \frac{A}{B} = \frac{2}{5} = \frac{18}{45}.$

7. The intensity of illumination I from a source of light varies inversely as the square of the distance d from the source. If the intensity is 120 candle power when the source is 3.5 feet away, find

a) the intensity when the source is 5 feet away.

EXAMPLE 7   The intensity of illumination I from a source of light varies inversely as the square of the distance d from the source. If the intensity is 150 candle power when the source is 4 feet away, find

a.   the intensity when the source is 5 feet away, and

b.   the distance of the source of light in order for the intensity to be 24 candle power.

Solutions:

I varies inversely as square of d. The resulting equation is $I = \dfrac{k}{d^2}$, where k is a constant of variation. It is given that $I = 150$ when $d = 4$.

Substituting these values in $I = \dfrac{k}{d^2}$, we get $150 = \dfrac{k}{4^2}$

$$k = 150 \cdot (16) = 2400$$

Therefore, the equation that expresses variation for the problem is

$$I = \frac{2400}{d^2} \qquad\qquad (1)$$

a.   To find the intensity when the source is 5 feet away, we substitute 5 for d in (1).

$$I = \frac{2400}{5^2} \longrightarrow I = \frac{2400}{25} = \mathbf{96}$$

So, the intensity is 96 candle power.

b. To find the distance from the light source to create a 24 candle power light, we substitute 24 for I in (1).

$$24 = \frac{2400}{d^2} \longrightarrow d^2 = \frac{2400}{24}$$

$$\longrightarrow d^2 = 100$$

$$\longrightarrow d = 10 \quad \text{or} \quad d = -10$$

Since the distance is always positive we reject the value $d = -10$. Hence the source of light should be 10 feet away in order to provide 24 candle power of illumination.

EXAMPLE 8 Find the constant of variation if x varies jointly as y and the cube of z; given $x = 32$, $y = 5$, and $z = 2$.

Solution:

If k is the constant of variation, then $x = kyz^3$.

Substitute 32 for x, 5 for y and 2 for z.

$$32 = k(5)(2^3) \longrightarrow 32 = k(5)(8)$$

$$\text{or} \quad 40k = 32$$

$$k = \frac{32}{40} = \frac{4}{5}$$

b) the distance of the source of light in order for the intensity to be 2 candle power.

8. The force F required to pull a wagon varies jointly as square of the velocity v and square root of the weight W. Given $F = 120$ lbs, $v = 10$ miles/hr and $W = 144$ lbs, find the constant of variation.

Answers:

6.   48

7. a) 58.8 candle power

b) $\sqrt{735}$ ft 8. $\frac{1}{10}$

EXERCISE 7.8

A. 1. One-third of a number is 3 less than one-half of the number. Find the number.

2. Five added to seven times a number gives 96. Find the number.

3. The numerator of a fraction is 3 less than its denominator. If $\frac{1}{10}$ is added to the fraction the result is $\frac{1}{2}$. What is the fraction?

4. One-third of a number is greater than one-fourth of its successor by 1. Find the number.

5. A certain number is twice another number. If the sum of their reciprocals is 4, find the numbers.

6. The numerator of a fraction is 3 less than the denominator. If the denominator is added to the numerator and numerator is subtracted from the denominator, the new fraction is $\frac{11}{3}$. Find the fraction.

7. When three times a number is added to four times its reciprocal, the result is 13. Find the number.

8. The denominator of a rational number is greater than its numerator by 3. If 3 is subtracted from the numerator and 2 is added to its denominator, the new fraction becomes $\frac{1}{5}$. Find the original number.

B. 9. A boat travels 20 miles upstream in the same time that it would take to travel 30 miles downstream. If the rate of the water is 5 miles per hour, find the speed of the boat alone.

10. A steamer goes down stream and covers the distance between two places in 4 hours while it covers the same distance going upstream in 5 hours. If the speed of the stream is 2 miles per hour, find the speed of the steamer in still water.

11. John can drive a motor boat 45 miles downstream in the same amount of time that he takes to drive 27 miles upstream. The speed of the motorboat in still water is 12 miles per hour. What is the rate of the stream?

12. The distance between two stations is 425 miles. Two trains start simultaneously from these stations on parallel tracks and travel towards each other. The speed of one of them is 5 miles per hour faster than the speed of the other. The distance between two trains after 3 hours of their start is 20 miles. Find the speed of each train.

13. A train travels 220 miles and returns the same distance. The total time taken by the train is $9\frac{1}{2}$ hours. If the speed of the train averaged 15 miles per hour more while going back, how fast did the train travel in each direction?

14. A passenger train takes 2 hours less for a journey of 300 miles if its speed is increased by 5 miles per hour from its usual speed. What is its usual speed?

15. An airplane flying against the wind travels 360 miles in the same time that it would take the same plane to travel 480 miles with the wind. If the wind speed is 20 miles per hour, find the speed of the airplane without wind effect.

16. A plane left 30 minutes later than the scheduled time. In order to reach its destination 1500 miles away on schedule, it has to increase its speed by 250 miles per hour from its usual speed. Find its usual speed.

17. Hoses A and B together can fill a swimming pool in 6 hours. If hose A alone takes 10 hours to fill the pool, how long would it take hose B to fill the pool?

18. Shannel and Lisa can finish a job in 12 days. If Shannel can finish the same work in 20 days, in how many days can Lisa finish the work?

19. Computer A can do a data analysis job in 4 hours. Computer B can do the same job in 6 hours. How long should it take to complete the job if both the computers were put to work together?

20. Roosevelt can finish a piece of work in 12 days and Manuel can do the same work in 24 days. In how many days can the two finish the same work?

21. A certain copier can do a printing job in 7 hours. Another copier can do the job in 12 hours. How long would it take to do the job if the two copiers worked together?

22. John and Paul can polish the floors of a building in 25 days. John alone can do $\frac{1}{3}$ of this job in 15 days. In how many days can Paul alone polish the floors of the building?

23. Kristy can clean the house in 5 hours, and her father can clean the house in 4 hours. Kristy's younger brother, Tom can completely mess up the house in 10 hours. If Kristy and her father clean the house, and if Tom plays in the house, all at the same time, how long will it take to clean the house?

24. Working 8 hours a day, Peter can copy a book in 18 days. How many hours a day should he work so as to finish the work in 12 days?

25. Cynthia can do a job in 5 hours. When Cynthia and her elder sister Cassandra work together, it takes them 3 hours to finish the same job. How long would it take Cassandra to complete the job alone?

26. If 12 boys earn $840 in 7 days, what will 15 boys earn in 6 days?

27. One half of the profits from a sale are to be given for two scholarships so that the value of one scholarship is $\frac{5}{4}$ times that of the other. If the profits from the sale amount to $1980 how much is the scholarship with lesser value?

28. An air bus covers a distance of 1542 miles in 2 hours. If it continues at the same rate, in how much time will it cover a distance of 3084 miles?

29. A 5-horsepower snow blower and a 9-horsepower snow blower can together clear a parking lot in 1 hour. The 5-horsepower snow blower alone can do this job in $3\frac{1}{2}$ hours. How long will it take the 9-horsepower snow blower to do this job all by itself?

C. 30. Suppose A varies directly as B. Given that A = 8 when B is 20, find B when A is 54.

31. The variable x varies directly as y. If $x = 7$, when $y = 2$, find x when y is 6.

32. Find the constant of variation if x varies jointly as y and the square of z; given $x = 64$, $y = 10$, and $z = 4$.

33. If v varies inversely as the cube of a and $v = 2$, when $a = 2$,
  (a) Find the constant of variation   **(b)** Find v, when $a = 4$.

34. If v varies inversely as the square of a and $v = 4$ when $a = 4$,
  (a) Find the constant of variation
  (b) Find v, when $a = 8$

35. The variable z varies jointly as x and y, and $z = 36$, when $x = 3$ and $y = 4$. Find z when $x = 5$ and $y = 2$.

36. The variable z varies jointly as x and y, and $z = 18$, when $x = 4$ and $y = 9$. Find z when $x = 10$ and $y = 4$.

37. When an object is dropped, the distance traveled by the object varies as the square of time. If the distance traveled by the object in 2 seconds is 64 feet, find the equation connecting the distance and the time.

38. If x varies directly as a cube of r and inversely as the cube of s, and $x = 8$ when $r = 8$ and $s = 4$.
  (a) Find an equation in terms of x, r and s.
  (b) Find x when $r = 2$ and $s = 3$.

39. If x varies directly as the square of r and inversely as the square of s, and $x = 4$ when $r = 4$ and $s = 2$.
  (a) Determine an equation connecting x, r, and s.
  (b) Find x when $r = 6$ and $s = 5$.

40. The variable z varies jointly as x and y, and $z = 15$, when $x = 5$ and $y = 3$. Find z when $x = 25$ and $y = 4$.

═══════════ **EXAMPLES** ═══════════

1. For what value of x is the equation
$$\frac{3x^2 + 4x - 1}{x^2 - x - 2} \text{ not defined?}$$
$$x^2 - x - 2 = 0$$
$$(x - 2)(x + 1) = 0$$
$$\rightarrow \quad x = 2, x = -1$$

2. Evaluate: $\dfrac{x^2 + 2}{x^2 + 1}$ for $x = 2$

$$\frac{(2)^2 + 2}{(2)^2 + 1} = \frac{6}{5}$$

3. $\dfrac{x^3 + x^2 - 2x}{x^2 + 2x}$

Numerator $= x(x - 1)(x + 2)$
Denominator $= x(x + 2)$
g.c.f. $= x(x + 2)$

$$\frac{x\,(x - 1)\,(x + 2)}{x\,(x + 2)} = x - 1$$

4. $\dfrac{x^2 + x}{x^2 - x - 2} \cdot \dfrac{x^2 - 1}{x^2 - 2x}$

$$= \frac{(x^2 + x)(x^2 - 1)}{(x^2 - x - 2)(x^2 - 2x)}$$

$$= \frac{x\,(x + 1)\,(x - 1)\,(x + 1)}{(x - 2)\,(x + 1)\,x\,(x - 2)}$$

$$= \frac{(x - 1)\,(x + 1)}{(x - 2)\,(x - 2)} \qquad \text{GCF} = x\,(x + 1)$$

RATIONAL EXPRESSIONS

1. To determine the values of the variable for which a rational expression is not defined, proceed as follows:

Step 1 Set the denominator of the rational expression to zero.

Step 2 Solve the equation obtained in Step 1.

Step 3 Solutions in step 2 are the values of the variable for which the expression is not defined.

2. To find the numerical value of an expression, substitute the value of the variable in the expression and carry out the computation.

SIMPLIFYING RATIONAL EXPRESSIONS

3. Steps to simplify a rational expression to lowest terms are:

Step 1 Factor the numerator completely.

Step 2 Factor the denominator completely.

Step 3 Determine the greatest common factor of the numerator and the denominator.

Step 4 Divide the numerator and the denominator by the greatest common factor.

MULTIPLICATION AND DIVISION

4. Steps to multiply two rational expressions:

Step 1 Multiply the numerators and the denominators, but do not expand.

Step 2 Factor the numerators and denominators.

Step 3 Write in lowest terms by dividing the numerator and denominator by the GCD.

5. Steps to divide a rational expression $\dfrac{P}{Q}$ by $\dfrac{R}{S}$:

Step **1** Multiply $\dfrac{P}{Q}$ and the reciprocal of $\dfrac{R}{S}$ *i.e.,*

multiply $\dfrac{P}{Q}$ and $\dfrac{S}{R}$

Step **2** Write the product in lowest terms.

5. $\dfrac{x^2 + x}{x^2 - x - 2} \div \dfrac{x^3 - x}{x^2 - 4}$

$= \dfrac{x^2 + x}{x^2 - x - 2} \cdot \dfrac{x^2 - 4}{x^3 - x}$

$= \dfrac{x\,(x + 1) \cdot (x - 2)\,(x + 2)}{(x - 2)\,(x + 1) \cdot x\,(x - 1)\,(x + 1)}$

$= \dfrac{x + 2}{(x - 1)\,(x + 1)}$

LEAST COMMON DENOMINATOR (LCD)

6. Steps to find the least common multiple (LCM) of polynomials:

Step **1** Factor each polynomial completely.

Step **2** Determine the different factors and their maximum exponents.

Step **3** The LCM of the polynomials is the product of distinct factors, each raised to its maximum exponent, as determined in step 2.

6. Find the LCM of $x^2 - x$, $x^2 - 1$, x^2.

Step 1 $x\,(x - 1)$, $(x - 1)\,(x + 1)$, x^2

Step 2 x^2, $(x - 1)^1$, $(x + 1)^1$

Step 3 $x^2(x - 1)\,(x + 1)$

7. The least common denominator (LCD) of fractions is defined to be the least common multiple of the denominators of the fractions.

7. Find the LCD of $\dfrac{x + 1}{x^2 - x}, \dfrac{x - 2}{x^2 - 1}$

$= \text{LCM of } x^2 - x,\ x^2 - 1$

$= x(x - 1)(x + 1)$

8. Steps for writing a rational expression as an equivalent fraction with a given expression as the new denominator:

Step **1** Find the quotient:

$\dfrac{\text{new denominator}}{\text{old denominator}} = k$

Step **2** Multiply the given fraction by $\dfrac{k}{k}$.

Step **3** Simplify and expand if necessary.

This process uses the basic rule $\dfrac{a}{b} = \dfrac{a \cdot k}{b \cdot k}$

8. Write $\dfrac{2x - 1}{x^2 - x}$ with $x\,(x - 1)(x + 1)$ as the new denominator.

$\dfrac{x\,(x - 1)\,(x + 1)}{x^2 - x} = \dfrac{x\,(x - 1)\,(x + 1)}{x\,(x - 1)}$

$= x + 1 = k$

$\dfrac{2x - 1}{x^2 - x} = \dfrac{2x - 1}{x\,(x - 1)} \cdot \dfrac{x + 1}{x + 1}$

$= \dfrac{(2x - 1)\,(x + 1)}{x\,(x - 1)\,(x + 1)}$

ADDITION AND SUBTRACTION

9. To add rational expressions with the same denominator we add the numerators and place the sum over the common denominator.

9. $\dfrac{3x - 1}{x - 1} + \dfrac{5}{x - 1}$

$= \dfrac{3x - 1 + 5}{x - 1} = \dfrac{3x + 4}{x - 1}$

10. $\dfrac{2x-1}{x^2-x} + \dfrac{x+2}{x^2-1}$

$x^2 - x = x(x-1)$

$x^2 - 1 = (x-1)(x+1)$

$\text{LCD} = x(x-1)(x+1)$

$\dfrac{2x-1}{x^2-x} = \dfrac{2x-1}{x(x-1)} \cdot \dfrac{x+1}{x+1}$

$\qquad = \dfrac{(2x-1)(x+1)}{x(x-1)(x+1)}$

$\dfrac{(x+2)}{x^2-1} = \dfrac{x+2}{(x-1)(x+1)} \cdot \dfrac{x}{x}$

$\qquad = \dfrac{x(x+2)}{x(x-1)(x+1)}$

$\dfrac{2x-1}{x^2-x} + \dfrac{x+2}{x^2-1}$

$= \dfrac{(2x-1)(x+1)}{x(x-1)(x+1)} + \dfrac{x(x+2)}{x(x-1)(x+1)}$

$= \dfrac{(2x-1)(x+1) + x(x+2)}{x(x-1)(x+1)}$

$= \dfrac{2x^2 + x - 1 + x^2 + 2x}{x(x-1)(x+1)}$

$= \dfrac{3x^2 + 3x - 1}{x(x-1)(x+1)}$

11. $\dfrac{1 + \dfrac{2}{x}}{\dfrac{3}{x} - 4}$

(Method 1) $\qquad$ LCD $= x$

$\dfrac{\left(1 + \dfrac{2}{x}\right)x}{\left(\dfrac{3}{x} - 4\right)x} = \dfrac{x+2}{3-4x}$

(Method 2)

$\dfrac{1 + \dfrac{2}{x}}{\dfrac{3}{x} - 4}$

$1 + \dfrac{2}{x} = \dfrac{x}{x} + \dfrac{2}{x} = \dfrac{x+2}{x}$

$\dfrac{3}{x} - 4 = \dfrac{3}{x} - \dfrac{4x}{x} = \dfrac{3-4x}{x}$

---

10. Steps for adding or subtracting rational expressions with different denominators are:

Step **1** Find the LCD of the denominator.

Step **2** Rewrite each rational expression with the LCD as the new denominator.

Step **3** Add or subtract the new equivalent fractions with the same denominators.

Step **4** Reduce the result to lowest terms.

COMPLEX FRACTIONS

11. Simplifying Complex Fractions:

METHOD 1:

Step **1** Find the LCD of all fractions appearing in the numerator and the denominator.

Step **2** Multiply both the numerator and the denominator by the LCD and simplify.

METHOD 2:

Step **1** Simplify the numerator.

Step **2** Simplify the denominator.

Step **3** Divide the numerator by the denominator, and simplify.

$$\frac{1+\dfrac{2}{x}}{\dfrac{3}{x}-4} = \frac{\dfrac{x+2}{x}}{\dfrac{3-4x}{x}}$$

$$= \frac{x+2}{x} \cdot \frac{x}{3-4x}$$

$$= \frac{x+2}{3-4x}$$

EQUATIONS WITH RATIONAL EXPRESSIONS

12. Solving equations with rational expressions:

Step **1** Find the LCD of all the rational expressions in the equation.

Step **2** Multiply both sides of the equation by the LCD and simplify.

Step **3** Solve the resulting equation.

Step **4** Verify the answer obtained in step 3 by substituting in the original equation. Reject any solution that makes the denominator zero.

12. $\dfrac{2}{y}+\dfrac{1}{2}=\dfrac{7}{2y}$ LCD $= 2y$

$$2y\left(\frac{2}{y}+\frac{1}{2}\right) = 2y\left(\frac{7}{2y}\right)$$

$$\rightarrow 4+y = 7$$
$$\rightarrow \quad y = 3$$

$$\frac{2}{3}+\frac{1}{2} = \frac{7}{2(3)}$$

$$\rightarrow \quad \frac{7}{6} = \frac{7}{6} \qquad \text{True}$$

APPLICATIONS

13. Steps to solve problems involving **numbers**:

Step **1** Identify the required number (unknown). Let the required number be x.

Step **2** Determine expressions for the other numbers in terms of the unknown.

Step **3** Use the given information to set up an equation.

Step **4** Solve the equation.

Step **5** Check the solution.

14. Steps to solve problems involving **distances**:

Step **1** Identify the unknown as distance, time, or rate.

Step **2** Use a table to organize the information regarding distance, time, and rate.

Step **3** Use the formula $d = rt$ or $t = \dfrac{d}{r}$ or $r = \dfrac{d}{t}$.

Step **4** Use the given information and set up an equation.

Step **5** Solve the equation.

Step **6** Check the solution.

15. Steps to solve problems involving **work**:

Step **1**   Identify the unknown.

Step **2**   Use a table to organize the given information.

Step **3**   Use the formula : Rate × Time = Work Done, where rate is the fraction of a job done in a unit of time.

Step **4**   Use the given relationship to form an equation.

Step **5**   Solve the equation.

Step **6**   Verify the solution.

16. *Variation:*

y varies directly as *x*:	$y = kx$
y varies directly as square of *x*:	$y = kx^2$
y varies inversely as *x*:	$y = \dfrac{k}{x}$
y varies inversely as square of *x*:	$y = \dfrac{k}{x^2}$
z varies jointly as *x* and *y*:	$z = kxy$
z varies jointly as square of *x* and inversely as cube of *y*:	$z = \dfrac{kx^2}{y^3}$

Use given (initial) information to find the constant *k*. Then use the value of *k* in the appropriate equation to find additional values.

7.10   REVIEW EXERCISES

In exercises 1-8, find the values for which the rational expression is not defined.

1. $\dfrac{4x-1}{3x-2}$

2. $\dfrac{3x+1}{2x+3}$

3. $\dfrac{2x^2+1}{x^2-4x+4}$

4. $\dfrac{3x+1}{x^2+7x+6}$

5. $\dfrac{1}{6p^2+p-1}$

6. $\dfrac{1}{3x^2+x-2}$

7. $\dfrac{2x+1}{x^3}$

8. $\dfrac{5+x}{3x^4}$

In exercises 9-16, evaluate the expression for the indicated value.

9. $\dfrac{3x+5}{4x-3}$; $x=-2$

10. $\dfrac{2x-3}{3x+5}$; $x=-3$

11. $\dfrac{4}{3x^2+1}$; $x=-1$

12. $\dfrac{2x}{4x^2-1}$; $x=2$

13. $\dfrac{3x^2+7x-2}{4x^3+3x+5}$; $x=\dfrac{1}{2}$

14. $\dfrac{2x^2-x+5}{3x^3+2x+1}$; $x=-2$

15. $\dfrac{x-1}{x^2-2x+2}$; $x=2$ **16.** $\dfrac{x+1}{x^3+x+1}$; $x=-3$

In exercises 17-30, write the rational expression in lowest terms.

17. $\dfrac{12p^3}{16p^5}$ **18.** $\dfrac{8x^4}{12x^6}$ **19.** $\dfrac{18x^2y^3}{27xy^4}$ **20.** $\dfrac{15x^3y^4}{25x^2y^6}$ **21.** $\dfrac{3x-4}{4-3x}$

22. $\dfrac{6-5x}{5x-6}$ **23.** $\dfrac{2(x^2-4)}{4(x-2)}$ **24.** $\dfrac{4\left(9-x^2\right)}{12(3+x)}$ **25.** $\dfrac{x^3-81x}{x^2-18x+81}$ **26.** $\dfrac{16x-x^3}{x^2+x-12}$

27. $\dfrac{9a^2-16b^2}{9a^2+24\,ab+16b^2}$ **28.** $\dfrac{16x^2-9y^2}{16x^2-24xy+9y^2}$

29. $\dfrac{8p^2-14pq-15q^2}{2p^2-5pq+4p-10q}$ **30.** $\dfrac{y^2+9x^2+6xy}{y^2+3y+3xy+9x}$

In exercises 31-52, perform the indicated operations.

31. $\dfrac{4x}{5y}\cdot\dfrac{3y^2}{2}$ **32.** $\dfrac{5y}{3z}\cdot\dfrac{4z^2}{10}$ **33.** $\dfrac{3x+2}{4x}\cdot\dfrac{5x^2}{2x+1}$ **34.** $\dfrac{2x-5}{3x}\cdot\dfrac{6x^3}{2x-3}$

35. $\dfrac{2x-3}{3x+5}\cdot\dfrac{4x-1}{2x+1}$ **36.** $\dfrac{x+2}{2x+1}\cdot\dfrac{x-1}{2x-1}$ **37.** $\dfrac{3x^3}{7}\div\dfrac{6x^2}{5}$ **38.** $\dfrac{5x^2}{6}\div\dfrac{2x}{3}$

39. $\dfrac{3x^2}{5x+7}\div\dfrac{2x^2}{x+1}$ **40.** $\dfrac{4x}{3x-5}\div\dfrac{8x}{x-1}$ **41.** $\dfrac{2p-3}{3p+5}\div\dfrac{4p-6}{9p+15}$ **42.** $\dfrac{3x-2}{2x+1}\div\dfrac{6x-4}{4x+2}$

43. $\dfrac{y^2-3y+2}{2y-1}\div\dfrac{y^2-6y+5}{2y^2+y-1}$ **44.** $\dfrac{x^2-3x-4}{x^2-9}\cdot\dfrac{x^2-x-6}{x^2+3x+2}$

45. $\dfrac{x^3+8}{x-2}\cdot\dfrac{x^2-4x+4}{x^2-2x+4}\div\dfrac{x+2}{x-1}$ **46.** $\dfrac{x^3-8}{x^2-4}\div\dfrac{(x+2)^2-2x}{x^2+6x+8}$

47. $\dfrac{x+2}{x-4}\div\dfrac{x-4}{x+3}\div\dfrac{x-4}{x+2}$ **48.** $\left(\dfrac{x+3}{x+2}\cdot\dfrac{x+2}{x+3}\right)\div\dfrac{x-2}{x+3}$

49. $\dfrac{ab-b^2}{a^2-ab}\cdot\dfrac{a^2+ab}{ab-b^2}\div\dfrac{ab+a^2}{a^2-ab}$ **50.** $\left(\dfrac{x+2}{x-5}\div\dfrac{x-5}{x+5}\right)\cdot\dfrac{x+5}{x+2}$

51. $\dfrac{p+3}{p-7}\div\dfrac{p-7}{p+5}\cdot\dfrac{p+5}{p+3}$ **52.** $\dfrac{x+2}{x-3}\div\dfrac{x-3}{x+4}\cdot\dfrac{x+4}{x+2}$

In exercises 53-58, find the least common denominator.

53. $\dfrac{1}{x}, \dfrac{3}{y}$

54. $\dfrac{1}{9x}, \dfrac{2}{3y}$

55. $\dfrac{3}{4-x}, \dfrac{2}{x-4}$

56. $\dfrac{2}{x-3}, \dfrac{5}{3-x}$

57. $\dfrac{3x+1}{x^2-2x+1}, \dfrac{4-5x}{2x^2-3x+1}$

58. $\dfrac{2x-1}{x^2+5x+4}, \dfrac{3x-2}{x^2+6x+8}$

In exercises 59-64, find the least common denominator of the rational expressions. In each case rewrite each expression with the LCD as the new denominator.

59. $\dfrac{x+1}{6x^2}, \dfrac{3x-1}{4x^3}$

60. $\dfrac{x-1}{2x}, \dfrac{2x+1}{5x^2}$

61. $\dfrac{3x}{(x+1)^2}, \dfrac{5}{2(x+1)}$

62. $\dfrac{2x}{(x-2)^3}, \dfrac{6}{3(x-2)^2}$

63. $\dfrac{2x}{x^2-9}, \dfrac{3x+1}{x^2-5x+6}$

64. $\dfrac{2x}{x^2-4}, \dfrac{2x-3}{x^2-5x+6}$

In exercises 65-78, perform the indicated operations.

65. $\dfrac{4}{x}+\dfrac{5}{x}$

66. $\dfrac{3}{x}-\dfrac{2}{x}$

67. $\dfrac{x-2}{4x}-\dfrac{3-x}{4x}$

68. $\dfrac{x+3}{2x}+\dfrac{2-x}{2x}$

69. $\dfrac{2a}{a-3}+\dfrac{3a}{3-a}$

70. $\dfrac{5x}{2-x}-\dfrac{3x}{x-2}$

71. $\dfrac{p+5}{p^2+2p-15}+\dfrac{2}{p-3}$

72. $\dfrac{x-2}{x^2-x-6}+\dfrac{5}{x+2}$

73. $\dfrac{1}{y-x}+\dfrac{x}{(x-y)^2}$

74. $\dfrac{3}{x-y}+\dfrac{x}{(y-x)^2}$

75. $\dfrac{x-1}{x^3-1}-\dfrac{x+1}{x^2+x+1}$

76. $\dfrac{x+1}{x^3+1}+\dfrac{1-x}{x^2-x+1}$

77. $\dfrac{4}{x^2-x}-\dfrac{1}{x^2+x-2}+\dfrac{6}{x^2+2x}$

78. $\dfrac{x+1}{x-1}+\dfrac{x-1}{x+1}-\dfrac{3x^2}{x-1}$

In exercises 79-82, simplify the complex fraction.

79. $\dfrac{\dfrac{3xy}{z}}{\dfrac{6x^3}{z^2}}$

80. $\dfrac{\dfrac{2x^2y^2}{z^2}}{\dfrac{8x^3}{y^2}}$

81. $\dfrac{\dfrac{x-y}{x+y}}{\dfrac{1}{x^2}-\dfrac{1}{y^2}}$

82. $\dfrac{\dfrac{x+y}{x-y}}{\dfrac{1}{x}-\dfrac{1}{y}}$

In exercises 83-90, solve the equation and check your answer(s).

83. $x+\dfrac{x}{x-2}=\dfrac{2}{x-2}$

84. $\dfrac{2}{x-3}+\dfrac{3}{x-4}=\dfrac{5}{x}$

85. $\dfrac{x}{x-2}+\dfrac{2}{x+3}=\dfrac{10}{x^2+x-6}$

86. $\dfrac{x}{x-1}+\dfrac{3}{x+2}=\dfrac{3}{x^2+x-2}$

87. $\dfrac{3}{x-3}+\dfrac{4}{x-4}=\dfrac{25}{x^2-7x+12}$

88. $\dfrac{2}{x+6}+\dfrac{3}{x-1}=\dfrac{5}{x^2+5x-6}$

89. $\dfrac{2x-4}{x+2}=5-\dfrac{3x+2}{x-1}$

90. $\dfrac{6x-7}{2x+1}-\dfrac{3x+1}{x+5}=0$

In exercises 91-94, solve for the specified variable.

91. $\dfrac{1}{x} = \dfrac{1}{y} + \dfrac{1}{z}$; for y

92. $\dfrac{1}{x} = \dfrac{1}{y} - \dfrac{1}{z}$; for z

93. $\dfrac{a}{b} = \dfrac{3b - c}{a + c}$; for c

94. $\dfrac{x}{y} = \dfrac{2y + z}{x + y}$; for z

95. The sum of the numerator and denominator of a fraction is 68. When 12 is added to the numerator and subtracted from the denominator, the result is $\dfrac{11}{6}$. Find the fraction.

96. The numerator of a fraction is 4 less than its denominator. If the numerator is decreased by 2 and the denominator is increased by 1, then the denominator is eight times the numerator. Find the fraction.

97. A number is twice another number. If the sum of their reciprocals is $\dfrac{5}{2}$, find the numbers.

98. The speed of a boat in still water is 10 miles per hour. If the boat can travel 26 miles downstream and 14 miles upstream in the same time, find the speed of stream.

99. An airplane flying against the wind travels 250 miles in the same time that it would travel 300 miles with the wind. The wind speed is 10 miles per hour. Find the speed of the airplane without wind effect.

100. The sum of two numbers is 8. If their sum is 4 times their difference, find the numbers.

101. A boat travels 20 miles upstream in the same time that it would take to travel 30 miles downstream. If the rate of the stream is 5 miles per hour, find the speed of the boat in still water.

102. A boat goes 8 miles downstream in 40 minutes and returns in one hour. Determine the speed of the boat in still water and the speed of the current.

103. Two photographers can complete an assignment in 4 hours working together. Working alone one of the photographers can complete the job in 6 hours. How long would it take the other photographer to complete the job?

104. John and Michael can do a job in 12 days. Michael and Thomas can complete the job in 15 days. Thomas and John can complete the job in 20 days. How long would each take separately to do the same work?

105. A printing press can print a magazine in 5 hours. After the press has been in operation for 2 hours, a second printing press joins the first one. If the job is finished in two more hours, how long will it take the second press to print the same magazine alone?

106. Two printers working together can finish a piece of work in 6 days and working alone one of the printers can do the same work in 9 days. How long would it take the other printer to complete the work?

107. The amount of garbage produced in a given location varies directly with the number of people living in the area. It is known that 25 tons of garbage are produced by 100 people in one year. If there is an influx of 5,000 people in a state, find the amount of additional garbage that will have to be picked up in one year in that state.

108. The amount of extension in an elastic spring varies directly as the weight hung on it. If a weight of 150 grams produces an extension of 2.9 cm, then what weight would produce an extension of 17.4 cm?

109. The volume of a sphere varies directly as the cube of its radius. The volume is 36p cubic inches when the radius is 3 inches. What is the volume of the sphere when the radius is 6 centimeters?

110. A car can finish a certain journey in 10 hours at the speed of 48 miles per hour. By how much should its speed be increased so that it would take only 8 hours to cover the same distance?

111. Newton's law of gravitation states that the gravitational attraction between two objects varies jointly as the product of their masses and inversely as the square of the distance between their centers of mass. What will be the change in attraction between the two objects if both masses are doubled, and the distance between their centers is cut in half?

112. If an object is dropped, it starts falling down vertically. It is known that the distance "d" meters through which it falls in "t" seconds varies directly as the square of "t". Given that in 2 seconds, the object falls through 20 meters, what distance would it fall in 10 seconds?

7.11 SELF TEST

1. Find the values of x for which $\dfrac{3x-1}{2x^2+3x-2}$ is not defined.

2. Find x for which $\dfrac{3-2x}{3x^2-2x-1}$ is not defined.

3. Evaluate $\dfrac{4t-1}{3t^2+5t-1}$ at $t = -2$.   **4.** Find $\dfrac{1-3x}{2x^2-x+2}$ at $x = -1$

5. Write the following expressions in lowest terms.

   (a) $\dfrac{3x^2}{4xy}$ (b) $\dfrac{3y^2z}{4xy}$ (c) $\dfrac{4a^3}{5ab}$ (d) $\dfrac{3x^2}{2yz}$ (e) $\dfrac{3x^2-3y^2}{x-y}$

In exercises 6-11, perform the indicated operation.

6. $\dfrac{20}{35} \div \dfrac{15}{28}$ **7.** $\dfrac{5x}{15y} \div \dfrac{6x}{4y}$ **8.** $\dfrac{(x-1)^2}{(x+2)^2} \cdot \dfrac{x^2-4}{x^2-1}$ **9.** $\dfrac{(x+1)^3}{x^2-9} \cdot \dfrac{x+3}{(x+1)^2}$

10. $\dfrac{p^2+p-2}{p-3} \div (p+2)$ **11.** $\dfrac{x^2-x-2}{x+2} \div (x+1)$

In exercises 12-13, find the least common denominator.

12. $\dfrac{4}{5x^3}, \dfrac{5}{12x^2}, -\dfrac{9}{20x}$ **13.** $\dfrac{3}{4x^2}, \dfrac{-4}{8x}, \dfrac{5}{12x^3}$

14. Identify the missing numerator: $\dfrac{32}{9x^2} = \dfrac{?}{18x^3-9x^2}$.

15. Identify the missing numerator: $\dfrac{15}{7x} = \dfrac{?}{14x^2-7x}$

In exercises 16-24, perform the indicated operation.

16. $\dfrac{2}{3x} + \dfrac{5}{4x}$

17. $\dfrac{3}{4a} + \dfrac{4}{5a}$

18. $\dfrac{2}{x^3} - \dfrac{3}{x^2} + \dfrac{5}{x}$

19. $\dfrac{3}{x^2} + \dfrac{1}{x^2} - \dfrac{4}{x^4}$

20. $\dfrac{3}{2x-3} - \dfrac{2}{9-4x^2}$

21. $\dfrac{4}{9x^2-25} + \dfrac{2}{5+3x}$

22. $\dfrac{b}{b-a} - \dfrac{a}{a+b} + \dfrac{a^2+b^2}{a^2-b^2}$

23. $\dfrac{3x+2}{x^2-16} + \dfrac{x-5}{(x+4)^2}$

24. $\dfrac{x}{2x+3} - \dfrac{2x}{2x-3} + \dfrac{4x^2+9}{4x^2-9}$

In exercises 25-28, simplify the complex fraction.

25. $\dfrac{2-\dfrac{1}{x}}{1+\dfrac{5}{x}}$

26. $\dfrac{3+\dfrac{1}{b}}{4-\dfrac{2}{b}}$

27. $\dfrac{\dfrac{x^2}{x-3}+\dfrac{x}{x-3}}{\dfrac{2x}{x-3}-\dfrac{x}{x+3}}$

28. $\dfrac{\dfrac{2y}{y+2}-\dfrac{y}{y-2}}{\dfrac{2y^2}{y-2}-\dfrac{y}{y+2}}$

In exercises 29-34, solve the equation and check the solution.

29. $x + \dfrac{2x}{x-1} = \dfrac{3-x}{x-1}$

30. $\dfrac{3}{x-1} + \dfrac{4}{x-2} = \dfrac{7}{x-3}$

31. $\dfrac{x}{x-2} - \dfrac{2}{x+4} = \dfrac{12}{x^2+2x-8}$

32. $\dfrac{x}{x-3} + \dfrac{1}{x-1} = \dfrac{13}{x^2-4x+3}$

33. $\dfrac{x}{x-2} - \dfrac{2}{x+4} = \dfrac{13x^2+26x-62}{7(x-2)(x+4)}$

34. $\dfrac{x}{x-1} - \dfrac{3}{x+2} = \dfrac{x^2-x+1}{x^2+x-2}$

35. Five times a number is added to three times the reciprocal of the number. The result is $\dfrac{17}{2}$. Find the number.

36. The sum of a number and its square is $\dfrac{35}{4}$. Find the number.

37. A boat goes 8 miles per hour in still water. It takes the same amount of time to go 40 miles downstream as it takes to go 24 miles upstream. Find the speed of the current.

38. A motor boat whose speed is 15 miles per hour in still water goes 30 miles downstream and comes back in a total of 4 hours 30 minutes. Determine the speed of the stream.

39. Using a small mower, a student can finish a job in 9 hours. After he had been working for one hour, another student joined him with a tractor. Together they complete the remaining job in 2 hours. How many hours would it take to do the job using the tractor only?

40. "A" and "B" working together can mow a field in 28 days and with the help of "C" they can mow it in 21 days. How long would "C" take by himself to do the entire job?

Roots and Radicals

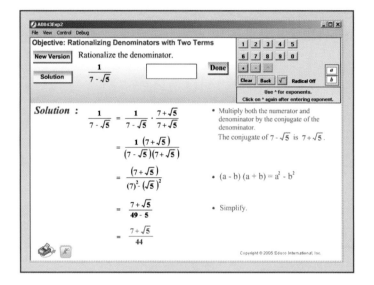

- A0843Exp2
- File View Control Debug
- **Objective: Rationalizing Denominators with Two Terms**
- **New Version** Rationalize the denominator.
- **Solution** $\dfrac{1}{7-\sqrt{5}}$ **Done**
- 1 2 3 4 5
- 6 7 8 9 0
- Clear Back √ Radical Off
- Use ^ for exponents.
- Click on ^ again after entering exponent.
- **Solution :**
$$\frac{1}{7-\sqrt{5}} = \frac{1}{7-\sqrt{5}} \cdot \frac{7+\sqrt{5}}{7+\sqrt{5}}$$
$$= \frac{1\,(7+\sqrt{5})}{(7-\sqrt{5})(7+\sqrt{5})}$$
$$= \frac{(7+\sqrt{5})}{(7)^2 - (\sqrt{5})^2}$$
$$= \frac{7+\sqrt{5}}{49-5}$$
$$= \frac{7+\sqrt{5}}{44}$$
- • Multiply both the numerator and denominator by the conjugate of the denominator.
  The conjugate of $7 - \sqrt{5}$ is $7 + \sqrt{5}$.
- • $(a - b)(a + b) = a^2 - b^2$
- • Simplify.
- Copyright © 2005 Educo International Inc.

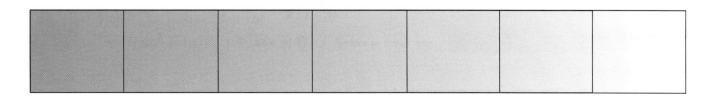

8
ROOTS AND RADICALS

In this chapter we will consider the expressions where the exponents are rational numbers. We will define different terms associated with rational exponents, establish rules for writing such expressions in different forms, and revisit the laws of exponents.

This chapter is divided into the following six sections:

8.1 FINDING ROOTS

In chapter 5 we defined the notation of exponents. We now use this application in reverse order. We will reverse the squaring process and find *square roots* of numbers.

Recall that the square of a number is the product of a number with itself. For example,

$$3^2 = 3 \cdot 3 = 9.$$
$$(-4)^2 = (-4)(-4) = 16.$$

The opposite of squaring a number is finding the square root.

Consider the equation $a^2 = 4$.

We know that the only possible values for a are -2 and 2. Recall that these values (-2 and 2) are called **square roots** of 4.

Similarly, consider $b^3 = -8.$

Here, $b = -2$ since $(-2)^3 = (-2)(-2)(-2) = -8.$

The number -2 is the **cube roots** of -8.

In general, if r is a real number and n is a *positive integer* then,

> a is an nth **root** of r if $r = a^n$.

1.   When $n = 2$, the nth root is called *square* root.

2.   When $n = 3$, the nth root is called *cube* root.

OBJECTIVES ■■■■

Upon completion of this section you will be able to:

A. Find roots;

B. Determine whether a root is a rational number, irrational number, or not a real number;

C. Find decimal approximations for irrational square roots and cube roots; and

D. Use the Pythagorean formula.

A. FINDING ROOTS

1. Find square roots of the following numbers:

   a) 81

   b) 121

   c) −144

2. Find the cube roots of the following numbers:

   a) 64

   b) $-\dfrac{1}{8}$

   c) 125

3. Find the fourth roots of the following numbers:

   a) 81

   b) −256

EXAMPLE 1 Find the square roots of the following numbers

   a. 36   b. 49   c. −81

Solutions:

   a. Since, $(6)^2 = 36$ and $(-6)^2 = 36$, therefore, **6 and −6 are square roots of 36**.

   b. We know that, $7^2 = 49$ and $(-7)^2 = 49$, therefore, **7 and −7 are square roots of 49**.

   c. Since the square of any real number is never negative, there is no real number whose square is −81. Therefore, the **square root of −81 *is not a real number*.**

   > A calculator may be used to find such roots. See example 1 of section 8.1 in Appendix B.

EXAMPLE 2 Find the cube roots of the following numbers:

   a. 27   b. −8   c. $\dfrac{1}{64}$

Solutions:

   a. We use the fact that 3 is the *only* real number whose cube is 27 or $3^3 = 27$. Therefore, **the cube root of 27 is 3.**

   b. −2 is the *only* real number whose cube is −8, or $(-2)^3 = -8$

   Therefore, **the cube root of −8 is −2.**

   c. $\dfrac{1}{4}$ is the *only* real number whose cube is $\dfrac{1}{64}$ since

   $$\left(\frac{1}{4}\right)^3 = \left(\frac{1}{4}\right)\left(\frac{1}{4}\right)\left(\frac{1}{4}\right) = \frac{1}{64}.$$

   Therefore, **the cube root of $\dfrac{1}{64}$ is $\dfrac{1}{4}$.**

EXAMPLE 3 Find the fourth roots of the following numbers:

   a. 16   b. −16

Solutions:

   a. Notice that $2^4 = 2 \cdot 2 \cdot 2 \cdot 2 = 16$ and

   $(-2)^4 = (-2)(-2)(-2)(-2) = 16$

   There is no other real number whose fourth power is 16. Therefore, the **fourth roots of 16 are 2 and −2.**

   b. Since the fourth power of any real number is always positive, the **fourth root of −16 is not a real number.**

Recall: Any real number raised to an *even* power has a non-negative result.

- Cube root of 27 is 3 because $3^3 = 27$

  Cube root of -8 is -2 because $(-2)^3 = -8$

  We may observe that **when *n* is odd**, we can define the *n*th root of any real number.

- Fourth root of 16 is 2 because $2^4 = 16$

  Fourth root of -16 is not defined because any number raised to the exponent 4 is always positive. We may observe that **when *n* is even**, the *n*th root can be defined for only *positive* real numbers.

  As seen in the above examples, there is only one odd root of a real number. But there are two even roots of a **positive** real number, one is positive and the other is negative.

  > If *a* is a non-negative real number and *n* is even, then the two *n*th roots of *a*
  >
  > are written symbolically as $\sqrt[n]{a}$ and $-\sqrt[n]{a}$.
  >
  > The *positive even root* $\sqrt[n]{a}$ is called the **principal *n*th root** of *a*.
  >
  > The principal **square root** of *a* is written simply as $\sqrt{a}$.

  If *n* is *odd*, then for **any** **real number** *a* there is only one real *n*th root, which is denoted by $\sqrt[n]{a}$.

Anatomy of a root symbol:

root index   radical sign

n is called the **root index**.

$\sqrt{}$ is called the **radical sign**.

$$\sqrt[n]{a}$$

→ radical expression

a is called the **radicand**.

$\sqrt[n]{a}$ is called the **radical expression**.

radicand

See example 4 of section 8.1 in Appendix B for another interpretation of square root.

EXAMPLE 4   Simplify the following radical expressions:

a. $\sqrt{121}$ b. $\sqrt{-36}$ c. $\sqrt{\dfrac{1}{81}}$ d. $\sqrt[5]{0}$

e. $\sqrt[3]{64}$ f. $\sqrt[3]{-729}$ g. $\sqrt[4]{16}$ h. $\sqrt[4]{-81}$

Solutions:

a. $\sqrt{121} = 11$, since $11^2 = \mathbf{121}$. $\sqrt{121}$ is a positive root.

b. $\sqrt{-36}$ **does not exist in real numbers.**   The radicand is negative.

c. $\sqrt{\dfrac{1}{81}} = \dfrac{1}{9}$, since $\left(\dfrac{1}{9}\right)^2 = \left(\dfrac{1}{9}\right)\left(\dfrac{1}{9}\right) = \dfrac{1}{\mathbf{81}}$.

d. $\sqrt[5]{0} = 0$, since $0^5 = \mathbf{0}$.

e. $\sqrt[3]{64} = 4$, since $4^3 = 4 \cdot 4 \cdot 4 = \mathbf{64}$.

f. $\sqrt[3]{-729} = -9$, since $(-9)^3 = (-9)\,(-9)\,(-9) = -\mathbf{729}$.

g. $\sqrt[4]{16} = 2$, since $2^4 = 2 \cdot 2 \cdot 2 \cdot 2 = \mathbf{16}$.

Note There are two square roots of 121. They are 11 and −11. However, there is only **one** principal square root of 121, it is $\sqrt{121}$ or 11.

---

h) $\sqrt[4]{-81}$

5. Simplify the following expressions:

a) $\left(-\sqrt{11}\right)^2$ b) $\left(\sqrt[2]{15}\right)^2$

c) $\left(-\sqrt[4]{9}\right)^4$ d) $\left(-\sqrt{2x+3}\right)^2$

e) $\left(-\sqrt[4]{(-3)^4}\right)$

Answers:

1. a) 9, – 9 b) 11, –11 c) no real solution

2. a) 4   b) $-\dfrac{1}{2}$ c) 5

3. a) 3, –3 b) no real solution

4. a) 12 b) no real solution c) $\dfrac{1}{2}$ d) 0
   e) 6   f) 2   g) 3   h) no real solution

5. a) 11 b) 15 c) 9   d) $2x+3$
   e) –3

h. $\sqrt[4]{-81}$ is not a real number, since the fourth power of every real number is positive.

EXAMPLE 5   Simplify the following expressions:

   a. $\left(\sqrt{13}\right)^2$ **b.** $\left(-\sqrt{15}\right)^2$ **c.** $\left(\sqrt[3]{7}\right)^3$

   d. $\left(\sqrt{8x^2+5}\right)^2$ **e.** $\sqrt{(-8)^2}$

Solutions:

   a. $\left(\sqrt{13}\right)^2 = \mathbf{13}$, since by definition, $\sqrt{13}$ is a positive number whose square is 13.

   b. $\left(-\sqrt{15}\right)^2 = \left(-\sqrt{15}\right)\left(-\sqrt{15}\right) = \left(\sqrt{15}\right)^2$
   $= \mathbf{15}$

   c. $\left(\sqrt[3]{7}\right)^3 = \mathbf{7}$

   d. $\left(\sqrt{8x^2+5}\right)^2 = \mathbf{8}x^2 + \mathbf{5}$

   e. $\sqrt{(-8)^2} = \sqrt{8^2} = \mathbf{8}$

   These examples show the following rule:

   Rule : $\sqrt[n]{a^n} = a$ if n is odd ; $\sqrt[n]{a^n} = |a|$ if n is even

B.   RATIONAL, IRRATIONAL, AND REAL NUMBERS

Recall that numbers of the type   4,   9, $\dfrac{4}{9}$, $\dfrac{9}{25}$, …

are all perfect squares of rational numbers.

$$4 = (2)^2, \qquad 9 = (3)^2, \qquad \frac{4}{9} = \left(\frac{2}{3}\right)^2, \qquad \frac{9}{25} = \left(\frac{3}{5}\right)^2 \dots$$

Therefore, the square roots of **perfect squares** are also rational numbers.

$$\sqrt{4} = 2, \qquad \sqrt{9} = 3, \qquad \sqrt{\frac{4}{9}} = \frac{2}{3}, \qquad \sqrt{\frac{9}{25}} = \frac{3}{5} \dots$$

What about **square roots** of rational numbers that are **not perfect squares**?
For example: $\sqrt{2}$, $\sqrt{3}$, $\sqrt{7}$ …...   Such numbers are examples of **irrational numbers**.

Similarly, cube roots of **perfect cubes** 8,   27,   125, $-\dfrac{1}{8}$…

are rational numbers: $\sqrt[3]{8} = 2$, $\sqrt[3]{27} = 3$, $\sqrt[3]{125} = 5$, $\sqrt[3]{-\dfrac{1}{8}} = -\dfrac{1}{2}$ …

What about **cube roots** of rational numbers that are **not perfect cubes**?
For example : $\sqrt[3]{7}, \sqrt[3]{2}, \sqrt[3]{10}$ …   Again, these are examples of **irrational numbers**. The number pi, written as the Greek letter π, the numerical value of the area of a unit circle, is an irrational number.

We know that there is no real number whose square is negative. Later in chapter 9, we will define new types of numbers to deal with square roots of negative numbers. At this time we want to emphasize that **if a is a negative number, then $\sqrt{a}$ is not a real number**.

EXAMPLE 6   Which of the following are rational, irrational, or not real?

a. $\sqrt{16}$ **b.** $\sqrt{17}$

c. $\sqrt{-4}$ **d.** $\sqrt{\dfrac{4}{9}}$

Solutions:

a. $\sqrt{16}$ is *rational*, because $16 = 4^2$ is a perfect square.

b. $\sqrt{17}$ is *irrational*, because 17 is not a perfect square.

c. $\sqrt{-4}$ is *not real*, because -4 is negative.

d. $\sqrt{\dfrac{4}{9}}$ is *rational*, because $\dfrac{4}{9} = \left(\dfrac{2}{3}\right)^2$ is a perfect square.

C.   DECIMAL APPROXIMATIONS FOR IRRATIONAL SQUARE ROOTS AND CUBE ROOTS

It is always possible to approximate irrational numbers by numbers in decimal form. This can be done with ease by using calculators. Scientific calculators have an exponential key which can be used to approximate any root of a number, when it is defined. Most other calculators have a square root key which can be used to approximate square roots of positive numbers.

Use a calculator to approximate the value of π, $\sqrt{2}$, and $\sqrt[3]{5}$.

$\pi \approx 3.142,$ $\sqrt{2} \approx 1.414,$ and $\sqrt[3]{5} \approx 1.7110$

D.   PYTHAGOREAN FORMULA AND SQUARE ROOTS

Recall the Pythagorean formula:

If a right triangle with legs a and b has hypotenuse c,

then $c^2 = a^2 + b^2$.

$(\text{hypotenuse})^2 = (\text{side 1})^2 + (\text{side 2})^2$

or **hypotenuse** $= \sqrt{(\textbf{base})^2 + (\textbf{height})^2}$

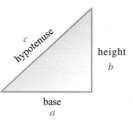

7. A right triangle has its legs equal to 4 cm and 6 cm. Find the hypotenuse.

EXAMPLE 7 A right triangle has its legs equal to 6 cm and 8 cm. Find the hypotenuse.

Solution:

Use the Pythagorean formula.

$(hypotenuse)^2 = (6)^2 + (8)^2 = 36 + 64 = 100$

Therefore, $hypotenuse = \sqrt{100} = 10$ cm.

8. The hypotenuse of a right triangle is 5. If one leg of the triangle is 3, find the other leg.

EXAMPLE 8 The hypotenuse of a right triangle is 12 cm. If one leg of the triangle is 5 cm, find the other leg. Approximate the answer to three decimal places (thousandth place).

Solution:

Suppose the second leg is x cm. Then

$$12^2 = 5^2 + x^2 \qquad \text{Pythagorean formula}$$
$$144 = 25 + x^2$$
$$x^2 = 144 - 25 = 119$$

Therefore, $\qquad x = \sqrt{119}$

$\qquad\qquad\qquad = 10.9087121$ Use the square root key on the calculator.

$\qquad\qquad\qquad \approx \mathbf{10.909}$ Round off to three decimal places.

9. Elizabeth is flying a kite on a 30 feet string. The vertical distance between the kite and the ground is 15 feet. What is the horizontal distance between Elizabeth and the kite.

EXAMPLE 9 Elizabeth is flying a kite on a 60 feet string. The horizontal distance between Elizabeth and a point directly below the kite is 25 feet. How high is the kite above Elizabeth's hand? Round off the answer to two decimal places.

Solution: Suppose the height of the kite above Elizabeth's hand is x feet.

By Pythagorean formula:
$$60^2 = 25^2 + x^2$$
$$x^2 = 60^2 - 25^2$$
$$= 3600 - 625$$
$$= 2975$$

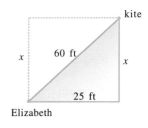

Therefore, $x = \sqrt{2975}$

$\qquad\qquad \approx 54.5435605$ Use the square root key on the calculator.

$\qquad\qquad \approx \mathbf{54.54}$ **feet** Round off to the hundredths place.

Answers:

7. $\sqrt{52}$ cm   8. 4

9. 25.98 feet

A. In exercises 1-10, find the principal square root of the given number.

1. 4   **2.** 9   **3.** 81   **4.** 225   **5.** $\dfrac{1}{25}$ **6.** $\dfrac{1}{625}$ **7.** 0   **8.** -25 **9.** -16 **10.** $\dfrac{4}{25}$

In exercises 11-22, find the indicated root.

11. 8; cube root   **12.** 27 ; cube root   **13.** -32; fifth root   **14.** 64 ; sixth root

15. 81; fourth root   **16.** -243; fifth root   **17.** -626; fourth root   **18.** -64 ; sixth root

19. 729; sixth root   **20.** $\dfrac{1}{32}$; fifth root   **21.** $\dfrac{8}{125}$; cube root   **22.** $\dfrac{16}{81}$; fourth root

In exercises 23-36, find the value of the radical.

23. $\sqrt{36}$ **24.** $\sqrt{81}$ **25.** $\sqrt{144}$ **26.** $\sqrt{256}$ **27.** $\sqrt[3]{-64}$ **28.** $\sqrt[3]{-125}$ **29.** $\sqrt[3]{\dfrac{1}{27}}$

30. $\sqrt[3]{64}$ **31.** $\sqrt[5]{\dfrac{32}{243}}$ **32.** $\sqrt[4]{\dfrac{81}{16}}$ **33.** $\sqrt[4]{625}$ **34.** $\sqrt[5]{243}$ **35.** $\sqrt{-121}$ **36.** $\sqrt[4]{-16}$

B. In exercises 37-46, identify the number as rational, irrational, or non-real.

37. $\sqrt{4}$ **38.** $\sqrt[3]{27}$ **39.** $\sqrt{18}$ **40.** $\sqrt[3]{18}$ **41.** $\sqrt{-25}$

42. $\sqrt{-36}$ **43.** $\sqrt{\dfrac{4}{49}}$ **44.** $\sqrt[3]{\dfrac{27}{64}}$ **45.** $-\sqrt{\dfrac{1}{16}}$ **46.** $-\sqrt{25}$

C. In exercises 47-52, find the decimal approximation for the irrational number.

47. $\sqrt{3}$ **48.** $\sqrt{7}$ **49.** $\sqrt[3]{13}$ **50.** $\sqrt[4]{17}$ **51.** 2π **52.** π^2

D. In exercises 53-56, determine the third side of a right triangle ABC, whose hypotenuse is AC. Approximate the value to three decimal places wherever necessary.

53. AB = 5 in, BC = 12 in, AC = ?   **54.** AB = 5 in, AC = 8 in, BC = ?

55. AC = 9 cm, BC = 4 cm, AB = ?   **56.** AB = 6 in, BC = 13 in, AC = ?

57. Mario is flying a kite with a string of 80 feet. The horizontal distance between Mario and the kite is 35 feet. How high is the kite above the ground if Mario's hands are 4 feet above the ground? Approximate the answer to the thousandths place.

58. The diagonal of a rectangular hall is 10 m. The width of the hall is 6 m. Find the length of the hall.

59. A ladder is 10 feet long and leans against a wall. The foot of the ladder is 5 feet from the wall. Approximate to two decimal places how high the top of the ladder is when resting against the wall?

60. The perimeter of a rectangle is 14 m and the length is 4 m. Find the width and the diagonal of the rectangle.

8.2 MULTIPLICATION AND DIVISION OF RADICALS

OBJECTIVES ■■■■

Upon completion of this section you will be able to :

A. Multiply radicals;

B. Simplify radicals with the product rule; and

C. Simplify quotients of radicals with the quotient rule.

A. PRODUCT RULE OF RADICALS

Two radicals $\sqrt[m]{a}$ and $\sqrt[n]{b}$ are said to be of the **same index** if $m = n$.

$\sqrt{3}$ and $\sqrt{4}$ are of the same index **2**.

$\sqrt[3]{5}$ and $\sqrt[3]{-7}$ are of the same index **3**.

The radicals $\sqrt{3}$ and $\sqrt[3]{5}$ are not of the same index.

We can multiply radicals of the same index using the following product rule.

> **Product Rule of Radicals**
>
> If a and b are any two positive real numbers then
>
> $$\sqrt[n]{a} \cdot \sqrt[n]{b} = \sqrt[n]{ab} \quad \text{where } n \text{ is an integer and } n \geq 2.$$

WARM-UP

1. Use the product rule for radicals to find each of the following products.

a) $\sqrt{3} \cdot \sqrt{5}$

b) $\sqrt[3]{6} \cdot \sqrt[3]{36}$

c) $\sqrt[5]{3} \cdot \sqrt[5]{2}$

d) $\sqrt{x+2} \cdot \sqrt{(x+2)^3}$

Answers:

1. a) $\sqrt{15}$ b) 6   c) $\sqrt[5]{6}$ d) $(x + 2)^2$

EXAMPLE 1   Use the product rule for radicals to find each of the following products.

    a. $\sqrt{2} \cdot \sqrt{5}$ **b.** $\sqrt[3]{4} \cdot \sqrt[3]{16}$

    c. $\sqrt[5]{3} \cdot \sqrt[5]{7}$ **d.** $\sqrt{13} \cdot \sqrt{x}$

Solutions:

a. $\sqrt{2} \cdot \sqrt{5} = \sqrt{2 \cdot 5}$ Same index.

            $= \sqrt{\mathbf{10}}$

b. $\sqrt[3]{4} \cdot \sqrt[3]{16} = \sqrt[3]{4 \cdot 16} = \sqrt[3]{64}$ Same index.

                         $= \mathbf{4}$

c. $\sqrt[5]{3} \cdot \sqrt[5]{7} = \sqrt[5]{3 \cdot 7}$ Same index.

                $= \sqrt[5]{\mathbf{21}}$

d. $\sqrt{13} \cdot \sqrt{x} = \sqrt{13x}$ Same index.

B. SIMPLIFYING RADICALS

We use the following steps to simplify radicals.

> **Step 1** Write the prime factorization of the radicand
>
> **Step 2** Apply the product rule $\sqrt[n]{xy} = \sqrt[n]{x} \cdot \sqrt[n]{y}$
>
> **Step 3** Simplify if possible. Factor out perfect n^{th} powers.

EXAMPLE 2   Simplify each of the following.

   a. $\sqrt{50}$ **b.** $\sqrt{96}$ **c.** $\sqrt[3]{243}$ **d.** $\sqrt[5]{480}$

Solutions:

a. $\sqrt{50}$:

Step 1 $50 = 2 \cdot 5 \cdot 5 = 2 \cdot 5^2$ Prime factorization of radicand.

Step 2 $\sqrt{50} = \sqrt{2 \cdot 5^2}$
$= \sqrt{2} \cdot \sqrt{5^2}$ Product rule.

Step 3 $\left(\sqrt{2}\right) \cdot \sqrt{5^2} = \sqrt{2} \cdot 5$ Square root of 5^2 is 5.
$= 5\sqrt{2}$

b. $\sqrt{96}$:

Step 1 $96 = (2 \cdot 2) \cdot (2 \cdot 2) \cdot 2 \cdot 3$ Prime factorization
$= 2^2 \cdot 2^2 \cdot 2 \cdot 3$ of radicand.

Step 2 $\sqrt{96} = \sqrt{2^2 \cdot 2^2 \cdot 2 \cdot 3}$
$= \sqrt{2^2} \cdot \sqrt{2^2} \cdot \sqrt{2} \cdot \sqrt{3}$ Product rule.

$\sqrt{96} = 2 \cdot 2 \cdot \sqrt{2} \cdot \sqrt{3}$
$= 4 \cdot \sqrt{2} \cdot \sqrt{3}$
$= 4 \cdot \sqrt{2 \cdot 3}$
$= 4\sqrt{6}$ Product rule.

c. $\sqrt[3]{243}$:

Step 1 $243 = (3 \cdot 3 \cdot 3) \cdot 3 \cdot 3 = 3^3 \cdot 3 \cdot 3$ Prime factorization of radicand.

Step 2 $\sqrt[3]{243} = \sqrt[3]{3^3 \cdot 3 \cdot 3}$
$= \sqrt[3]{3^3} \ \sqrt[3]{3 \cdot 3} = 3 \cdot \sqrt[3]{3 \cdot 3}$ Product rule.
$= 3\sqrt[3]{9}$ $\sqrt[3]{a^3} = a$

d. $\sqrt[5]{480}$:

Step 1 $480 = 2 \cdot 2 \cdot 2 \cdot 2 \cdot 2 \cdot 3 \cdot 5 = 2^5 \cdot 3 \cdot 5$
Prime factorization of radicand.

Step 2 $\sqrt[5]{480} = \sqrt[5]{2^5 \cdot 3 \cdot 5}$
$= \sqrt[5]{2^5} \ \sqrt[5]{3 \cdot 5}$ Product rule.
$= 2\sqrt[5]{15}$

WARM-UP

3. Find each of the following products and simplify.

a) $\sqrt{32}\cdot\sqrt{20}$

b) $\sqrt{5}\cdot\sqrt{35}$

c) $\sqrt[3]{25}\cdot\sqrt[3]{160}$

Answers:

2. a) $4\sqrt{3}$ b) $6\sqrt{3}$ c) $3\sqrt[3]{3}$ d) $\sqrt[5]{16}$

3. a) $8\sqrt{10}$ b) $5\sqrt{7}$ c) $10\sqrt[3]{4}$

EXAMPLE 3   Find each of the following products and simplify.

a. $\sqrt{8}\cdot\sqrt{98}$ b. $\sqrt{6}\cdot\sqrt{90}$ c. $\sqrt[3]{45}\cdot\sqrt[3]{150}$

Solutions:

a. $\sqrt{8}\cdot\sqrt{98} = \sqrt{8\cdot98}$ Product rule.

$= \sqrt{(2\cdot2\cdot2)(2\cdot7\cdot7)}$ Prime factorization.

$= \sqrt{2\cdot2\cdot2\cdot2\cdot7\cdot7}$

$= \sqrt{2^2\cdot2^2\cdot7^2} = \sqrt{2^2}\cdot\sqrt{2^2}\cdot\sqrt{7^2} = 2\cdot2\cdot7$

$= \mathbf{28}$

b. $\sqrt{6}\cdot\sqrt{90} = \sqrt{6\cdot90}$ Product rule.

$= \sqrt{(2\cdot3)(2\cdot3\cdot3\cdot5)}$ Prime factorization.

$= \sqrt{2^2\cdot3^2\cdot3\cdot5}$

$= \sqrt{2^2}\cdot\sqrt{3^2}\cdot\sqrt{3\cdot5} = 2\cdot3\cdot\sqrt{3\cdot5}$

$= \mathbf{6\sqrt{15}}$

c. $\sqrt[3]{45}\cdot\sqrt[3]{150} = \sqrt[3]{45\cdot150}$ Product rule.

$= \sqrt[3]{(3\cdot3\cdot5)(2\cdot3\cdot5\cdot5)}$ Prime factorization.

$= \sqrt[3]{3^3\cdot5^3\cdot2} = \sqrt[3]{3^3}\cdot\sqrt[3]{5^3}\cdot\sqrt[3]{2} = 3\cdot5\cdot\sqrt[3]{2}$

$= \mathbf{15\sqrt[3]{2}}$

C. QUOTIENT RULE OF RADICALS

If a and b are non-negative real numbers, and $b \neq 0$ then for any integer $n \geq 2$

$$\frac{\sqrt[n]{a}}{\sqrt[n]{b}} = \sqrt[n]{\frac{a}{b}}\ .$$

In particular, for $n = 2$, $\dfrac{\sqrt{a}}{\sqrt{b}} = \sqrt{\dfrac{a}{b}}.$

EXAMPLE 4   Find the quotients.

a. $\dfrac{\sqrt{20}}{\sqrt{5}}$ b. $\dfrac{\sqrt{5a^2b}}{\sqrt{125b^3}}$

Solutions:

a. $\dfrac{\sqrt{20}}{\sqrt{5}} = \sqrt{\dfrac{20}{5}} = \sqrt{4} = \mathbf{2}$ Quotient rule

b. $\dfrac{\sqrt{5a^2b}}{\sqrt{125b^3}} = \sqrt{\dfrac{5a^2b}{125b^3}} = \sqrt{\dfrac{a^2}{25b^2}} = \sqrt{\left(\dfrac{a}{5b}\right)^2}$

$$= \dfrac{a}{5b}$$

EXAMPLE 5   Simplify each of the following radicals.

a. $\dfrac{\sqrt{216}}{\sqrt{6}}$ b. $\dfrac{\sqrt[4]{729}}{\sqrt[4]{9}}$

c. $\sqrt{\dfrac{25x}{x^3}}$ d. $\sqrt{\dfrac{4}{7}} \cdot \sqrt{\dfrac{2}{35}}$

Solutions:

a. $\dfrac{\sqrt{216}}{\sqrt{6}} = \sqrt{\dfrac{216}{6}} = \sqrt{36} = \sqrt{6^2}$ Quotient rule.

$$= 6$$ $\sqrt{a^2} = |a|$

b. $\dfrac{\sqrt[4]{729}}{\sqrt[4]{9}} = \sqrt[4]{\dfrac{729}{9}} = \sqrt[4]{81}$ Quotient rule.

$$= \sqrt[4]{3^4} = 3$$ $\sqrt[4]{a^4} = |a|$

c. $\sqrt{\dfrac{25x}{x^3}} = \sqrt{\dfrac{25}{x^2}} = \dfrac{\sqrt{25}}{\sqrt{x^2}} = \dfrac{5}{x}$ $(x > 0)$

d. $\sqrt{\dfrac{4}{7}} \cdot \sqrt{\dfrac{2}{35}} = \sqrt{\dfrac{4}{7} \cdot \dfrac{2}{35}} = \sqrt{\dfrac{2 \cdot 2 \cdot 2}{7 \cdot 7 \cdot 5}} = \dfrac{\sqrt{2^2} \cdot \sqrt{2}}{\sqrt{7^2} \cdot \sqrt{5}}$

$$= \dfrac{2\sqrt{2}}{7\sqrt{5}}$$

EXAMPLE 6   Simplify the following, given that all variables are strictly positive:

a. $\sqrt[3]{72y^8z^9}$ b. $\sqrt{\dfrac{20x^3}{y^2}}$ c. $\dfrac{5a^2b^3}{\sqrt[3]{8a^3b^3}}$

Solutions:

a. $\sqrt[3]{72y^8z^9}$

$$= \sqrt[3]{2 \cdot 2 \cdot 2 \cdot 3 \cdot 3 \cdot y^3 \cdot y^3 \cdot y^2 \cdot z^3 \cdot z^3 \cdot z^3}$$ Factorization.

$$= \sqrt[3]{2^3 \cdot 3^2 \cdot y^3 \cdot y^3 \cdot y^2 \cdot z^3 \cdot z^3 \cdot z^3}$$

$$= \sqrt[3]{2^3} \cdot \sqrt[3]{3^2} \cdot \sqrt[3]{y^3} \cdot \sqrt[3]{y^3} \cdot \sqrt[3]{y^2} \cdot \sqrt[3]{z^3} \cdot \sqrt[3]{z^3} \cdot \sqrt[3]{z^3}$$ Product rule.

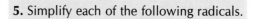

$$= 2 \cdot \sqrt[3]{3^2} \cdot y \cdot y \cdot \sqrt[3]{y^2} \cdot z \cdot z \cdot z$$

$$= 2 \sqrt[3]{9} \, y^2 z^3 \sqrt[3]{y^2} = 2y^2 z^3 \sqrt[3]{9} \sqrt[3]{y^2} = \mathbf{2y^2 z^3 \sqrt[3]{9y^2}}$$

c) $\dfrac{3a^3 b^4}{\sqrt[3]{64a^3 b^6}}$

b. $\sqrt{\dfrac{20x^3}{y^2}} = \dfrac{\sqrt{20x^3}}{\sqrt{y^2}} = \dfrac{\sqrt{20}\sqrt{x^3}}{\sqrt{y^2}} = \dfrac{\sqrt{2 \cdot 2 \cdot 5}\,\sqrt{x^2 \cdot x}}{\sqrt{y^2}}$

$$= \dfrac{\sqrt{2^2 \cdot 5}\,\sqrt{x^2 \cdot x}}{\sqrt{y^2}} = \dfrac{\sqrt{2^2} \cdot \sqrt{5} \cdot \sqrt{x^2} \cdot \sqrt{x}}{\sqrt{y^2}}$$

$$= \dfrac{2 \cdot \sqrt{5} \cdot x \cdot \sqrt{x}}{y}$$

$$= \dfrac{2x\sqrt{5x}}{y}$$

c. $\dfrac{5a^2 b^3}{\sqrt[3]{8a^3 b^3}} = \dfrac{5a^2 b^3}{\sqrt[3]{2 \cdot 2 \cdot 2 \cdot a^3 b^3}} = \dfrac{5a^2 b^3}{\sqrt[3]{2^3}\sqrt[3]{a^3}\sqrt[3]{b^3}} = \dfrac{5a^2 b^3}{2ab}$

$$= \dfrac{5ab^2}{2}$$

Answers:

4. a) 2 b) $\sqrt{\dfrac{b}{3a}}$

5. a) 15 b) 3 c) $\dfrac{7}{x^2}$ d) $\dfrac{4}{5}$

6. a) $3y^2 z^2 \sqrt[3]{3z}$ b) $\dfrac{2x^2}{y}\sqrt{\dfrac{15x}{y}}$

   c) $\dfrac{3a^2 b^2}{4}$

EXERCISE 8.2

A. In exercises 1-14, use the product rule to write the expression under one radical. Assume that all variables are positive.

1. $\sqrt{4} \cdot \sqrt{7}$ 2. $\sqrt{9} \cdot \sqrt{10}$ 3. $\sqrt{5} \cdot \sqrt{8}$ 4. $\sqrt{3} \cdot \sqrt{5}$ 5. $\sqrt[4]{2} \cdot \sqrt[4]{9}$

6. $\sqrt[3]{2} \cdot \sqrt[3]{5}$ 7. $\sqrt[3]{-25} \cdot \sqrt[3]{35}$ 8. $\sqrt[3]{27} \cdot \sqrt[3]{2}$ 9. $\sqrt[5]{7} \cdot \sqrt[5]{9}$ 10. $\sqrt[4]{3} \cdot \sqrt[4]{11}$

11. $\sqrt{13} \cdot \sqrt{x^3}$ 12. $\sqrt{a} \cdot \sqrt{y^4}$ 13. $\sqrt[3]{x} \cdot \sqrt[3]{y^2}$ 14. $\sqrt[4]{a} \cdot \sqrt[4]{b^2}$

B. In exercises 15-24, use the product rule and simplify the expression. Assume that all variables are positive.

15. $\sqrt{8} \cdot \sqrt{50}$ 16. $\sqrt{27} \cdot \sqrt{48}$ 17. $\sqrt[3]{16} \cdot \sqrt[3]{500}$ 18. $\sqrt[4]{40} \cdot \sqrt[4]{250}$

19. $\sqrt{2xy^3} \cdot \sqrt{18x^3 y}$ 20. $\sqrt{98x^5 y^3} \cdot \sqrt{4x^2 y^2}$ 21. $\sqrt[3]{15x^2 y} \cdot \sqrt[3]{50x^2 y^2}$ 22. $\sqrt[3]{16u^2 v^4} \cdot \sqrt[3]{8u^2 v^2}$

23. $\sqrt[4]{24uv^3} \cdot \sqrt[4]{64u^3 v^2}$ 24. $\sqrt[5]{16u^4 v} \cdot \sqrt[5]{64u^2 v^4}$

C. In exercises 25-32, use the quotient rule and simplify.

25. $\dfrac{\sqrt{7}}{\sqrt{20}}$ 26. $\dfrac{\sqrt[3]{5}}{\sqrt[3]{25}}$ 27. $\dfrac{\sqrt[3]{25}}{\sqrt[3]{8}}$ 28. $\dfrac{\sqrt{25}}{\sqrt{4}}$

29. $\dfrac{\sqrt{x^2 y}}{\sqrt{y}}$, $y > 0$ 30. $\dfrac{\sqrt[4]{ab^4}}{\sqrt[4]{a}}$, $a > 0$ 31. $\dfrac{\sqrt[5]{p^2 q}}{\sqrt[5]{r^3}}$, $r \neq 0$ 32. $\dfrac{\sqrt[4]{x^3 y}}{\sqrt[4]{z^3}}$, $z \neq 0$

In exercises 33-50, simplify radicals.

33. $\sqrt{48}$ 34. $\sqrt{12}$ 35. $\sqrt{128}$ 36. $\sqrt{150}$ 37. $\sqrt{54}$ 38. $\sqrt{147}$

39. $\sqrt{120}$ **40.** $\sqrt{80}$ **41.** $\sqrt[3]{1080}$ **42.** $\sqrt[3]{720}$ **43.** $\sqrt[4]{240}$ **44.** $\sqrt[5]{256}$

45. $\sqrt[5]{-288}$ **46.** $\sqrt[3]{-270}$ **47.** $\sqrt[3]{-3125}$ **48.** $\sqrt[3]{270}$ **49.** $\sqrt[3]{3125}$ **50.** $\sqrt[6]{320}$

In exercises 51-77, perform the indicated operations and simplify (the variables represent positive numbers).

51. $\sqrt{32p^5}$ **52.** $\sqrt{18x^3}$ **53.** $\sqrt{a^2b^5}$ **54.** $\sqrt{x^3y^4}$ **55.** $\sqrt[3]{a^5b^4}$ **56.** $\sqrt[4]{x^5y^6}$

57. $\sqrt{\dfrac{2000}{81}}$ **58.** $\sqrt{\dfrac{256}{729}}$ **59.** $\sqrt[3]{-\dfrac{216}{125}}$ **60.** $\sqrt[3]{-\dfrac{27}{64}}$ **61.** $\dfrac{\sqrt[4]{3x^2y}}{\sqrt[4]{48x^7y^3}}$

62. $\dfrac{\sqrt[3]{4a^3b}}{\sqrt[3]{20a^5b}}$ **63.** $\sqrt{x^6}$ **64.** $\sqrt{a^{10}}$ **65.** $\sqrt{y^{11}}$ **66.** $\sqrt{x^4y^4}$ **67.** $\sqrt{4a^6}$

68. $\sqrt{x^{12}y^4}$ **69.** $y\sqrt{x^3y^4}$ **70.** $5\sqrt{9a^4b}$ **71.** $2x\sqrt{8x^4y^5}$ **72.** $3a\sqrt{12a^7b^5}$

73. $\sqrt{x^{12}y^4}$ **74.** $\dfrac{\sqrt{15x^3y}}{\sqrt{3xy}}$ **75.** $\dfrac{\sqrt{9xy^2}}{\sqrt{27x}}$ **76.** $\dfrac{\sqrt{12a^3b}}{\sqrt{24a^2b^2}}$ **77.** $\dfrac{\sqrt{25a^4b}\cdot\sqrt{49a^3b^3}}{\sqrt{144ab}}$

8.3   ADDITION AND SUBTRACTION OF RADICALS

Two radical expressions which have the *same radicand* and the *same index* are called *like* radicals.

A. ADDING AND SUBTRACTING LIKE RADICALS

Like radicals are added or subtracted using the distributive property: $a\sqrt{x}+b\sqrt{x}=(a+b)\sqrt{x}$.

EXAMPLE 1   Perform the indicated operation.

   a. $2\sqrt{5}+7\sqrt{5}$ **b.** $6\sqrt[3]{12}-4\sqrt[3]{12}$ **c.** $\sqrt[4]{7}-5\sqrt[4]{7}$

Solutions:

   a. $2\sqrt{5}+7\sqrt{5}=(2+7)\sqrt{5}$ Distributive property.

                $=9\sqrt{5}$

   b. $6\sqrt[3]{12}-4\sqrt[3]{12}=(6-4)\sqrt[3]{12}$ Distributive property.

                  $=2\sqrt[3]{12}$

   c. $\sqrt[4]{7}-5\sqrt[4]{7}=1\cdot\sqrt[4]{7}-5\sqrt[4]{7}$

                  $=(1-5)\sqrt[4]{7}=-4\sqrt[4]{7}$ Distributive property.

OBJECTIVES ■■■

Upon completion of this section you will be able to:

A.   Add and subtract like radicals.

B.   Simplify radical sums and differences.

B. SIMPLIFYING RADICAL SUMS AND DIFFERENCES

The radicals of the type $\sqrt{2}$ and $\sqrt{5}$ cannot be added together. However, some radical expressions can be simplified and may become like radicals after simplification.

For example $\sqrt{8}$ and $\sqrt{18}$ can be simplified as:

$$\sqrt{8} = \sqrt{4 \cdot 2} = \sqrt{4} \cdot \sqrt{2}$$
$$= \mathbf{2\sqrt{2}} \qquad \text{and}$$
$$\sqrt{18} = \sqrt{9 \cdot 2} = \sqrt{9} \cdot \sqrt{2}$$
$$= \mathbf{3\sqrt{2}}$$

Such radical expressions can be added or subtracted after simplification.

WARM-UP

2. Simplify

a) $3\sqrt{2} + 3\sqrt{8}$

b) $12\sqrt{12} - 3\sqrt{48}$

c) $13\sqrt[3]{320} + 2\sqrt[3]{40}$

EXAMPLE 2   Simplify: **a.** $4\sqrt{3} - 6\sqrt{27}$

b. $5\sqrt{15} + \sqrt{60}$ **c.** $\sqrt[3]{81} + 4\sqrt[3]{375}$

Solutions:

We will simplify each of the radicals by using the prime factorization of the radicands.

a. $4\sqrt{3} - 6\sqrt{27} = 4\sqrt{3} - 6\sqrt{3 \cdot 3 \cdot 3}$ Prime factorization.

$\qquad\qquad = 4\sqrt{3} - 6\sqrt{3^2 \cdot 3}$

$\qquad\qquad = 4\sqrt{3} - 6\sqrt{3^2} \cdot \sqrt{3}$ Product rule.

$\qquad\qquad = 4\sqrt{3} - 6 \cdot 3 \cdot \sqrt{3}$

$\qquad\qquad = 4\sqrt{3} - 18\sqrt{3}$

$\qquad\qquad = \mathbf{-14\sqrt{3}}$ Subtract.

b. $5\sqrt{15} + \sqrt{60} = 5\sqrt{3 \cdot 5} + \sqrt{2 \cdot 2 \cdot 3 \cdot 5}$ Prime factorization.

$\qquad\qquad = 5\sqrt{3 \cdot 5} + \sqrt{2^2 \cdot 3 \cdot 5}$

$\qquad\qquad = 5\sqrt{3 \cdot 5} + 2\sqrt{3 \cdot 5}$ Product rule.

$\qquad\qquad = 5\sqrt{15} + 2\sqrt{15}$ Prime factorization.

$\qquad\qquad = \mathbf{7\sqrt{15}}$ Add.

c. $\sqrt[3]{81} + 4\sqrt[3]{375} = \sqrt[3]{3 \cdot 3 \cdot 3 \cdot 3} + 4\sqrt[3]{5 \cdot 5 \cdot 5 \cdot 3}$ Prime factorization.

$\qquad\qquad = \sqrt[3]{3^3 \cdot 3} + 4\sqrt[3]{5^3 \cdot 3}$

$\qquad\qquad = \sqrt[3]{3^3} \cdot \sqrt[3]{3} + 4\sqrt[3]{5^3} \cdot \sqrt[3]{3}$ Product rule.

$\qquad\qquad = 3\sqrt[3]{3} + 4 \cdot 5 \cdot \sqrt[3]{3}$ $\sqrt[3]{a^3} = a$

$\qquad\qquad = 3\sqrt[3]{3} + 20\sqrt[3]{3}$

$\qquad\qquad = \mathbf{23\sqrt[3]{3}}$ Add.

EXAMPLE 3   Simplify:

    a. $\sqrt{25}+\sqrt{4}$ **b.** $4\sqrt{3}-2\sqrt{75}$

    c. $3+2\sqrt{4}+5\sqrt{6}-3\sqrt{24}$

    d. $\sqrt{80}-\sqrt{128}+\sqrt{288}$

Solutions:

a. $\sqrt{25}+\sqrt{4}=\sqrt{5^2}+\sqrt{2^2}=5+2=\mathbf{7}$

b. $4\sqrt{3}-2\sqrt{75}=4\sqrt{3}-2\sqrt{5\cdot5\cdot3}$ Prime factorization.

                $=4\sqrt{3}-2\sqrt{5^2\cdot3}$

                $=4\sqrt{3}-2\sqrt{5^2}\cdot\sqrt{3}$ Product rule.

                $=4\sqrt{3}-2\cdot5\cdot\sqrt{3}$ $\sqrt{5^2}=5$

                $=4\sqrt{3}-10\sqrt{3}$ Combine like radicals.

                $=\mathbf{-6\sqrt{3}}$ Subract

c. $3+2\sqrt{4}+5\sqrt{6}-3\sqrt{24}$

     $=3+2\sqrt{2^2}+5\sqrt{2\cdot3}-3\sqrt{2\cdot2\cdot2\cdot3}$

     $=3+2\sqrt{2^2}+5\sqrt{2\cdot3}-3\sqrt{2^2}\cdot\sqrt{2\cdot3}$

     $=3+2\cdot2+5\sqrt{2\cdot3}-3\cdot2\cdot\sqrt{2\cdot3}$

     $=3+4+5\sqrt{6}-6\sqrt{6}$

     $=\mathbf{7-\sqrt{6}}$

d. $\sqrt{80}-\sqrt{128}+\sqrt{288}$

     $=\sqrt{16\cdot5}-\sqrt{64\cdot2}+\sqrt{144\cdot2}$ Factor perfect squares 4, 9, 16, ...

     $=4\cdot\sqrt{5}-8\cdot\sqrt{2}+12\cdot\sqrt{2}$

     $=\mathbf{4\sqrt{5}+4\sqrt{2}}$

EXAMPLE 5   Simplify the following expressions:

    a. $3\sqrt{3}\left(4\sqrt{8}-5\sqrt{27}\right)$

    b. $\left(\sqrt{5}+\sqrt{2}\right)\left(\sqrt{5}-\sqrt{2}\right)$

    c. $4\sqrt{15}\cdot\sqrt{5}-3\sqrt{3}$

    d. $\left(2\sqrt{a}-4\sqrt{b}\right)^2, a\geq0, b\geq0$

    e. $\left(\sqrt{x}+2\sqrt{y}\right)\left(2\sqrt{x}-3\sqrt{y}\right), x\geq0, y\geq0$

WARM-UP

3. Simplify:

a) $\sqrt{36}+\sqrt{1}$

b) $4\sqrt{60}-2\sqrt{15}$

c) $11+3\sqrt{16}+5\sqrt{8}-6\sqrt{2}$

d) $\sqrt{32}-\sqrt{98}+\sqrt{242}$

4. Simplify the following expressions:

a) $2\sqrt{3}\left(2\sqrt{5}-4\sqrt{6}\right)$

Solutions:

b) $\left(\sqrt{4}-\sqrt{2}\right)\left(\sqrt{4}+\sqrt{2}\right)$

c) $3\sqrt{12}\cdot\sqrt{4}-2\sqrt{12}$

d) $\left(3\sqrt{a}-2\sqrt{b}\right)^2$

e) $\left(\sqrt{x}-2\sqrt{y}\right)\left(3\sqrt{x}+\sqrt{y}\right)$

Answers:

2. a) $9\sqrt{2}$ b) $12\sqrt{3}$ c) $56\sqrt[3]{5}$

3. a) 7 b) $6\sqrt{15}$

    c) $23+4\sqrt{2}$ d) $8\sqrt{2}$

4. a) $4\sqrt{15}-24\sqrt{2}$ b) 2 c) $8\sqrt{3}$

    d) $9a-12\sqrt{ab}+4b$ e) $3x-5\sqrt{xy}-2y$

a. $3\sqrt{3}\left(4\sqrt{8}-5\sqrt{27}\right)$

$= \left(3\sqrt{3}\right)\left(4\sqrt{8}\right)-\left(3\sqrt{3}\right)\left(5\sqrt{27}\right)$ Distributive property.

$= 12\sqrt{3\cdot 8}-15\sqrt{3\cdot 27}$ Product rule.

$= 12\sqrt{24}-15\sqrt{81}$

$= 12\sqrt{2^2\cdot 6}-15\sqrt{9^2}$

$= 12\cdot 2\sqrt{6}-15\cdot 9$

$= \mathbf{24\sqrt{6}-135}$

b. $\left(\sqrt{5}+\sqrt{2}\right)\left(\sqrt{5}-\sqrt{2}\right)=\left(\sqrt{5}\right)^2-\left(\sqrt{2}\right)^2$

$= 5-2=\mathbf{3}$ $(a+b)(a-b)=a^2-b^2$

c. $4\sqrt{15}\cdot\sqrt{5}-3\sqrt{3}=4\sqrt{75}-3\sqrt{3}$

$= 4\sqrt{3\cdot 25}-3\sqrt{3}$

$= 4\sqrt{3\cdot 5^2}-3\sqrt{3}$

$= 4\sqrt{3}\cdot\sqrt{5^2}-3\sqrt{3}$

$= \left(4\sqrt{3}\right)(5)-3\sqrt{3}$

$= 20\sqrt{3}-3\sqrt{3}=\mathbf{17\sqrt{3}}$

d. $\left(2\sqrt{a}-4\sqrt{b}\right)^2=\left(2\sqrt{a}\right)^2-2\left(2\sqrt{a}\right)\left(4\sqrt{b}\right)+\left(4\sqrt{b}\right)^2$

$= 4\left(\sqrt{a}\right)^2-16\sqrt{a}\sqrt{b}+16\left(\sqrt{b}\right)^2$

$= 4a-16\sqrt{a}\sqrt{b}+16b$

$= 4a-16\sqrt{ab}+16b$

$= \mathbf{4a+16b-16\sqrt{ab}}$

e. $\left(\sqrt{x}+2\sqrt{y}\right)\left(2\sqrt{x}-3\sqrt{y}\right)$

$= \left(\sqrt{x}\right)\left(2\sqrt{x}\right)+\sqrt{x}\left(-3\sqrt{y}\right)+\left(2\sqrt{y}\right)\left(2\sqrt{x}\right)+\left(2\sqrt{y}\left(-3\sqrt{y}\right)\right)$

$= 2\left(\sqrt{x}\right)^2-3\sqrt{x}\sqrt{y}+4\sqrt{y}\cdot\sqrt{x}-6\left(\sqrt{y}\right)^2$

$= \mathbf{2x}-3\sqrt{x}\sqrt{y}+4\sqrt{y}\cdot\sqrt{x}-6y$

$= 2x-\mathbf{3\sqrt{xy}}+4\sqrt{xy}-6y$

$= \mathbf{2x+\sqrt{xy}-6y}$

EXERCISE 8.3

A. In exercises 1-27, perform the indicated operations.

1. $3\sqrt{2} - 4\sqrt{2}$

2. $4\sqrt{3} - 5\sqrt{3}$

3. $5\sqrt{7} - 2\sqrt{7}$

4. $3\sqrt{5} + 5\sqrt{5}$

5. $-8\sqrt{3} + 11\sqrt{3}$

6. $5\sqrt{11} - 11\sqrt{11}$

7. $-\sqrt[3]{4} + 4\sqrt[3]{4}$

8. $-\sqrt[3]{2} + 5\sqrt[3]{2}$

9. $-\sqrt[4]{2} - 3\sqrt[4]{2}$

10. $2\sqrt[5]{3} - 5\sqrt[5]{3}$

11. $-5\sqrt[3]{5} + 7\sqrt[3]{5}$

12. $4\sqrt[4]{3} - 8\sqrt[4]{3}$

13. $-\sqrt[4]{6} - 6\sqrt[4]{6}$

14. $-3\sqrt[5]{5} + 2\sqrt[5]{5}$

15. $2\sqrt[5]{3} - 3\sqrt[5]{3} + 7\sqrt[5]{3}$

16. $3\sqrt[3]{5} - 2\sqrt[3]{5} + 4\sqrt[3]{5}$

17. $\frac{7}{8}\sqrt{15} - \frac{4}{5}\sqrt{15}$

18. $\frac{1}{2}\sqrt{10} + \frac{2}{3}\sqrt{10}$

19. $\frac{5}{6}\sqrt[4]{11} + \frac{4}{9}\sqrt[4]{11}$

20. $\frac{1}{3}\sqrt[3]{2} + \frac{2}{5}\sqrt[3]{2}$

21. $\frac{3}{4}\sqrt[3]{4} - \frac{5}{6}\sqrt[3]{4}$

22. $\frac{7}{8}\sqrt[3]{9} - \frac{5}{6}\sqrt[3]{9}$

23. $\sqrt{8} \cdot \sqrt{3} - 2\sqrt{6}$

24. $\sqrt{8} \cdot \sqrt{3} - 4\sqrt{6}$

25. $-\sqrt{27} \cdot \sqrt{5} + 4\sqrt{15}$

26. $\sqrt{18} \cdot \sqrt{5} - 2\sqrt{10}$

27. $-\sqrt{12} \cdot \sqrt{8} + 6\sqrt{6}$

B. In exercises 28-55, perform the indicated operations and simplify. Assume that the variables represent non-negative real numbers.

28. $\sqrt{2}\left(\sqrt{2} - \sqrt{3}\right)$

29. $\sqrt{5}\left(\sqrt{5} - \sqrt{6}\right)$

30. $\sqrt{7}\left(\sqrt{3} + \sqrt{7}\right)$

31. $\sqrt{a}\left(\sqrt{a} - \sqrt{b}\right)$

32. $\sqrt{b}\left(2\sqrt{a} + 3\sqrt{b}\right)$

33. $\sqrt{10}\left(\sqrt{20} - \sqrt{a}\right)$

34. $3\sqrt{2}\left(9\sqrt{8} - 5\sqrt{2}\right)$

35. $2\sqrt{3}\left(4\sqrt{27} - 5\sqrt{32}\right)$

36. $2\sqrt{5}\left(3\sqrt{20} - 2\sqrt{45}\right)$

37. $4\sqrt{2}\left(-3\sqrt{2} + 8\sqrt{8}\right)$

38. $3\sqrt{2}\left(5\sqrt{8} - \sqrt{18}\right)$

39. $\left(2\sqrt{3} - \sqrt{5}\right)\left(2\sqrt{3} + \sqrt{5}\right)$

40. $\left(3\sqrt{4} + \sqrt{6}\right)\left(3\sqrt{4} - \sqrt{6}\right)$

41. $\left(2\sqrt{2} - 3\sqrt{3}\right)\left(2\sqrt{2} + 3\sqrt{3}\right)$

42. $\left(\sqrt{3} - 2\sqrt{2}\right)\left(\sqrt{3} + 2\sqrt{2}\right)$

43. $\left(3\sqrt{x} - 5\sqrt{y}\right)\left(3\sqrt{x} + 5\sqrt{y}\right)$

44. $\left(2\sqrt{a} + \sqrt{b}\right) \cdot \left(5\sqrt{a} + 4\sqrt{b}\right)$

45. $\left(3\sqrt{x} + \sqrt{y}\right)\left(3\sqrt{x} - \sqrt{y}\right)$

46. $\left(7\sqrt{x} + 2\sqrt{y}\right)\left(7\sqrt{x} - 2\sqrt{y}\right)$

47. $\left(3\sqrt{x} + 5\sqrt{y}\right)^2$

48. $\left(4\sqrt{y} + 3\sqrt{x}\right)^2$

49. $\left(2\sqrt{x} - 3\sqrt{y}\right)^2$

50. $\left(5\sqrt{p} - 2\sqrt{q}\right) \cdot \left(3\sqrt{p} - 4\sqrt{q}\right)$

51. $\left(3\sqrt{a} - 2b\right) \cdot \left(5\sqrt{a} - 4b\right)$

52. $\left(\sqrt{p} + 3\sqrt{q^3}\right)\left(4\sqrt{p} - 2\sqrt{q}\right)$

53. $\left(\sqrt{q} + 5\sqrt{p^3}\right)\left(\sqrt{q} - 5\sqrt{p^3}\right)$

54. $\left(\sqrt{p} - 3q\sqrt{q}\right)\left(\sqrt{p} - 4q\sqrt{q}\right)$

55. $\left(\sqrt{x} + 2\sqrt{y}\right)\left(\sqrt{x} - 3\sqrt{y}\right)$

8.4 RATIONALIZING THE DENOMINATOR

Upon completion of this section you will be able to:

A. Rationalize denominators with one term;

B. Write radicals in simplified form; and

C. Rationalize denominators involving two terms.

Rationalizing the denominator means changing the given radical expression so that the denominator is free of radicals. If the denominator does not have radicals, then it is a *rational* denominator

A. RATIONALIZING DENOMINATORS WITH ONE TERM

To rationalize the denominator of $\dfrac{5}{\sqrt{xy}}$, we need to rewrite this expression so that the denominator becomes

$\sqrt{x^2 y^2}$ $(= xy)$ which is free of any radical. How do we rewrite the given expression? We multiply both numerator and denominator by the same expression so that the radicand in the denominator is a perfect square.

This can be done using fundamental property of rational expressions that states; $\dfrac{PK}{QK} = \dfrac{P}{Q}$ for any non-zero number or expression.

> **In general for rationalizing the denominator the basic idea is to be able to rewrite the denominator in the form** $\sqrt[n]{a^n}$.

We can rationalize the denominator using the following step by step approach:

Step 1   Simplify the given expression as far as possible.

Step 2   Identify an expression K that when used as a factor in the denominator can make the denominator rational.

Step 3   Multilpy the expression with $\dfrac{K}{K}$.

Step 4   Simplify the result in step 3.

We explain this step by step approach through the following examples.

━━━ **WARM-UP** ━━━

1. Rationalize the denominators.

a) $\dfrac{4}{\sqrt{3}}$

EXAMPLE 1   Rationalize the denominators.

a. $\dfrac{3}{\sqrt{7}}$ b. $\dfrac{4}{\sqrt{8}}$ c. $\dfrac{5}{4\sqrt{3}}$

Solutions:

a. $\dfrac{3}{\sqrt{7}} = \dfrac{3}{\sqrt{7}} \cdot \dfrac{\sqrt{7}}{\sqrt{7}}$

$= \dfrac{3\sqrt{7}}{\sqrt{7} \cdot \sqrt{7}}$

$= \dfrac{3\sqrt{7}}{7}$

Step 2 $K = \dfrac{\sqrt{7^2}}{\sqrt{7}} = \sqrt{\dfrac{7^2}{7}} = \sqrt{7}$

Step 3 Multiply by $\dfrac{K}{K}$.

Step 4 Simplify.

b. $\dfrac{4}{\sqrt{8}} = \dfrac{4}{\sqrt{8}} \cdot \dfrac{\sqrt{8}}{\sqrt{8}}$ Multiply by $\frac{K}{K}$.

$= \dfrac{4\sqrt{8}}{\sqrt{8}\cdot\sqrt{8}} = \dfrac{4\sqrt{8}}{8} = \dfrac{\sqrt{8}}{2}$ Simplify

$\dfrac{\sqrt{8}}{2}$ can be further simplified as $\dfrac{2\sqrt{2}}{2} = \sqrt{2}$.

c. $\dfrac{5}{4\sqrt{3}} = \dfrac{5}{4\sqrt{3}} \cdot \dfrac{\sqrt{3}}{\sqrt{3}} = \dfrac{5\sqrt{3}}{4\sqrt{3^2}} = \dfrac{5\sqrt{3}}{4\cdot 3} = \dfrac{5\sqrt{3}}{12}$

EXAMPLE 2 Rationalize the following denominators.

a. $\dfrac{4}{\sqrt[3]{2}}$ **b.** $\dfrac{1}{\sqrt[4]{9}}$

Solutions:

a. $\dfrac{4}{\sqrt[3]{2}} = \dfrac{4}{\sqrt[3]{2}} \cdot \dfrac{\sqrt[3]{4}}{\sqrt[3]{4}}$ Look for the perfect cubes: 1, 8, 27, ...

$K = \sqrt[3]{4}$, Multiply by $\frac{K}{K}$.

$= \dfrac{4\sqrt[3]{4}}{\sqrt[3]{2}\cdot\sqrt[3]{4}} = \dfrac{4\sqrt[3]{4}}{\sqrt[3]{8}} = \dfrac{4\sqrt[3]{4}}{2}$ Simplify.

$= 2\sqrt[3]{4}$

b. $\dfrac{1}{\sqrt[4]{9}} = \dfrac{1}{\sqrt[4]{9}} \cdot \dfrac{\sqrt[4]{9}}{\sqrt[4]{9}}$ $K = \sqrt[4]{9}$, Multiply by $\frac{K}{K}$.

$= \dfrac{\sqrt[4]{9}}{\sqrt[4]{81}} = \dfrac{\sqrt[4]{9}}{3}$ Simplify.

B. WRITING SQUARE ROOTS IN SIMPLIFIED FORM

A *square root* radical is said to be in simplified form if:

- The radicand does not contain any factor, different from 1, which is a perfect square.
- The radicand does not contain fractions.
- No denominator contains a radical.

The third condition above means that, if needed, the denominator must be rationalized.

EXAMPLE 3 Simplify the following:

a. $\sqrt{\dfrac{8}{3}}$ **b.** $\sqrt{\dfrac{5}{6}} \cdot \sqrt{\dfrac{3}{8}}$ **c.** $\sqrt{\dfrac{3x^2}{y}}$ $(x > 0, y > 0)$

a) $\sqrt{\dfrac{3}{5}}$

b) $\sqrt{\dfrac{3}{7} \cdot \dfrac{21}{9}}$

c) $\sqrt{\dfrac{5x^3}{y^3}}$ $(x \geq 0, \; y > 0)$

Answers:

3. a) $\dfrac{\sqrt{15}}{5}$ b) 1   c) $\dfrac{x\sqrt{5xy}}{y^2}$

Solutions:

a. $\sqrt{\dfrac{8}{3}} = \dfrac{\sqrt{8}}{\sqrt{3}} \cdot \dfrac{\sqrt{3}}{\sqrt{3}} = \dfrac{\sqrt{24}}{\sqrt{9}}$

$= \dfrac{\sqrt{4 \cdot 6}}{3} = \dfrac{2\sqrt{6}}{3}$

b. $\sqrt{\dfrac{5}{6}} \cdot \sqrt{\dfrac{3}{8}} = \sqrt{\dfrac{5}{6} \cdot \dfrac{3}{8}} = \sqrt{\dfrac{5}{16}} = \dfrac{\sqrt{5}}{4}$

c. $\sqrt{\dfrac{3x^2}{y}} = \dfrac{\sqrt{3x^2}}{\sqrt{y}} = \dfrac{\sqrt{3}\sqrt{x^2}}{\sqrt{y}}$

$= \dfrac{\sqrt{3} \cdot x}{\sqrt{y}} = \dfrac{x\sqrt{3}}{\sqrt{y}} \cdot \dfrac{\sqrt{y}}{\sqrt{y}} = \dfrac{x\sqrt{3} \cdot \sqrt{y}}{\sqrt{y} \cdot \sqrt{y}}$

$= \dfrac{x\sqrt{3} \cdot \sqrt{y}}{y} = \dfrac{x\sqrt{3y}}{y}$

C. RATIONALIZING DENOMINATORS WITH TWO TERMS

We will see how the formula $(a + b)(a - b) = a^2 - b^2$, learned earlier in chapter 5, can be used to rationalize denominators with two terms.

> Two binomials which differ only in the sign between the two terms are called **conjugate binomials.** Thus $a + \sqrt{b}$ and $a - \sqrt{b}$ are conjugates of each other.

WARM-UP

4. Write down the conjugate.

a) $\sqrt{5} - \sqrt{2}$

b) $2\sqrt{8} - \sqrt{5}$

c) $8 - 6\sqrt{2}$

d) $-13\sqrt{5} + \sqrt{7}$

EXAMPLE 4   Find the conjugate of each expression.

a. $\sqrt{3} + \sqrt{5}$ b. $2\sqrt{7} - \sqrt{6}$

c. $3 - 5\sqrt{2}$ d. $-4\sqrt{6} + 2\sqrt{8}$

Solutions:

a. The conjugate of $\sqrt{3} + \sqrt{5}$ is $\sqrt{3} - \sqrt{5}$.

b. The conjugate of $2\sqrt{7} - \sqrt{6}$ is $\mathbf{2\sqrt{7} + \sqrt{6}}$.

c. The conjugate of $3 - 5\sqrt{2}$ is $\mathbf{3 + 5\sqrt{2}}$.

d. The conjugate of $-4\sqrt{6} + 2\sqrt{8}$ is $\mathbf{-4\sqrt{6} - 2\sqrt{8}}$.

EXAMPLE 5   Rationalize the denominators.

a. $\dfrac{1}{3-\sqrt{5}}$ b. $\dfrac{\sqrt{2}+3}{2\sqrt{2}+\sqrt{5}}$

Solutions:

a. $\dfrac{1}{3-\sqrt{5}}$:

Step 1   Multiply both the numerator and denominator by the conjugate of the denominator. The conjugate of

$3-\sqrt{5}$ is $3+\sqrt{5}$.

$\dfrac{1}{3-\sqrt{5}} = \dfrac{1}{3-\sqrt{5}} \cdot \dfrac{3+\sqrt{5}}{3+\sqrt{5}}$

$= \dfrac{1\left(3+\sqrt{5}\right)}{\left(3-\sqrt{5}\right)\left(3+\sqrt{5}\right)}$

$= \dfrac{\left(3+\sqrt{5}\right)}{(3)^2-\left(\sqrt{5}\right)^2}$ $(a-b)(a+b) = a^2 - b^2$

Step 2   Simplify: $\dfrac{3+\sqrt{5}}{(3)^2-\left(\sqrt{5}\right)^2} = \dfrac{3+\sqrt{5}}{9-5} = \dfrac{3+\sqrt{5}}{4}$

b. $\dfrac{\sqrt{2}+3}{2\sqrt{2}+\sqrt{5}}$:   The conjugate of $2\sqrt{2}+\sqrt{5}$ is $2\sqrt{2}-\sqrt{5}$.

$\dfrac{\sqrt{2}+3}{2\sqrt{2}+\sqrt{5}} = \dfrac{\sqrt{2}+3}{2\sqrt{2}+\sqrt{5}} \cdot \dfrac{2\sqrt{2}-\sqrt{5}}{2\sqrt{2}-\sqrt{5}}$

$= \dfrac{\left(\sqrt{2}+3\right)\left(2\sqrt{2}-\sqrt{5}\right)}{\left(2\sqrt{2}\right)^2-\left(\sqrt{5}\right)^2}$

$= \dfrac{\left(\sqrt{2}\right)\left(2\sqrt{2}\right)+\sqrt{2}\left(-\sqrt{5}\right)+\left(3\cdot2\sqrt{2}\right)+3\left(-\sqrt{5}\right)}{\left(2\sqrt{2}\right)^2-\left(\sqrt{5}\right)^2}$

$= \dfrac{2\cdot2-\sqrt{10}+6\sqrt{2}-3\sqrt{5}}{8-5}$

$= \dfrac{4-\sqrt{10}+6\sqrt{2}-3\sqrt{5}}{3}$

EXERCISE 8.4

A. In exercises 1-36, rationalize the denominator and simplify.

1. $\dfrac{3}{\sqrt{2}}$ 2. $\dfrac{5}{\sqrt{3}}$ 3. $\dfrac{4}{\sqrt{5}}$ 4. $\dfrac{3}{\sqrt{7}}$ 5. $\dfrac{4}{\sqrt{6}}$ 6. $\dfrac{5}{\sqrt{10}}$

7. $\dfrac{3}{2\sqrt{18}}$ 8. $\dfrac{5}{3\sqrt{50}}$ 9. $\dfrac{12}{\sqrt{32}}$ 10. $\dfrac{6}{\sqrt{72}}$ 11. $\dfrac{10}{2\sqrt{125}}$ 12. $\dfrac{7}{3\sqrt{98}}$

13. $\dfrac{8}{\sqrt{48}}$ 14. $\dfrac{3}{\sqrt{75}}$ 15. $\dfrac{12}{\sqrt{108}}$ 16. $\dfrac{2}{\sqrt[3]{2}}$ 17. $\dfrac{4}{\sqrt[3]{10}}$ 18. $\dfrac{3}{\sqrt[3]{3}}$

19. $\dfrac{5}{\sqrt[3]{40}}$ 20. $\dfrac{8}{\sqrt[3]{72}}$ 21. $\dfrac{4}{\sqrt[3]{100}}$ 22. $\dfrac{6}{\sqrt[3]{81}}$ 23. $\dfrac{4}{\sqrt[4]{32}}$ 24. $\dfrac{5}{\sqrt[4]{162}}$

25. $\dfrac{5}{2\sqrt[4]{4}}$ 26. $\dfrac{3}{4\sqrt[4]{3}}$ 27. $\dfrac{\sqrt[4]{3}}{2\sqrt[4]{4}}$ 28. $\dfrac{\sqrt[3]{5}}{3\sqrt[3]{6}}$ 29. $\dfrac{3\sqrt{15}}{5\sqrt{6}}$ 30. $\dfrac{4\sqrt{6}}{7\sqrt{15}}$

31. $\dfrac{\sqrt{45}}{\sqrt{5}}$ 32. $\dfrac{\sqrt{48}}{\sqrt{3}}$ 33. $\sqrt{\dfrac{16}{7}}$ 34. $\sqrt{\dfrac{25}{6}}$ 35. $\sqrt{\dfrac{40}{3}}$ 36. $\sqrt{\dfrac{20}{6}}$

B. In exercises 37-54, rationalize the denominator and express the result in the simplified form. (Assume that $x > 0, y > 0$)

37. $\sqrt{\dfrac{2}{5}} \cdot \sqrt{\dfrac{3}{10}}$ 38. $\sqrt{\dfrac{3}{7}} \cdot \sqrt{\dfrac{3}{14}}$ 39. $\sqrt{\dfrac{1}{13}} \cdot \sqrt{\dfrac{39}{10}}$ 40. $\sqrt{\dfrac{1}{7}} \cdot \sqrt{\dfrac{14}{5}}$ 41. $\sqrt{\dfrac{1}{10}} \cdot \sqrt{\dfrac{20}{3}}$

42. $\sqrt{\dfrac{1}{8}} \cdot \sqrt{\dfrac{24}{6}}$ 43. $\sqrt{\dfrac{4}{x}}$ 44. $\sqrt{\dfrac{9}{2x}}$ 45. $\sqrt{\dfrac{6x^3}{4y}}$ 46. $\sqrt{\dfrac{8x}{4y}}$

47. $\dfrac{\sqrt{8a^2 b}}{\sqrt{2a^4 b^2}}$ 48. $\dfrac{\sqrt{6ab^3}}{\sqrt{4a^3 b}}$ 49. $\dfrac{\sqrt{50a^3 b^4}}{\sqrt{25ab^2}}$ 50. $\dfrac{\sqrt{18ab^2}}{\sqrt{8a^3 b^4}}$ 51. $\dfrac{\sqrt{25x}}{\sqrt{36xz^2}}$

52. $\dfrac{\sqrt{8x^3 z^4}}{\sqrt{32xz^2}}$ 53. $\dfrac{\sqrt{28z^5 x}}{\sqrt{63z^3 x^3}}$ 54. $\dfrac{\sqrt{16z}}{\sqrt{49zx}}$

C. In exercises 55-60, find the conjugate of the given expression.

55. $4 - 3\sqrt{2}$ 56. $\sqrt{7} + \sqrt{5}$ 57. $2\sqrt{5} - 3\sqrt{3}$

58. $-3\sqrt{7} + 5\sqrt{6}$ 59. $-2\sqrt{3} - 7\sqrt{7}$ 60. $-11\sqrt{5} - 13\sqrt{3}$

In exercises 61-80, rationalize the denominator and simplify.

61. $\dfrac{2}{\sqrt{3} - \sqrt{2}}$ 62. $\dfrac{3}{\sqrt{5} + \sqrt{3}}$ 63. $\dfrac{3}{\sqrt{5} + 1}$ 64. $\dfrac{2}{\sqrt{5} - \sqrt{3}}$ 65. $\dfrac{\sqrt{7} - \sqrt{2}}{\sqrt{2} + \sqrt{7}}$

66. $\dfrac{\sqrt{3} + \sqrt{2}}{\sqrt{3} - \sqrt{2}}$ 67. $\dfrac{\sqrt{3} - 1}{\sqrt{3} + 1}$ 68. $\dfrac{2 + \sqrt{3}}{2 - \sqrt{3}}$ 69. $\dfrac{\sqrt{x} + \sqrt{y}}{\sqrt{x} - \sqrt{y}}$ 70. $\dfrac{\sqrt{3} - 3\sqrt{5}}{\sqrt{5}}$

71. $\dfrac{3\sqrt{2} - 8\sqrt{2}}{\sqrt{2}}$ 72. $\dfrac{2\sqrt{8} + 3\sqrt{2}}{\sqrt{32}}$ 73. $\dfrac{5\sqrt{8} - 3\sqrt{2}}{\sqrt{2}}$ 74. $\dfrac{6 - 2\sqrt{3}}{4 + 3\sqrt{3}}$ 75. $\dfrac{\sqrt{x} - 4}{2\sqrt{x} + 2}$

76. $\dfrac{2 + \sqrt{x}}{\sqrt{x} - 3}$ 77. $\dfrac{2\sqrt{3} - \sqrt{6}}{5\sqrt{3} + 2\sqrt{6}}$ 78. $\dfrac{\sqrt{ab}}{\sqrt{a} - \sqrt{b}}$ 79. $\dfrac{\sqrt{a} - \sqrt{b}}{\sqrt{a} + \sqrt{b}}$ 80. $\dfrac{2\sqrt{a} + 3\sqrt{b}}{2\sqrt{a} - 3\sqrt{b}}$

8.5 FRACTIONAL EXPONENTS

We have already discussed laws of exponents where exponents are integers. In this section we discuss fractional exponents.

A. DEFINITION OF $a^{1/n}$

For any *non-negative* number *a* and a positive integer *n*, $a^{1/n} = \sqrt[n]{a}$.

The denominator of the fractional exponents becomes the index of the radical.

Thus, $\qquad a^{1/2} = \sqrt[2]{a} = \sqrt{a} \qquad\qquad a^{1/5} = \sqrt[5]{a}$

(If there is no index in the radical then it is understood that the index is 2.)

EXAMPLE 1 Simplify **a.** $9^{1/2}$ **b.** $8^{1/3}$
  c. $256^{1/4}$ **d.** $243^{1/5}$

Solutions:

a. $\quad 9^{1/2} = \sqrt{9} = 3 \qquad$ $9 = 3 \cdot 3 = 3^2$

b. $\quad 8^{1/3} = \sqrt[3]{8} = 2 \qquad$ $8 = 2^3$

c. $\quad 256^{1/4} = \sqrt[4]{256} = 4 \qquad$ $256 = 4^4$

d. $\quad 243^{1/5} = \sqrt[5]{243} = 3 \qquad$ $243 = 3^5$

*For a real number **a**, and a positive integer **n***

- $\quad a^{1/n} = \sqrt[n]{a} \qquad$ if $a > 0$

- $\quad a^{1/n} = 0 \qquad$ if $a = 0$

- $\quad a^{1/n}$ is not a real number if $a < 0$ and n is even.

EXAMPLE 2 Simplify each of the following expressions.
  a. $125^{1/3}$ **b.** $(-125)^{1/3}$ **c.** $-125^{1/3}$
  d. $0^{1/10}$ **e.** $(-256)^{1/4}$ **f.** $-256^{1/4}$

Solutions:

a. $\quad \mathbf{125^{1/3}} = \sqrt[3]{125} = \mathbf{5} \qquad$ $125 = 5^3$

b. $\quad \mathbf{(-125)^{1/3}} = \sqrt[3]{-125} = \mathbf{-5} \qquad$ $-125 = (-5)^3$

c. $\quad \mathbf{-125^{1/3}} = -\left(\sqrt[3]{125}\right) = \mathbf{-5}$

d. $\quad \mathbf{0^{1/10}} = \mathbf{0}$

e. $\quad \mathbf{(-256)^{1/4}}$ is not a real number since -256 is negative and $n = 4$ is even.

WARM-UP

1. Simplify

a) $196^{1/2}$

b) $729^{1/3}$

c) $81^{1/4}$

d) $1024^{1/5}$

2. Simplify the following expressions.

a) $(-729)^{1/3}$

b) $(216)^{1/3}$

c) $-216^{1/3}$

d) $(-625)^{1/4}$

e) $(625)^{1/4}$

f) $-625^{1/4}$

f. $\quad -256^{1/4} = -\left(\sqrt[4]{256}\right) = -4$ $\qquad\qquad$ $256 = 4^4$

Note $\qquad$ $-256^{1/4}$ $\qquad\quad \neq \qquad\quad$ $(-256)^{1/4}$

$\qquad\qquad\qquad\quad \downarrow \qquad\qquad\qquad\qquad\quad \downarrow$

$\qquad\qquad\qquad$ Base of the $\qquad\qquad$ Base of the

$\qquad\qquad\qquad$ exponent is 256 $\qquad$ exponent is −256

B. DEFINITION OF $a^{m/n}$

$a^{m/n}$ is defined so as to follow the general power rule of exponents.

$a^{m/n} = (a^m)^{1/n} = (a^{1/n})^m$, for all real a, and non-zero integers m, and n except when $a < 0$ and n is even.

We can also write $a^{m/n} = \sqrt[n]{a^m} = \left(\sqrt[n]{a}\right)^m$

Observe that, the denominator of the fractional exponent becomes the index of the radical.

WARM-UP

3. Simplify

a) $27^{2/3}$

b) $9^{3/2}$

c) $(-64)^{4/3}$

EXAMPLE 3 $\qquad$ Simplify:

$\qquad$ **a.** $8^{2/3}$ $\qquad$ **b.** $4^{3/2}$ $\qquad$ **c.** $(-27)^{4/3}$

$\qquad$ **d.** $a^{1/2} \cdot a^{2/3}$ $\quad$ **e.** $\left(a^{3/4}\right)^2$ $\quad$ **f.** $\left(2x^{4/3}y^{-2/3}\right)^3$

Solutions:

$\qquad$ **a.** $\quad 8^{2/3} = (8^2)^{1/3} = (64)^{1/3} = (2 \cdot 2 \cdot 2 \cdot 2 \cdot 2 \cdot 2)^{1/3}$

$\qquad\qquad\qquad\qquad\qquad = (4^3)^{1/3} = \sqrt[3]{4^3} = 4$

$\qquad$ **Alternatively,** $\quad 8^{2/3} = \left(8^{1/3}\right)^2 = \left(\sqrt[3]{8}\right)^2 = 2^2$

$\qquad\qquad\qquad\qquad\qquad\qquad\qquad\qquad = 4$

$\qquad$ **b.** $\quad 4^{3/2} = \left(4^3\right)^{1/2} = 64^{1/2} = \sqrt{64} = 8$

$\qquad$ **Alternatively,** $\quad 4^{3/2} = \left(4^{1/2}\right)^3$

$\qquad\qquad\qquad\qquad\qquad\qquad = \left(\sqrt{4}\right)^3 = 2^3 = 8$

$\qquad$ **c.** $\quad (-27)^{4/3} = [(-27)^4]^{1/3}$

$\qquad\qquad\qquad\qquad = [(-27)(-27)(-27)(-27)]^{1/3}$

$\qquad\qquad\qquad\qquad = (27 \cdot 27 \cdot 27 \cdot 27)^{1/3}$

$\qquad\qquad\qquad\qquad = \sqrt[3]{3^3 \cdot 3^3 \cdot 3^3 \cdot 3^3}$

$\qquad\qquad\qquad\qquad = \sqrt[3]{3^3} \cdot \sqrt[3]{3^3} \cdot \sqrt[3]{3^3} \cdot \sqrt[3]{3^3}$

$\qquad\qquad\qquad\qquad = 3 \cdot 3 \cdot 3 \cdot 3 = 81$

$\qquad$ **Alternatively,** $(-27)^{4/3} = [(-27)^{1/3}]^4 = \left(\sqrt[3]{-27}\right)^4$

$\qquad\qquad\qquad\qquad\qquad\qquad\qquad = (-3)^4 = 81$

Note: It is usually easier to take root first and then the power.

d. $a^{1/2} \cdot a^{2/3} = a^{1/2\,+\,2/3} = a^{7/6}$ $\quad a^m \cdot a^n = a^{m+n}$

e. $(a^{3/4})^2 = a^{(3/4 \cdot 2)} = a^{3/2}$ $\quad (a^m)^n = a^{m \cdot n}$

f. $(2x^{4/3}y^{-2/3})^3 = 2^3 (x^{4/3})^3 (y^{-2/3})^3$ $\quad (ab)^m = a^m b^m$

$\qquad = 2^3 \cdot x^{\left(\frac{4}{3} \cdot 3\right)} \cdot y^{\left(-\frac{2}{3} \cdot 3\right)}$ $\quad (a^m)^n = a^{mn}$

$\qquad = 8 \cdot x^4 \cdot y^{-2} = \dfrac{8x^4}{y^2}$ $\quad a^{-n} = \dfrac{1}{a^n}$

EXAMPLE 4   Simplify:

$$\textbf{a.}\quad \frac{4x^{2/3}\,y^{-1/3}}{12x^{-1/3}\,y^{2/3}} \qquad \textbf{b.}\quad \left(\frac{8x^{-2/3}\,p^{1/2}}{50x^{4/3}\,p^{-3/2}}\right)^{1/2}$$

$$\textbf{c.}\quad (x\,y^{p-q})^{p+q} \cdot (x\,y^{q+p})^{q-p}$$

Solutions:

a. $\dfrac{4x^{2/3}\,y^{-1/3}}{12x^{-1/3}\,y^{2/3}} = \dfrac{1 \cdot x^{2/3\,+\,1/3}}{3 \cdot y^{2/3\,+\,1/3}}$ $\quad \dfrac{4}{12} = \dfrac{1}{3},\ \dfrac{1}{x^{-1/3}} = x^{1/3},\ y^{-1/3} = \dfrac{1}{y^{1/3}}$

$\qquad = \dfrac{x^{3/3}}{3y^{3/3}} = \dfrac{x}{3y}$

b. $\left(\dfrac{8x^{-2/3}\,p^{1/2}}{50x^{4/3}\,p^{-3/2}}\right)^{1/2} = \left(\dfrac{4p^{1/2\,+\,3/2}}{25x^{4/3\,+\,2/3}}\right)^{1/2}$ $\quad \dfrac{8}{50} = \dfrac{4}{25},\ x^{-2/3} = \dfrac{1}{x^{2/3}},$

$\qquad\qquad\qquad\qquad\qquad\qquad\qquad \dfrac{1}{p^{-3/2}} = p^{3/2}$

$\qquad = \left(\dfrac{4p^2}{25x^2}\right)^{1/2}$ $\quad \dfrac{1}{2} + \dfrac{3}{2} = \dfrac{4}{2} = 2$

$\qquad\qquad\qquad\qquad \dfrac{4}{3} + \dfrac{2}{3} = \dfrac{6}{3} = 2$

$\qquad = \dfrac{4^{1/2} (p^2)^{1/2}}{25^{1/2} (x^2)^{1/2}} = \dfrac{2p}{5x}$

c. $(x\,y^{p-q})^{p+q} \cdot (x\,y^{q+p})^{q-p}$

$\qquad = x^{p+q}\, y^{(p-q)(p+q)} \cdot x^{q-p}\, y^{(q+p)(q-p)}$

$\qquad = \left(x^{p+q} \cdot x^{q-p}\right)\left(y^{p^2-q^2} \cdot y^{q^2-p^2}\right)$

$\qquad = x^{p+q+q-p} \cdot y^{p^2-q^2+q^2-p^2}$

$\qquad = x^{2q} \cdot y^0 = x^{2q}$

WARM-UP

d) $a^{2/3} \cdot a^{4/3}$

e) $(b^{3/6})^2$

f) $(3x^{4/6}\,y^{-1/3})^6$

4. Simplify

a) $\dfrac{24\,a^{5/4}\,b^{-1/3}}{60\,a^{-3/4}\,b^{5/3}}$

b) $\left(\dfrac{18\,m^{-2/5}\,n^{4/7}}{98\,m^{8/5}\,n^{-10/7}}\right)^{1/2}$

c) $\left(p^{x-y}\right)^{x+y} \cdot \left(q^{x+y}\right)^{y-x}$

Answers:

3. **a)** 9   **b)** 27   **c)** 256

$\quad$ **d)** a^2 **e)** b **f)** $\dfrac{729x^4}{y^2}$

4. **a)** $\dfrac{2a^2}{5b^2}$ **b)** $\dfrac{3n}{7m}$ **c)** $p^{x-y^2} \times q^{y^2-x^2}$

A. In exercises 1-18, write the expression in radical form and simplify.

1. $16^{1/2}$ 2. $64^{1/2}$ 3. $36^{1/2}$ 4. $27^{2/3}$

5. $8^{1/3}$ 6. $81^{1/4}$ 7. $-8^{1/3}$ 8. $-27^{1/3}$

9. $(-8)^{1/3}$ 10. $(-27)^{2/3}$ 11. $4^{5/2}$ 12. $25^{3/2}$ 13. $27^{-2/3}$

14. $(625)^{-3/4}$ 15. $121^{3/2}$ 16. $64^{2/3}$ 17. $(81)^{3/4}$ 18. $(-128)^{4/7}$

B. In exercises 19-50, simplify the expression. (Assume that all variables are positive).

19. $(8x)^{1/3}$ 20. $(27y)^{-1/3}$ 21. $(8x^2 y^{-1})^{-1/3}$ 22. $(16x^{-1}y^2)^{1/4}$ 23. $\left(16x^4\right)^{\frac{1}{4}}$

24. $\left(8x^3\right)^{-\frac{1}{3}}$ 25. $\left(16x^4 y^{-4}\right)^{-\frac{1}{4}}$ 26. $\left(27x^3 y^{-3}\right)^{\frac{1}{3}}$ 27. $\left(a^{\frac{3}{4}}b^{-\frac{5}{4}}\right)^4$ 28. $\left(3x^{\frac{1}{3}}y^{-\frac{4}{3}}\right)^3$

29. $\left(8x^{-3}y^6\right)^{\frac{1}{3}}$ 30. $\left(2x^{\frac{2}{5}}y^{-\frac{3}{5}}\right)^5$ 31. $\left(\dfrac{4p^3 q}{9pq}\right)^{1/2}$ 32. $\left(\dfrac{25x^5 y^2}{16xy^2}\right)^{1/2}$ 33. $\left(x^3 y^3\right)^{1/6}$

34. $\left(x^4 y^4\right)^{1/8}$ 35. $\dfrac{y^{3/4}\cdot y^{7/4}}{2y^{5/4}}$ 36. $\dfrac{x^{1/3}\cdot x^{6/3}}{3\,x^{4/3}}$ 37. $\dfrac{x^{3/5}\cdot x^{8/5}}{4\,x^{1/5}}$ 38. $\dfrac{x^{1/5}\cdot x^{9/5}}{x}$

39. $\dfrac{5x^{3/4}\cdot x^{-1/4}}{6x^{-1/2}}$ 40. $\dfrac{3x^{3/4}\cdot x^{5/6}}{4x^2}$ 41. $\dfrac{x^{2/5}\cdot x^{-7/5}}{x^{4/3}\cdot x^{-1/3}}$ 42. $\left(\dfrac{x^{3/4}\cdot x^{5/4}}{y^{5/2}\cdot y^{3/2}}\right)^{1/2}$ 43. $\left(\dfrac{x^6\, y^7}{y\, x^3}\right)^{1/3}$

44. $\left(\dfrac{2^3 x^6\, y^{-2}}{x^{-3}y}\right)^{\frac{1}{3}}$ 45. $\left(\dfrac{x^{8/3}\, y^{7/3}}{y^{-2/3}x^{2/3}}\right)$ 46. $\left(\dfrac{18\,x^{3/2}\cdot y^{3/2}}{50\,y^{7/2}\cdot x^{-5/2}}\right)^{1/2}$ 47. $\left(\dfrac{16\,x^{4/5}\cdot y^{5/2}}{54\,y^{-1/2}\cdot x^{1/5}}\right)^{1/3}$

48. $\left(\dfrac{8\,x^{6/5}\cdot y^{3/2}}{125\,y^{-5/2}\cdot x^{3/5}}\right)^{1/3}$ 49. $\left(x^{a+b}\right)^{a-b}\left(x^{b+c}\right)^{b-c}\left(x^{c+a}\right)^{c-a}$ 50. $\left(\alpha\, x^{a+b}\right)^{a-b}\left(\alpha\, x^{b+c}\right)^{b-c}\left(\alpha\, x^{c+a}\right)^{c-a}$

8.6 SOLVING EQUATIONS WITH RADICALS

To solve equations involving radicals we use the following *equality rule for exponents*.

If $a = b$ then $a^n = b^n$ for all integers n.

OBJECTIVES ▪▪▪▪

Upon completion of this section you will be able to solve equations with radicals.

SOLVING EQUATIONS WITH RADICALS

We solve equations with radicals using the following steps.

> **Step 1** Apply the properties of numbers and transfer terms so that one side of the equation contains only one radical.
>
> **Step 2** Raise both sides to a suitable power to remove this radical.
>
> Use $\left(\sqrt[n]{a}\right)^n = a$.
>
> **Step 3** Combine like terms.
>
> **Step 4** If the resulting equation still has a radical, repeat steps 1-3.
>
> **Step 5** Solve the equation obtained above.
>
> **Step 6** Check the solution obtained in step 5 by substituting the value in the *original equation*. For radical equations, checking is required because the process of raising to a power can induce extraneous values.

A solution obtained in step 5 which does not satisfy the original equation is called an **extraneous solution**.

The process is explained in the following examples.

EXAMPLE 1 Solve the equation $\sqrt{2x} = 5$.

Solution:

Step 1 Not needed.

Step 2 Square both sides. $\left(\sqrt{2x}\right)^2 = 5^2 \longrightarrow 2x = 25$

Step 3, 4 Not needed.

Step 5 Solve the equation. $x = \dfrac{25}{2}$.

Step 6 Check the solution: $\sqrt{2x} = 5$

$\sqrt{2 \cdot \dfrac{25}{2}} = 5$ or $\sqrt{25} = 5$ True

Therefore, $x = \dfrac{25}{2}$ is a solution.

2. Solve the equation

$$\sqrt{x+4} = 3$$

EXAMPLE 2   Solve the equation $\sqrt{x-3}=4$.

Solution:

• Square both sides

$$\left(\sqrt{x-3}\right)^2 = 4^2$$

$$x - 3 = 16 \longrightarrow x = 16 + 3 \longrightarrow x = 19$$

• *Check* the solution: $\sqrt{x-3} = 4$

$$\longrightarrow \sqrt{19-3} = 4 \longrightarrow \sqrt{16} = 4$$

$$\longrightarrow 4 = 4 \quad \text{True}$$

Therefore, $x = 19$ is a solution.

 We can solve equations with radicals using a calculator. See example 1 of 8.6 in Appendix B.

3. Solve the equation

$$q-\sqrt{q-2} = 2$$

EXAMPLE 3   Solve the equation $p - \sqrt{p-2}=4$

Solution:

• $p - 4 = \sqrt{p-2}$

• Square both sides.

$$(p - 4)^2 = \left(\sqrt{p-2}\right)^2$$

$$p^2 - 8p + 16 = p - 2 \qquad {\scriptstyle (a - b)^2 = a^2 - 2ab + b^2}$$

• $p^2 - 9p + 18 = 0$

• Solve the equation.

$$(p - 6)(p - 3) = 0$$

$$\longrightarrow \quad p - 6 = 0 \quad \text{or} \quad p - 3 = 0$$

$$\longrightarrow \quad p = 6 \quad \text{or} \quad p = 3$$

• *Check* the solution:

(i)   **For $p = 6$:** $p-\sqrt{p-2} = 4$

$$6-\sqrt{6-2}=4 \longrightarrow 6-\sqrt{4}=4$$

$$\longrightarrow 6 - 2 = 4$$

$$\longrightarrow 4 = 4 \qquad \text{True}$$

Therefore, **$p = 6$ is a solution.**

(ii)   **For $p = 3$:**

$$p-\sqrt{p-2} = 4$$

$$3-\sqrt{3-2}=4 \longrightarrow 3-\sqrt{1}=4 \longrightarrow 3 - 1 = 4$$

$$\longrightarrow 2 = 4 \qquad \text{Not True}$$

Therefore, **$p = 3$** is an ***extraneous solution***.

Thus **$p = 6$** is the only solution.

EXAMPLE 4   Solve the equation: $\sqrt{5x-1} - \sqrt{x+2} = 1$.

Solution:

- $\sqrt{5x-1} = 1 + \sqrt{x+2}$

- Square both sides.

$$\left(\sqrt{5x-1}\right)^2 = \left(1 + \sqrt{x+2}\right)^2 \qquad (a+b)^2 = a^2 + 2ab + b^2$$

$$5x - 1 = 1 + 2\sqrt{x+2} + \left(\sqrt{x+2}\right)^2$$

$$5x - 1 = 1 + 2\sqrt{x+2} + x + 2$$

- Simplify

- $5x - 1 = x + 3 + 2\sqrt{x+2}$

$$\longrightarrow \quad 4x - 4 = 2\sqrt{x+2}$$

$$\longrightarrow \quad 2x - 2 = \sqrt{x+2} \qquad \text{Divide both sides by 2.}$$

- The equation still contains a radical, so we repeat steps 1-3.

$$\sqrt{x+2} = 2x - 2 \qquad\qquad \textit{Step 1}$$

$$\left(\sqrt{x+2}\right)^2 = (2x-2)^2 \qquad\qquad \textit{Step 2}$$

$$(x+2) = 4x^2 - 8x + 4$$

$$4x^2 - 8x - x + 4 - 2 = 0$$

$$4x^2 - 9x + 2 = 0 \qquad\qquad \textit{Step 3}$$

- Solve the equation.

- $4x^2 - 9x + 2 = 0$

$$(x-2)(4x-1) = 0$$

$$\longrightarrow \qquad x - 2 = 0 \quad \text{or} \quad 4x - 1 = 0$$

$$\longrightarrow \qquad\qquad x = 2 \quad \text{or} \qquad x = \frac{1}{4}$$

- ***Check*** the solution: $\sqrt{5x-1} - \sqrt{x+2} = 1$

$x = 2$: $\sqrt{5(2)-1} - \sqrt{2+2} = 1 \longrightarrow \sqrt{9} - \sqrt{4} = 1$ True

Therefore, $x = 2$ is a solution.

$x = \dfrac{1}{4}$: $\sqrt{5\left(\dfrac{1}{4}\right) - 1} - \sqrt{\dfrac{1}{4} + 2} = 1$

$$\longrightarrow \sqrt{\frac{1}{4}} - \sqrt{\frac{9}{4}} = 1 \longrightarrow \frac{1}{2} - \frac{3}{2} = 1 \quad \text{Not true}$$

Therefore, $x = \dfrac{1}{4}$ is an extraneous solution.

Thus $x = 2$ is the only solution.

WARM-UP

4. Solve the equation:

$$\sqrt{4x-7} = 1 + \sqrt{2x}$$

Answers:

1. 5   **2.** 5   **3.** 2, 3

4. 8, 2

EXERCISE 8.6

In exercises 1-71, solve the equations.

1. $\sqrt{x} = 3$

2. $\sqrt{y} = 6$

3. $\sqrt{x} = 4$

4. $\sqrt{z} = 5$

5. $\sqrt{a} = 12$

6. $\sqrt{5x} = 5$

7. $\sqrt{4x} = 8$

8. $\sqrt{4a} + 5 = 2$

9. $\sqrt{3a} - 1 = 2$

10. $\sqrt{5a} + 3 = 5$

11. $-\sqrt{7a} + 4 = 3$

12. $\sqrt{x-3} = 5$

13. $\sqrt{y-5} = 0$

14. $\sqrt{2x-3} = 0$

15. $\sqrt{t+5} = -2$

16. $\sqrt{x-2} = -5$

17. $\sqrt{z} + 3 = 7$

18. $\sqrt{x} + 5 = 8$

19. $\sqrt{x} - 4 = 5$

20. $\sqrt{y} - 3 = 7$

21. $\sqrt{2x+1} = 7$

22. $\sqrt{3x-2} = 4$

23. $\sqrt{2x+3} = 2$

24. $\sqrt{3x-2} = 2$

25. $\sqrt{2x-3} = 1$

26. $\sqrt{3x-5} = 1$

27. $\sqrt{5y+2} = 0$

28. $0 = \sqrt{3x-9} - 6$

29. $\sqrt{t+8} = 5$

30. $\sqrt{x-6} = 2$

31. $\sqrt{x} - 3 = 1$

32. $3 + \sqrt{x} = 6$

33. $\sqrt{2x-2} = 2$

34. $x = \dfrac{\sqrt{18x-9}}{3}$

35. $x = \dfrac{\sqrt{16x-12}}{2}$

36. $\sqrt{x} + 2x = 1$

37. $\sqrt{24-5t} = 6-t$

38. $\sqrt{-t+2} = t-2$

39. $\sqrt{t+2} = 4-t$

40. $\sqrt{x+2} = \sqrt{4-x}$

41. $\sqrt{217-x} = x-7$

42. $\sqrt{-5x+24} = 6-x$

43. $x = \sqrt{2x-1}$

44. $\sqrt{2x+9} + x = 13$

45. $\sqrt{p+2} = p$

46. $\sqrt{x-3} = \sqrt{x} + 3$

47. $\sqrt{x} + \sqrt{3} = \sqrt{x+3}$

48. $2 + \sqrt{x} = \sqrt{2x+7}$

49. $\sqrt{6x+1} - 3\sqrt{x} = -1$

50. $\sqrt{6-x} = \sqrt{2x+3}$

51. $\sqrt{4x-2} = \sqrt{5x-3}$

52. $\sqrt{2x-3} = 2\sqrt{3x-2}$

53. $\sqrt{8x-4} = \sqrt{7x+2}$

54. $\sqrt{x+4} = \sqrt{2x+3}$

55. $\sqrt{x+2} = \sqrt{3x-4}$

56. $\sqrt{5x-8} = \sqrt{3x-4}$

57. $\sqrt{a^2-5a+6} = \sqrt{a^2-8a+9}$

58. $\sqrt{a^2-a+1} = \sqrt{a^2-3a+9}$

59. $\sqrt{x^2+2x-3} = \sqrt{x^2-3x+7}$

60. $\sqrt{2x^2-5x+3} = \sqrt{x^2-3x+11}$

61. $\sqrt{x+7} = \sqrt{x+4} - 3$

62. $\sqrt{13-x^2} = x+5$

63. $\sqrt{x-1} = 3 - \sqrt{x+2}$

64. $\sqrt{4x-3} + \sqrt{2x+3} = 6$

65. $\sqrt{8x+20} - \sqrt{7x+11} = 1$

66. $\sqrt{4-x} + \sqrt{x+9} = 5$

67. $\sqrt{2x-1} = 4 - \sqrt{x-4}$

68. $\sqrt{2x+9} = 3 + \sqrt{x-4}$

69. $\sqrt{3x+4} = \sqrt{2x+1} + 1$

70. $\sqrt{y+1} + \sqrt{2y-5} = 3$

71. $\sqrt{5x-1} - \sqrt{3x-2} = 1$

8.7 CHAPTER SUMMARY

FINDING ROOTS

1. If r is a real number and n is a positive integer such that $r = a^n$, then a is called the **nth root** of r.

1.
- $81 = (-3)^4 \rightarrow -3$ is a fourth root of 81.
- $32 = 2^5 \rightarrow 2$ is a fifth root of 32.

2. No real number can be an even root of a negative real number.

2.
- There is no real number a such that $a^4 = -16$.
- $\sqrt{-16}$ is not a real number.

3. For a positive rational number r:
- $\sqrt{r}$ is rational if r is a perfect square.
- $\sqrt{r}$ is irrational if r is not a perfect square.

3.
- $\sqrt{16} = 4$, $\sqrt{\dfrac{9}{16}} = \dfrac{3}{4}$ are rational numbers.
- $\sqrt{17}$, $\sqrt{\dfrac{5}{9}}$, are irrational numbers.

4. Each real number has exactly one real cube root.

4.
- $\sqrt[3]{8} = 2$ $\sqrt[3]{-27} = -3$

5. For a positive rational number r :
- $\sqrt[3]{r}$ is rational if r is a perfect cube.
- $\sqrt[3]{r}$ is irrational if r is not a perfect cube.

5.
- $\sqrt[3]{-8} = -2$, $\sqrt[3]{\dfrac{27}{64}} = \dfrac{3}{4}$ are rational numbers.
- $\sqrt[3]{7}$, $\sqrt[3]{\dfrac{5}{11}}$ are irrational numbers.

MULTIPLICATION AND DIVISION OF RADICALS

Product rule for Radicals

6. If x and y are non-negative real numbers, then $\sqrt{x} \cdot \sqrt{y} = \sqrt{xy}$.

6.
- $\sqrt{2} \cdot \sqrt{3} = \sqrt{6}$
- $\sqrt{2} \cdot \sqrt{18} = \sqrt{36} = 6$

7. If $\sqrt[n]{x}$ and $\sqrt[n]{y}$ are real, then $\sqrt[n]{x} \cdot \sqrt[n]{y} = \sqrt[n]{xy}$

7.
- $\sqrt[3]{5} \cdot \sqrt[3]{4} = \sqrt[3]{20}$,
- $\sqrt[5]{8} \cdot \sqrt[5]{-4} = \sqrt[5]{-32} = -2$

Quotient Rule for Radicals

8. If x and y are non-negative real numbers and y is non-zero then $\dfrac{\sqrt{x}}{\sqrt{y}} = \sqrt{\dfrac{x}{y}}$.

8.
- $\dfrac{\sqrt{18}}{\sqrt{2}} = \sqrt{\dfrac{18}{2}} = \sqrt{9} = 3$
- $\sqrt{\dfrac{9}{16}} = \dfrac{\sqrt{9}}{\sqrt{16}} = \dfrac{3}{4}$

9. If $\sqrt[n]{x}$ and $\sqrt[n]{y}$ are real and y is non-zero then $\dfrac{\sqrt[n]{x}}{\sqrt[n]{y}} = \sqrt[n]{\dfrac{x}{y}}$.

9.
- $\dfrac{\sqrt[5]{12}}{\sqrt[5]{3}} = \sqrt[5]{\dfrac{12}{3}} = \sqrt[5]{4}$

10. Simplify $\sqrt[3]{120}$

- $120 = 2 \cdot 2 \cdot 2 \cdot 3 \cdot 5$

- $\sqrt[3]{120} = \sqrt[3]{2^3} \cdot \sqrt[3]{3} \cdot \sqrt[3]{5}$

$$= 2\sqrt[3]{3} \cdot \sqrt[3]{5}$$

$$= 2\sqrt[3]{15}$$

Alternatively:

$$\sqrt[3]{120} = \sqrt[3]{8 \cdot 15}$$

$$= \sqrt[3]{8} \cdot \sqrt[3]{15} = 2\sqrt[3]{15}$$

11.
- $3\sqrt{5} + 4\sqrt{5} = (3+4)\sqrt{5} = 7\sqrt{5}$

- $2\sqrt{27} + 5\sqrt{3} = 2(3\sqrt{3}) + 5\sqrt{3}$

$$= 6\sqrt{3} + 5\sqrt{3}$$

$$= (6+5)\sqrt{3} = 11\sqrt{3}$$

12.
- $5\sqrt{3} - 7\sqrt{3} = (5-7)\sqrt{3}$

$$= -2\sqrt{3}$$

- $\sqrt{18} - \sqrt{8} = 3\sqrt{2} - 2\sqrt{2} = \sqrt{2}$

13. $\sqrt{2} + \sqrt{3}$ or $3\sqrt{5} - 2\sqrt{7}$ cannot be combined.

14.
- $\dfrac{3}{\sqrt{5}} = \dfrac{3}{\sqrt{5}} \cdot \dfrac{\sqrt{5}}{\sqrt{5}} = \dfrac{3\sqrt{5}}{5}$

- $\dfrac{5x}{\sqrt[3]{y}} = \dfrac{5x \cdot \sqrt[3]{y^2}}{\sqrt[3]{y} \cdot \sqrt[3]{y^2}} = \dfrac{5x\sqrt[3]{y^2}}{y}$

15.
- The conjugate of $2 + 5\sqrt{3}$ is $2 - 5\sqrt{3}$
- The conjugate of $1 - \sqrt{2}$ is $1 + \sqrt{2}$

16. Rationalize $\dfrac{4 + 2\sqrt{3}}{3 - \sqrt{5}}$.

The conjugate of $3 - \sqrt{5} = 3 + \sqrt{5}$.

$$\frac{4 + 2\sqrt{3}}{3 - \sqrt{5}} = \frac{4 + 2\sqrt{3}}{3 - \sqrt{5}} \cdot \frac{3 + \sqrt{5}}{3 + \sqrt{5}}$$

Simplifying Radicals

10. Steps to simplify radicals

Step **1** Write the prime factorization of the radicand.

Step **2** Apply the product rule.

Step **3** Use $\sqrt[n]{a^n} = \begin{cases} |a| \text{ if } n \text{ is even} \\ a \text{ if } n \text{ is odd} \end{cases}$

ADDITION AND SUBTRACTION OF RADICALS

11. Addition of Radicals

We add *like* radicals by using the distributive property.

12. Subtraction of Radicals

We subtract *like* radicals by using the distributive property.

13. Unlike radicals cannot be combined.

RATIONALIZING THE DENOMINATOR

14. A radical expression is said to be rationalized when its denominator contains no radicals.

15. Two binomials $a + \sqrt{b}$ and $a - \sqrt{b}$, which differ only in the sign of the radical term, are called conjugates of each other.

16. To rationalize an expression whose denominator is of the form $a + c\sqrt{d}$ or $a\sqrt{b} + c\sqrt{d}$, we multiply the numerator and the denominator by the conjugate of the denominator and simplify.

$$= \frac{(4+2\sqrt{3})(3+\sqrt{5})}{(3-\sqrt{5})(3+\sqrt{5})}$$

$$= \frac{12+4\sqrt{5}+6\sqrt{3}+(2\sqrt{3})\sqrt{5}}{(3)^2-(\sqrt{5})^2}$$

$$= \frac{12+4\sqrt{5}+6\sqrt{3}+2\sqrt{15}}{9-5}$$

$$= \frac{6+2\sqrt{5}+3\sqrt{3}+\sqrt{15}}{2}$$

FRACTIONAL EXPONENTS

17. For any non-negative real number a and positive integer n, the principal root of $\sqrt[n]{a}$ **is written as** $a^{1/n}$.

17. • $\sqrt[3]{5} = 5^{\frac{1}{3}}$ • $\sqrt{7} = 7^{\frac{1}{2}}$

18. $a^{\frac{m}{n}} = \sqrt[n]{a^m} = \left(\sqrt[n]{a}\right)^m$ for all a, m, and n except when n is even and $a < 0$.

18. • $(27)^{2/3} = \left(\sqrt[3]{27}\right)^2 = 3^2 = 9$

EQUATIONS WITH RADICALS

19. To solve an equation with radicals, we use the following steps:

Step **1** Apply the properties of numbers and transfer terms so that **at least one side** of the equation contains **only one radical**.

Step **2** Raise both sides to a suitable power to remove this radical. Use $\left(\sqrt[n]{a}\right)^n = a$

Step **3** Combine like terms

Step **4** If the resulting equation still has a radical term, repeat steps 1 - 3.

Step **5** Solve the equation obtained above.

Step **6** Check all solutions obtained in Step 5 by substituting the values into the original equation.

A solution which does not satisfy the original equation is called an **extraneous solution**.

19. Solve $\sqrt{x+8} - x = 2$.

$$\sqrt{x+8} - x = 2 \;\to\; \sqrt{x+8} = 2 + x$$

Since the left hand side is a square root, we square both sides.

$$\left(\sqrt{x+8}\right)^2 = (2+x)^2 \;\to\; x+8 = 4 + 4x + x^2$$

$$x^2 + 3x - 4 = 0$$

$$x^2 + 3x - 4 = 0 \;\to\; (x+4)(x-1) = 0$$
$$\to\; x = -4 \text{ or } x = 1$$

Verify that $x = 1$ is a solution of the original equation but $x = -4$ is not a solution.

In the example 19 above, $x = -4$ is an extraneous solution.

8.8 REVIEW EXERCISES

In exercises 1-6, simplify the expression.

1. $\sqrt{25}$ **2.** $\sqrt{81}$ **3.** $\sqrt{-\dfrac{1}{16}}$ **4.** $\sqrt{-\dfrac{49}{4}}$ **5.** $\sqrt[3]{729}$ **6.** $\sqrt[4]{1296}$

In exercises 7-12, identify the given number as rational, irrational or non-real.

7. $\sqrt{\dfrac{48}{81}}$ **8.** $\sqrt{\dfrac{36}{15}}$ **9.** $\sqrt{-49}$ **10.** $\sqrt[3]{-125}$ **11.** $\sqrt{36}$ **12.** $\sqrt{\dfrac{1}{25}}$

13. **Find the square roots.** **a)** 144 **b)** $\dfrac{81}{16}$

14. **Find the square roots.** **a)** 169 **b)** $\dfrac{625}{81}$

15. One of the sides of a right triangle is 9 cm and its hypotenuse is 11 cm. Find the length of the third side.

16. A ladder 25 m long reaches a window of a house 20 m above the ground. Determine the distance of the foot of the ladder from the house.

17. A boat is being pulled into dock with a rope attached to its front. When the boat is 6 feet from the dock, the end of the rope is 3 feet above the dock. Approximate the length of the extended rope to the hundredths place.

18. A man goes 10 m due east and then 30 m due north. Find his distance from the starting point.

In exercises 19-34, simplify the expression. (Assume all variables are positive)

19. $\sqrt{5} \cdot \sqrt{6}$ **20.** $\sqrt{7} \cdot \sqrt{3}$ **21.** $\sqrt[3]{16} \cdot \sqrt[3]{-4}$ **22.** $\sqrt[4]{32} \cdot \sqrt[4]{8}$

23. $\sqrt[3]{x^2 y} \cdot \sqrt[3]{xy^2}$ **24.** $\sqrt[4]{x^3 y^2} \cdot \sqrt[4]{x^5 y^2}$ **25.** $\sqrt[3]{3r^2 s} \cdot \sqrt[3]{9r^3 s^4}$ **26.** $\sqrt{2x^2 y} \cdot \sqrt{8x^4 y^3}$

27. $\dfrac{\sqrt[3]{48}}{\sqrt[3]{-6}}$ **28.** $\dfrac{\sqrt{72}}{\sqrt{2}}$ **29.** $\dfrac{\sqrt[4]{6x^2 y}}{\sqrt[4]{96x^6 y^9}}$ **30.** $\dfrac{\sqrt[3]{12xy^7}}{\sqrt[3]{96x^4 y}}$

31. $\sqrt{3ab}\,\sqrt{6a}$ **32.** $\sqrt{4x^3 y} \cdot \sqrt{8xy^2}$ **33.** $\dfrac{\sqrt{3ab^2}}{\sqrt{12a}}$ **34.** $\dfrac{\sqrt{5x^2 y}}{\sqrt{20y}}$

In exercises 35-44, perform the indicated operations and simplify as far as possible.

35. $3\sqrt{2} + 5\sqrt{3} - 4\sqrt{18}$ **36.** $\sqrt{8} + \sqrt{32} - \sqrt{2}$ **37.** $\left(2\sqrt{2} - \sqrt{3}\right)\left(2\sqrt{2} + \sqrt{3}\right)$

38. $\left(5\sqrt{3} + \sqrt{2}\right)\left(5\sqrt{3} - \sqrt{2}\right)$ **39.** $\left(x - \sqrt{2y}\right)^2$ **40.** $\left(x + \sqrt{3y}\right)^2$

41. $\left(x + \sqrt{2y}\right)^2$ **42.** $\left(2y - \sqrt{3z}\right)^2$ **43.** $\left(\sqrt{x} - \sqrt{3}\right)\left(2\sqrt{x} + \sqrt{7}\right)$

44. $\left(\sqrt{a} + \sqrt{2}\right)\left(3\sqrt{a} - \sqrt{3}\right)$

In exercise 45-62, rationalize the denominator and simplify.

45. $\dfrac{7}{\sqrt{6}}$

46. $\dfrac{5}{\sqrt{7}}$

47. $\dfrac{3x}{4\sqrt{x}}$; $x > 0$

48. $\dfrac{3x}{\sqrt{4a}}$; $a > 0$

49. $\dfrac{5}{\sqrt[3]{4}}$

50. $\dfrac{7}{\sqrt[3]{9}}$

51. $\dfrac{5}{3+\sqrt{5}}$

52. $\dfrac{3}{\sqrt{3}+2}$

53. $\dfrac{2+\sqrt{5}}{4-\sqrt{3}}$

54. $\dfrac{4-\sqrt{3}}{4+\sqrt{3}}$

55. $\dfrac{\sqrt{5}-\sqrt{3}}{\sqrt{5}+\sqrt{3}}$

56. $\dfrac{\sqrt{7}+\sqrt{5}}{\sqrt{7}-\sqrt{5}}$

57. $\dfrac{2\sqrt{a}+\sqrt{b}}{\sqrt{a}-\sqrt{b}}$;

$a \neq b; a, b > 0$

58. $\dfrac{3\sqrt{x}-\sqrt{y}}{\sqrt{x}-\sqrt{y}}$;

$x \neq y; x, y > 0$

59. $\sqrt{\dfrac{5p^3}{4p^5}}$

60. $\sqrt{\dfrac{25x^5}{16y^3}}$

61. $\dfrac{\sqrt{3a}}{\sqrt{a}+\sqrt{3}}$; $a > 0$

62. $\dfrac{\sqrt{2x}}{\sqrt{x}+\sqrt{2}}$; $x > 0$

In exercises 63-68, simplify the expression.

63. $25^{1/2}$

64. $49^{1/2}$

65. $(-27)^{1/3}$

66. $(-64)^{1/3}$

67. $(25)^{3/2}$

68. $(8)^{2/3}$

In exercises 69-72, simplify the expression and write your answer in terms of positive exponents only.

69. $(8x^2)^{1/3}$

70. $(125x^3)^{1/3}$

71. $(4a^{-2}b)^{-3/2}$

72. $(8xy^{-3})^{2/3}$

In exercises 73-78, solve the equation.

73. $\sqrt{2y-3} = 3$

74. $\sqrt{3x+2} = 5$

75. $\sqrt{x-2}+4 = x$

76. $\sqrt{x+4}-x+2 = 0$

77. $\sqrt{p-2}+3 = \sqrt{p+13}$

78. $\sqrt{x+1}+\sqrt{x+3} = 4$

79. The sum of two numbers is 11. The smaller number is the square root of one more than the greater number. Find the numbers.

80. The sum of the squares of two numbers is 130. The sum of the smaller number and twice the larger number is 25. Determine the numbers.

[*Hint:* Let smaller of the two numbers be x i.e. $x^2 + (\text{larger number})^2 = 130 \Rightarrow \text{larger number} = \sqrt{130 - x^2}$]

81. The radius r of a circle is given by the formula $r = \sqrt{\dfrac{A}{\pi}}$, where A is the area measure of the circle. For a circle with radius 3 inches, find the area measure of the circle rounded to three places of decimal.

[π is an irrational number. The value of π approximated to three places of decimal is 3.142. Use your calculator to find the approximation of π to different number of decimal places.]

8.9 SELF TEST

Note : Assume that all variables represent positive real numbers.

In exercises 1-20, simplify.

1. $\sqrt{169}$

2. $\sqrt{289}$

3. $\sqrt[3]{-343}$

4. $\sqrt[5]{-1024}$

5. $\sqrt{27x^2}$

6. $\sqrt{125x^4}$

7. $\sqrt{\dfrac{25}{81}}$

8. $\sqrt[3]{\dfrac{-125}{64}}$

9. $\sqrt[5]{-8} \cdot \sqrt[5]{16}$

10. $\sqrt[3]{-27} \cdot \sqrt[3]{64}$

11. $\sqrt[4]{256x^5y^{11}} \cdot \sqrt[4]{48x^6y^2}$

12. $\sqrt{196x^3} \cdot \sqrt{50xy^5}$

13. $3\sqrt{3} + \sqrt{12} - \sqrt{27}$

14. $3\sqrt{2} - \sqrt{8} + \sqrt{32}$

15. $3\sqrt{27p} - 2\sqrt{48p} + 5\sqrt{75}$

16. $5\sqrt{64x} - 3\sqrt{25x} + 3\sqrt{27}$

17. $\left(\sqrt{5} - 2\sqrt{3}\right)\left(\sqrt{5} + 2\sqrt{3}\right)$

18. $\left(\sqrt{8} + 3\sqrt{2}\right)\left(\sqrt{8} - 3\sqrt{2}\right)$

19. $\left(\sqrt{2y} + 7\right)\left(\sqrt{3y} - 7\right)$

20. $\left(\sqrt{5x} - 3\right)\left(\sqrt{3x} + 3\right)$

In exercises 21-26, rationalize and simplify.

21. $\dfrac{\sqrt{2}}{3 - \sqrt{5}}$

22. $\dfrac{\sqrt{5}}{9 - \sqrt{7}}$

23. $\dfrac{3\sqrt{2} + \sqrt{3}}{2\sqrt{2} - 3\sqrt{3}}$

24. $\dfrac{5\sqrt{3} + \sqrt{2}}{\sqrt{3} - \sqrt{2}}$

25. $\dfrac{5\sqrt{x} + 3\sqrt{y}}{5\sqrt{x} - 3\sqrt{y}}$

26. $\dfrac{3\sqrt{y} - 2\sqrt{x}}{3\sqrt{y} + 2\sqrt{x}}$

In exercises 27-30, solve the equation.

27. $\sqrt{x-3} = 1 - \sqrt{x}$

28. $6\sqrt{a} - 3 = a + 2$

29. $\sqrt{25 - x^2} + 1 = x$

30. $\sqrt{x+2} + 1 = \sqrt{x}$

Solution of Quadratic Equations

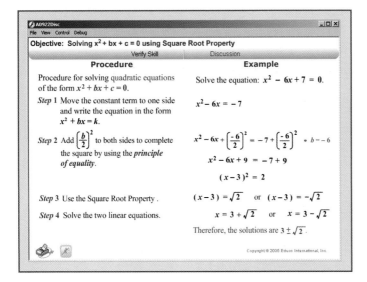

Objective: Solving $x^2 + bx + c = 0$ using Square Root Property

Verify Skill		Discussion

Procedure | **Example**

Procedure for solving quadratic equations of the form $x^2 + bx + c = 0$.

Solve the equation: $x^2 - 6x + 7 = 0$.

Step 1 Move the constant term to one side and write the equation in the form $x^2 + bx = k$.

$x^2 - 6x = -7$

Step 2 Add $\left(\dfrac{b}{2}\right)^2$ to both sides to complete the square by using the *principle of equality*.

$x^2 - 6x + \left(\dfrac{-6}{2}\right)^2 = -7 + \left(\dfrac{-6}{2}\right)^2$ $\bullet$ $b = -6$

$x^2 - 6x + 9 = -7 + 9$

$(x - 3)^2 = 2$

Step 3 Use the Square Root Property .

$(x - 3) = \sqrt{2}$ or $(x - 3) = -\sqrt{2}$

Step 4 Solve the two linear equations.

$x = 3 + \sqrt{2}$ or $x = 3 - \sqrt{2}$

Therefore, the solutions are $3 \pm \sqrt{2}$.

Copyright © 2005 Educo International, Inc.

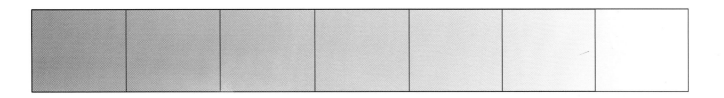

9

SOLUTION OF QUADRATIC EQUATIONS

In Chapter 6 we learned how to solve quadratic equations by factoring. In this chapter we will learn how to solve a quadratic equation by other methods that are applicable even when the quadratic expression is not factorable. These methods are completing the square, the quadratic formula, and graphing quadratic functions. Basic to all these methods is the **square root property** of equations discussed below in Section 9.1.

- Recall, all quadratic equations can be written as $ax^2 + bx + c = 0$, where a, b, and c are real numbers and $a \neq 0$.

- A quadratic equation always has two solutions. The two solutions can be rational numbers (integers or fractions), or irrational numbers, or numbers that are not real.

- Numbers that are not real are called complex numbers. Such numbers are beyond the scope of this text. Therefore, quadratic equations with complex number solutions will not be discussed in this chapter. One simple example of such an equation is $x^2 + 1 = 0$:

$$x^2 + 1 = 0 \quad \Rightarrow \quad x^2 = -1.$$

  This equation does not have any real number solution because there is no real number whose square is -1.

- Quadratic equations whose solutions are rational numbers can be easily solved by factoring and using zero factor property, as discussed in Chapter 6, and revisited below.

  Zero factor property states that,

$$
\begin{aligned}
a \cdot b = 0 \quad &\longrightarrow \quad a = 0 \quad \text{or} \quad b = 0 \\
(x - 2)(x - 3) = 0 \quad &\longrightarrow \quad x - 2 = 0 \quad \text{or} \quad x - 3 = 0 \\
&\longrightarrow \quad x = \mathbf{2} \quad \text{or} \quad x = \mathbf{3} \\
x^2 - 7x + 12 = 0 \quad &\longrightarrow \quad (x - 3)(x - 4) = 0 \\
&\longrightarrow \quad x - 3 = 0 \quad \text{or} \quad x - 4 = 0 \\
&\longrightarrow \quad x = \mathbf{3} \quad \text{or} \quad x = \mathbf{4} \\
6x^2 + 5x - 4 = 0 \quad &\longrightarrow \quad (2x - 1)(3x + 4) = 0 \\
&\longrightarrow \quad 2x - 1 = 0 \quad \text{or} \quad 3x + 4 = 0 \\
&\longrightarrow \quad x = \frac{\mathbf{1}}{\mathbf{2}} \quad \text{or} \quad x = -\frac{\mathbf{4}}{\mathbf{3}}
\end{aligned}
$$

- In this chapter, we will discuss the methods that can be used to solve any quadratic equation having real number solutions; Integers, Fractions, or even Irrational numbers. This chapter is divided into four sections:

  9.1 *Square Root Property;*

  9.2 *Solution by Completing the Square;*

  9.3 *Solution using The Quadratic Formula; and*

  9.4 *Solution by Graphing.*

9.1 SQUARE ROOT PROPERTY

In this section we use the square root property to solve certain quadratic equations. Recall that a quadratic equation can always be written in the form $ax^2 + bx + c = 0$, where a, b, c are real numbers, and $a \neq 0$.

SQUARE ROOT PROPERTY

Recall that we used the addition and multiplication properties of equality to solve linear equations. The **square root property** will be used to solve quadratic equations.

For example if $x^2 = 4$ then $x = +\sqrt{4}$ or $x = -\sqrt{4}$ which means that $x = +2$ or $x = -2$. Note that there are two solutions. These solutions can also be written as $x = \pm 2$. This short hand form of the solution is read as "x is equal to plus or minus two".

> **Square Root Property:**
>
> If b is a positive number then $a^2 = b$ implies $a = \sqrt{b}$ or $a = -\sqrt{b}$.

Note: Not all quadratic equations have real number solutions. For instance, $x^2 = -9$ has no real solution because this would imply that there is a real number x, such that $x^2 = -9$. Keep this possibility in mind as you complete the exercises in this section.

WARM-UP

1. Use the square root property to solve the following equations.

a) $x^2 = 64$

b) $x^2 - 9 = 0$

EXAMPLE 1 Use the square root property to solve the following equations.

a. $x^2 = 9$ b. $x^2 - 27 = 0$ c. $9x^2 = 36$
d. $x^2 = -5$ e. $5x^2 - 34 = 26$

Solutions:

a. $x^2 = 9$ $x = \sqrt{9}$ or $-\sqrt{9}$ Square root property.

$x = 3$ or -3

Therefore, the solutions of the equation $x^2 = 9$ are $x = \pm 3$.

b. $x^2 - 27 = 0$

$x^2 = 27$

$x = \sqrt{27}$ or $-\sqrt{27}$ Square root property.

$x = 3\sqrt{3}$ or $-3\sqrt{3}$

Therefore, the solutions of the equation $x^2 = 27$ are

$x = \pm 3\sqrt{3}$.

c. $9x^2 = 36$

$\qquad x^2 = \dfrac{36}{9}$

$\qquad x^2 = 4$ Square root property.

$\qquad x = \sqrt{4}$ or $x = -\sqrt{4}$

$\qquad x = 2$ or -2

Hence, the solutions of the equation $9x^2 = 36$ are $x = \pm 2$.

d. $x^2 = -5$

Since -5 is a **negative number, the square root property cannot be applied.** In fact, we know that there is no real number whose square is negative. Therefore, $x^2 = -5$ has no real solution.

e. $5x^2 - 34 = 26$

$\qquad 5x^2 = 26 + 34$

$\qquad 5x^2 = 60$

$\qquad x^2 = \dfrac{60}{5}$

$\qquad x^2 = 12$

$\qquad x = \sqrt{12} = \mathbf{2\sqrt{3}}$ or $x = -\sqrt{12} = \mathbf{-2\sqrt{3}}$

Therefore, the solutions of the equation $5x^2 - 34 = 26$ are $x = \pm\mathbf{2\sqrt{3}}$.

EXAMPLE 2   Solve the following equations.

$\qquad$ **a.** $(x + 1)^2 = 25$ $\qquad$ **b.** $(2y - 3)^2 = 45$

$\qquad$ **c.** $(3x - 1)^2 = -1$ $\qquad$ **d.** $(3t - 5)^2 + 6 = 8$

Solutions:

a.   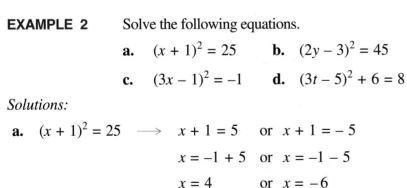 $(x + 1)^2 = 25 \longrightarrow \quad x + 1 = 5 \quad$ or $\quad x + 1 = -5$

$\qquad\qquad\qquad\qquad\qquad x = -1 + 5 \quad$ or $\quad x = -1 - 5$

$\qquad\qquad\qquad\qquad\qquad x = 4 \qquad\qquad$ or $\quad x = -6$

Therefore, the solutions are $x = \mathbf{4}$ and $x = -\mathbf{6}$.

Check: $\qquad\qquad x = 4 \qquad\qquad\qquad\qquad x = -6$

$\qquad\qquad\quad (\mathbf{4} + 1)^2 = 25 \qquad\qquad (-6 + 1)^2 = 25$

$\qquad\qquad\qquad\quad 5^2 = 25 \qquad\qquad\qquad (-5)^2 = 25$

$\qquad\qquad\qquad 25 = 25$ True $\qquad\qquad 25 = 25$ True

---

c) $6x^2 = 54$

d) $x^2 = -6$

e) $4x^2 - 46 = 54$

2.   Solve the following equations.

$\quad$ a) $(x + 2)^2 = 49$

---

b) $(2y + 3)^2 = 1$

c) $(3x + 2)^2 = -9$

d) $(4t - 7)^2 - 6 = 4$

b. $(2y - 3)^2 = 45$

$2y - 3 = +\sqrt{45}$ or $2y - 3 = -\sqrt{45}$ $45 = 3\sqrt{5}$

$2y = 3 + 3\sqrt{5}$ or $2y = 3 - 3\sqrt{5}$

$y = \dfrac{3 + 3\sqrt{5}}{2}$ or $y = \dfrac{3 - 3\sqrt{5}}{2}$

Therefore, the solutions of the equation are $y = \dfrac{3 \pm 3\sqrt{5}}{2}$.

c. $(3x - 1)^2 = -1$

Since -1 is a negative number, the square root property cannot be applied. $(3x - 1)^2 = -1$ has **no real solution**.

d. $(3t - 5)^2 + 6 = 8$

$(3t - 5)^2 = 8 - 6 = 2$

$3t - 5 = \sqrt{2}$ or $3t - 5 = -\sqrt{2}$

$3t = 5 + \sqrt{2}$ or $3t = 5 - \sqrt{2}$

$t = \dfrac{5 + \sqrt{2}}{3}$ or $t = \dfrac{5 - \sqrt{2}}{3}$

Therefore, the solutions of the equation are $t = \dfrac{5 \pm \sqrt{2}}{3}$.

Answers:

1. **a)** $8, -8$ **b)** $3, -3$
    c) $3, -3$ **d)** No real solution
    e) $5, -5$

2. **a)** $5, -9$ **b)** $-1, -2$
    c) No real solution
    d) $\dfrac{7 + \sqrt{10}}{4}, \dfrac{7 - \sqrt{10}}{4}$

EXERCISE 9.1

In exercises 1-75, solve the equation.

1. $x^2 = 25$

2. $y^2 = 64$

3. $x^2 = 81$

4. $y^2 = 625$

5. $x^2 = 98$

6. $y^2 = 72$

7. $y^2 = 44$

8. $x^2 = 99$

9. $3a^2 = 27$

10. $4x^2 = 64$

11. $-5x^2 = -25$

12. $15x^2 = -60$

13. $x^2 + 2 = 6$

14. $y^2 - 2 = 18$

15. $p^2 - 10 = 17$

16. $z^2 - 5 = 20$

17. $3t^2 - 5 = 10$

18. $4x^2 + 8 = 24$

19. $4x^2 + 3 = 15$

20. $3x^2 - 4 = 71$

21. $(3y - 1)^2 = 4$

22. $(2x + 1)^2 = 9$

23. $(2m + 5)^2 = 8$

24. $(3x - 4)^2 = 10$

25. $(5x + 1)^2 = 25$

26. $(5x - 2)^2 = 16$

27. $(7x - 1)^2 = 4$

28. $(6x + 5)^2 = 9$

29. $(6x - 7)^2 = 7$

30. $(2x - 5)^2 = 0$

31. $3(2x - 1)^2 = 24$

32. $2(3y + 1)^2 = 16$

33. $(4p - 1)^2 + 6 = 10$

34. $(5x + 1)^2 - 7 = 13$

35. $(2t + 7)^2 - 6 = 6$

36. $(7 - 2x)^2 + 1 = 13$ **37.** $(2y - 3)^2 - 1 = 8$ **38.** $-(2x + 3)^2 + 6 = 7$ **39.** $(6x - 3)^2 - 2 = 7$

40. $-(5x + 4)^2 + 3 = -13$ **41.** $(3 - 5z)^2 = 18$ **42.** $(2 - 3x)^2 = 8$ **43.** $(5t - 3)^2 + 5 = 11$

44. $(2t + 7)^2 + 11 = 12$ **45.** $x^2 = -1$ **46.** $2x^2 + 3 = 0$ **47.** $(x - 2)^2 = -3$

48. $(2x + 3)^2 = -1$ **49.** $(5x - 6)^2 = -4$ **50.** $\left(5x - \dfrac{2}{3}\right)^2 + \dfrac{9}{4} = 1$ **51.** $5x^2 + 13 = 4$

52. $(3x + 5)^2 + 13 = 7$ **53.** $(2x + 1)^2 = -4$ **54.** $2(3y - 1)^2 = -5$ **55.** $(3x + 5)^2 + 4 = -4$

56. $(4 - 2x)^2 + 6 = 4$ **57.** $(5 - 6y)^2 + 3 = 1$ **58.** $(3x + 1)^2 + \dfrac{7}{3} = \dfrac{2}{3}$ **59.** $5\left(2x - \dfrac{1}{5}\right)^2 = 20$

60. $4\left(3x - \dfrac{1}{4}\right)^2 = 32$ **61.** $3\left(x - \dfrac{1}{3}\right)^2 = 15$ **62.** $\dfrac{2}{9}\left(2x + \dfrac{1}{4}\right)^2 = \dfrac{1}{2}$ **63.** $4\left(y - \dfrac{2}{3}\right)^2 = 2$

64. $2\left(2x + \dfrac{1}{3}\right)^2 = 7$ **65.** $\dfrac{1}{4}(x - 2)^2 = 3$ **66.** $\dfrac{1}{4}(x - 2)^2 - \dfrac{1}{5} = 0$ **67.** $3\left(x - \dfrac{2}{3}\right)^2 = \dfrac{1}{4}$

68. $\left(3x - \dfrac{1}{4}\right)^2 = \dfrac{9}{25}$ **69.** $\left(5x - \dfrac{1}{5}\right)^2 = \dfrac{4}{9}$ **70.** $\left(7x + \dfrac{2}{3}\right)^2 = \dfrac{16}{25}$ **71.** $\left(2t + \dfrac{3}{2}\right)^2 = \dfrac{4}{49}$

72. $\left(3t - \dfrac{1}{2}\right)^2 = \dfrac{4}{25}$ **73.** $\left(t + \dfrac{1}{2}\right)^2 = \dfrac{2}{9}$ **74.** $\left(t - \dfrac{2}{3}\right)^2 = \dfrac{25}{36}$ **75.** $\left(2t + \dfrac{3}{4}\right)^2 + \dfrac{11}{16} = \dfrac{15}{16}$

9.2 SOLUTION BY COMPLETING THE SQUARE

We used the Square Root Property to solve any equation of the form $a^2 = b$. It is possible to write any quadratic equation in the form $a^2 = b$. This process is called *completing the square*.

The basic steps in this process are explained below.

Before we describe the steps, recall the results of special products we discussed in Chapter 5.

$(x - 2)^2 = x^2 - 4x + 4$

$(x + 3)^2 = x^2 + 6x + 9$

$(x + 7)^2 = x^2 + 14x + 49$

OBJECTIVES ■■■■

Upon completion of this section you will be able to:

A. Identify a new term for making $x^2 + bx$ a perfect square binomial;

B. Solve equations of the type $x^2 + bx + c = 0$ using the method of completing the square; and

C. Solve equations of the type $ax^2 + bx + c = 0$ using the method of completing the squares.

Observe the pattern in these expressions.

$$\overset{\text{Same sign}}{(x + 7)^2} = x^2 + 14x + 49$$

$$7 \text{ is } \frac{1}{2} \text{ of } 14 \qquad 49 = \left(\frac{1}{2} \text{ of } 14\right)^2$$

In general we have;

$$(x + a)^2 = x^2 + 2ax + a^2$$

A. IDENTIFY A NEW TERM FOR MAKING $x^2 + bx$ A PERFECT SQUARE BINOMIAL

What constant must be added to $x^2 + bx$ to make it a perfect square of a binomial?

$$x^2 + bx + ? = (x + ?)^2$$

Examine the illustration given above. If we add the square of half the coefficient of x then the sum is a perfect square of a binomial.

$$x^2 + bx + \left(\frac{b}{2}\right)^2 = \left(x + \frac{b}{2}\right)^2$$

Square of half the coefficient of x

$$x^2 + \underset{\text{Same sign}}{bx + \left(\frac{b}{2}\right)^2} = \left(x + \frac{b}{2}\right)^2$$

In a similar way identify what should be added to $x^2 - bx$ so that the sum is a perfect square of a binomial.

$$x^2 - bx = x^2 + (-b)x$$

Add the square of half the coefficient of x.

$$x^2 + (-b)x + \left(-\frac{b}{2}\right)^2 = \left(x + \frac{-b}{2}\right)^2$$

$$x^2 \underset{\text{Same sign}}{- bx + \left(\frac{b}{2}\right)^2} = \left(x - \frac{b}{2}\right)^2$$

Consider for example $x^2 + 6x$. What should be added to $x^2 + 6x$ so that the sum is a perfect square of a binomial?

Coefficient of x in $x^2 + 6x$ is 6.

Half the coefficient of $x = \frac{1}{2} \cdot 6 = 3$.

Therefore, we add 3^2 or **9** to $x^2 + 6x$.

$$x^2 + 6x + 9 = \left(x + \frac{6}{2}\right)^2$$
$$= (x + 3)^2$$

Consider $x^2 - 8x$. What should be added to $x^2 - 8x$ so that the sum is a perfect square binomial.

Coefficient of x in $x^2 - 8x$ is -8.

Half the coefficient of $x = \frac{1}{2}(-8) = -4$.

Therefore, we add $(-4)^2$ or 16 to $x^2 - 8x$, so that the sum is a perfect square binomial.

$$x^2 - 8x + 16 = \left(x + \frac{-8}{2}\right)^2 = (x - 4)^2$$

EXAMPLE 1 Identify the constant which when added to the given expression makes it a perfect square of a binomial. Find that binomial.

a. $x^2 - 14x$ b. $x^2 + 12x$ c. $x^2 - 7x$

Solutions:

a. $x^2 - 14x$: Compare this with $x^2 + bx$, where $b = -14$

$$\text{The constant (c)} = \left(\frac{b}{2}\right)^2 = \left(\frac{-14}{2}\right)^2$$

$$= (-7)^2 = 49$$

$$x^2 - 14x + \left(\frac{-14}{2}\right)^2 = x^2 - 14x + (-7)^2 \quad \text{Perfect square trinomial.}$$

$$= (x - 7)^2 \quad \text{Square of a binomial.}$$

b. $x^2 + 12x$: Compare this with $x^2 + bx$, where $b = 12$.

$$\text{The constant (c)} = \left(\frac{b}{2}\right)^2 = \left(\frac{12}{2}\right)^2 = (6)^2$$

$$x^2 + 12x + \left(\frac{12}{2}\right)^2 = x^2 + 12x + (6)^2 \quad \text{Trinomial.}$$

$$= (x + 6)^2 \quad \text{Square of a binomial.}$$

c. $x^2 - 7x$: Compare this with $x^2 + bx$, where $b = -7$.

$$\text{The constant (c)} = \left(\frac{b}{2}\right)^2 = \left(\frac{-7}{2}\right)^2 = \frac{49}{4}$$

$$x^2 - 7x + \left(\frac{-7}{2}\right)^2 = x^2 - 7x + \frac{49}{4} \quad \text{Perfect square trinomial.}$$

$$= \left(x - \frac{7}{2}\right)^2 \quad \text{Square of a binomial.}$$

B. SOLVING QUADRATIC EQUATIONS OF THE FORM $x^2 + bx + c = 0$.

The method of completing the square can be used to solve any quadratic equation $x^2 + bx + c = 0$.

Completing the square:

Step 1 Move the constant term to one side and write the equation in the form $x^2 + bx = k$.

Step 2 Add $\left(\dfrac{b}{2}\right)^2$ to both sides to complete the square.

Step 3 Use the square root property.

Step 4 Solve the two linear equations.

> *Note* While using this procedure, remember the **principle of equality**, *i.e.* adding the same constant to both sides of the equation.

2. Solve the following equations.

a) $x^2 - 4x + 3 = 0$

b) $x^2 + 5x = 6$

EXAMPLE 2 Solve the following equations.

    a. $x^2 - 6x + 7 = 0$ **b.** $x^2 + 7x = 4$

Solutions:

a. $x^2 - 6x + 7 = 0$

Step 1 $\quad x^2 - 6x = -7$

Step 2 $\quad x^2 - 6x + \left(\dfrac{-6}{2}\right)^2 = -7 + \left(\dfrac{-6}{2}\right)^2$

$$x^2 - 6x + 9 = -7 + 9$$
$$(x - 3)^2 = 2$$

Step 3 $\quad x - 3 = \sqrt{2} \qquad$ or $\qquad x - 3 = -\sqrt{2}$.

$\qquad\qquad x = 3 + \sqrt{2} \qquad$ or $\qquad x = 3 - \sqrt{2}$.

Therefore, the solutions are $3 \pm \sqrt{2}$.

b. $x^2 + 7x = 4$

Step 1 Already in the form $x^2 + bx = k$

Step 2 $\quad x^2 + 7x + \left(\dfrac{7}{2}\right)^2 = 4 + \left(\dfrac{7}{2}\right)^2$

$$x^2 + 7x + \dfrac{49}{4} = 4 + \dfrac{49}{4}$$

$$\left(x + \dfrac{7}{2}\right)^2 = \dfrac{65}{4}$$

$$x + \dfrac{7}{2} = +\sqrt{\dfrac{65}{4}} \quad \text{or} \quad x + \dfrac{7}{2} = -\sqrt{\dfrac{65}{4}}$$

$$x = -\dfrac{7}{2} + \dfrac{\sqrt{65}}{2} \quad \text{or} \quad x = -\dfrac{7}{2} - \dfrac{\sqrt{65}}{2}$$

Therefore, the solutions are $-\dfrac{7}{2} \pm \dfrac{\sqrt{65}}{2}$.

EXAMPLE 3   Solve the equation $x^2 + 4x + 4 = 0$.

Solution:

Already a perfect square trinomial.

$$(x + 2)^2 = 0$$

$$x + 2 = 0$$

$$x = -2$$

The equation has repeated roots: **–2, –2**.

Check:

$$x^2 + 4x + 4 = 0$$

$$(-2)^2 + 4(-2) + 4 = 0$$

$$4 - 8 + 4 = 0 \qquad \text{True}$$

C.   SOLVING QUADRATIC EQUATIONS OF THE FORM $ax^2 + bx + c = 0$.

If the coefficient of the second degree term of an equation is different from 1, then we divide all the terms of the equation by *this coefficient* to reduce the equation to the form $x^2 + bx + c = 0$ and then follow the same procedure as in objective B to solve the equation.

For example:

(i) $3x^2 + 5x + 9 = 0$ $\longrightarrow$ $\dfrac{3x^2}{3} + \dfrac{5x}{3} + \dfrac{9}{3} = \dfrac{0}{3}$ $\longrightarrow$ $x^2 + \dfrac{5}{3}x + 3 = 0$

(ii) $-2x^2 + 7x = 8$ $\longrightarrow$ $\dfrac{-2x^2}{-2} + \dfrac{7x}{-2} = \dfrac{8}{-2}$ $\longrightarrow$ $x^2 - \dfrac{7}{2}x = -4$

EXAMPLE 4   Solve the equations

     a. $4p^2 + 8p = 21$ **b.** $-3z^2 - 8z + 1 = 0$

Solutions:

a. $4p^2 + 8p = 21$

$$\frac{4p^2}{4} + \frac{8p}{4} = \frac{21}{4} \qquad \text{\small Divide all terms by 4.}$$

$$p^2 + 2p = \frac{21}{4}$$

$$p^2 + 2p + \left(\frac{2}{2}\right)^2 = \frac{21}{4} + \left(\frac{2}{2}\right)^2 \qquad \text{\small Add } \left(\tfrac{2}{2}\right)^2 \text{ to both sides.}$$

$$p^2 + 2p + 1 = \frac{25}{4}$$

$$(p + 1)^2 = \frac{25}{4}$$

$$p + 1 = \pm\frac{5}{2}$$

$$p + 1 = \frac{5}{2} \qquad \text{or} \qquad p + 1 = -\frac{5}{2}$$

$$\longrightarrow \qquad p = -1 + \frac{5}{2} \qquad \text{or} \qquad p = -1 - \frac{5}{2}$$

$$\longrightarrow \qquad p = \frac{3}{2} \qquad \text{or} \qquad p = -\frac{7}{2}$$

The solutions are $p = \dfrac{3}{2}$ and $-\dfrac{7}{2}$.

b) $-3z^2 + 10z - 2 = 0$

b. $-3z^2 - 8z + 1 = 0$

$$-3z^2 - 8z = -1$$

$$\frac{-3z^2}{-3} - \frac{8z}{-3} = \frac{-1}{-3} \qquad \text{Divide by } -3.$$

$$z^2 + \frac{8z}{3} = \frac{1}{3} \qquad \tfrac{1}{2} \text{ the coefficient of } z = \tfrac{4}{3}.$$

$$z^2 + 2 \cdot \frac{4}{3} z + \left(\frac{4}{3}\right)^2 = \frac{1}{3} + \left(\frac{4}{3}\right)^2 \qquad \text{Add } \left(\tfrac{4}{3}\right)^2 \text{ to both sides.}$$

$$\left(z + \frac{4}{3}\right)^2 = \frac{19}{9}$$

$$z + \frac{4}{3} = \sqrt{\frac{19}{9}} \qquad \text{or} \qquad z + \frac{4}{3} = -\sqrt{\frac{19}{9}}$$

$$z = -\frac{4}{3} + \frac{\sqrt{19}}{9} \qquad \text{or} \qquad z = -\frac{4}{3} - \sqrt{\frac{19}{9}}$$

$$z = \frac{-4}{3} \pm \frac{\sqrt{19}}{3}$$

The solutions are $z = \dfrac{-4 \pm \sqrt{19}}{3}$.

5. Solve $(3x + 2)(x + 5) = 16$

EXAMPLE 5 Solve $(2x + 1)(x - 5) = 3$

Solution:

$$(2x + 1)(x - 5) = 3$$

$$2x^2 - 9x - 5 = 3$$

$$2x^2 - 9x = 8$$

$$\frac{2x^2}{2} - \frac{9x}{2} = \frac{8}{2} \qquad \text{Divide both sides by 2.}$$

$$x^2 - \frac{9}{2}x = 4$$

$$x^2 - 2 \cdot \frac{9}{4}x + \left(\frac{9}{4}\right)^2 = 4 + \left(\frac{9}{4}\right)^2 \quad \text{Add } \left(\frac{1}{2} \cdot \frac{9}{2}\right)^2 \text{ to both sides.}$$

$$\left(x - \frac{9}{4}\right)^2 = \frac{145}{16} \qquad 4 + \left(\frac{9}{4}\right)^2 = \frac{145}{16}$$

$$x - \frac{9}{4} = \frac{\sqrt{145}}{4} \quad \text{or} \quad x - \frac{9}{4} = -\frac{\sqrt{145}}{4}$$

$$x = \frac{9}{4} + \frac{\sqrt{145}}{4} \quad \text{or} \quad x = \frac{9}{4} - \frac{\sqrt{145}}{4}$$

The solutions are: $\quad x = \dfrac{9 \pm \sqrt{145}}{4}$.

Answers:

4. a) $x = -1, \dfrac{5}{2}$ b) $z = \dfrac{5 \pm \sqrt{19}}{3}$

5. $-6, \dfrac{1}{3}$

EXERCISE 9.2

A. **In exercises 1-24, find the number that should be added to the expression to make it a perfect square.**

1. $x^2 + 4x$ 2. $a^2 - 5a$ 3. $y^2 + 7y$ 4. $x^2 + 3x$ 5. $p^2 - 6p$ 6. $y^2 - 8y$

7. $t^2 - t$ 8. $b^2 + 18b$ 9. $x^2 + 2x$ 10. $x^2 + 9x$ 11. $x^2 + 6x$ 12. $x^2 - 10x$

13. $x^2 + 8x$ 14. $x^2 - 14x$ 15. $x^2 + 12x$ 16. $x^2 - 4x$ 17. $u^2 - \frac{1}{4}u$ 18. $u^2 - 9u$

19. $u^2 + 3u$ 20. $u^2 - 11u$ 21. $x^2 - 14x$ 22. $x^2 + 5x$ 23. $x^2 + \frac{3}{4}x$ 24. $x^2 + \frac{4}{7}x$

In exercises 25-44, complete the square.

25. $x^2 + 8x + 9$ 26. $x^2 - 2x + 5$ 27. $x^2 - 7x + 5$ 28. $x^2 + 3x - 6$

29. $y^2 + y - 10$ 30. $a^2 - a + 5$ 31. $z^2 - 3z + 7$ 32. $y^2 - 5y + 4$

33. $3x^2 - 2x + 9$ 34. $2x^2 + 12x - 3$ 35. $4x^2 - 3x + 16$ 36. $-2x^2 + 3x - 1$

37. $4x^2 + 6x - 2$ 38. $2x^2 + 8x + 1$ 39. $9x^2 - 24x + 7$ 40. $16x^2 + 8x - 9$

41. $4u^2 - 3u - 2$ 42. $4u^2 - 4u - 3$ 43. $2u^2 - 6u + 3$ 44. $2u^2 - 7u - 2$

B. **In exercises 45-60, solve the equation using the method of completing the square.**

45. $x^2 + 4x + 2 = 0$ 46. $x^2 - 6x + 2 = 0$ 47. $z^2 + z - 10 = 0$ 48. $x^2 - x + 5 = 0$

49. $y^2 - 3y - 9 = 0$ 50. $x^2 + 2x - 5 = 0$ 51. $a^2 - a - 1 = 0$ 52. $x^2 - 3x = 0$

53. $x^2 + 5x = 0$ 54. $2x^2 - 4x = 0$ 55. $x^2 + 7x = 7$ 56. $y^2 + 4y = 5$

57. $t^2 + 6t = -8$ 58. $x^2 - 6x + 7 = 0$ 59. $a^2 - 5a = 3$ 60. $x^2 - 2x = 4$

C. **In exercises 61-80, solve the quadratic equation of the form $ax^2 + bx + C = 0$ using the method of completing the square.**

61. $2r^2 - 7r = 1$ 62. $2z^2 - 4z = 4$ 63. $3x^2 = 2x + 1$ 64. $2x^2 + 6x - 1 = 0$

65. $-5y^2 + 4y + 3 = 0$ 66. $3x^2 + 6x = 2$ 67. $4k^2 - 3k - 2 = 0$ 68. $4x^2 - 4x + 1 = 0$

69. $(x - 2)(x + 5) = 4$ 70. $6x - 3 = 2x^2$ 71. $(3p + 7)(p + 4) = 5$ 72. $(y + 2)(y - 3) = 4$

73. $3x^2 + 7x = 0$ 74. $\dfrac{x}{2} + \dfrac{2}{x} = \dfrac{9}{4}$ 75. $\dfrac{x^2}{3} + \dfrac{x}{2} = 4$ 76. $\dfrac{2x^2}{5} = 4x + 1$

77. $\dfrac{x^2}{8} - \dfrac{x}{4} = 1$ 78. $\dfrac{x^2}{4} + \dfrac{x}{3} = \dfrac{5}{6}$ 79. $\dfrac{x^2}{30} + \dfrac{x}{5} + \dfrac{1}{6} = 0$ 80. $\dfrac{x^2}{18} - \dfrac{x}{6} - 1 = 0$

9.3 SOLUTION USING THE QUADRATIC FORMULA

OBJECTIVES ■■■■

Upon completion of this section you will be able to:

A. Develop the quadratic formula; use the quadratic formula for solving quadratic equations; and

B. Use the quadratic formula for solving applied problems.

Another method for solving quadratic equations involves the Quadratic Formula. This formula is derived by using the "**Completing the square**" method applied to the general quadratic equation:

$$ax^2 + bx + c = 0$$

A. DEVELOP AND USE THE QUADRATIC FORMULA FOR SOLVING QUADRATIC EQUATIONS

The formula is obtained by completing the square for a general quadratic equation. Consider the general quadratic equation in standard form.

$$ax^2 + bx + c = 0$$

Coefficient of x^2 is a.

$$ax^2 + bx = -c$$

$$\frac{ax^2}{a} + \frac{bx}{a} = -\frac{c}{a}$$

Divide by a.

$$x^2 + \frac{b}{a}x = -\frac{c}{a}$$

Simplify.

$$x^2 + 2 \cdot \frac{b}{2a} \cdot x + \left(\frac{b}{2a}\right)^2 = -\frac{c}{a} + \left(\frac{b}{2a}\right)^2$$

Completing the Square.

$$\left(x + \frac{b}{2a}\right)^2 = -\frac{c}{a} + \frac{b^2}{4a^2}$$

Replace left side with the binomial square.

$$\left(x + \frac{b}{2a}\right)^2 = \frac{b^2}{4a^2} - \frac{c}{a}$$

Switch terms on the right side.

$$\left(x + \frac{b}{2a}\right)^2 = \frac{b^2}{4a^2} - \frac{4a\,c}{4a \cdot a}$$

$$= \frac{b^2}{4a^2} - \frac{4a\,c}{4a^2}$$

Combine fractions on right side.

$$= \frac{b^2 - 4a\,c}{4a^2}$$

$$x + \frac{b}{2a} = \pm\sqrt{\frac{b^2 - 4ac}{4a^2}} = \pm\frac{\sqrt{b^2 - 4ac}}{2a}$$

Square Root Property.

$$x = -\frac{b}{2a} \pm \frac{\sqrt{b^2 - 4ac}}{2a} = \frac{-b \pm \sqrt{b^2 - 4ac}}{2a}$$

The solutions of $ax^2 + bx + c = 0$, $a \neq 0$ are $x = \dfrac{-b \pm \sqrt{b^2 - 4ac}}{2a}$.

This is generally referred to as the **quadratic formula.** The expression under the radical sign $b^2 - 4ac$ is called the **discriminant.**

The solutions of $ax^2 + bx + c = 0$, $a \neq 0$ are given by the Quadratic Formula

$$x = \dfrac{-b \pm \sqrt{b^2 - 4ac}}{2a}$$

The expression under the radical, $b^2 - 4ac$, is called the **discriminant.** The discriminant will reveal the type of solutions to a quadratic equation.

> For any quadratic equation in the form $ax^2 + bx + c = 0$,
>
> 1. If $b^2 - 4ac > 0$, the equation has **two** real solutions.
> 2. If $b^2 - 4ac = 0$, the equation has **one (repeated)** real solution.
> 3. If $b^2 - 4ac < 0$, the equation has **no real** number solution.

We use the following steps to apply the quadratic formula for solving quadratic equations.

Solving the Quadratic Equation:

Step 1 Write the quadratic equation in the standard form $ax^2 + bx + c = 0$.

Step 2 Identify a, the coefficient of x^2; the b, coefficient of x; and c, the constant term.

$$ax^2 \quad + \quad bx \quad + \quad c$$

Coeff. of $x^2 = a$ Coeff. of $x = b$ Constant Term $= c$

Step 3 Compute the value of the discriminant $b^2 - 4ac$.

Step 4 Substitute the value of the discriminant in $x = \dfrac{-b \pm \sqrt{b^2 - 4ac}}{2a}$ and simplify.

Step 5 Check the solution with calculator.

Easy way to check solutions (Optional) :

If the solutions of a quadratic equation are simple whole numbers then we can check the solutions by directly substituting the values of x in the given equation. But if the solutions are irrational numbers then checking by direct substitution may involve lots of calculations. One way to check solutions in such a situation is to use calculator, but another easy way to check the solutions is to use the following fact.

The quadratic equation $ax^2 + bx + c = 0$ has two solutions.

$$x = \dfrac{-b + \sqrt{b^2 - 4ac}}{2a} \qquad x = \dfrac{-b - \sqrt{b^2 - 4ac}}{2a}$$

Fact 1: Verify that the sum of the solutions is $= -\dfrac{b}{a} = -\dfrac{\text{coefficient of } x}{\text{coefficient of } x^2}$.

Fact 2: Verify that the product of these solutions $= \dfrac{c}{a} = \dfrac{\text{constant term}}{\text{coefficient of } x^2}$.

During the discussion in this section we will not use the direct substitution method for checking, if the solutions are irrational numbers. Instead we will either refer to the use of calculator or use the above facts; fact 1 for partial check, and fact 1 and fact 2 for complete check.

WARM-UP

1. Use the quadratic formula to solve the following quadratic equations.

   a) $x^2 - 3x - 4 = 0$

EXAMPLE 1   Use the quadratic formula to solve the following quadratic equations.

   a. $x^2 - 4x - 5 = 0$ b. $5x - 2x^2 = 2$

   c. $3x^2 - 5 = 0$ d. $4x^2 + 4x + 1 = 0$

Solutions:

   a. $x^2 - 4x - 5 = 0$

Step 1   The equation is already in the standard form $ax^2 + bx + c = 0$.

Step 2   Here $a = 1$, $b = -4$, $c = -5$.

Step 3 $b^2 - 4ac = (-4)^2 - 4(1)(-5) = 16 + 20 = 36$

Step 4   Substituting these values in the quadratic formula, we get

$$x = \frac{-b \pm \sqrt{b^2 - 4ac}}{2a} \quad \text{Quadratic Formula}$$

$$= \frac{-(-4) \pm \sqrt{36}}{2(1)} \quad \text{Substitute the values}$$

$$= \frac{4 \pm \sqrt{36}}{2} \longrightarrow x = \frac{4 \pm 6}{2}$$

$$\longrightarrow x = \frac{4 + 6}{2} \quad \text{or} \quad x = \frac{4 - 6}{2}$$

$$\longrightarrow x = 5 \quad \text{or} \quad x = -1$$

The solutions are **5 and –1**.

Step 5   **Check the solutions:** $x^2 - 4x - 5 = 0$

   $x = 5$:   **$x = -1$:**

   $(5)^2 - 4(5) - 5 = 0$ $(-1)^2 - 4(-1) - 5 = 0$

   $\qquad\qquad 0 = 0$ True $1 + 4 - 5 = 0$

   $\qquad\qquad\qquad\qquad\qquad\qquad 0 = 0$ True

You may also check the solutions using a calculator. See section 9.4 of Appendix B for illustrations.

Observation

The discriminant is > 0, therefore the equation has two real solutions, 5 and –1.

---

b. $5x - 2x^2 = 2$

Step 1   Rewrite the equation in the form $ax^2 + bx + c = 0$.
$$-2x^2 + 5x - 2 = 0$$

Step 2   Here $a = -2, \quad b = 5, \quad c = -2$.

Step 3 $b^2 - 4ac = (5)^2 - 4(-2)(-2) = 25 - 16 = 9$

Step 4 $x = \dfrac{-b \pm \sqrt{b^2 - 4ac}}{2a}$

$$= \frac{-5 \pm \sqrt{9}}{2(-2)} \; = \; \frac{-5 \pm 3}{-4}$$

$$\longrightarrow \quad x = \frac{-5 + 3}{-4} \qquad \text{or} \qquad x = \frac{-5 - 3}{-4}$$

$$\longrightarrow \quad x = \frac{-2}{-4} = \frac{1}{2} \qquad \text{or} \qquad x = \frac{-8}{-4} = 2$$

The solutions are $\dfrac{1}{2}$ **and 2.**

Step 5   **Check the solutions:** $5x - 2x^2 = 2$

$$x = \frac{1}{2}: \quad 5\left(\frac{1}{2}\right) - 2\left(\frac{1}{2}\right)^2 = 2$$

$$\frac{5}{2} - \frac{1}{2} = 2$$

$$2 = 2 \qquad \text{True}$$

$$x = 2: \quad 5(2) - 2(2)^2 = 2$$

$$10 - 8 = 2$$

$$2 = 2 \qquad \text{True}$$

Observation

The discriminant is a perfect square $[9 = 3^2]$, and the two solutions

are *rational* numbers $\left(\dfrac{1}{2} \text{ and } 2\right)$.

---

c. $3x^2 - 5 = 0$

Step 1   Rewrite $3x^2 - 5 = 0$ in the form $ax^2 + bx + c = 0$.
$$3x^2 + \mathbf{0} \cdot x - 5 = 0$$

Step 2 $a = 3, \quad b = 0, \quad c = -5$.

Step 3 $b^2 - 4ac = (0)^2 - 4(3)(-5) = 60$

Step 4 $x = \dfrac{-b \pm \sqrt{b^2 - 4ac}}{2a} = \dfrac{-0 \pm \sqrt{60}}{2(3)}$

$$= \frac{\pm \sqrt{60}}{6} = \frac{\pm 2\sqrt{15}}{6} = \frac{\pm \sqrt{15}}{3}$$

b) $2x^2 + 3x - 5 = 0$

c) $4x^2 - 7 = 0$

$$x = \frac{\sqrt{15}}{3} \quad \text{or} \quad x = \frac{-\sqrt{15}}{3}.$$

The solutions are $\frac{\sqrt{15}}{3}$ and $-\frac{\sqrt{15}}{3}$.

Step 5   ***Check the solution:*** $3x^2 - 5 = 0$

$$x = \pm\frac{\sqrt{15}}{3}: \quad 3\left(\pm\frac{\sqrt{15}}{3}\right)^2 - 5 = 0$$

$$3 \cdot \frac{15}{9} - 5 = 0$$

$$5 - 5 = 0 \qquad \text{True}$$

Observation

The discriminant is a positive whole number but not a perfect square, and the solutions are *irrational* numbers.

---

d) $9x^2 + 6x + 1 = 0$

d. $\boldsymbol{4x^2 + 4x + 1 = 0}$

Step 1   The equation is already in the standard form.

Step 2 $a = 4$, $b = 4$, $c = 1$.

Step 3 $b^2 - 4ac = (4)^2 - 4(4)(1) = 16 - 16 = 0$

Step 4 $x = \dfrac{-4 \pm \sqrt{0}}{2 \cdot 4} = \dfrac{-4 \pm 0}{8}$

$$x = \frac{-4}{8} \quad \text{or} \quad x = \frac{-4}{8}$$

$$x = -\frac{1}{2} \quad \text{or} \quad x = -\frac{1}{2}$$

The solution $-\dfrac{1}{2}$ is repeated.

Step 5   ***Check the solution:*** $4x^2 + 4x + 1 = 0$

$$x = -\frac{1}{2}: \quad 4\left(-\frac{1}{2}\right)^2 + 4\left(-\frac{1}{2}\right) + 1 = 0$$

$$4 \cdot \frac{1}{4} - \frac{4}{2} + 1 = 0$$

$$1 - 2 + 1 = 0 \qquad \text{True}$$

Observation

The discriminant is 0 and the equation has one *repeated* solution. $4x^2 + 4x + 1$ is a perfect square so $(2x + 1)^2 = 0$

$$x = -\frac{1}{2}.$$

EXAMPLE 2   Solve the equations.

           a. $3x^2 - 7x + 2 = 0$ **b.** $2x^2 + 4x + 1 = 0$

Solutions:

a. $3x^2 - 7x + 2 = 0$ Here, $a = 3$, $b = -7$, $c = 2$.

$b^2 - 4ac = (-7)^2 - 4(3)(2) = 49 - 24 = 25$

$$x = \frac{-b \pm \sqrt{b^2 - 4ac}}{2a}$$ Quadratic formula.

$$= \frac{-(-7) \pm \sqrt{25}}{2(3)} = \frac{7 \pm \sqrt{25}}{6}$$

$$x = \frac{7 + \sqrt{25}}{6} \quad \text{or} \quad x = \frac{7 - \sqrt{25}}{6}$$

$$x = \frac{7 + 5}{6} = \mathbf{2} \quad \text{or} \quad x = \frac{7 - 5}{6} = \frac{\mathbf{1}}{\mathbf{3}}$$

The solutions are $x = \mathbf{2}$ and $x = \dfrac{\mathbf{1}}{\mathbf{3}}$.

Check : $3x^2 - 7x + 2 = 0$

$x = \mathbf{2}$: $3(\mathbf{2})^2 - 7(\mathbf{2}) + 2 = 0$

              $12 - 14 + 2 = 0$

                    $0 = 0$ True

$x = \dfrac{1}{3}$: $3\left(\dfrac{1}{3}\right)^2 - 7\left(\dfrac{1}{3}\right) + 2 = 0$

              $\dfrac{1}{3} - \dfrac{7}{3} + 2 = 0$

              $-\dfrac{6}{3} + 2 = 0$

              $-2 + 2 = 0$ True

Observation

The discriminant is a positive non-zero number which is a perfect square, and the solutions are *rational* numbers.

---

b. $2x^2 + 4x + 1 = 0$ Here, $a = 2$, $b = 4$, $c = 1$.

$b^2 - 4ac = (4)^2 - 4(2)(1) = 16 - 8 = 8$

$$x = \frac{-b \pm \sqrt{b^2 - 4ac}}{2a}$$

$$= \frac{-4 \pm \sqrt{8}}{4} = \frac{-4 \pm 2\sqrt{2}}{4} = \frac{2(-2 \pm \sqrt{2})}{4} = \frac{-2 \pm \sqrt{2}}{2}$$

$$x = \frac{-2 + \sqrt{2}}{2} \quad \text{or} \quad x = \frac{-2 - \sqrt{2}}{2}$$

The solutions are $\dfrac{-2 + \sqrt{2}}{2}$ and $\dfrac{-2 - \sqrt{2}}{2}$.

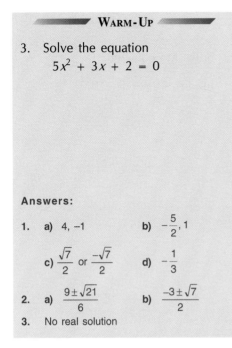

WARM-UP

3. Solve the equation
$$5x^2 + 3x + 2 = 0$$

Answers:

1. a) $4, -1$ b) $-\frac{5}{2}, 1$

   c) $\frac{\sqrt{7}}{2}$ or $\frac{-\sqrt{7}}{2}$ d) $-\frac{1}{3}$

2. a) $\frac{9 \pm \sqrt{21}}{6}$ b) $\frac{-3 \pm \sqrt{7}}{2}$

3. No real solution

EXAMPLE 3   Solve the equation: $7x^2 + 4x + 3 = 0$

Solution:

$$7x^2 + 4x + 3 = 0 \qquad \text{Here, } a = 7, \ b = 4, \ c = 3.$$

$$b^2 - 4ac = (4)^2 - 4(7)(3) = 16 - 84 = \mathbf{-68}$$

$$x = \frac{-b \pm \sqrt{b^2 - 4ac}}{2a}$$

$$= \frac{-4 \pm \sqrt{-68}}{14}$$

$\sqrt{-68}$ is not defined in real numbers. Therefore, this equation has no solution in real numbers.

Observation

If the discriminant is a negative number then there are no real solutions.

The observations from the above three examples are summarized below.

1. If the discriminant is **positive**, the solutions are **real and distinct numbers**.
    • If the discriminant is a perfect square the solutions are rational numbers, otherwise the solutions are irrational numbers.
2. If the discriminant is **zero**, there is only **one real** (Repeated) solution.
3. If the discriminant is **negative**, there are no real solutions.

B.   QUADRATIC FORMULA FOR SOLVING APPLICATIONS

Recall the strategy for solving an applied problem:
• Read the problem carefully.
• Interpret the given information and prepare a mathematical model.
• Solve the equations involved in the model.
• Interpret the result.

WARM-UP

4. The sum of squares of two consecutive positive integers is 61. Find the integers.

EXAMPLE 4   The sum of the squares of two consecutive positive integers is 145. Find the integers.

Solution: We have to find **two consecutive positive integers**. The sum of the squares of the integers must be 145. Suppose the **smaller** of the two positive integers is x. The **next** positive integer is $x + 1$.

Now the sum of the squares is 145 means:

$$x^2 + (x + 1)^2 = 145 \qquad \text{Given condition.}$$
$$x^2 + x^2 + 2x + 1 = 145 \qquad \text{Simplify.}$$
$$2x^2 + 2x - 144 = 0$$

We divide both sides by 2 and get $x^2 + x - 72 = 0$

We use the quadratic formula to solve this quadratic equation.

$$a = 1, \quad b = 1, \quad \text{and} \quad c = -72$$

$$b^2 - 4ac = (1)^2 - 4(1)(-72) = 1 + 288 = \mathbf{289}$$

$$x = \frac{-b \pm \sqrt{b^2 - 4ac}}{2a}$$

$$= \frac{-1 \pm \sqrt{289}}{2} = \frac{-1 \pm 17}{2}$$

$$x = \frac{-1 + 17}{2} \qquad \text{or} \qquad x = \frac{-1 - 17}{2}$$

$$\longrightarrow \quad x = 8 \qquad \text{or} \qquad x = -9$$

Since the required integers are positive, the only possible solution is $x = 8$. Thus, the two integers are **8 and 9**.

Check : The sum of squares = $8^2 + 9^2 = 64 + 81 = 145$.   True

EXAMPLE 5   Michael purchased a certain number of shares of one stock for a total of $1400. The second stock was selling for $6 less per share. Michael could have bought 3 more shares of the second stock for the same amount of money. How many shares of the first stock did Michael purchase? How much did each share cost?

Solution:

Suppose Michael purchased x shares of the first stock.

Price per share of first stock $= \dfrac{\text{Total money invested}}{\text{Total number of shares purchased}} = \dfrac{1400}{x}$

Price per share of second stock $= \dfrac{1400}{x} - 6$ Given

Number of shares of second stock which could be purchased for $1400 is $x + 3$.

The above information is summarized in the following model.

	Number	×	Price =	Total Amount
First Stock	x		$\dfrac{1400}{x}$	1400
Second Stock	$x + 3$		$\dfrac{1400}{x} - 6$	$(x+3)\left(\dfrac{1400}{x} - 6\right)$

5.   Bob purchased a certain number of instruments for physics laboratory for a total of $600. Same instrument offered by a different manufacturer were selling for $5 less per instrument. Bob could have purchased 10 more instruments for the same amount of money. How many instruments did Bob purchase from the first vendor? How much did each instrument cost?

Thus, $(x+3)\left(\dfrac{1400}{x}-6\right) = 1400$

$$x\left(\dfrac{1400}{x}-6\right)+3\left(\dfrac{1400}{x}-6\right) = 1400$$

$$1400 - 6x + \dfrac{4200}{x} - 18 = 1400 \longrightarrow -6x + \dfrac{4200}{x} - 18 = 0$$

$$\longrightarrow -6x^2 - 18x + 4200 = 0$$

$$\longrightarrow x^2 + 3x - 700 = 0$$

We can use quadratic formula to solve this equation.

Here, $a = 1$, $b = 3$, $c = -700$.

$$b^2 - 4ac = (3)^2 - 4(1)(-700) = 9 + 2800 = 2809$$

$$x = \dfrac{-b \pm \sqrt{b^2 - 4ac}}{2a} = \dfrac{-3 \pm \sqrt{2809}}{2} = \dfrac{-3 \pm 53}{2}$$

$$x = \dfrac{-3 + 53}{2} \quad \text{or} \quad x = \dfrac{-3 - 53}{2}.$$

$$x = 25 \quad \text{or} \quad x = -28.$$

The number of shares **cannot be negative**. Therefore, the acceptable solution is **$x = 25$**.

(i) Michael bought 25 shares of the first stock.

(ii) Price of each share = $\dfrac{1400}{25}$ = \$56.

6. Harry and Patrick work together as a team and unload a truck in 2 hours. Harry is stronger and works faster than Patrick. Working alone, Harry would take 3 hours less than Patrick to unload the same truck. How long does it take for Patrick to unload the truck?

EXAMPLE 6 Two cranes can unload a ship together in 4 hours. The faster crane takes 6 hours less than the slower crane, if each were to unload the same ship alone. How long does it take for each crane to unload this ship?

Solution:

Let the number of hours required by the faster crane to unload the ship = x.

Then the slower crane unloads the ship in $(x + 6)$ hours.

Crane	Rate	×	Time	=	Work Done
Faster Crane	$\dfrac{1}{x}$		4		$\dfrac{4}{x}$
Slower Crane	$\dfrac{1}{x+6}$		4		$\dfrac{4}{x+6}$

Since the ship is unloaded by the two cranes working together in 4 hours, we get:

$$\frac{4}{x} + \frac{4}{x+6} = 1$$

$$x(x+6)\left[\frac{4}{x} + \frac{4}{x+6}\right] = x(x+6)$$

Multiply both sides by the LCD: $x(x+6)$

$$4(x+6) + 4x = x(x+6)$$

$$4x + 24 + 4x = x^2 + 6x$$ Simplify.

$$x^2 - 2x - 24 = 0$$

Now we solve $x^2 - 2x - 24 = 0$.

Here, $a = 1$, $b = -2$, $c = -24$.

$$b^2 - 4ac = (-2)^2 - 4(1)(-24) = 4 + 96 = \mathbf{100}$$

$$x = \frac{-(-2) \pm \sqrt{100}}{2}$$

$$= \frac{2 \pm \sqrt{100}}{2}$$

$$= \frac{2 \pm 10}{2}$$

$$x = \mathbf{6} \quad \text{or} \quad x = \mathbf{-4}$$

Since -4 is not a feasible solution, the faster crane unloads the ship in $x = \mathbf{6\ hours}$, and the slower crane unloads the ship in $x + 6 = \mathbf{12\ hours}$.

Answers:

4. 5, 6
5. 30 instruments at $20 each
6. 6 hours

EXERCISE 9.3

A. **In exercises 1-34, use the quadratic formula to solve the equation.**

1. $x^2 - 3x + 2 = 0$

2. $x^2 + 3x - 4 = 0$

3. $y^2 + 6y + 5 = 0$

4. $x^2 + 8x - 105 = 0$

5. $2x^2 - 3x + 1 = 0$

6. $3x^2 + 10x + 3 = 0$

7. $5x^2 + 6x + 1 = 0$

8. $3x^2 - 11x + 6 = 0$

9. $6z - 3z^2 = 3$

10. $48x^2 - 13x = 1$

11. $9x^2 + 12x + 4 = 0$

12. $4x^2 - 20x + 25 = 0$

13. $t^2 + 5t = 4$

14. $x^2 = 15x - 26$

15. $p^2 - 7p + 2 = 0$

16. $x^2 = 8x + 65$

17. $3x^2 + 15x + 8 = 0$

18. $8x^2 = 2$

19. $5x^2 + 7x - 2 = 0$

20. $x^2 + 13x = 68$

21. $3x^2 - 5x - 13 = 0$

22. $2x^2 + 4x + 1 = 0$

23. $4x^2 - 12x + 9 = 0$

24. $2x^2 - 5x + 2 = 0$

25. $3x^2 - 6x + 2 = 0$

26. $x^2 + 2x + 3 = 0$

27. $3x^2 - 8x + 5 = 0$

28. $4x^2 + 3x - 28 = 0$

29. $6x^2 - 5x = 4$

30. $3x^2 + 7x = 12$

31. $x^2 - \left(\frac{10}{3}\right)x + \frac{25}{9}$

32. $-2x^2 + 9x + 35 = 0$

33. $-\left(\dfrac{3}{2}\right)x^2 - 3x + \dfrac{1}{6} = 0$　　　　　**34.** $-\dfrac{5}{2}y^2 + \dfrac{2}{3}y - 4 = 0$

B.　In exercises 35-50, solve the application problem.

35.　The product of two consecutive positive even integers is 224. Find the integers.

36.　The sum of the squares of three consecutive natural numbers is 110. Find the numbers.

37.　The sum of the reciprocals of two consecutive odd integers is $\dfrac{8}{15}$. Find the numbers.

38.　Find two consecutive positive odd integers the sum of whose squares is 130.

39.　The sum of an integer and its reciprocal is $\dfrac{37}{6}$. Find the integer.

40.　The length of a prayer hall is 3 meters more than its width. If the area of the hall is 36 m^2, calculate nearest to one-tenth of a meter, the length and width of the hall.

41.　A ball is thrown upwards. The height h, measured in feet, attained by it after being in air for t seconds follows the rule:
$h = -16t^2 + 32t + 50$.
　(i)　From what height was the ball thrown upwards?
　(ii)　When will the ball be 30 feet above the ground?

42.　In a group of children, each child gives a gift to every other child. If the number of gifts is 132, find the number of children.

43.　Diane invested $12,000 for a certain number of shares of a stock. If the price of each share of stock were $20 more, Diane would get 20 shares less for the same amount of money. How many shares did Diane buy?

44.　The product of John's age (in years) five years ago with his age 9 years later is 15. Find his present age.

45.　A salesman worked for certain number of days to earn $240. If he had been paid $8 more per day he would have earned the same amount of money in five fewer days. How many days did he work?

46.　A car traveling at a speed of x miles per hour requires approximately d feet to stop when the brakes are applied, where d is given by $d = \dfrac{x^2}{10} + \dfrac{x}{2}$.

　　If it took the car 200 feet to stop, how fast was the car moving at the time when the brakes were applied?

47.　The hypotenuse of a right triangle is 10 cm. It is known that its sides are x and $\sqrt{2x+1}$. Find the dimensions of the triangle.

48.　From each corner of a square piece of an aluminum sheet, a square piece of side 16 cm is cut out. The edges are turned up to form an open box. If the box holds 400 cubic fm, find the dimensions of the box.

49.　An object is thrown from the top of a 1,280 feet tall building with an initial velocity of 32 feet per second. The distance s of the object after t seconds is given by the formula
$$s = 32t + 16t^2$$
After how many seconds will the object hit the ground?

50.　A diver jumps from the ten meter springboard. His height in meters above the water level t seconds after he jumps off the board is given by
$$h = -4.2t^2 + 5t + 12.$$
After how many seconds he will pass the springboard again? Approximate your answer correct to two decimal places.

9.4 SOLUTION BY GRAPHING

In Chapter 3, we learned how to graph linear equations, whose graphs were straight lines. In this section, we will study the graphs of quadratic functions.

A quadratic function of x can be written in the form $y = ax^2 + bx + c$, $a \neq 0$. The graph of a quadratic function is called a parabola. Parabolas are cup shaped like the reflective piece from a flashlight.

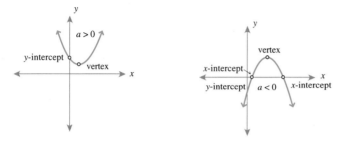

The graph of $y = ax^2 + bx + c$:

1. Opens upwards if a is **positive** (Examples 1-4).

2. Opens downwards if a is **negative** (Example 5).

3. There is a point on the graph which is the *lowest* if the graph opens *upwards*, and is the *highest* if the graph opens *downwards*. This point is called the **vertex** of the parabola.

4. The graph is symmetrical about the vertical line through the vertex. This line is called the **axis** of symmetry.

A. GRAPHING A QUADRATIC EQUATION

The simplest quadratic equation is $y = x^2$. The graph of $y = x^2$ is most fundamental, since graphs of all equations $y = ax^2 + bx + c$ can be derived from the graph of $y = x^2$. Our first example explains how to graph $y = x^2$.

EXAMPLE 1   Graph $y = x^2$.

Solution:

Make a table for several x- and y-values.

x	$y = x^2$	Point (x, y)
3	9	(3, 9)
2	4	(2, 4)
1	1	(1, 1)
0	0	(0, 0)
−1	1	(−1, 1)
−2	4	(−2, 4)
−3	9	(−3, 9)

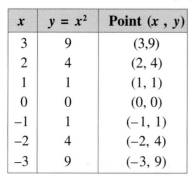

Figure 9.1

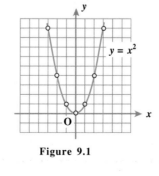

WARM-UP

1. Graph $y = -x^2$

Plot these points on a graph paper. Draw a smooth curve containing these points. The graph is shown in Figure 9.1.

2. Graph $y = x^2 - 3$

EXAMPLE 2   Graph $y = x^2 - 9$.

Solution:

Make a table for several x- and y-values.

x	$y = x^2 - 9$	(x, y)
4	7	(4, 7)
3	0	(3, 0)
2	–5	(2, –5)
1	–8	(1, – 8)
0	–9	(0, – 9)
–1	–8	(–1, – 8)
–2	–5	(–2, –5)
–3	0	(–3, 0)
–4	7	(– 4, 7)

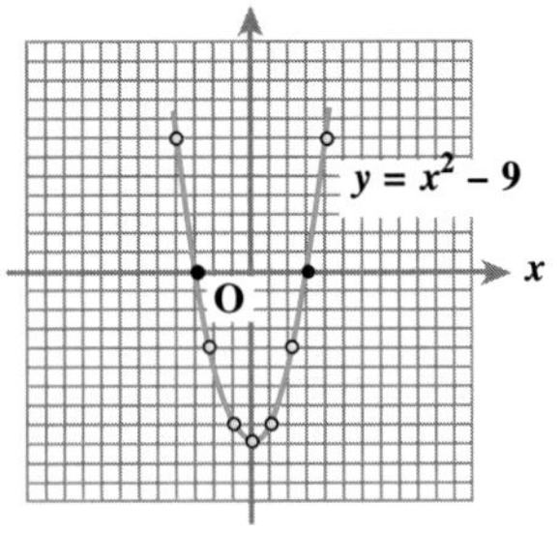

Figure 9.2

Plot these points on a graph paper. Draw a smooth curve containing these points. The graph is shown in Figure 9.2. **Observe that the graph of $y = x^2 - 9$ is the same as the graph of $y = x^2$ shifted vertically down by 9 units.** Think about it and draw a general inference. Use your inference to determine how the graph of the following can be obtained from the graph of $y = x^2$.

(a) $y = x^2 - 1$ **(b)** $y = x^2 + 2$ **(c)** $y = x^2 - 4$

We can compare these graphs easily using a graphing calculator. See example 1 of 9.5 in the Appendix B.

3. Graph $y = (x - 3)^2 + 5$

EXAMPLE 3:   Graph $y = (x - 2)^2 + 6$.

Solution:

Make a table for several x- and y-values.

x	y	(x, y)
5	15	(5,15)
4	10	(4, 10)
3	7	(3, 7)
2	6	(2, 6)
1	7	(1, 7)
0	10	(0, 10)
–1	15	(–1, 15)

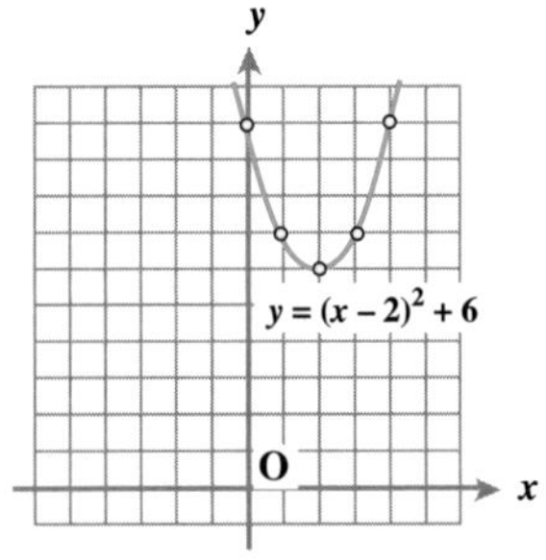

Figure 9.3

Plot these points on a graph paper. Draw a smooth curve containing these points. The graph is shown as in Figure 9.3. **Observe that the graph of $y = (x - 2)^2 + 6$ is the same as the graph of $y = x^2$ shifted two units to the right and six units**

vertically up. Think about this result and draw a general inference. Use your inference to determine how the graphs of

a) $y = (x + 1)^2 + 1$ **b)** $y = (x + 3)^2 - 4$

can be obtained from the graph of $y = x^2$.

EXAMPLE 4 Graph $y = 2x^2$.

Solution:

Make a table for several x- and y-values.

x	y	(x, y)
–1.5	4.5	(–1.5, 4.5)
–1	2	(–1, 2)
–.5	.5	(–.5, .5)
0	0	(0, 0)
.5	.5	(.5, .5)
1	2	(1, 2)
1.5	4.5	(1.5, 4.5)

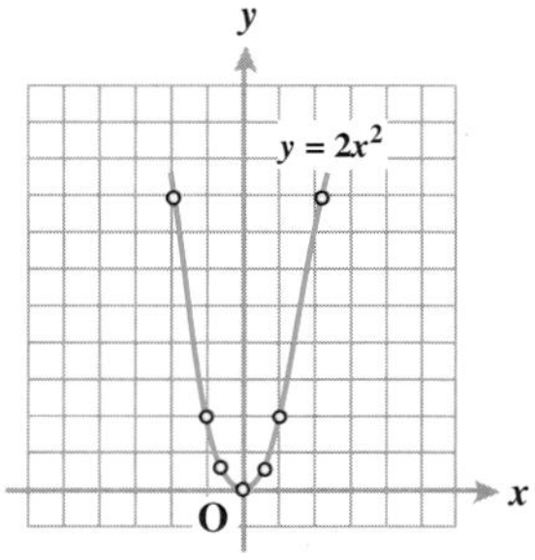

Figure 9.4

Plot these points. Draw a smooth curve containing these points. The graph is shown in Figure 9.4. **Observe that the graph of $y = 2x^2$ is similar to the graph of $y = x^2$ but is narrower or closer to the y - axis.** Think about this result and draw a general inference. Use your inference to determine how the graph of $y = \frac{1}{2}x^2$ is related to the graph of $y = x^2$.

EXAMPLE 5 Graph $y = -2x^2 + 5x - 2$

Solution:

Make a table for several x- and y-values.

x	y	(x, y)
–1	–9	(–1,– 9)
0	– 2	(0, –2)
1	1	(1, 1)
2	0	(2, 0)
3	–5	(3, –5)
4	–14	(4, –14)

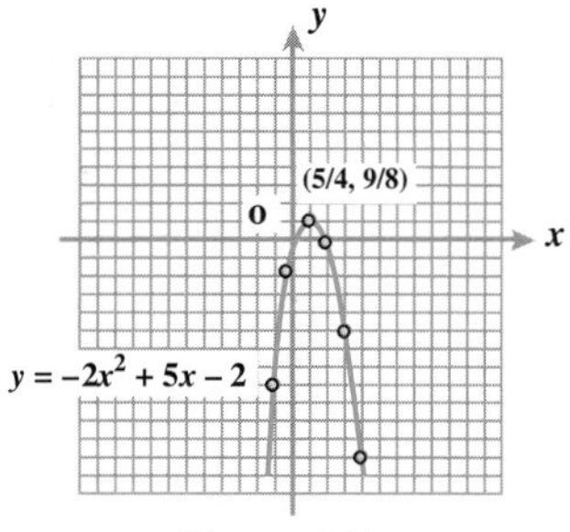

Figure 9.5

We may graph this equation using a calculator. See Example 1 of 9.5 in the Appendix B for illustration.

Plot these points on a graph paper. Draw a smooth curve containing these points. The graph is shown in Figure 9.5. Notice that the graph opens downwards and the coefficient of x^2 is negative.

WARM-UP

4. Graph $y = 3x^2$

5. Graph $y = 3x^2 + 7x - 6$

Answers:

1.

2.

3.

4.

5.

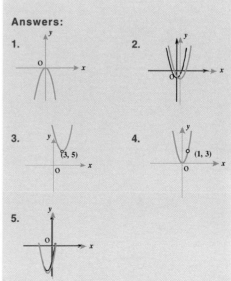

In Example 1, the vertex of the parabola is at the origin, and the axis of symmetry is the *y*-axis. The following graphs are the graphs of Example 3 and Example 5, respectively. We have marked the vertex as V and the axis of symmetry by a dotted line.

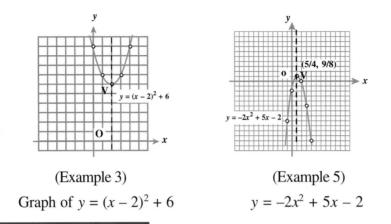

(Example 3)	(Example 5)
Graph of $y = (x - 2)^2 + 6$	$y = -2x^2 + 5x - 2$

B. FINDING THE VERTEX OF A PARABOLA

The vertex of a parabola can be found by determining the coefficients a, b and c of the quadratic equation

$$y = ax^2 + bx + c = a\left(x + \frac{b}{2a}\right)^2 + \frac{4ac - b^2}{4a} \,.$$

1. The *x*-coordinate of the vertex will be $x = -\dfrac{b}{2a}$.

2. Find the *y*-coordinate of the vertex by substituting the *x*-coordinate in the equation.

━━━━━ WARM-UP ━━━━━

6. Find the vertex of the parabola.

$$y = -2x^2 - 3x + 5$$

EXAMPLE 6   Find the vertex of the parabola.

$$y = -2x^2 + 5x - 2$$

Solution: $a = -2, \quad b = 5, \quad c = -2$

$$x = -\frac{b}{2a}$$

$$x = \frac{-5}{2(-2)}$$

$$x = \frac{5}{4}$$

The *y*-coordinate of the vertex is:

$$y = -2\left(\frac{5}{4}\right)^2 + 5\left(\frac{5}{4}\right) - 2$$

$$y = \frac{9}{8}$$

Vertex: $\left(\dfrac{5}{4}, \dfrac{9}{8}\right)$

General method for Graphing a Quadratic Function.

1. Find the vertex.

2. Find the *x*-intercept(s) and the *y*-intercept, if any. If none, additional points must be determined.

3. Find the direction of the parabola using the leading coefficient, *a*.

4. Graph the parabola.

EXAMPLE 7   Graph $y = -2x^2 + 5x - 2$

Solution:

Step 1   The vertex is $\left(\dfrac{5}{4}, \dfrac{9}{8}\right)$ from Example 6.

Step 2   Find the *x*-intercepts, if any, by replacing *y* by 0 and solving for *x*.

$-2x^2 + 5x - 2 = 0$

$a = -2, \quad b = 5, \quad c = -2$

$x = \dfrac{-5 \pm \sqrt{(5)^2 - 4(-2)(-2)}}{2(-2)}$

$\quad = \dfrac{-5 \pm \sqrt{9}}{-4} = \dfrac{-5 + 3}{-4}, \text{ or } \dfrac{-5 - 3}{-4} = \dfrac{1}{2}, \text{ or } 2$

$x = \dfrac{1}{2}$ or $x = 2$. The *x*-intercepts are: $\left(\dfrac{1}{2}, \mathbf{0}\right)$ and **(2, 0)**.

Find the *y*-intercept by replacing *x* by 0 and evaluating *y*.

$y = -2(0)^2 + 5(0) - 2$

$y = -2$

The *y*-intercept is **(0, –2)**.

Step 3   Since $a = -2$, the parabola opens downwards.

Step 4   Graph the parabola.

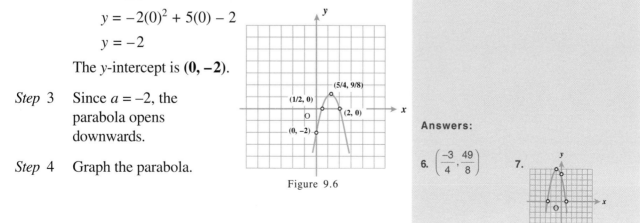

Figure 9.6

7.   Graph : $y = -2x^2 - 3x + 5$

Answers:

6. $\left(\dfrac{-3}{4}, \dfrac{49}{8}\right)$ 7.

C. APPROXIMATING REAL SOLUTIONS OF A QUADRATIC EQUATION GRAPHICALLY

- If a quadratic equation $ax^2 + bx + c = 0$ has real solutions, the graph of the parabola $y = ax^2 + bx + c$ will intersect the x-axis. The x-coordinates of the point of intersection will be the solutions.

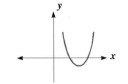

It may not be possible to read the x-coordinates of the points of intersection exactly. That is why we say that this method provides approximate values of the solutions.

- If the vertex of the parabola lies on the x-axis (*i.e.* the parabola meets the x-axis in only one point) then the equation $ax^2 + bx + c = 0$ has only one solution.

- The equation $ax^2 + bx + c = 0$ will have no real solution if the parabola does not meet (intersect) the x-axis.

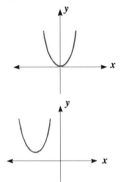

━━━ WARM-UP ━━━

8. Use graph to find the number of real solutions.

a) $x^2 + 6x + 9 = 0$

EXAMPLE 8 Use the graph to find the number of real solutions of the following equations.

a. $x^2 - 6x + 9 = 0$ **b.** $x^2 - 2x + 4 = 0$

c. $-x^2 + 3x + 5 = 0$

Solutions:

a. Solve $x^2 - 6x + 9 = 0$. Draw the graph of $y = x^2 - 6x + 9$.

Step 1 Determine coordinates of the vertex.
$a = 1$, $b = -6$, $c = 9$.

The x-coordinate of the vertex $= \dfrac{-b}{2a} = \dfrac{-(-6)}{2(1)} = 3$

The y-coordinate of the vertex is given by :
$y = 3^2 - 6 \cdot 3 + 9 = 0$. The vertex is $(3, 0)$.

Step 2 Make a table for several x– and y– values on both sides of the vertex.

x	y	(x, y)
0	9	(0, 9)
1	4	(1, 4)
2	1	(2, 1)
3	**0**	**(3, 0)**
4	1	(4, 1)
5	4	(5, 4)
6	9	(6, 9)

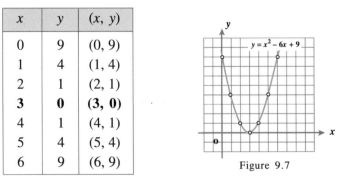

Figure 9.7

🖩 We can solve the equation graphically using a calculator. See example 2 of section 9.5 in Appendix B.

Step 3 Plot the above points and draw a smooth curve.

Conclusion:

The vertex lies on the *x*-axis. In other words the parabola meets the *x*-axis in exactly one point, which is (3, 0). Therefore, the equation $x^2 - 6x + 9 = 0$ has only one real solution. The solution of the equation is **x = 3**.

b. Solve $x^2 - 2x + 4 = 0$.

Draw the graph of $y = x^2 - 2x + 4$.

Here, $a = 1$, $b = -2$, $c = 4$.

b) $x^2 + x + 3 = 0$

Step 1 The *x*-coordinate of the vertex = $\dfrac{-b}{2a} = \dfrac{-(-2)}{2(1)} = 1$

The *y*-coordinate of the vertex is given by

$y = 1^2 - 2 \cdot 1 + 4 = 3$

The vertex is (1, 3).

> The vertex is (1, 3) and $a = 1 > 0$, therefore the parabola opens upward. You can infer that the graph has no *x*-intercepts (Figure 9.8), so the equation has no real solution.

Step 2 Make a table for several *x*- and *y*-values on both sides of the vertex.

x	*y*	(*x*, *y*)
-2	12	(-2, 12)
-1	7	(-1, 7)
0	4	(0, 4)
1	**3**	**(1, 3)**
2	4	(2, 4)
3	7	(3, 7)
4	12	(4, 12)

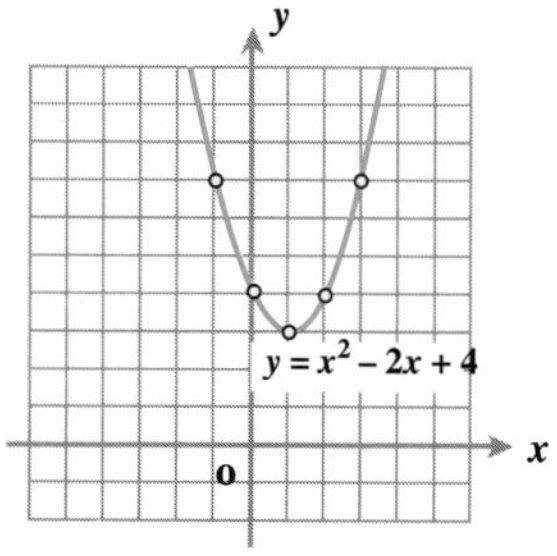

Figure 9.8

Step 3 Plot the above points and draw a smooth curve.

Conclusion:

Since the graph does not intersect the *x*-axis, the equation $x^2 - 2x + 4 = 0$ has **no real solution.**

c. Solve $-x^2 + 3x + 5 = 0$

Draw the graph of $y = -x^2 + 3x + 5$.

c) $2x^2 + 5x - 7 = 0$

Step 1 Determine coordinates of the vertex.

Here, $a = -1$, $b = 3$, $c = 5$.

The *x*-coordinate of the vertex = $\dfrac{-b}{2a} = -\dfrac{3}{2(-1)} = \dfrac{3}{2}$

The *y*-coordinate of the vertex is given by

$$y = -\left(\dfrac{3}{2}\right)^2 + 3\left(\dfrac{3}{2}\right) + 5 = \dfrac{29}{4}$$

The vertex is $\left(\dfrac{3}{2}, \dfrac{29}{4}\right)$.

Answers:

8\. a) One repeated real solution $x = -3$

b) No real solution

c) Two distinct real solutions: $x = -\frac{7}{2}$ and $x = 1$

Step 2 Make a table for several x- and y-values on both sides of the vertex.

x	y	(x, y)
−2	−5	(−2, −5)
−1	1	(−1, 1)
0	5	(0, 5)
1	7	(1, 7)
2	7	(2, 7)
3	5	(3, 5)
4	1	(4, 1)
5	−5	(5, −5)

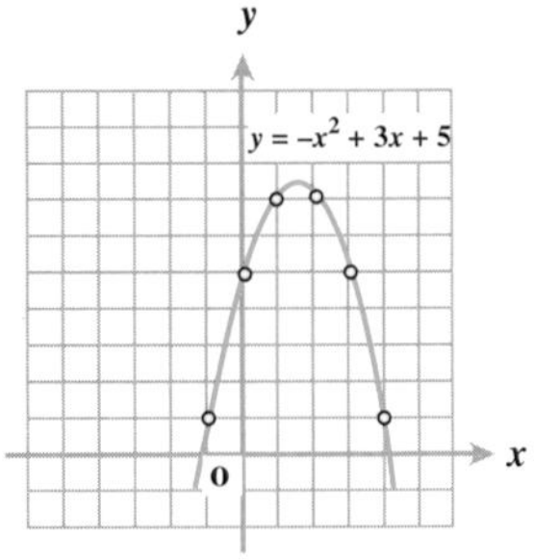

Figure 9.9

Step 3 Plot these points and draw a smooth curve.

Conclusion:

Since the graph intersects the x-axis in two points, $-x^2 + 3x + 5 = 0$ has two real solutions, the x coordinates of the points of intersection. If we read carefully the points of intersection of the graph with the x-axis, we will notice that the solutions are **approximately** $x = -1$ and $x = 4$.

Observation

The knowledge of the position of the vertex and whether the parabola opens upwards or downwards is sufficient to determine the number of real solutions.

EXERCISE 9.4

A. In exercises 1-16, draw the graph of the equation and identify the vertex.

1. $y = 4x^2$ 2. $y = 3x^2$ 3. $y = -4x^2$ 4. $y = -3x^2$
5. $y = x^2 + 2x + 1$ 6. $y = x^2 - 2x + 1$ 7. $y = x^2 - 4x + 4$ 8. $y = x^2 + 6x + 9$
9. $y = 2(x-1)^2 + 3$ 10. $y = 2(x+1)^2 + 4$ 11. $y = -2(x+2)^2 + 8$ 12. $y = -(x-2)^2 + 6$
13. $y = x^2 + 2x + 4$ 14. $y = x^2 - 2x + 3$ 15. $y = 3x^2 + 4x + 1$ 16. $y = -x^2 + 2x - 3$

In exercises 17-24, determine which parabola opens upward and which opens downward.

17. $y = 2x^2 - 5x + 7$ 18. $y = x^2 + 5x - 4$ 19. $y = -x^2 + 4x + 2$ 20. $y = -2x^2 + 3x + 1$
21. $y = 3 + 4x - 2x^2$ 22. $y = -(-2x + 4x^2 + 5)$ 23. $y = -(3 + 4x - 5x^2)$ 24. $y = -(5 + x + 3x^2)$

B. In exercises 25-40, find the vertex and draw appropriate graph to determine graphically the approximate values of the intercepts of the graph.

25. $y = 2x^2 - 8x + 8$ 26. $y = x^2 + 4x + 4$ 27. $y = 4x^2 - 6x + 5$ 28. $y = 2x^2 + 4x + 1$
29. $y = 4 + 2x - 3x^2$ 30. $y = x^2 + 2x + 1$ 31. $y = -2x^2 - 5x + 1$ 32. $y = -x^2 - 2x - 1$
33. $y = x^2 - 2x + 1$ 34. $y = x^2 + 3x - 4$ 35. $y = x^2 - 3x - 4$ 36. $y = x^2 - 5x + 6$
37. $y = 2x^2 - 5x + 4$ 38. $y = -x^2 + 2x + 3$ 39. $y = -x^2 + 7x - 10$ 40. $y = x^2 + 6x + 8$

C. In exercises 41-56, use the graphs of exercises 25-40 to find the approximate real solutions of the equation.

41. $2x^2 - 8x + 8 = 0$ 42. $x^2 + 4x + 4 = 0$ 43. $4x^2 - 6x + 5 = 0$ 44. $2x^2 + 4x + 1 = 0$
45. $4 + 2x - 3x^2 = 0$ 46. $x^2 + 2x + 1 = 0$ 47. $-2x^2 - 5x + 1 = 0$ 48. $-x^2 - 2x - 1 = 0$
49. $x^2 - 2x + 1 = 0$ 50. $x^2 + 3x - 4 = 0$ 51. $x^2 - 3x - 4 = 0$ 52. $x^2 - 5x + 6 = 0$
53. $2x^2 - 5x + 4 = 0$ 54. $-x^2 + 2x + 3 = 0$ 55. $-x^2 + 7x - 10 = 0$ 56. $x^2 + 6x + 8 = 0$

9.5 CHAPTER SUMMARY

THE SQUARE ROOT PROPERTY

1. The square root property of equations: If b is a positive number then

$$a^2 = b \longrightarrow a = \sqrt{b} \quad \text{or} \quad a = -\sqrt{b}.$$

1. $x^2 = 4 \rightarrow x = \sqrt{4} \quad \text{or} \quad x = -\sqrt{4}$

$\rightarrow \quad x = 2 \quad \text{or} \quad x = -2$

2. We can solve equations of the type $(x - a)^2 = b$, $b > 0$, using the square root property.

2. $(3x - 2)^2 = 8$

$\rightarrow \quad 3x - 2 = \pm\sqrt{8}$

$\rightarrow \quad 3x - 2 = \pm 2\sqrt{2}$

$\rightarrow \quad 3x = 2 \pm 2\sqrt{2}$

$\rightarrow \quad x = \dfrac{2 \pm 2\sqrt{2}}{3}$

COMPLETING THE SQUARE

3. Completing the square for $x^2 + bx = k$

- Add $\left(\dfrac{b}{2}\right)^2$ to both sides of the equation.

- The first three terms form a perfect square.

3. $x^2 + 6x + 8 = 0$

$\rightarrow \quad x^2 + 6x = -8$

$\rightarrow x^2 + 6x + 9 = -8 + 9$

$(x + 3)^2 = 1$

4. Solving: $x^2 + bx + c = 0$:

- Complete the square.

- Solve the equation using square root method.

4. $x^2 + 6x + 8 = 0$

$(x + 3)^2 = 1$

$x + 3 = \pm 1$

$\rightarrow x = -3 \pm 1$

$\rightarrow x = -4, -2$

5. Solving: $ax^2 + bx + c = 0$:

- Write the equation in the standard form.

- First divide both sides by a to change the coefficient of the x^2 term to 1.

- We solve the new equation just like we solved $x^2 + bx + c = 0$.

5.

$3x^2 + 8x = 1$

$3x^2 + 8x = 1$

$3x^2 + 8x - 1 = 0$

$x^2 + \dfrac{8}{3}x - \dfrac{1}{3} = 0$

$x^2 + 2\left(\dfrac{4}{3}x\right) + \left(\dfrac{4}{3}\right)^2 - \dfrac{1}{3} - \left(\dfrac{4}{3}\right)^2 = 0$

$\left(x + \dfrac{4}{3}\right)^2 - \dfrac{19}{9} = 0 \quad \rightarrow \quad \left(x + \dfrac{4}{3}\right)^2 = \dfrac{19}{9}$

$x + \dfrac{4}{3} = \pm\sqrt{\dfrac{19}{9}} \quad \rightarrow \quad x = -\dfrac{4}{3} \pm \dfrac{\sqrt{19}}{3}$

QUADRATIC FORMULA

6. Solutions of $ax^2 + bx + c = 0$, $a \neq 0$, are :

$$x = \dfrac{-b \pm \sqrt{b^2 - 4ac}}{2a}.$$

7. $b^2 - 4ac$ is called the **discriminant** of the equation.

8. **(a)** $x^2 - 3x + 2 = 0$, $b^2 - 4ac = 1$

 (b) $x^2 + 9x + 2 = 0$, $b^2 - 4ac = 73$

 (c) $x^2 - 4x + 4 = 0$, $b^2 - 4ac = 0$

 (d) $x^2 + x + 1 = 0$, $b^2 - 4ac = -3$

9. $2x^2 + 4x - 3 = 0$

$a = 2$, $b = 4$, $c = -3$

$b^2 - 4ac = 16 - 4(2)(-3)$

$\qquad = 16 + 24 = 40$

Discriminant is not a perfect square.

Solutions are irrational.

$x = \dfrac{-b \pm \sqrt{b^2 - 4ac}}{2a}$

$\quad = \dfrac{-4 \pm \sqrt{40}}{4}$

$\quad = \dfrac{-2 + \sqrt{10}}{2}, \dfrac{-2 - \sqrt{10}}{2}$

10. $y = 2x^2 \qquad (2 > 0)$

$\quad y = -2x^2 \quad (-2 < 0)$

11. $y = x^2 - 2x + 5$

$a = 1$, $b = -2$, $c = 5$

Vertex: $x = -\dfrac{b}{2a} = \dfrac{-(-2)}{2} = 1$

$\qquad\qquad y = (1)^2 - 2(1) + 5 = 4$

The vertex is $(1, 4)$

12. $y = x^2 - 2x + 5$

The vertex is $(1, 4)$

x intercepts: $x^2 - 2x + 5 = 0$

---

8. For the quadratic equation $ax^2 + bx + c = 0$, $a \neq 0$, solutions are:

 • two real distinct numbers if $b^2 - 4ac$ is positive.

 • the same (repeated solution) if $b^2 - 4ac = 0$, and

 • not real numbers if $b^2 - 4ac < 0$.

9. Use the following steps to solve a quadratic equation by the quadratic formula.

 • Rewrite the equation in the form $ax^2 + bx + c = 0$.

 • Identify a, b, c.

 • Compute the discriminant $b^2 - 4ac$.

 • Identify the nature of the solutions.

 • Use the quadratic formula to find the exact solutions.

SOLVING QUADRATIC EQUATIONS GRAPHICALLY

10. The graph of $y = ax^2 + bx + c$; $a \neq 0$ is a parabola, which opens upward if $a > 0$ and downwards if $a < 0$.

11. Coordinates of the vertex of the parabola:

$$y = ax^2 + bx + c = a\left(x + \frac{b}{2a}\right)^2 + \frac{4ac - b^2}{4a}$$

$$x = -\frac{b}{2a}$$

Substitute this value of x in the equation of the parabola to find the y-coordinate of the vertex.

12. To graph $y = ax^2 + bx + c$, $(a \neq 0)$ carefully, we use the following steps:

 Step 1 Determine the coordinate of the vertex.

 Step 2 Find x-intercepts, if any, and find the y-intercepts.

Step 3 Plot these points and draw a smooth curve through them.

$b^2 - 4ac < 0$, no x-intercepts, no real solution.

y-intercept: $(0, 5)$

Plot a few more points.

x	–2	–1	0	**1**	2	3	4
y	13	8	5	**4**	5	8	13

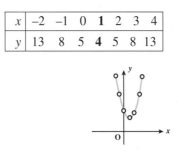

13. The solutions of the equation $ax^2 + bx + c = 0$ are given by the x-intercepts of $y = ax^2 + bx + c$.

13. The equation $x^2 - 2x + 5 = 0$ has no solution since the graph of $y = x^2 - 2x + 5$ has no x-intercepts.

14. It is often difficult to read the exact value or the x-intercept from the graph. Therefore, solutions obtained graphically are usually approximate solutions.

9.6 REVIEW EXERCISES

In exercises 1-14, solve the equation in the set of real numbers.

1. $x^2 = 9$ **2.** $y^2 = 64$ **3.** $x^2 = 16$ **4.** $y^2 = 121$ **5.** $-8p^2 = -1$

6. $-12x^2 = -2$ **7.** $4a^2 - 3 = 13$ **8.** $3x^2 - 3 = 9$ **9.** $(3y - 1)^2 = 36$ **10.** $(2x + 1)^2 = 25$

11. $(1 - 2z)^2 - 13 = 36$ **12.** $(1 + 3x)^2 - 12 = 52$ **13.** $(2y - 5)^2 = 27$ **14.** $(3x + 2)^2 = 8$

In exercises 15-20, complete the square.

15. $x^2 - 6x + 4$ **16.** $y^2 + 8y - 4$ **17.** $x^2 + 3x + 2$ **18.** $y^2 + 5y - 3$ **19.** $x^2 - 7x - 8$ **20.** $x^2 - 3x + 4$

In exercises 21-28, solve the equations using the method of completing the square.

21. $x^2 + 6x + 8 = 0$ **22.** $x^2 - 3x + 2 = 0$ **23.** $2y^2 + 6y = 5$ **24.** $3x^2 - 6x = 12$

25. $-t^2 + 4t - 2 = 0$ **26.** $-x^2 + 6x - 5 = 0$ **27.** $(2x - 1)(x + 2) = 1$ **28.** $(x + 1)(x - 2) = -2$

In exercises 29-33, use quadratic formula to solve the equation.

29. $3x^2 + 5x + 2 = 0$ **30.** $2x^2 + 3x - 4 = 0$ **31.** $4x^2 - 4x + 1 = 0$ **32.** $9x^2 - 6x + 1 = 0$ **33.** $x^3 - x^2 - x = 0$

34. The difference of the reciprocals of two consecutive even integers is $\dfrac{1}{24}$. Find the integers.

35. If an integer is added to its square the sum is 90. Find the integer.

36. The perimeter of a rectangle is 80 cm. Area of the rectangle is 351 sq cm. Find the dimensions of the rectangle.

37. There are three consecutive integers such that the square of the first increased by the product of the other two gives 154. What are the integers.

38. A certain projectile is $d = 2t^2 - 5t + 7$ feet from the ground after being in the air for t seconds. How many seconds will it take the projectile to be 25 feet from the ground?

39. The sum of two numbers is 48 and their product is 432. Find the numbers.

40. The base of a triangle is 3 inches more than the altitude drawn to it. If the area of the triangle is 35 square inches, find the base of the triangle.

41. The perimeter of a rectangle is 54 meters and its area is 180 sq meters. Find its length and width.

42. The height h, measured in feet, reached by a model rocket t seconds after take-off is given by $h(t) = -16t^2 + 480t$. After how many seconds will the rocket be at a height of 3200 ft?

43. Find the side of a square room such that if its length and width are each increased by 4 meters, the area is increased by 120 square meters.

44. A positive number is the average of two integers which differ by 4. If the product of the two integers is 357, find the number.

45. The measures of the sides of a rectangular strip are reciprocals of each other. If the perimeter of the rectangle is 20.2 inches, find the dimensions of the strip.

46. A company charges $200 for each television set on orders upto 150 sets. A large chain store orders a certain number of television sets with a deal that the price of each television set will be reduced by x dollars if the order is x sets more than 150 sets and less than or equal to 200 sets. If the order was for $30,600 how many sets did the chain store order?

47. The profit P (in millions of dollars) of a company after selling x (in thousands) units of an item is given by
$$P = -.05x^2 + 2.3x + 10$$
For what sales will the profit be 5 million dollars?

48. A polygon with n sides has $\frac{1}{2}n(n-3)$ diagonals. Does there exist a polygon with 98 diagonals? Explain your answer.

In exercises 49-54, find the vertex of the parabola. Answer whether the parabola opens upward or downward.

49. $y = 2x^2 - 6x + 1$ **50.** $y = 2x^2 - 4x - 1$ **51.** $y = x^2 + 8x + 16$

52. $y = x^2 + 12x + 36$ **53.** $y = -2x^2 + 4x - 5$ **54.** $y = -x^2 + 2x - 4$

9.7 SELF TEST

1. Solve for t using the square root property: $(1 - 5t)^2 = 49$

2. Solve for x using the square root property: $(1 + 3x)^2 = 25$

In exercises 3-6, complete the square.

3. $x^2 + 7x - 3$

4. $y^2 - 6y + 5$

5. $x^2 - 11x + 8$

6. $z^2 + 8z - 4$

In exercises 7-20, solve the quadratic equation by any method.

7. $x^2 - 3x = 7$

8. $(y + 2)^2 = -4$

9. $(x - 1)^2 = -1$

10. $y^2 - 5y = -4$

11. $-2x^2 + 3x = 1$

12. $-3x^2 - 2x = -4$

13. $\dfrac{x^2 - 7}{3} = \dfrac{x}{2}$

14. $\dfrac{x^2 + 5}{2} = \dfrac{x}{3}$

15. $2x^2 - 3x = 5 - 2x$

16. $3x^2 + 5 = -2x$

17. $(2x + 1)(x + 2) = -3$

18. $(x - 3)(x - 1) = 4$

19. $\dfrac{1}{x-1} + \dfrac{1}{x+2} = 1$

20. $\dfrac{1}{y+1} + \dfrac{1}{y-2} = 1$

21. The sum of a number and its reciprocal is $\dfrac{29}{10}$. Find the number.

22. A number exceeds its positive square root by 12. Find the number.

23. The percent markup on the cost price of a dress is the same as the cost price in dollars. If the dress is sold for $24, what was the cost price of the dress?

24. The sum of a number and its reciprocal is $\dfrac{50}{7}$. Find the number.

In exercises 25-30, graph the equation.

25. $y = x^2 + 3$

26. $y = x^2 - 4$

27. $y = x^2 + 6x + 4$

28. $y = x^2 + 4x + 2$

29. $y = -9 - 6x - x^2$

30. $y = -x^2 - 4x - 2$

31. From your graphs in exercises 25, 27, and 29, determine how many real solutions do the following equations have?

i) $x^2 + 3 = 0$ ii) $x^2 + 6x + 4 = 0$ iii) $-9 - 6x - x^2 = 0$

Give reasons for your answers.

32. From your graphs in exercises 26, 28, and 30, determine how many real solutions do the following equations have?

i) $x^2 - 4 = 0$ ii) $x^2 + 4x + 2 = 0$ iii) $-x^2 - 4x - 2 = 0$

Give reasons for your answers.

ANSWERS

ANSWERS

CHAPTER 1

SECTION 1.1

1. 5 **3.** 13 **5.** 3 **7.** 13 **9.** 3 **11.** 16, −16 **13.** None **15.** 8, − 6

17.

19. 5 **21.** −13 **23.** − 1 **25.** 5

27. −37 **29.** − 2 **31.** − 12 **33.** −2

35. −125 **37.** − 77 **39.** − 8 **41.** − 12 **43.** 5 **45.** − 4 **47.** − 2 **49.** −35 **51.** 24

53. − 96 **55.** − 960 **57.** −120 **59.** −5 **61.** 9 **63.** − 1 **65.** −8 **67.** 2 **69.** − 11 **71.** 21

73. −12 **75.** −3 **77.** −4 **79.** 21 **81.** −1 **83.** 34 **85.** 30 **87.** 1

SECTION 1.2

1. (a), (d), (e), and (f) **3.** (a) $\frac{8}{12}$ (b) $\frac{-9}{15}$ (c) $\frac{-20}{55}$ (d) $\frac{30}{72}$ **5.** (a) $\frac{2}{3}$ (b) $-\frac{4}{9}$ (c) $\frac{5}{12}$ (d) $\frac{1}{2}$ (e) $\frac{5}{12}$

7. (a) $\frac{6}{5}$ (b) $\frac{4}{5}$ (c) $-\frac{21}{25}$ (d) 2 **9.** (a) $\frac{1}{2}$ (b) $\frac{4}{3}$ (c) $\frac{3}{4}$ (d) $\frac{6}{7}$ (e) $\frac{5}{3}$ **11.** (a) $\frac{2}{5}$ (b) $\frac{23}{20}$

(c) $\frac{-17}{8}$ (d) $\frac{22}{15}$ (e) $\frac{-11}{15}$ **13.** (a) $-37\frac{3}{8}$ or $-\frac{299}{8}$ (b) $-1\frac{11}{13}$ or $-\frac{24}{13}$ (c) $-\frac{11}{96}$ (d) 3 **15.** 1 **17.** $\frac{-32}{45}$

SECTION 1.3

1. (a) Two and four tenths, (b) Negative two and four hundredths (c) Four hundred thirty-four and one hundred thirty-four thousandths

(d) Negative four thousandths. (e) Thirty-seven thousand, four hundred fifty-two and four thousand two hundred ninety-one ten-thousandths.

3. (a) 4.8, (b) −79.09, (c) 294.080 (d) 18.9 **5.** (a) −85,000 (b) 1.0 (c) −90 (d) 4,700

7. (a) −40.96 (b) 82.12, (c) − 618.31 (d) 28,737.46 **9.** (a) 25.5 (b) 31.3 (c) −107.2 **11.** (a) −7,483

(b) 874,920 (c) 0.473 (d) −0.417923 (e) 0.00925434 **13.** (a) −1.25 (b) 0.375 (c) 0.8 (d) −5.4

(e) $-0.\overline{6}$ (f) $-20.8\overline{3}$ (g) 132.142857 **15.** (a) −7.40 (b) −18.33 (c) 2170.50 (d) −2.23 (e) −15.38

SECTION 1.4

1. (a) 5% (b) 7.5% (c) 0.5% (d) 12% (e) 125% **3.** (a) 0.27 (b) 0.075 (c) .123 (d) 1.23 (e) .005

5. (a) 10% (b) 40% (c) 19% (d) 10% **7.** (a) $35 (b) $67.50 (c) $40 (d) $51 **9.** (a) 10%

(b) $33.\overline{3}\%$ (c) $58\frac{14}{17}\%$ or 58.82% **11.** $84, $131.67 **13.** 61.76% **15.** $13

SECTION 1.5

1. Whole numbers {0, 4}; Integers {0, 4, −8} ; Rational Numbers, {all}

3. Whole numbers, {5, 7, 11}; Integers {−1, 5, 7, 11}; Rational Numbers {all} **5.** Whole numbers **7.** Rational Numbers

9.

11. True **13.** True **15.** True **17.** False

19. False **21.** False **23.** True **25.** True

27. -6 **29.** 6.32 **31.** $-\dfrac{1}{2}$ **33.** $-\sqrt{3}$ **35.** $-2\dfrac{1}{4}$ **37.** -4.09 **39.** -2 **41.** $-\dfrac{1}{3}$ **43.** $0+(-8)=-8$

45. $7+0=7$ **47.** $(-19)\cdot 1=-19$ **49.** $-6\cdot 1=-6$ **51.** $1\cdot\left(-\dfrac{2}{3}\right)=-\dfrac{2}{3}$ **53.** $3+(-7)=(-7)+3$

55. $-6+(-8)=(-8)+(-6)$ **57.** $\left(-1\dfrac{2}{3}\right)+\left(2\dfrac{1}{5}\right)=2\dfrac{1}{5}+\left(-1\dfrac{2}{3}\right)$ **59.** $5\cdot(-6)=(-6)\cdot 5$ **61.** $(-6)\cdot\left(-\dfrac{1}{3}\right)=\left(-\dfrac{1}{3}\right)\cdot(-6)$

63. $(4+6)+(-2)$ **65.** $-19+(7+4)$ **67.** $[(-2)\cdot 4]\cdot(-8)$ **69.** $61+\left[\left(-\dfrac{2}{3}\right)+\left(-5\dfrac{1}{6}\right)\right]$

71. $-19\cdot\left(\dfrac{1}{-19}\right)=1$ **73.** $\dfrac{-5}{6}+\dfrac{5}{6}=0$ **75.** $1\cdot 1=1$ **77.** $\dfrac{3}{-2}\cdot\dfrac{-2}{3}=1$

79. Additive Inverse   **81.** Additive Inverse   **83.** Additive Inverse   **95.** Inverse   **97.** Distributive

99. Identity   **101.** Inverse   **103.** Distributive

SECTION 1.6

1. $4\cdot 7$ **3.** $x+9$ **5.** $7-2x$ **7.** $x+9$ **9.** $\dfrac{11}{x}$ **11.** $20-\dfrac{7}{x}$ **13.** $2x+5$ **15.** $\dfrac{3}{5}x+4$

17. $4+3\cdot 5=19$ **19.** $3^4=9^2$ **21.** $7\times 6=\dfrac{84}{2}$ **23.** $20-5\cdot 3\neq 6$ **25.** Expression   **27.** Equation

29. Equation   **31.** Expression   **33.** $x=7$ **35.** $x=2$ **37.** $y=10$ **39.** $z=2$ **41.** no solution in the set

43. 2 **45.** $4x-7=1,\ 2$ **47.** $x+\dfrac{1}{x}=1$, no solution in the set   **49.** $3+2x=12$, no solution in the set

51. $3-2x=x,\ \ x=1$ **53.** $x^2-x=0;\ \ x=0,\ \ x=1$ **55.** $\dfrac{2}{x}=x+\dfrac{1}{x};\ \ x=1$ **57.** $2x^2-1=x;\ \ x=1$

59. (a) $\neq$ or $<,\ \le$ (b) $\neq$ or $>,\ \ge$ (c) $=$ or $\ge$ or $\le$ **61.** $11>5$ **63.** $6<8$ **65.** $15>7$ **67.** $3^2\le 4^2$

69. False   **71.** True   **73.** True   **75.** False   **77.** True   **79.** $8+5>10$ **81.** $\dfrac{20}{4}=5$

83. $\dfrac{30}{5}<9$ **85.** $5\cdot 6\neq 21$ **87.** $17-2\cdot 5>3$ **89.** $9^4\neq 4^9$ **91.** -1 and 21 **93.** 29 and 7 **95.** $\dfrac{11}{9}$ and $\dfrac{33}{68}$

97. $\dfrac{3}{4}$ and $\dfrac{83}{19}$ or $4\dfrac{7}{19}$ **99.** $\dfrac{3}{2}$ **101.** 2415 **103.** 31

SELF TEST 1.7

1. -3 **3.** 8 **5.** -11 **7.**   **9.** 12 **11.** 15

13. $\dfrac{1}{2},-\dfrac{1}{2}$ **15.** $2,\ -2$ **17.** -3 **19.** -94 **21.** -16 **23.** 4 **25.** Divisible by 2, 5, and 8

27. Divisible by 2 and 8   **29.** Divisible by 2 and 5   **31.** $\dfrac{3}{5}$ **33.** $\dfrac{25}{63}$ **35.** $\dfrac{53}{80}$

37. $\dfrac{1}{5}$ **39.** $\dfrac{29}{34}$ **41.** $\dfrac{1}{4}$ **43.** $\dfrac{21}{20}$ **45.** Equivalent   **47.** Equivalent

49. Equivalent   **51.** $\dfrac{1}{7},\dfrac{1}{6},\dfrac{1}{5}$ **53.** $\dfrac{29}{30}$ **55.** $\dfrac{5}{6}$ **57.** (a) $1\dfrac{29}{36}$ (b) $1\dfrac{1}{32}$ (c) $5\dfrac{4}{9}$

59. (a) 41.01 (b) $1,000,321.006$ **61.** (a) 72 (b) $90,000$ (c) $240,000$

63. (a) $345,230$ (b) $9,932,560,000,000$ (c) 3.14835 (d) 0.007895123

65. (a) 25% (b) 150% (c) 60% (d) 175% (e) 250% (f) 180% **67.** \$75, \$183.75

69. \$2,000   **71.** (a) $1,\ 0$ (b) $1,\ 0,\ -1$ (c) $-\dfrac{4}{3},\ 1,\ 0.54,0,-1,\ 3.\overline{4},\ 6.\overline{38}$ **73.** $-\dfrac{2}{3}$ **75.** $3.8\overline{9}$

77. 4, Commutative Property of Addition   **79.** 7, Inverse Property of Addition   **81.** 1, Multiplication Identity

83. -5, Associative Property of Addition   **85.** 4 Distributive Property

87. (a) -48 (b) 11 (c) -10 (d) $-\dfrac{7}{18}$

CHAPTER 2

SECTION 2.1

1. -15 3. 6 5. -7 7. 4 9. -1 11. 1 13. -1 15. x^2, 2

17. xy, 2 19. x^2y^2, 1 21. y^2zx, -3 23. No variable part, -7 25. x^2, 1 27. x^2y, -4 29. Unlike terms

31. Like tems   33. Like terms   35. Unlike terms   37. Like terms   39. Unlike terms   41. $-3m$ 43. $11s - 18$

45. $8t^2 + 28$ 47. $17 - 6x$ 49. $y^2 + 3y + 13x$ 51. $y - 8x$ 53. $20x + y$ 55. $2z^3 - 11z^2 + 5z + 39$

57. $-18p - 8pq - 10q$ 59. $x + \dfrac{y}{3} + 4$ 61. $12a + 45$ 63. $3x + 114$ 65. $\dfrac{3}{2}x + \dfrac{7}{2}$ 67. $2x$

69. x^2 71. $2x + 14.8$ 73. $3x + 9$ 75. $5x - 21$ 77. $-12x + 7$ 79. $2x - 4$ 81. $3x - 16$ 83. $-4x - 13$

85. $-4x + 27$ 87. $3a - 11$ 89. $-2x + 12$ 91. $-x + 20$ 93. $6a + 16$ 95. $-2x + 2y$ 97. $-5x + \dfrac{1}{2}$

99. $3y + 14$ 101. $12x^2 - 20x + 8$ 103. $x + 8x$; $9x$ 105. $x + 2(x + 1)$; $3x + 2$ 107. $2x - 10$

109. $\dfrac{2x + 6}{x}$ 111. $x^3 - 10x$ 113. $x + 4 - 2x$; $4 - x$ 115. $(8 - 3x)(x - 4)$

SECTION 2.2

1. Linear   3. Non-linear   5. Linear   7. Linear   9. Linear   11. Non-linear   13. Yes   15. Yes   17. No

19. Yes   21. Yes   23. $x = 3$ 25. $x = -1$ 27. $x = 16$ 29. $x = -3$ 31. $x = 33$ 33. $x = 3$ 35. $x = -5$

37. $x = 9$ 39. $x = -24$ 41. $x = 9$ 43. $x = 1$ 45. $x = \dfrac{7}{3}$ 47. $x = \dfrac{9}{5}$ 49. $x = \dfrac{-2}{9}$ 51. $x = \dfrac{7}{10}$

53. $x = \dfrac{-29}{36}$ 55. $x = 13.9$ 57. $x = -6$ 59. $x = -1.4$ 61. $x = -2.3$ 63. $x = 5.1$ 65. $x = \dfrac{2}{3}$ 67. $x = \dfrac{-9}{5}$

69. $x = 2$ 71. $x = -2$ 73. $x = \dfrac{-8}{3}$ 75. $x = \dfrac{-5}{7}$ 77. $x = \dfrac{1}{3}$ 79. $x = -\dfrac{3}{4}$ 81. $x = \dfrac{1}{3}$ 83. $x = \dfrac{7}{4}$

85. $x = 2$ 87. $x = \dfrac{9}{5}$ 89. $x = \dfrac{1}{3}$ 91. $x = \dfrac{11}{7}$ 93. $x = \dfrac{3}{4}$ 95. $x = -4$ 97. $x = -3$ 99. $x = -4$

101. $x = -\dfrac{4}{5}$ 103. $x = \dfrac{7}{2}$ 105. $x = -1$ 107. $x = -2$ 109. $x = -\dfrac{3}{7}$ 111. $x = -\dfrac{5}{3}$ 113. $x = -\dfrac{4}{3}$ 115. $x = -\dfrac{9}{7}$

117. $x = -\dfrac{9}{4}$ 119. $x = \dfrac{5}{11}$ 121. $x = \dfrac{14}{5}$ 123. $x = 42.9$ 125. $a = 10$ 127. $a = -\dfrac{8}{5}$ 129. $y = \dfrac{20}{3}$ 131. $x = 50$

133. $x = -14$ 135. $x = 25$ 137. $y = -12$ 139. $x = 0$ 141. $x = 1$ 143. $x = 6$ 145. $x = \dfrac{1}{2}$ 147. $x = 1$

149. $x = 4$ 151. $x = -3\dfrac{3}{4}$ 153. $x = 7$ 155. $x = 2$ 157. $x = -2$ 159. $x = 5$ 161. $x = -9$ 163. $x = \dfrac{5}{2}$

165. $x = \dfrac{11}{6}$ 167. $x = 3$ 169. $x = \dfrac{9}{4}$ 171. $x = \dfrac{27}{20}$ 173. $x = \dfrac{1}{2}$ 175. $x = -2$ 177. $x = \dfrac{14}{27}$ 179. $x = 5$

181. $x + 7 = 10$; $x = 3$ 183. $2x + 10 = x - 5$; $x = -15$ 185. $x + (x + 1) = 11$; 5 and 6

187. $2(x - 20) = 4x$, $x = -20$

SECTION 2.3

1. $x = 1$ 3. $a = \dfrac{1}{2}$ 5. $x = 2$ 7. $x = 28$ 9. $x = \dfrac{29}{2}$ 11. $x = \dfrac{-3}{77}$ 13. $x = -2$ 15. $x = \dfrac{33}{4}$

17. $x = 4$ 19. $x = \dfrac{-7}{6}$ 21. $x = -7.9$ 23. $x = -2.56$ or $\dfrac{64}{25}$ 25. $x = -1.5$ 27. $x = 10$ 29. $x = 5.1$

31. $x = 20$ 33. $x = -1.7$ 35. $x = 8.88$ 37. $x = \dfrac{-85}{27}$ 39. $x = \dfrac{-12}{7}$ 41. $x = \dfrac{-25}{4}$ 43. $a = 60$ 45. $x = 3$

47. $x = 0.175$ or $-\dfrac{7}{40}$ **49.** $x = 10.248$ **51.** $x = -14.83$ **53.** $t = 81.2$ **55.** $x = 20$ **57.** $y = 13.31$

59. $x = 1.71$ **61.** $x = 4.8$ **63.** $x = 7.09$ **65.** $x = -1.5$ **67.** Identity   **69.** Identity   **71.** Identity   **73.** Identity

75. No solution   **77.** Only one solution   **79.** Identity   **81.** No solution   **83.** No solution   **85.** Identity

SECTION 2.4

1. 5   **3.** 8   **5.** -2 **7.** 0   **9.** 18 cents   **11.** 9 quarters ,7 dimes   **13.** 18 cents, $.18 **15.** $w = 4\,\text{cm}$, $l = 13\,\text{cm}$

17. Roosters = 56, Hens = 94   **19.** 9, 19, 29 inches   **21.** $25°$ **23.** Tranquilizers = 30 , Painkillers = 42

25. 16 cm, 13 cm, 13 cm   **27.** 32 yrs, 8 yrs   **29.** $400   **31.** 97   **33.** 40 years

SECTION 2.5

1. 4   **3.** 4   **5.** 1525   **7.** 4   **9.** 95   **11.** $4\dfrac{1}{3}$ **13.** $x = 6 - 2y$ **15.** $x = \dfrac{3y+5}{2}$ **17.** $x = \dfrac{3-y}{6}$ **19.** $x = \dfrac{5y+2}{3}$

21. $y = \dfrac{-5x-1}{6}$ **23.** $\dfrac{2A}{b}$ **25.** $\dfrac{p-2w}{2}$ **27.** $\dfrac{A-P}{Pr}$ **29.** $\dfrac{5(F-32)}{9} = c$ **31.** $m = \dfrac{y-b}{x}$ **33.** $n = \dfrac{b-a}{d} + 1$ or $\left(\dfrac{b-a+d}{d}\right)$

35. $T = \dfrac{VP}{NR}$ **37.** $m = \dfrac{E}{c^2}$ **39.** $w = \dfrac{T+gm}{f}$ **41.** $b_1 = \dfrac{2A - h\,b_2}{h}$ **43.** $y = \dfrac{-2}{5}x + \dfrac{4}{5}$ **45.** 6, 7, 8

47. Kennedy : 303 votes, Nixon : 219 votes   **49.** 30 yds   **51.** 21 cms   **53.** $107°, 73°$ **55.** $20°$, $70°$

SECTION 2.6

1. $\dfrac{3}{5}$ **3.** $\dfrac{4}{3}$ **5.** $\dfrac{2}{3}$ **7.** $\dfrac{4}{3}$ **9.** $\dfrac{4}{5}$ **11.** 16   **13.** $\dfrac{5}{3}$ **15.** 2   **17.** $\dfrac{16}{3}$

19. $\dfrac{5}{12}$ **21.** Not a proportion   **23.** Proportion   **25.** Proportion   **27.** Not a proportion   **29.** Proportion

31. Proportion   **33.** $a = 24$ **35.** 42   **37.** $x = 10$ **39.** $y = 100$ **41.** $k = \dfrac{35}{8}$ or 4.375   **43.** $m = \dfrac{20}{7}$ or $2\dfrac{6}{7}$ **45.** $x = 10$

47. $x = -80$ **49.** $x = 16$ **51.** $x = -10$ **53.** 10.5   **55.** $x = 4$ **57.** $7.80   **59.** 387.38 miles   **61.** 2176.2 miles

63. 250.75 miles   **65.** 35 oz for $2.19   **67.** 15.75 lb   **69.** 220 tickets   **71.** 159 tickets

73. 8.081 lbs   **75.** 9.75 in   **77.** 13.36 lb   **79.** 15 ft   **81.** 45 ft   **83.** 7.67 ft or 7 ft 8 inches

SECTION 2.7

1. Caramels ; 2 lbs, Chocolate ; 3 lbs   **3.** 40 lbs   **5.** 45 gallons   **7.** 40 liters   **9.** 50 quarts   **11.** $440,000

13. $250   **15.** $45,000   **17.** 9%   **19.** 40 miles   **21.** 3 hrs   **23.** 2mi/hr   **25.** 9 p.m.

27. 1 hour   **29.** 1.1 hour   **31.** 14 gallons   **33.** 3 lbs of 20% and 2 lbs of 15%   **35.** $64,177.04

SECTION 2.8

1.   **3.**   **5.**

7.   **9.**   **11.**

13.   **15.**   **17.** $-2 < x < 5$ **19.** $4 \le x \le 10$ **21.** $x > 4$

23. $x \le -12$ **25.** $x < 1$ **27.** $x \le -7$ **29.** $x \le -9$ **31.** $x < 9$ **33.** $x \le 10$ **35.** $x > -4$

37. $x \ge -2$ **39.** $x > 9$ **41.** $x > 3$ **43.** $x > -12$ **45.** $x < 2$ **47.** $x \le \dfrac{-1}{6}$ **49.** $x \le \dfrac{8}{7}$

51. $x \le \dfrac{11}{8}$ **53.** $x \le \dfrac{2}{7}$ **55.** $x > 0.1$ **57.** $x > 20$ **59.** $x \le -0.6$ **61.** $x > 0.4$ **63.** $x > 23$

Answers

65. $p > -2$

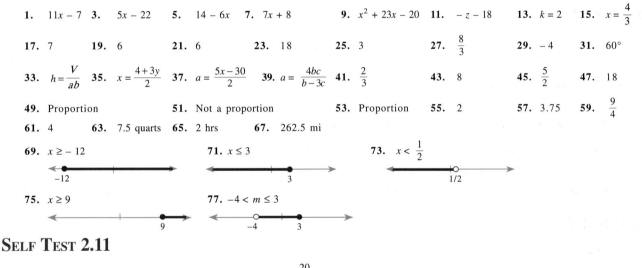

67. $x \le 3$

69. $z < -1$

71. $k \le -3$

73. $x \le -5$

75. $x \ge 5$

77. $x < 5$

79. $x \ge -3$ **81.** All real numbers   **83.** $x > \dfrac{-5}{16}$ **85.** $y < -\dfrac{1}{8}$ **87.** $x \ge \dfrac{1}{4}$

89. $x \le 1$ **91.** $x < \dfrac{13}{17}$ **93.** $x > \dfrac{7}{3}$ **95.** $1 < x < 3$ **97.** $-9 \le x < -3$ **99.** $-9 < x \le -7$

101. $9 < x \le 15$ **103.** $-11 \le x \le -6$ **105.** $\dfrac{3}{2} < x \le 2$ **107.** $\dfrac{3}{4} < x \le \dfrac{11}{4}$ **109.** $\dfrac{-3}{7} \le x < \dfrac{3}{7}$ **111.** $\dfrac{5}{8} \le x \le 1$

113. $\dfrac{-5}{4} \le x \le 0$ **115.** $\dfrac{-4}{9} < x \le -\dfrac{1}{3}$ **117.** $-10 \le x < -4$ **119.** $1000 \le p \le 15{,}000$ **121.** $50 < S < 100$

123. $4000 \le A < 9000$ **125.** $.15 < F < .25$ **127.** Profit $\le \$75$ **129.** $5000   **131.** No   **133.** 103; Not Possible

135. 1.89 hrs   **137.** 23 min   **139.** $805 < 23.7 \times 35.8 < 864$ **141.** 23 years

REVIEW EXERCISES 2.10

1. $11x - 7$ **3.** $5x - 22$ **5.** $14 - 6x$ **7.** $7x + 8$ **9.** $x^2 + 23x - 20$ **11.** $-z - 18$ **13.** $k = 2$ **15.** $x = \dfrac{4}{3}$

17. 7   **19.** 6   **21.** 6   **23.** 18   **25.** 3   **27.** $\dfrac{8}{3}$ **29.** -4 **31.** $60°$

33. $h = \dfrac{V}{ab}$ **35.** $x = \dfrac{4 + 3y}{2}$ **37.** $a = \dfrac{5x - 30}{2}$ **39.** $a = \dfrac{4bc}{b - 3c}$ **41.** $\dfrac{2}{3}$ **43.** 8   **45.** $\dfrac{5}{2}$ **47.** 18

49. Proportion   **51.** Not a proportion   **53.** Proportion   **55.** 2   **57.** 3.75   **59.** $\dfrac{9}{4}$

61. 4   **63.** 7.5 quarts   **65.** 2 hrs   **67.** 262.5 mi

69. $x \ge -12$ **71.** $x \le 3$ **73.** $x < \dfrac{1}{2}$

75. $x \ge 9$ **77.** $-4 < m \le 3$

SELF TEST 2.11

1. $2x + 7y - 3$ **3.** $-6x - 4y$ **5.** $p = -20$ **7.** $y = \dfrac{20}{3}$ **9.** -20 **11.** No solution   **13.** Identity : all real numbers are solutions

15. 14   **17.** $-\dfrac{8}{9}$ **19.** $\dfrac{11}{3}$ **21.** $50°$ **23.** $h = \dfrac{S - 2ab}{2(a + b)}$ **25.** $9000 at 7.5% , $5000 at 6.5%

27. $x < 4$ **29.** $x \le \dfrac{3}{2}$ **31.** $a > 3$

33. $-1 \le k \le 2$ **35.** $-11 \le x < 14$ **37.** $x \ge -1$

CHAPTER 3
SECTION 3.1

1. No   **3.** Yes   **5.** Yes   **7.** No   **9.** No   **11.** Yes   **13.** Yes   **15.** Yes   **17.** (0, 2)   **19.** (1, 0)

21. (0, 7)   **23.** (2, 2)   **25.** (2, 0)   **27.** (2, 8)   **29.** (9, −1)

31.
x	y
3	0
0	2
−3	4
6	−2

33.
x	y
0	1
2	0
−6	4
−4	3

35.
x	y
1	4
4	13
5	16

37.
x	y
4	3
0	−3
2	0

39.
x	y
1	1
4	0
−2	2

41.
x	y
0	6
2	0
1	3

43.
x	y
1	−1
2	1
−1	−5

45.
x	y
−4	0
0	2
2	3

47.
x	y
5	−3
5	4
5	7

49.
x	y
0	−4
−1	−4
4	−4

51.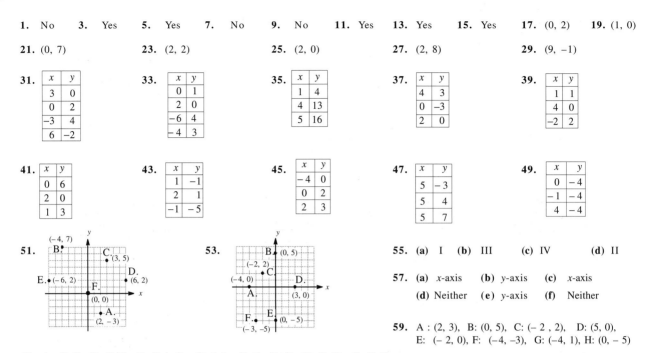

53.

55. **(a)** I   **(b)** III   **(c)** IV   **(d)** II

57. **(a)** x-axis   **(b)** y-axis   **(c)** x-axis
(d) Neither   **(e)** y-axis   **(f)** Neither

59. A : (2, 3), B: (0, 5), C: (− 2 , 2),   D: (5, 0), E: (− 2, 0), F: (−4, −3), G: (−4, 1), H: (0, − 5)

61. A : (2, 5), B: (5, 1), C: (3 , −1),   D: (−1, −6), E: (4, 0), F: (0, 3), G: (0, 0)

63. A : (1, 5), B: (4, 1), C: (2 , 0),   D: (0, −2), E: (3, 4), F: (−5, −1), G: (−6, −1), H: (−4, 3)   **65.** $y = -2x$ **67.** $y = \frac{x}{2} - 1$

69. $y = 2x + 2$ **71.** $y = 2x + 1$ **73.** $y = 3x - 2$ **75.** $y = x + 3$ **77.** $y = 3x - 2$ **79.** $y = x - 3$

81. $y = 2x - 4$ **83.** $y = 4x - 3$ **85.** $y = \frac{1}{3}x - 2$ **87.** $y = \frac{-2}{3}x + 4$

SECTION 3.2

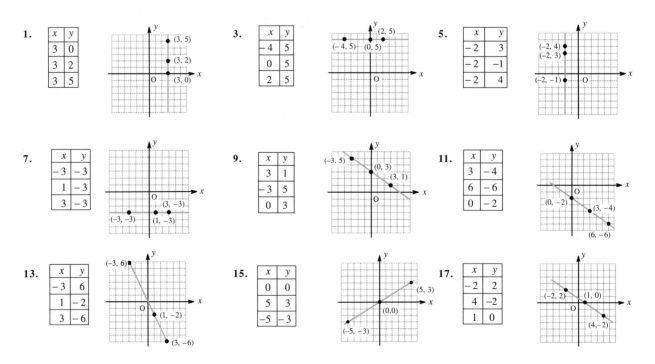

1.
x	y
3	0
3	2
3	5

3.
x	y
−4	5
0	5
2	5

5.
x	y
−2	3
−2	−1
−2	4

7.
x	y
−3	−3
1	−3
3	−3

9.
x	y
3	1
−3	5
0	3

11.
x	y
3	−4
6	−6
0	−2

13.
x	y
−3	6
1	−2
3	−6

15.
x	y
0	0
5	3
−5	−3

17.
x	y
−2	2
4	−2
1	0

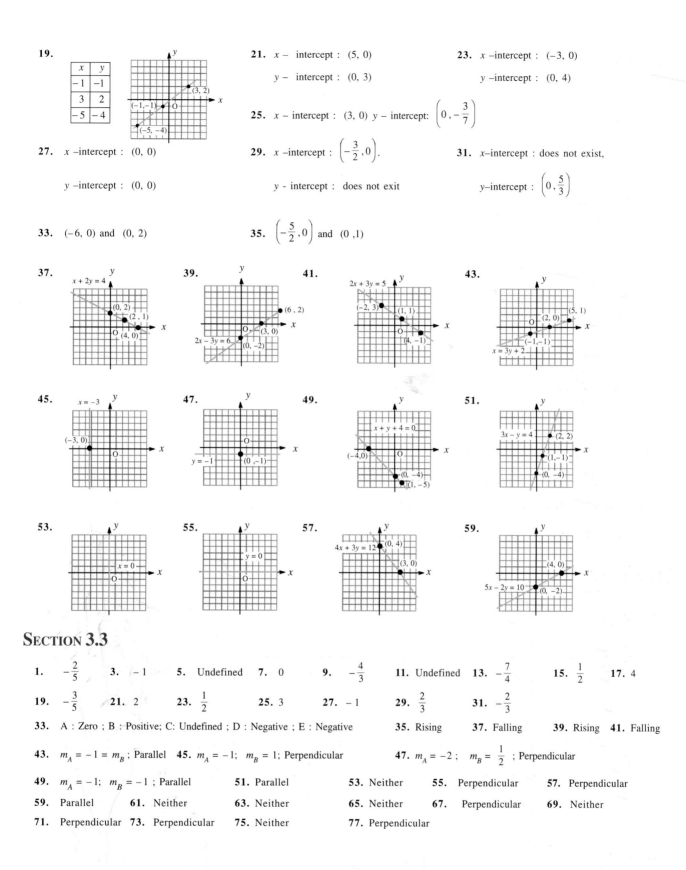

19.

x	y
−1	−1
3	2
−5	−4

21. $x-$ intercept : $(5, 0)$

$y-$ intercept : $(0, 3)$

23. x –intercept : $(-3, 0)$

y –intercept : $(0, 4)$

25. $x-$ intercept : $(3, 0)$ $y-$ intercept: $\left(0, -\dfrac{3}{7}\right)$

27. x –intercept : $(0, 0)$

y –intercept : $(0, 0)$

29. x –intercept : $\left(-\dfrac{3}{2}, 0\right)$.

y - intercept : does not exit

31. x–intercept : does not exist,

y–intercept : $\left(0, \dfrac{5}{3}\right)$

33. $(-6, 0)$ and $(0, 2)$

35. $\left(-\dfrac{5}{2}, 0\right)$ and $(0, 1)$

SECTION 3.3

1. $-\dfrac{2}{5}$ **3.** -1 **5.** Undefined **7.** 0 **9.** $-\dfrac{4}{3}$ **11.** Undefined **13.** $-\dfrac{7}{4}$ **15.** $\dfrac{1}{2}$ **17.** 4

19. $-\dfrac{3}{5}$ **21.** 2 **23.** $\dfrac{1}{2}$ **25.** 3 **27.** -1 **29.** $\dfrac{2}{3}$ **31.** $-\dfrac{2}{3}$

33. A : Zero ; B : Positive; C: Undefined ; D : Negative ; E : Negative **35.** Rising **37.** Falling **39.** Rising **41.** Falling

43. $m_A = -1 = m_B$; Parallel **45.** $m_A = -1$; $m_B = 1$; Perpendicular **47.** $m_A = -2$; $m_B = \dfrac{1}{2}$; Perpendicular

49. $m_A = -1$; $m_B = -1$; Parallel **51.** Parallel **53.** Neither **55.** Perpendicular **57.** Perpendicular

59. Parallel **61.** Neither **63.** Neither **65.** Neither **67.** Perpendicular **69.** Neither

71. Perpendicular **73.** Perpendicular **75.** Neither **77.** Perpendicular

Section 3.4

1. $y = 2x + 3$
3. $y = -3x - 2$
5. $y = -x + \dfrac{2}{3}$
7. $y = \dfrac{3}{5}x + 4$
9. $y = -\dfrac{1}{2}$

11.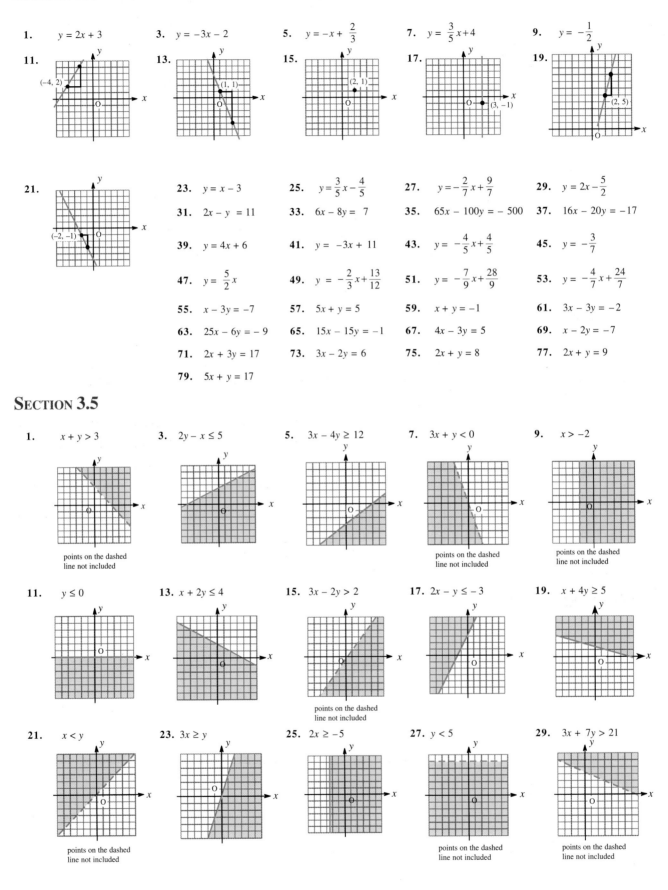
13.
15.
17.
19.

21.

23. $y = x - 3$
25. $y = \dfrac{3}{5}x - \dfrac{4}{5}$
27. $y = -\dfrac{2}{7}x + \dfrac{9}{7}$
29. $y = 2x - \dfrac{5}{2}$

31. $2x - y = 11$
33. $6x - 8y = 7$
35. $65x - 100y = -500$
37. $16x - 20y = -17$

39. $y = 4x + 6$
41. $y = -3x + 11$
43. $y = -\dfrac{4}{5}x + \dfrac{4}{5}$
45. $y = -\dfrac{3}{7}$

47. $y = \dfrac{5}{2}x$
49. $y = -\dfrac{2}{3}x + \dfrac{13}{12}$
51. $y = -\dfrac{7}{9}x + \dfrac{28}{9}$
53. $y = -\dfrac{4}{7}x + \dfrac{24}{7}$

55. $x - 3y = -7$
57. $5x + y = 5$
59. $x + y = -1$
61. $3x - 3y = -2$

63. $25x - 6y = -9$
65. $15x - 15y = -1$
67. $4x - 3y = 5$
69. $x - 2y = -7$

71. $2x + 3y = 17$
73. $3x - 2y = 6$
75. $2x + y = 8$
77. $2x + y = 9$

79. $5x + y = 17$

Section 3.5

1. $x + y > 3$
3. $2y - x \le 5$
5. $3x - 4y \ge 12$
7. $3x + y < 0$
9. $x > -2$

points on the dashed line not included

points on the dashed line not included

points on the dashed line not included

11. $y \le 0$
13. $x + 2y \le 4$
15. $3x - 2y > 2$
17. $2x - y \le -3$
19. $x + 4y \ge 5$

points on the dashed line not included

21. $x < y$
23. $3x \ge y$
25. $2x \ge -5$
27. $y < 5$
29. $3x + 7y > 21$

points on the dashed line not included

points on the dashed line not included

points on the dashed line not included

Answers

A.8

31. $2x + 3y < 6$ **33.** $y < 5x + 2$ **35.** $y \geq \dfrac{3}{4}x + \dfrac{5}{4}$ **37.** $y > \dfrac{-x}{4} - \dfrac{1}{4}$ **39.** $2 + y < 3$

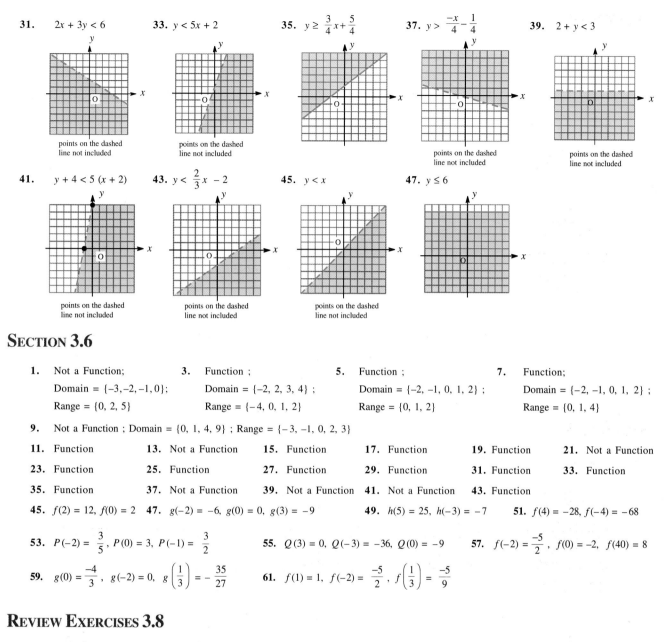

points on the dashed line not included   points on the dashed line not included   points on the dashed line not included   points on the dashed line not included

41. $y + 4 < 5\,(x + 2)$ **43.** $y < \dfrac{2}{3}x - 2$ **45.** $y < x$ **47.** $y \leq 6$

points on the dashed line not included   points on the dashed line not included   points on the dashed line not included

SECTION 3.6

1. Not a Function;
Domain = $\{-3, -2, -1, 0\}$;
Range = $\{0, 2, 5\}$

3. Function ;
Domain = $\{-2, 2, 3, 4\}$;
Range = $\{-4, 0, 1, 2\}$

5. Function ;
Domain = $\{-2, -1, 0, 1, 2\}$;
Range = $\{0, 1, 2\}$

7. Function;
Domain = $\{-2, -1, 0, 1, 2\}$;
Range = $\{0, 1, 4\}$

9. Not a Function ; Domain = $\{0, 1, 4, 9\}$; Range = $\{-3, -1, 0, 2, 3\}$

11. Function   **13.** Not a Function   **15.** Function   **17.** Function   **19.** Function   **21.** Not a Function

23. Function   **25.** Function   **27.** Function   **29.** Function   **31.** Function   **33.** Function

35. Function   **37.** Not a Function   **39.** Not a Function   **41.** Not a Function   **43.** Function

45. $f(2) = 12,\ f(0) = 2$ **47.** $g(-2) = -6,\ g(0) = 0,\ g(3) = -9$ **49.** $h(5) = 25,\ h(-3) = -7$ **51.** $f(4) = -28,\ f(-4) = -68$

53. $P(-2) = \dfrac{3}{5},\ P(0) = 3,\ P(-1) = \dfrac{3}{2}$ **55.** $Q(3) = 0,\ Q(-3) = -36,\ Q(0) = -9$ **57.** $f(-2) = \dfrac{-5}{2},\ f(0) = -2,\ f(40) = 8$

59. $g(0) = \dfrac{-4}{3},\ g(-2) = 0,\ g\left(\dfrac{1}{3}\right) = -\dfrac{35}{27}$ **61.** $f(1) = 1,\ f(-2) = \dfrac{-5}{2},\ f\left(\dfrac{1}{3}\right) = \dfrac{-5}{9}$

REVIEW EXERCISES 3.8

1. Yes   **3.** No   **5.** Yes   **7.** $(11, -2)$ **9.** $(-4, -5)$

11.

x	y
1	−2
−3	−10
7 / 2	3
3	2

13.

x	y
−2	−1
−2	2
−2	0

15.

x	y
4	−3
4	1
4	2

17.

x	y
−2	−5
0	−5
3	−5

19.

x	y
−3	−2
0	0
3	2

21.

x	y
−1	1
3	−2
−5	4

23.

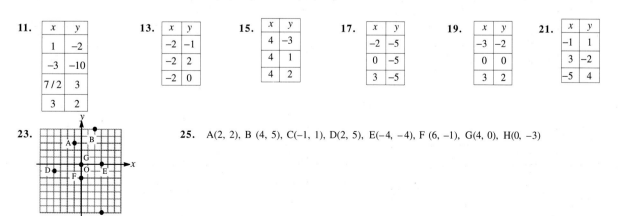

25. A(2, 2), B (4, 5), C(−1, 1), D(2, 5), E(−4, −4), F (6, −1), G(4, 0), H(0, −3)

27. x – intercept : $(2, 0)$
y – intercept : $(0, 3)$

29. x – intercept : $(5, 0)$
y – intercept : $(0, -4)$

31.

33.

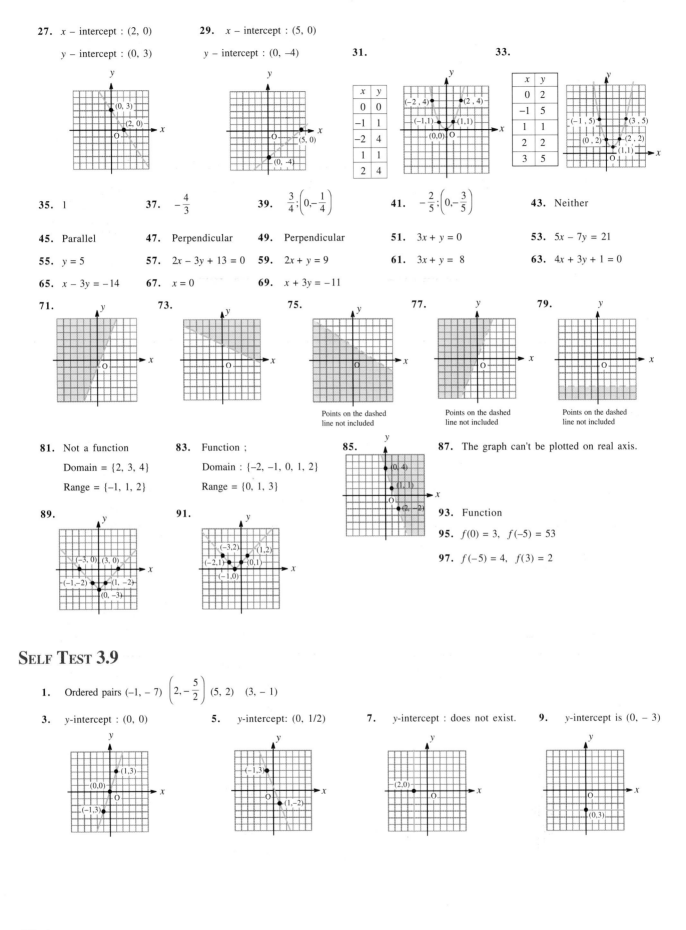

x	y
0	0
-1	1
-2	4
1	1
2	4

x	y
0	2
-1	5
1	1
2	2
3	5

35. 1

37. $-\dfrac{4}{3}$

39. $\dfrac{3}{4}; \left(0, -\dfrac{1}{4}\right)$

41. $-\dfrac{2}{5}; \left(0, -\dfrac{3}{5}\right)$

43. Neither

45. Parallel

47. Perpendicular

49. Perpendicular

51. $3x + y = 0$

53. $5x - 7y = 21$

55. $y = 5$

57. $2x - 3y + 13 = 0$

59. $2x + y = 9$

61. $3x + y = 8$

63. $4x + 3y + 1 = 0$

65. $x - 3y = -14$

67. $x = 0$

69. $x + 3y = -11$

71.

73.

75.
Points on the dashed
line not included

77.
Points on the dashed
line not included

79.
Points on the dashed
line not included

81. Not a function
Domain = {2, 3, 4}
Range = {-1, 1, 2}

83. Function ;
Domain : {-2, -1, 0, 1, 2}
Range = {0, 1, 3}

85.

87. The graph can't be plotted on real axis.

89.

91.

93. Function

95. $f(0) = 3$, $f(-5) = 53$

97. $f(-5) = 4$, $f(3) = 2$

SELF TEST 3.9

1. Ordered pairs $(-1, -7)$ $\left(2, -\dfrac{5}{2}\right)$ $(5, 2)$ $(3, -1)$

3. y-intercept : $(0, 0)$

5. y-intercept: $(0, 1/2)$

7. y-intercept : does not exist.

9. y-intercept is $(0, -3)$

11. $m = \dfrac{2}{5}$ **13.** $m = 0$ **15.** m = undefined; vertical line   **17.** $m = \dfrac{-3}{2}$ y-intercept $\left(0, \dfrac{7}{2}\right)$

y-intercept $\left(0, -\dfrac{3}{2}\right)$ y-intercept : does not exist

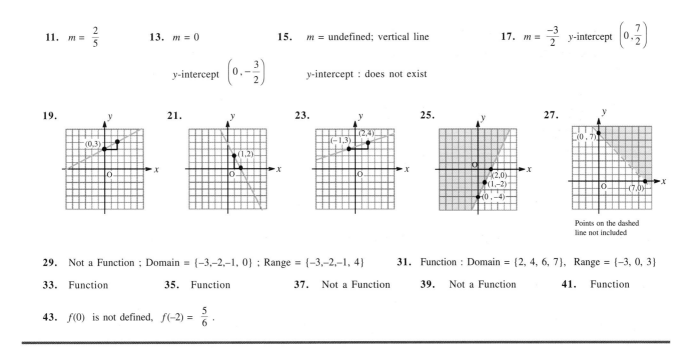

19.   **21.**   **23.**   **25.**   **27.**

Points on the dashed line not included

29. Not a Function ; Domain = {–3,–2,–1, 0} ; Range = {–3,–2,–1, 4}   **31.** Function : Domain = {2, 4, 6, 7}, Range = {–3, 0, 3}

33. Function   **35.** Function   **37.** Not a Function   **39.** Not a Function   **41.** Function

43. $f(0)$ is not defined, $f(–2) = \dfrac{5}{6}$.

Chapter 4

Section 4.1

1. Solution   **3.** Solution   **5.** Not a solution   **7.** Not a solution   **9.** Not a solution
11. Solution   **13.** Not a solution   **15.** Solution   **17.** Solution

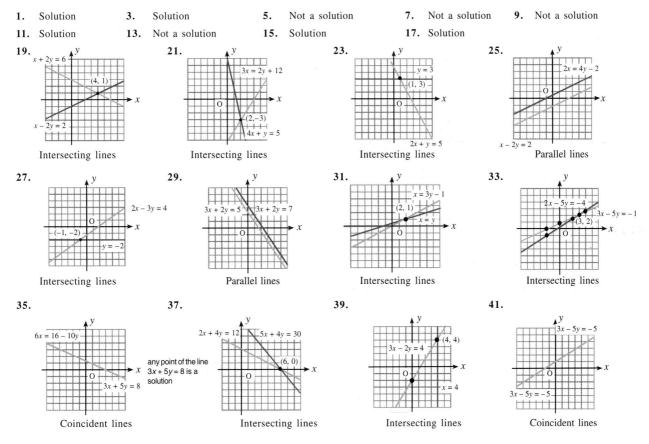

19. Intersecting lines   **21.** Intersecting lines   **23.** Intersecting lines   **25.** Parallel lines

27. Intersecting lines   **29.** Parallel lines   **31.** Intersecting lines   **33.** Intersecting lines

35. Coincident lines   **37.** any point of the line $3x + 5y = 8$ is a solution   Intersecting lines   **39.** Intersecting lines   **41.** Coincident lines

43. $y = \frac{3}{4}x - \frac{7}{4}$, $y = x + 7$; Intersecting   **45.** $y = \frac{-5}{2}x + 4$, $y = \frac{2}{5}x + \frac{1}{5}$; Intersecting

47. $y = \frac{2}{3}x - \frac{2}{3}$, $y = \frac{2}{3}x + \frac{5}{9}$; Parallel   **49.** $y = 2x - 4$, $y = 2x + 9$; Parallel

51. $y = x$, $y = x - 1$; Parallel   **53.** $y = x - 1$, $y = -x + 1$; Intersecting

55. $y = x$; $y = -2x + 2$; Intersecting   **57.** $y = x - 4$, $y = 0$; Intersecting

59. $y = \frac{-2}{3}x + \frac{7}{3}$, $y = \frac{-2}{3}x + \frac{7}{3}$; Coincident   **61.** $y = \frac{-9}{35}x + \frac{30}{7}$, $y = -\frac{6}{7}x - \frac{15}{2}$; Intersecting

Section 4.2

1. $(3, 2)$ **3.** $(4, -1)$ **5.** $\left(-\frac{1}{2}, 4\right)$ **7.** $(5, 2)$ **9.** $(3, -1)$

11. Many solutions ; Coincident   **13.** $\left(\frac{9}{2}, \frac{3}{2}\right)$ **15.** $(-3, 2)$ **17.** $(3, -7)$ **19.** $(0, 2)$

21. $\left(\frac{1}{7}, \frac{45}{14}\right)$ **23.** $(8, 10)$ **25.** No solutions; Parallel   **27.** $(2, 3)$ **29.** $\left(\frac{7}{5}, \frac{-2}{5}\right)$

31. $(1, -3)$; Intersecting   **33.** $(3, 1)$; Intersecting   **35.** $(2, -1)$; Intersecting   **37.** $\left(\frac{1}{4}, \frac{2}{3}\right)$; Intersecting   **39.** $\left(\frac{1}{2}, \frac{3}{2}\right)$; Intersecting

41. $\left(\frac{-1}{3}, 1\right)$; Intersecting   **43.** $(7, 0)$; Intersecting   **45.** $\left(\frac{4}{5}, \frac{-7}{5}\right)$; Intersecting   **47.** $\left(\frac{35}{11}, \frac{20}{11}\right)$; Intersecting   **49.** $(10, 5)$ Intersecting

51. No solution; Parallel   **53.** Many solutions; Coincident   **55.** $(1.2, -2.4)$; Intersecting   **57.** $\left(\frac{-2}{3}, \frac{-5}{2}\right)$; Intersecting

59. $(-2.5, 1.7)$; Intersecting   **61.** No solutions; Parallel   **63.** $(112.8, 67.2)$; Intersecting   **65.** $(4, 0)$; Intersecting

Section 4.3

1. $(5, -2)$ **3.** $\left(\frac{7}{2}, \frac{3}{2}\right)$ **5.** $(-3, 1)$ **7.** $\left(\frac{1}{2}, \frac{3}{2}\right)$ **9.** No solution   **11.** $\left(0, \frac{4}{5}\right)$ **13.** $(1, 2)$ **15.** $\left(\frac{1}{2}, \frac{2}{3}\right)$

17. $\left(\frac{5}{3}, 0\right)$ **19.** $(2, -5)$ **21.** $(-1, 5)$ **23.** No solution   **25.** $(8, -9)$ **27.** $\left(\frac{1}{3}, \frac{1}{3}\right)$ **29.** Infinetly ; Many solutions

31. No solutions; Parallel   **33.** No solutions; Parallel   **35.** $\left(\frac{3}{10}, \frac{1}{2}\right)$; Intersecting   **37.** $(4, 8)$; Intersecting   **39.** $\left(\frac{1}{2}, -3\right)$; Intersecting

41. $(-1, -2)$; Intersecting   **43.** $(4, 0)$; Intersecting   **45.** No solutions; Parallel   **47.** $(6.84, -5.84)$; Intersecting   **49.** $\left(\frac{8}{5}, \frac{-3}{10}\right)$; Intersecting

51. No solutions; Parallel   **53.** $(0, -3)$; Intersecting   **55.** No solutions; Parallel

Section 4.4

1.   **3.**   **5.**   **7.**   **9.**

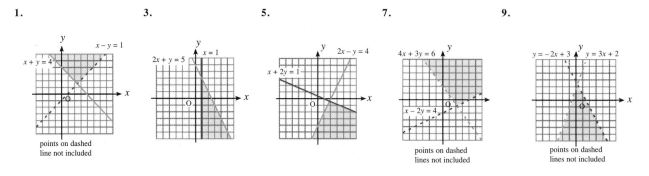

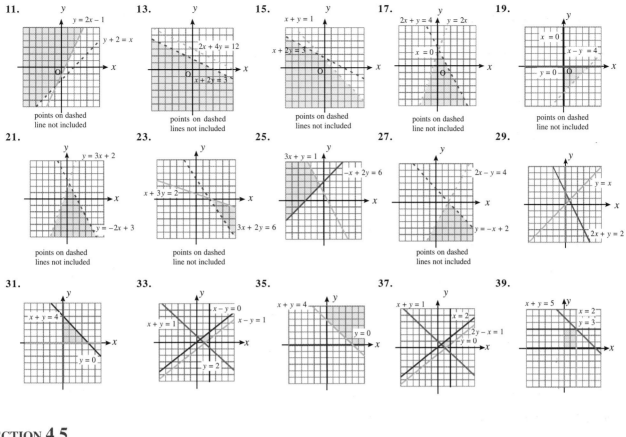

11. $y = 2x - 1$
$y + 2 = x$
points on dashed line not included

13. $2x + 4y = 12$
$x + 2y = 3$
points on dashed lines not included

15. $x + y = 1$
$x + 2y = 3$
points on dashed lines not included

17. $2x + y = 4$ $y = 2x$
$x = 0$
points on dashed line not included

19. $x = 0$
$x - y = 4$
$y = 0$
points on dashed line not included

21. $y = 3x + 2$
$y = -2x + 3$
points on dashed lines not included

23. $x + 3y = 2$
$3x + 2y = 6$
points on dashed line not included

25. $3x + y = 1$
$-x + 2y = 6$

27. $2x - y = 4$
$y = -x + 2$
points on dashed lines not included

29. $y = x$
$2x + y = 2$

31. $x + y = 4$
$y = 0$

33. $x - y = 0$
$x + y = 1$
$x - y = 1$
$y = 2$

35. $x + y = 4$
$y = 0$

37. $x + y = 1$
$x = 2$
$2y - x = 1$
$y = 0$

39. $x + y = 5$
$x = 2$
$y = 3$

SECTION 4.5

1. -6 and 12
3. $36, 27$
5. Length $= 20$ cm ; Width $= 16$ cm
7. $20°$
9. Adult : 140; Children : 50
11. Steak : $\$2.40$; Hamburger : $\$1.25$
13. $\$1,000$
15. Big : 110 ; Small : 75
17. 20 cent stamps $= 12$; 10 cent stamps $= 16$
19. Algebra : 6,700 ; Trigonometry 4,800
21. 3,800 at 10% ; 2,200 at 8%
23. 400 oz
25. 30% solution : 36 liters ; 80% solution : 24 liters
27. 15% solution : 180 milliliters ; 40% solution : 120 milliliters
29. $\$1.50$ per pound coffee : 16 lbs $\$2.00$ per pound coffee : 9 lbs
31. 150 mi/hour
33. 55 mi/hour ; 45 mi/hour
35. 198 mi/hour
37. 23

REVIEW EXERCISES 4.7

1. **(a)** No **(b)** No
3. Intersecting
5. Intersecting
7. Parallel
9. Coincident
11. Intersecting

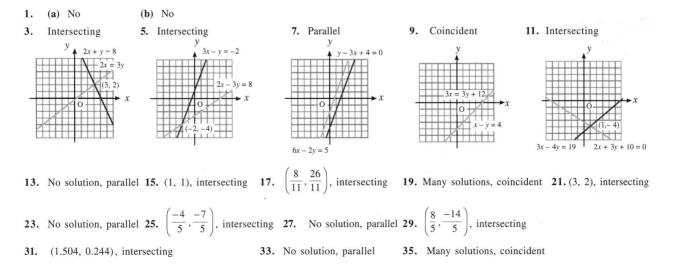

13. No solution, parallel 15. $(1, 1)$, intersecting 17. $\left(\frac{8}{11}, \frac{26}{11}\right)$, intersecting 19. Many solutions, coincident 21. $(3, 2)$, intersecting

23. No solution, parallel 25. $\left(\frac{-4}{5}, \frac{-7}{5}\right)$, intersecting 27. No solution, parallel 29. $\left(\frac{8}{5}, \frac{-14}{5}\right)$, intersecting

31. $(1.504, 0.244)$, intersecting 33. No solution, parallel 35. Many solutions, coincident

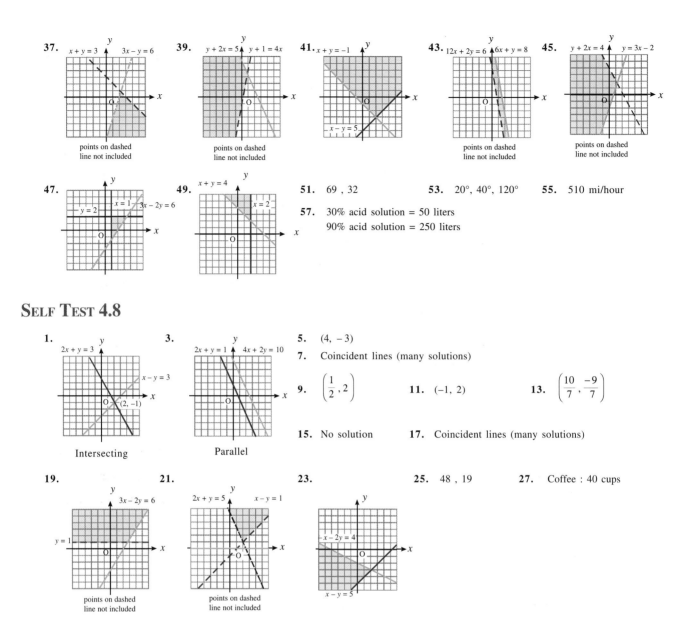

37. $x + y = 3$ $3x - y = 6$

points on dashed line not included

39. $y + 2x = 5$ $y + 1 = 4x$

points on dashed line not included

41. $x + y = -1$ $x - y = 5$

43. $12x + 2y = 6$ $6x + y = 8$

points on dashed line not included

45. $y + 2x = 4$ $y = 3x - 2$

points on dashed line not included

47. $y = 2$ $x = 1$ $3x - 2y = 6$

49. $x + y = 4$ $x = 2$

51. 69 , 32   **53.** 20°, 40°, 120°   **55.** 510 mi/hour

57. 30% acid solution = 50 liters
90% acid solution = 250 liters

Self Test 4.8

1. $2x + y = 3$ $x - y = 3$ (2, –1)

Intersecting

3. $2x + y = 1$ $4x + 2y = 10$

Parallel

5. $(4, -3)$

7. Coincident lines (many solutions)

9. $\left(\dfrac{1}{2}, 2 \right)$ **11.** $(-1, 2)$ **13.** $\left(\dfrac{10}{7}, \dfrac{-9}{7} \right)$

15. No solution   **17.** Coincident lines (many solutions)

19. $3x - 2y = 6$ $y = 1$

points on dashed line not included

21. $2x + y = 5$ $x - y = 1$

points on dashed line not included

23. $x - 2y = 4$ $x - y = 5$

25. 48 , 19   **27.** Coffee : 40 cups

CHAPTER 5

Section 5.1

1. Base = 3 ; Exponent = 6   **3.** Base = 3 ; Exponent = 6   **5.** Base = –3; Exponent = 6   **7.** Base = –5x ; Exponent = 7

9. Base = 5y ; Exponent = 7   **11.** Base = y ; Exponent = 7   **13.** $x^5 y^6$ **15.** $16x^4$ **17.** $\dfrac{x^6}{y^4}$ **19.** $\dfrac{x^7}{y^6}$

21. $6y^5$ **23.** $-392\,a^5$ **25.** p^{16} **27.** $-48a^4$ **29.** $3y^2$ **31.** $6x^2$ **33.** $x^6 y^5$ **35.** $-10a^6$

37. $\dfrac{8}{9}$ **39.** 250   **41.** 72   **43.** $\dfrac{544}{243}$ **45.** 8   **47.** 200   **49.** -64 **51.** $\dfrac{1}{3}$

53. $\dfrac{1}{4}$ **55.** 4   **57.** -56 **59.** -54 **61.** $x^2 y^4$ **63.** $25a^4 b^6$ **65.** $16a^8 b^8$ **67.** $8x^5 y^2$

69. $\dfrac{8x^6}{27}$ **71.** False   **73.** True   **75.** False   **77.** False   **79.** True   **81.** $18x^3$ **83.** $-7x^7y^4$

85. $-11a^9$ **87.** $6x^3y^2$ **89.** $6x^8$ **91.** $16m^6$ **93.** $\dfrac{9\pi}{4}a^8$

SECTION 5.2

1. a polynomial   **3.** a polynomial   **5.** not a polynomial   **7.** not a polynomial   **9.** a polynomial

11. $-3x^4 + 4x^3 + 3x^2 + 7x$;
degree = 4,
constant term = 0

13. $-4x^5 + 8x^3 + 7x^2 - 5$;
degree = 5,
constant term = -5

15. $-9x^8 + 7x^6 - 3x^5 + x^4$;
degree = 8,
constant term = 0

17. $7x^5 - 6x^4 - 2x^3 - 4x^2 + 1$;
degree = 5,
constant term = 1

19. Binomial ; 2   **21.** Monomial ; 3   **23.** Binomial ; 3   **25.** Trinomial ; 5   **27.** Polynomial ; 10

29. Trinomial ; 2   **31.** 3 ; 31   **33.** -10; 54   **35.** -13 ; -77 **37.** 127 ; 231

39. $4x^3 + 4x^2 - 5x + 7$ **41.** $x^4 + 16x^3 + 10x^2 + 8x$ **43.** $7p^2 - p + 2$ **45.** $11z^2 + 11z$ **47.** $-2y^3 - 2y^2 + y + 1$

49. $7y^3 + 4y^2 + 5y - 14$ **51.** $5x^2 + 7x$ **53.** $6a^2 + 3a + 6$ **55.** $-p^2 + 10p + 1$ **57.** $8x^2 - 2xy + 3y^2$

59. $9t^3 - 13t^2 + 12t + 3$ **61.** $2r^3 - 8r^2 + 7r + 19$ **63.** $7x^2 + 5x + 16$ **65.** $-5r^3 - 5r^2 - 2r - 8$ **67.** $m^3 - 10\ m - 10$

69. $7y^5 + y^4 - 16$ **71.** $-7x + 9$ **73.** $x^3 - 2x^2 - 4x + 6$ **75.** $7x^3 + 5x^2 + 4x + 9$ **77.** $-t^2 - 11$

79. $3n^5 - 4n^4 + 9n^3 - 8n^2 + 12$ **81.** $-2y^2 - 6xy$ **83.** $-2x^3 + x^2 + 3$ **85.** $-2y^3 + 7y^2 - 2y - 7$ **87.** $8u^3 + 6u^2 + 3u + 1$

89. $3u^3 - 2u^2 + 8u - 17$ **91.** $x^3 + 8x^2 - 1$ **93.** $8x^2 + 16x - 20$

SECTION 5.3

1. $15x^5$ **3.** $-4x^{15}$ **5.** $8x^8$ **7.** $-21x^6$ **9.** $15x^5$ **11.** $3x^2$ **13.** $-a^5b^5$

15. $-6x^3y^3$ **17.** $x^2 - 4x$ **19.** $3a^3 - 12a^2$ **21.** $6x^3 - 6x^2$ **23.** $6y^4 - 15y^3$ **25.** $-x^3y + xy^3$ **27.** $-2y^9 - 2y^8 + 2y^7$

29. $3a^3b - 5a^2b^2 - 6ab^3$ **31.** $30x^3 - 32x^2 - 14x$ **33.** $40x^{11} - 24x^9 - 15x^4 + 9x^2$ **35.** $20x^3 + 47x^2y^2 + 24xy^4$

37. $12x^2y - 8x^4 + 8y^2$ **39.** $6y^3 + 8x^2 - 8xy^2 - 6xy$ **41.** $12q^3 - 25q^2 + 7q$ **43.** $12x^6 - 24x^5 - 8x^3 + 16x^2$

45. $\dfrac{8}{3}x^3 - \dfrac{4}{15}x^2 - \dfrac{3}{2}x + \dfrac{3}{20}$ **47.** $12x^4 + x^3 - 32x^2 - 5x$ **49.** $5x^{12} + 5x^{11} - 3x^5 - 3x^4 + 7x^3 + 7x^2$ **51.** $9x^2 + 30x + 25$

53. $y^{12} - 7y^{10} - 10y^9 + 70y^7 + 8y^4 - 56y^2$ **55.** $9x^{10} - 30x^8 + 25x^6 + 42x^5 - 70x^3 + 49$ **57.** $a^3 - 4a^2 + 11a - 14$

59. $-10y^3 + 14y^2 - 6y + 2$ **61.** $6a^3 - 8a^2 - 10a + 4$ **63.** $2y^4 - 5y^3 + 3y^2 + 3y - 3$ **65.** $12x^2 - 13x - 35$

67. $27x^4 + 15x^3 + 63x^2 + 35x$ **69.** $6s^2 - s - 12$ **71.** $12t^2 - 8t - 15$ **73.** $16k^2 - 25l^2$

75. $12n^2 - 25mn + 12m^2$ **77.** $6y^7 - 14y^6 - 9y^3 + 21y^2$ **79.** $x^2 + 6x + 5$ **81.** $y^2 + 4y - 32$ **83.** $4y^2 - 2y - 6$

85. $2x^2 + 3xy + y^2$ **87.** $9x^2 + 6xy - 35y^2$ **89.** $22x^2 + 61xy + 15y^2$ **91.** $y^2 - 25$

SECTION 5.4

1. $x^2 - 4x + 4$ **3.** $y^2 + 8y + 16$ **5.** $4m^2 - 20m + 25$ **7.** $9t^2 + 42t + 49$ **9.** $25m^2 - 30mn + 9n^2$

11. $49r^2 + 70rs + 25s^2$ **13.** $x^2 + 2x + 1$ **15.** $x^2 + 8x + 16$ **17.** $4x^2 + 12xy + 9y^2$ **19.** $\dfrac{9}{16}x^2 + xy + \dfrac{4}{9}y^2$

21. $\dfrac{25}{49}u^2 - \dfrac{8}{7}uv + \dfrac{16}{25}v^2$ **23.** $t^2 - 36$ **25.** $16t^2 - 25$ **27.** $49x^2 - 9y^2$ **29.** $4x^4 - 1$

31. $4 - y^2$ **33.** $16x^2 - 25y^2$ **35.** $x^4 - 1$ **37.** $16 - r^4$ **39.** $9x^4 - y^2$

41. $9u^4 - v^4$ **43.** $\dfrac{9}{4}u^4 - \dfrac{4}{9}v^2$ **45.** $\dfrac{4}{9}u^6 - v^2$ **47.** $\dfrac{u^2}{v^2} - \dfrac{v^2}{u^2}$ **49.** $\dfrac{9}{16u^6} - \dfrac{1}{4v^4}$

51. $m^3 - 9m^2 + 27m - 27$ **53.** $8x^3 + 12x^2y + 6xy^2 + y^3$ **55.** $64x^3 - 144x^2y + 108xy^2 - 27y^3$

57. $8u^3 - 36u^2v + 54uv^2 - 27v^3$ **59.** $\dfrac{27}{u^3} - \dfrac{108}{u^2v} + \dfrac{144}{uv^2} - \dfrac{64}{v^3}$

Section 5.5

1. 4 **3.** $\dfrac{8}{27}$ **5.** $-\dfrac{64}{125}$ **7.** $\dfrac{625}{81}$ **9.** $\dfrac{1}{4}$ **11.** 8 **13.** $\dfrac{1}{125}$ **15.** 1 **17.** $\dfrac{1}{x^{20}}$ **19.** $\dfrac{y^6}{x^9}$

21. $r^3 s^{15}$ **23.** $\dfrac{1}{k}$ **25.** $2a^4$ **27.** 1 **29.** $\dfrac{1}{q^2}$ **31.** $\dfrac{2}{5m^3 n^8}$ **33.** $\dfrac{2b^2}{3a^5 c^2}$ **35.** $-\dfrac{27}{125x^{18} y^6}$ **37.** 64 **39.** $27k^2 l^7$

41. $\dfrac{a^{18}}{b^{12}}$ **43.** $\dfrac{9}{x^2 y^4}$ **45.** $-\dfrac{2}{x^8}$ **47.** $-x^2$ **49.** x^2 **51.** $\dfrac{y^9}{8x^4}$ **53.** $\dfrac{8x^5}{y^5}$ **55.** 72 **57.** $\dfrac{81}{4}$ **59.** $\dfrac{27}{8}$

61. $\dfrac{113}{72}$ **63.** $-\dfrac{1}{16}$ **65.** $\dfrac{29}{675}$ **67.** $\dfrac{13}{36}$ **69.** $\dfrac{4}{81}$ **71.** $\dfrac{x^4}{4y^4}$ **73.** $-\dfrac{1}{8x^6 y^3}$ **75.** $\dfrac{x^2}{25}$ **77.** $\dfrac{y^5}{x^4}$ **79.** x^8

Section 5.6

1. $7x^2$ **3.** $8x^2$ **5.** $-4yz$ **7.** $-3st$ **9.** $2x + 3$ **11.** $5y - 4$ **13.** $-3y + 9$ **15.** $17x + 2$

17. $a^2 - 2ab$ **19.** $3y^2 + \dfrac{4}{x}$ **21.** $2xz + \dfrac{1}{2}y$ **23.** $\dfrac{x^3}{2} - \dfrac{5x}{6} + \dfrac{1}{x}$ **25.** $\dfrac{3a^2}{5} - a + \dfrac{6}{5} - \dfrac{1}{a} + \dfrac{1}{a^2}$

27. $\dfrac{3}{5}y^2 z + \dfrac{2}{5}y^3 z^4 - \dfrac{4}{5z}$ **29.** $9p + 6 - 3q$

31. Divisor $= 2k - 3$, Dividend $= 8k^4 - 12k^3 - 2k^2 + 7k - 6$, Quotient $= 4k^3 - k + 2$, Remainder $= 0$

33. Divisor $= m^2 - 2$, Dividend $= -6m - m^2 + m^4$, Quotient $= m^2 + 1$, Remainder $= -6m + 2$

35. $Q = x + 3 : R = 0$ **37.** $Q = x - 3 : R = 0$ **39.** $Q = 3y + 4 : R = 0$ **41.** $Q = t^2 + 3t - 2 : R = 0$ **43.** $Q = x - 7 : R = 0$

45. $Q = 2a - 4 : R = 0$ **47.** $Q = a - 6 : R = 26$ **49.** $Q = 3y - 5 : R = 0$ **51.** $Q = 4x^3 - 3x^2 + 3x + 1 : R = 0$

53. $Q = 9a^2 - 6a + 4$ **55.** $Q = x^2 - 1$ **57.** $Q = t^4 + 2t^3 + 4t^2 + 8t + 16$ **59.** $Q = 3x^2 + 7x + 3$
     $R = 0$ $R = 0$ $R = 0$ $R = 0$

61. $Q = 8x^2 - 12x + 25$ **63.** $Q = y - \dfrac{9}{2}$ **65.** $12x^3 - 34x^2 + 34x - 10$

     $R = -130$ $R = 15$ **67.** $-4x^5 + 23x^3 - 2x^2 - 26x + 5$

Section 5.7

1. 4.501×10^3 **3.** 9.537×10^1 **5.** -8.47509×10^2 **7.** 4.0009×10^2 **9.** 3.4×10^{-2} **11.** 8.09×10^{-3}
13. 2.456×10^6 **15.** 4.3×10^{-5} **17.** -8.19×10^8 **19.** 5.29×10^3 **21.** 7.75×10^7 **23.** 3.7×10^{-6}
25. 6.78×10^{-7} **27.** 786 **29.** $359,000$ **31.** $49,705$ **33.** 0.52349 **35.** -345.7
37. -0.003456 **39.** 0.000000057095 **41.** 0.0009725 **43.** 230 **45.** $25,000,000$
47. 0.000000000713 **49.** 1.08×10^9 Km **51.** 7.15×10^{-4} oz

Review Exercises 5.9

1. $\dfrac{81}{2}$ **3.** -5 **5.** -3 **7.** $1,000$ **9.** $2 \cdot 3x^4 \cdot x^3 y^2$ **11.** $2^3 \cdot 3x^4$ **13.** $\dfrac{y^4}{x^6}$ **15.** $\dfrac{y^2}{x^2 z^2}$ **17.** 67 **19.** -1

21. $-5x^7 + 4x^3 + 3x^2 - 7x - 2$, Degree : 7 **23.** $5x^5 + 3x^4 + 5x^2 - 7x - 5$, Degree : 5 **25.** $4p^3 - 5p + 5$

27. $4x^4 - 3x^3 - 8x^2 + 3x$ **29.** $-4p^3 + 6p^2 - 7p + 3$ **31.** $-14x^4$ **33.** $12x^5 - 20x^4 + 8x^3$

35. $21x^5 - 6x^4 + 35x^3 - 3x^2 - 2x$ **37.** $15y^3 - 19y^2 + 6y$ **39.** $12x^3 - 11x^2 - 15x$ **41.** $\dfrac{16}{25}x^2 + \dfrac{24}{5}xy^2 + 9y^4$

43. $\dfrac{9}{4}x^4 - 21x^2 + 49$ **45.** $25x^2 - 9y^4$ **47.** $\dfrac{1}{x^3}$ **49.** $\dfrac{b^8}{a^7}$ **51.** $\dfrac{12b^2}{a^4}$

53. $\dfrac{24p}{q^{18}} = \dfrac{2^3 \cdot 3p}{q^{18}}$ **55.** $\dfrac{2}{3}t - 1 + \dfrac{4}{3t}$ **57.** Quotient : $2a + \dfrac{1}{2}$; Remainder : $\dfrac{17}{2}$

59. Quotient $= 5x + 5$; **61.** Quotient $y^2 + 4y + 4$; **63. a)** 1.357×10^6 ; **b)** 3.57×10^{-3} ; **c)** 1.23456×10^7 ; **d)** 4.56×10^{-2}

     Remainder $= 14x + 2$ Remainder $= -8y - 1$

SELF TEST 5.10

1. $\dfrac{25}{27}$ **3.** -2 **5. (a)** 9.784×10^3 **(b)** 2.35×10^{-4} **(c)** 3.485×10^1 **(d)** 3.21×10^{-3}

7. $7x^2 + 5x - 6$; Trinomial ; Degree 2   **9.** $4x^2 - 1$; Binomial ; Degree 2   **11.** $15x^5$; Monomial ; Degree 5   **13.** $5x^4 + 4x^3 + 9x^2 + 15x + 3$

15. $5x^3 - 10x^2 - 5x + 3$ **17.** $-x^4 + 5x^3 - 2x^2 + x + 1$ **19.** $-15x^7 + 10x^5 - 15x^3$

21. $12x^5 + 20x^4 - 10x^3 + 33x^2 - 37x - 7$ **23.** $-3x + 4 + \dfrac{4}{x} - \dfrac{1}{x^2}$ **25.** Quotient $= 15x^3 - 15x^2 - 7x + 30$; Remainder $= -23x - 21$

CHAPTER 6

SECTION 6.1

1. GCF $= 2$ **3.** GCF $= 15$ **5.** GCF $= 12$ **7.** GCF $= 3$ **9.** GCF $= 4mn^2$

11. GCF $= 7xy^2$ **13.** $36 = 4(\underline{9}\,)$ **15.** $5x^2 = x(\,\underline{5x}\,)$ **17.** $3x^4y^5 = 3x^2\left(\underline{x^2y^5}\right)$ **19.** $24p^4q^5 = 3p^3q^2\left(\underline{8pq^3}\right)$

21. No   **23.** No   **25.** Yes   **27.** No   **29.** $2x(2 + 3x^2)$

31. $14x^2(2 + 3x)$ **33.** $4y^3(2 - y^2)$ **35.** No factors   **37.** $2(a + 1)$ **39.** $4(4 - y)$

41. $7x(x - 3)$ **43.** $3a^2(a^2 - 3)$ **45.** No factors   **47.** $9(2x^2y^2 - a^2b^2)$ **49.** $5y(y^2 - 4y + 2)$

51. $x^3(2x^2 - 3x + 2)$ **53.** $25m^3(m^2 - 2m + 4)$ **55.** $9mn(5mn^2 - 4n + 7m^2)$ **57.** $(1 - 5b)\,(3a - 4b)$

59. $(r - 2s)(r + s)$ **61.** $(x - 4)\,(a - b)$ **63.** $(a - 2)\,(c + b)$ **65.** $(2 + c)\,(4x - 3y)$ **67.** $-(3 - x)$

69. $-x(x + 5)$ **71.** $-5(2x - 3)$ **73.** $(x - 5)\,(x - y)$ **75.** $(a + b)\,(r - 1)$ **77.** $(x + 2y)\,(x + 3)$

79. $(y - 1)\,(x^2 - 3)$ **81.** $(x - 1)\,(x^3 - x^2 + 1)$ **83.** $(a + b)\,(3a - b)$ **85.** $(2y + 5)\,(y + 3)$ **87.** $(2x - 3y)\,(x - y)$

89. $(m + 2)\,(m^3 + 2m^2 + 2)$

SECTION 6.2

1. $(x + 5)$ **3.** $(x + 7)$ **5.** $(t + 3)$ **7.** $(3r + 1)$ **9.** $2y(2y + 1)\,(y - 3)$

11. $2x^2(x - 3)\,(x - 4)$ **13.** $(x - 11)\,(x + 2)$ **15.** $(x - 5)^2$ **17.** $(z - 6)\,(z + 5)$ **19.** $(x - 3)\,(x + 2)$

21. $(x + 3)\,(x - 2)$ **23.** $(x - 3)\,(x - 2)$ **25.** $(x - 1)\,(x - 4)$ **27.** $(x - 4)\,(x + 1)$ **29.** $(x + 4)\,(x - 1)$

31. $(x - 5)\,(x + 1)$ **33.** $(x + 5)\,(x - 1)$ **35.** $(x - 5)\,(x - 1)$ **37.** $(x - 7)\,(x + 2)$ **39.** $(x + 7)\,(x - 2)$

41. $(x - 7)\,(x - 2)$ **43.** $(x + 7)\,(x - 3)$ **45.** $(x - 7)\,(x + 3)$ **47.** $(x - 3)\,(x - 7)$ **49.** $2(x + 1)\,(x + 2)$

51. $3(x - 2)\,(x + 3)$ **53.** $2p(p + 1)\,(p + 2)$ **55.** $3x(x - 3)\,(x + 4)$ **57.** $(2x - 1)\,(x + 3)$ **59.** $(2x + 1)\,(x - 3)$

61. $(3x + 1)\,(x - 2)$ **63.** $(3x - 1)\,(x + 2)$ **65.** $(4x + 5)\,(x - 3)$ **67.** $(4x - 5)\,(x + 3)$ **69.** $(3x - 1)\,(2x + 3)$

71. $(3x + 1)\,(2x - 3)$ **73.** $(3x - 1)\,(2x - 3)$ **75.** $(3x + 1)\,(2x + 3)$ **77.** $(3x - 1)\,(2x - 1)$ **79.** $(3x + 1)\,(2x - 1)$

81. $(3x - 1)\,(2x + 1)$ **83.** $(3x + 1)\,(2x + 1)$ **85.** $(5x - 2)\,(2x + 3)$ **87.** $(5x + 2)\,(2x - 3)$ **89.** $(5x + 2)\,(2x + 3)$

91. $(5x - 2)\,(2x - 3)$ **93.** $(r + 4)\,(8 - r)$ **95.** $-5(t + 5)\,(t + 3)$

SECTION 6.3

1. $(x + 3)\,(x - 3)$ **3.** $(2x + 5)\,(2x - 5)$ **5.** Not factorable   **7.** $(9a - 5b)\,(9a + 5b)$ **9.** $2(a - 2b)\,(a + 2b)$

11. $3(x - 2y)\,(x + 2y)$ **13.** $2(1 + 2t)\,(1 - 2t)$ **15.** $2(3 + 5a)\,(3 - 5a)$ **17.** $x(y - x)\,(y + x)$ **19.** $2b(a + 3b)\,(a - 3b)$

21. $5a(a - 2b)\,(a + 2b)$ **23.** $3(t + 3)\,(t - 3)$ **25.** $bc(a - b)\,(a + b)$ **27.** $(m + 3)\,(m - 3)(m^2 + 9)$ **29.** $9(p^2 + q^2)$

31. $(r^2 + 7)\,(r^2 - 7)$ **33.** $(a - 8)\,(a + 8)$ **35.** $(2y - 1)\,(2y + 1)$ **37.** $(3y - 1)\,(3y + 1)$ **39.** Not factorable

41. $(4 - ab)\,(4 + ab)$ **43.** $(x - 3)^2$ **45.** $(x + 4)^2$ **47.** $(a + 5)^2$ **49.** $(r - 7)^2$

51. $\left(y - \dfrac{7}{2}\right)^2$ **53.** $\left(t + \dfrac{5}{2}\right)^2$ **55.** $2(x - 2)^2$ **57.** $3(a + 3)^2$ **59.** $b(a - b)^2$

61. $(2x + 7)^2$ **63.** $(2p - 9q)^2$ **65.** $(3 + 4x)^2$ **67.** $2x(x - 2y)^2$ **69.** $2a(4b - 3)^2$

71. $(4a + 3b)^2$ **73.** $(7z - 2t)^2$ **75.** $x^2(3 + 8y)^2$ **77.** $a^2b^2(x - 10)^2$ **79.** $(x + 3)(x^2 - 3x + 9)$

81. $(4r + 5s)(16r^2 - 20rs + 25s^2)$ **83.** $(5x + 2y)(25x^2 - 10xy + 4y^2)$

85. $8(x^2 + 2y^2)(x^4 - 2x^2y^2 + 4y^4)$ **87.** $(x - 1)(x^2 + x + 1)$ **89.** $(3a - b)(9a^2 + 3ab + b^2)$

91. $(9p - 10q)(81p^2 + 90pq + 100q^2)$ **93.** $(x - y)(x + y)(x^4 + x^2y^2 + y^4)$

Section 6.4

1. $5, \dfrac{-4}{3}$ **3.** $-\dfrac{3}{2}, \dfrac{-5}{3}$ **5.** $0, 2$ **7.** $-1, \dfrac{3}{2}$ **9.** $0, 5, 7$ **11.** $-3, -2$ **13.** $4, -5$ **15.** $0, -4$ **17.** $0, 7$

19. $3, -3$ **21.** $2, -2$ **23.** $2, 5$ **25.** $-6, -4$ **27.** $-1, 7$ **29.** $-2, -1$ **31.** $\dfrac{8}{3}, -\dfrac{8}{3}$ **33.** $\dfrac{2}{5}, \dfrac{2}{5}$ **35.** $5, 3$

37. $-7, 3$ **39.** $-4, \dfrac{1}{2}$ **41.** $3, 9$ **43.** $4, -7$ **45.** $-2, -3$ **47.** $-5, 2$ **49.** $-2, \dfrac{5}{2}$ **51.** $0, \dfrac{7}{15}$ **53.** $-2, 11$

55. $\dfrac{1}{2}, 2$ **57.** $-\dfrac{1}{2}, 1$ **59.** $\dfrac{-5}{6}, 2$ **61.** $5, -\dfrac{3}{2}$ **63.** $0, -2$ **65.** $0, -\dfrac{5}{2}, \dfrac{5}{2}$ **67.** $0, -1, 9$ **69.** $0, 0, -\dfrac{5}{7}, 1$

71. $0, -\dfrac{1}{6}, -\dfrac{3}{2}$ **73.** $-2, -1, 1, 2$ **75.** $0, 1, -1$ **77.** $0, 3, -3$ **79.** $0, 0, 4, -4$

Section 6.5

1. 12, 14; $-14, -12$ **3.** 17, 19 ; $-17, -19$ **5.** 7, 8, 9; $-9, -8, -7$ **7.** 3 seconds **9.** 11, 12 ; $-12, -11$

11. 8 and 9 **13.** 15, 20 ; $-20, -15$ **15.** 14 meters **17.** 44 yards **19.** 8 units

21. 9 feet by 12 feet **23.** 8 feet, 3 feet **25.** 10 feet **27.** 60 cm^2 **29.** 6 meters **31.** 48°

Review Exercises 6.7

1. 3 **3.** 1 **5.** $4qp^2$ **7.** 1 **9.** $9x^2(3x - 4)$ **11.** $7(9y^2 - 2z^2)$ **13.** $15pq^2(2pq + 3p^3 - 5q^2)$

15. $(4s + 5t^2)(3s - 5t)$ **17.** $(3x + 4y)(4x - 5)$ **19.** $(4x^2 + y)(3x - y)$ **21.** $(r + 3)(r^3 + 3r - 2)$ **23.** $(3x^3 - 2y^2 + 1)(x^2 - y)$

25. $(x + 5)(x - 3)$ **27.** $(4x + 7)(3x - 2)$ **29.** $(x + 8)(x - 2)$ **31.** $(x - 4)(x - 2)$ **33.** $(6x - 1)(6x + 1)$

35. $(4t + 1)^2$ **37.** $2(4y + 1)(y - 1)$ **39.** $(3p + 2)(p - 4)$ **41.** $x(2x + 1)(x - 3)$ **43.** $(x + 2)(x + 1)$

45. $(x^2 - 2)(x^2 + 3)$ **47.** $(2x^2 + 1)(x + 2)(x - 2)$ **49.** Cannot be factored **51.** Cannot be factored

53. $(p + 4)(p - 4)$ **55.** $(2a + 7)(2a - 7)$ **57.** Cannot be factored **59.** $(x^2 + 6)(x^2 - 6)$

61. $(2x - 3)(2x + 3)(4x^2 + 9)$ **63.** $(y - 4)^2$ **65.** $2(z + 3)^2$ **67.** $\left(x - \dfrac{5}{2}\right)\left(x - \dfrac{5}{2}\right)$ **69.** $(3x + 5y)^2$

71. $(3x - 5y)(9x^2 + 15xy + 25y^2)$ **73.** $(2rs + 3t)(4r^2s^2 - 6rst + 9t^2)$ **75.** $(6ab^2 - 5c^2)(36a^2b^4 + 30ab^2c^2 + 25c^4)$

77. $-4, \dfrac{5}{3}$ **79.** $\dfrac{-3}{2}$ **81.** $-10, -5$ **83.** $5, 10$ **85.** $-5, 20$ **87.** $0, \dfrac{-1}{2}$ **89.** $\dfrac{-1}{2}, -\dfrac{1}{2}$

91. $-4, 3$ **93.** $\dfrac{-3}{2}, -1$ **95.** $\dfrac{-1}{2}, \dfrac{2}{3}$ **97.** No solution **99.** $-2, 2, 3, -3$ **101.** $-13, -11$; 11, 13

103. $-11, -10$; 10, 11 **105.** 7 **107.** 11 ft, 14 ft **109.** 8 feet and 4 feet **111.** 5 inch, 12 inch, 13 inch

113. 7 miles **115.** 140°

Self Test 6.8

1. $8xy(3x^2y^3 + 5x - 8y)$ **3.** $(3a - 5b)(4b - a)$ **5.** $(4x - 3y)(3x + 5)$ **7.** $(3x - y)(4x^2 + 3y - 2)$

9. $(4p - 3q)(2p + q - 5)$ **11.** $(2x - 5)(3x + 4)$ **13.** $(5a - 1)(5a - 1)$ **15.** Cannot be factored

17. $x(x - 6)(x + 3)$ **19.** $(4x + 5)(2x - 3)$ **21.** $3(2p - 3q)(2p + 3q)$ **23.** Cannot be factored

25. $(2m + n^2)(4m^2 - 2mn^2 + n^4)$ **27.** $-3, 6$ **29.** $-2, \dfrac{1}{3}$ **31.** $-3, 3$ **33.** $0, -2, \dfrac{5}{6}$

35. 4, 6 **37.** 10 meters **39.** 10 feet **41.** Since $4x^2 - 9$ can be further factored as $(2x - 3)(2x + 3)$

CHAPTER 7

SECTION 7.1

1. 0   **3.** $\dfrac{2}{5}$ **5.** -3 **7.** $\dfrac{1}{2},-\dfrac{1}{2}$ **9.** $2,-2$ **11.** -1 **13.** $-1,1$ **15.** $\dfrac{1}{3},-\dfrac{1}{3}$

17. $2,3$ **19.** $2,4$ **21.** $\dfrac{1}{2},-\dfrac{1}{3}$ **23.** None   **25.** None   **27.** $-6,-3$ **29.** $2,-4$ **31.** $0,-\dfrac{2}{3}$

33. 1   **35.** -13 **37.** $\dfrac{5}{3}$ **39.** $-\dfrac{29}{19}$ **41.** $-\dfrac{2}{7}$ **43.** $-\dfrac{7}{68}$ **45.** $\dfrac{7}{8}$ **47.** $\dfrac{1}{5}$

49. $\dfrac{2}{5}$ **51.** $\dfrac{9}{7}$ **53.** $\dfrac{17}{64}$ **55.** 1   **57.** $-\dfrac{3}{5}$ **59.** $-\dfrac{168}{359}$

SECTION 7.2

1. $\dfrac{2}{3}$ **3.** $5x^2$ **5.** $\dfrac{-2q^4}{3p}$ **7.** $\dfrac{-2u}{5v^2}$ **9.** $\dfrac{8}{5}x^5$ **11.** $\dfrac{4t-5}{2}$ **13.** $\dfrac{a}{3}$ **15.** $\dfrac{3p}{2}$

17. $\dfrac{3t}{4(s-t)}$; for $s \neq t$ **19.** $\dfrac{3}{2a-1}$; for $a \neq -4$ **21.** $x+y$ **23.** $\dfrac{2}{5y(y-z)}$; for $y \neq z$ **25.** $\dfrac{1}{2x-2y}$ **27.** $\dfrac{x-3}{x-5}$

29. $\dfrac{3}{x-2}$ **31.** $-\dfrac{y}{3}$ **33.** $\dfrac{x-1}{3x+1}$ **35.** $\dfrac{(x+2)}{\left(x^2+2x+4\right)}$ **37.** $\dfrac{(x-3y)(x+3y)}{(x+3)(x+y)}$ **39.** $t-1$

41. $\dfrac{(x+1)\left(x^2+1-x\right)}{(x+a)\left(x^2+a^2-xa\right)}$ **43.** $\dfrac{(x+3)\left(x^2-3x+9\right)}{(x-3)^2}$ **45.** $a+b$ **47.** $\dfrac{(x-2y)}{\left(x^2+2xy+4y^2\right)}$ **49.** $a-b$ **51.** $\dfrac{2(x-y)}{x+2}$

53. $\dfrac{1}{p+3}$ **55.** $\dfrac{4p+5q}{4p-5q}$ **57.** $\dfrac{4p-5q}{4p+5q}$ **59.** $\dfrac{2x+1}{2-x}$ **61.** $\dfrac{3t-5}{t+2}$ **63.** $\dfrac{-2a}{3}$ **65.** $\dfrac{y+4}{y-6}$ **67.** $\dfrac{2y-1}{2y+3}$

SECTION 7.3

1. $\dfrac{3}{5}$ **3.** $\dfrac{5a^2}{6}$ **5.** $\dfrac{y^2q^2}{xp^3}$ **7.** $\dfrac{2x^3}{3y^4}$ **9.** $\dfrac{2}{3xy}$ **11.** $\dfrac{2ab}{xy}$ **13.** $\dfrac{27s}{2r^2}$ **15.** $\dfrac{3}{2p}$ **17.** $\dfrac{50x}{27}$

19. $\dfrac{a}{6}$ **21.** $\dfrac{1}{x+2}$ **23.** $\dfrac{x+1}{2}$ **25.** $\dfrac{a-2}{a+1}$ **27.** $\dfrac{1}{x+1}$ **29.** $\dfrac{4}{3(x+3)}$ **31.** $\dfrac{(a+1)^2}{a-1}$ **33.** $\dfrac{18}{x-1}$ **35.** -3

37. $(t-6)(t+3)$ **39.** $\dfrac{2}{9}$ **41.** $\dfrac{b^2}{a}$ **43.** $\dfrac{y^4(x-1)}{x(x+10)}$ **45.** $\dfrac{x-6}{x-5}$ **47.** $\dfrac{x-3}{2x}$ **49.** -1 **51.** $-\dfrac{x+1}{x+3}$ **53.** 1

55. -1 **57.** $a-5$ **59.** $\dfrac{(t-2)(5t+2)}{(4t+1)(t+2)}$ **61.** $\dfrac{(x-2)(2x+3)}{2(x+1)}$ **63.** $\dfrac{2y}{y-3}$ **65.** $\dfrac{z^2-9}{(z-2)^2}$ **67.** $\dfrac{-a^2}{(3a+2)(a-1)}$

69. $\dfrac{a^2(a+4)}{y^2(a+2)}$ **71.** $\dfrac{x+3}{x+7}$ **73.** $\dfrac{x^2-4}{x(3x-1)}$ **75.** $\dfrac{10(t+5)}{t^2+15t+30}$ **77.** 1   **79.** $-\dfrac{(p+2)(p-3)}{p^2\left(p^2+1\right)\left(p^2-1\right)}$

SECTION 7.4

1. ab **3.** x^2 **5.** x^2-5x+4 **7.** $p-4$ **9.** $(x-1)(x+6)$ **11.** $(x+3)(x+6)$ **13.** $-(x-3)$

15. $(x-1)(x+2)$ **17.** $(3x-2)(2x-1)(2x+3)$ **19.** $(t+6)(t-2)(t-5)(t-4)$

21. LCD $= 6(x-2)$; $\dfrac{4}{6(x-2)}, \dfrac{3}{6(x-2)}$ **23.** LCD $= 8(x+2)(x-1)$; $\dfrac{x-1}{8(x+2)(x-1)}, \dfrac{16}{8(x+2)(x-1)}$

25. LCD $= (t-2)(t+2)$; $\dfrac{(3+t)}{(t-2)(t+2)}, \dfrac{(t+2)}{(t-2)(t+2)}$ **27.** LCD $= (p+1)(p-4)$; $\dfrac{2p}{(p+1)(p-4)}, \dfrac{p-4}{(p+1)(p-4)}$

29. LCD $= a(a-3)(a+3)$; $\dfrac{2a^2-5a-3}{a(a-3)(a+3)}, \dfrac{a}{a(a-3)(a+3)}$ **31.** LCD $= (x+3)^2$; $\dfrac{5(x+3)}{(x+3)^2}; \dfrac{2x}{(x+3)^2}$

33. LCD = $(x - 3)(x + 5)$; $\dfrac{4(x+5)}{(x-3)(x+5)}$; $\dfrac{5(x-3)}{(x-3)(x+5)}$

35. LCD = $(x - 3)(x + 3)$; $\dfrac{(x-1)(x+3)}{(x-3)(x+3)}$; $\dfrac{(x-2)(x-3)}{(x-3)(x+3)}$

37. LCD = $(4a + 5b)(4a - 5b)$; $\dfrac{3a(4a-5b)}{(4a-5b)(4a+5b)}$; $\dfrac{2b(4a+5b)}{(4a-5b)(4a+5b)}$

39. LCD = $(3c - d)(3c + d)$; $\dfrac{c(3c+d)}{(3c-d)(3c+d)}$; $\dfrac{d(3c-d)}{(3c-d)(3c+d)}$

41. LCD = $(x + 2)(2x + 3)$; $\dfrac{5(x+2)}{(2x+3)(x+2)}$; $\dfrac{4(2x+3)}{(2x+3)(x+2)}$

43. LCD = $a(x - 4)$; $\dfrac{a(x-1)}{a(x-4)}$; $\dfrac{(x+1)}{a(x-4)}$

45. LCD = $20x^3$; $\dfrac{16x}{20x^3}$; $\dfrac{15}{20x^3}$

47. LCD = $(x - 3)(x + 3)$; $\dfrac{(x-1)(x+3)}{(x-3)(x+3)}$; $\dfrac{(x+1)(x-3)}{(x-3)(x+3)}$; $\dfrac{x}{(x-3)(x+3)}$

49. LCD = $(x + 3)^2(x^2 - 3x + 9)$; $\dfrac{x(x+3)}{(x+3)^2(x^2-3x+9)}$, $\dfrac{-2\left(x^2-3x+9\right)}{(x+3)^2(x^2-3x+9)}$

51. LCD = $(x + 2)(x - 4)$; $\dfrac{3x-12}{(x+2)(x-4)}$, $\dfrac{x+2}{(x+2)(x-4)}$

53. LCD = z; $\dfrac{z^2}{z}$; $\dfrac{1}{z}$

55. LCD = $t^2(t - 1)(t + 1)$; $\dfrac{3t^3-3t^2}{t^2(t-1)(t+1)}$, $\dfrac{2t^2-2}{t^2(t-1)(t+1)}$, $\dfrac{t^4+t^3}{t^2(t-1)(t+1)}$

Section 7.5

1. $\dfrac{5}{x}$ **3.** $\dfrac{4x+4}{x^2}$ **5.** 2 **7.** $\dfrac{8}{x^2}$ **9.** $t+2$ **11.** $\dfrac{3x+10}{24}$ **13.** $\dfrac{4x-7}{2x}$

15. $\dfrac{y+3}{y^2}$ **17.** $\dfrac{x^2+2x-5}{4x^2}$ **19.** $\dfrac{3y^2+8}{3y}$ **21.** $\dfrac{2a-5}{a-7}$ **23.** $\dfrac{5-2x}{y-3}$ **25.** $\dfrac{2x^2-1}{x+1}$ **27.** $\dfrac{t-2}{6(3t+2)}$

29. $\dfrac{x-2}{6(x+2)}$ **31.** $\dfrac{4x-6}{3x}$ **33.** $\dfrac{-3}{x}$ **35.** $\dfrac{-7}{x+2}$ **37.** $\dfrac{x+1}{x^2+x+1}$ **39.** $\dfrac{4}{x-3}$

41. 1 **43.** $-\dfrac{2x^2+2x+3}{18x^2}$ **45.** $\dfrac{9}{x-2}$ **47.** $\dfrac{-a^2+7a-16}{4\left(a^2-1\right)}$ **49.** $\dfrac{-a\left(7a+1\right)}{(a-2)(a+1)(a+3)}$ **51.** $\dfrac{2b}{(3a-2b)(3a+2b)}$

53. $\dfrac{1}{z+4}$ **55.** $\dfrac{13x-x^2}{(x-1)(x+2)(x+3)}$ **57.** $\dfrac{2m^2-2m+1}{m(m-1)}$ **59.** $\dfrac{16s+rs-6r}{r^2 s^2}$ **61.** $\dfrac{2x+47}{10x}$

63. $\dfrac{7a-4}{(a-1)(a+1)}$ **65.** $\dfrac{1}{x+2}$ **67.** $\dfrac{4x^2-13x-10}{2x(x-1)(x+1)}$ **69.** $\dfrac{3x^3-4x^2+x+4}{(x-1)^2(x+1)}$ **71.** $\dfrac{3x^2+26x+80}{2x(x-4)(x+4)}$

73. $\dfrac{-2}{(x-3)(x+3)}$ **75.** $\dfrac{-x^2+7x+2}{(x-1)(x-5)(x+5)}$ **77.** $\dfrac{x^2-x+10}{(x-2)(x+2)}$ **79.** $\dfrac{-1}{(x-1)(x+1)}$ **81.** $\dfrac{5}{(x-2)(x+2)}$

Section 7.6

1. $\dfrac{9}{10}$ **3.** $\dfrac{1}{10}$ **5.** $\dfrac{22}{5}$ **7.** $-\dfrac{2}{3}$ **9.** $-\dfrac{5}{6}$ **11.** $\dfrac{1}{7}$ **13.** $\dfrac{pq}{5}$ **15.** $\dfrac{2(t+3)}{t(t-4)}$

17. $\dfrac{24x^4}{1+x}$ **19.** $-\dfrac{3}{x}$ **21.** $\dfrac{5(y+4)}{y+5}$ **23.** $-\dfrac{1}{a+b}$ **25.** $\dfrac{3t^2-3t-6}{2t^3}$ **27.** $\dfrac{a^3-a^2+2a}{(a-3)(a+2)}$ **29.** $4x(x+4)$

31. $-9x(x+9)$ **33.** $\dfrac{2x+1}{x-2}$ **35.** $\dfrac{a^2+b}{a^2-b}$ **37.** $\dfrac{y}{y-3}$ **39.** $\dfrac{3y}{5(y-2)}$ **41.** $\dfrac{5t}{t+2}$ **43.** $-3x$ **45.** $\dfrac{b-3}{b+5}$ **47.** $\dfrac{x-6}{x-2}$

49. $\dfrac{-y-1}{4y-3}$ **51.** $\dfrac{64-t}{2(t-4)}$ **53.** $\dfrac{t(4-t)}{4}$ **55.** $\dfrac{\left(2t^2-7t+21\right)(3-t)}{3t}$ **57.** $\dfrac{-\left(3x^2+23x+48\right)}{(x+4)(5x+18)}$ **59.** 3

Section 7.7

1. $\dfrac{11}{30}$ **3.** $\dfrac{7}{3}$ **5.** $-1\dfrac{1}{8}$ **7.** $2\dfrac{9}{23}$ **9.** 12 **11.** 3 **13.** $\dfrac{9}{2}$ **15.** $a = 2$

17. $x = 4$ **19.** $t = \dfrac{3}{4}$ **21.** $a = -1$ **23.** $a = 5$ **25.** $z = \dfrac{10}{3}, 1$ **27.** 12 **29.** 4, -1 **31.** 1, -11

33. $\dfrac{12}{7}$ **35.** $3, -\dfrac{6}{7}$ **37.** $x = 2$ is an extraneous solution **39.** No Solution **41.** 1 is an extraneous solution

43. $x = 3$ is an extraneous solution **45.** 5 ; 3 is an extraneous solution **47.** $P = \dfrac{RT}{V}$ **49.** $R = \dfrac{E}{I} - r$ **51.** $p = \dfrac{qr}{3q - r}$

53. $a = \dfrac{V - u}{t}$ **55.** $h = \dfrac{V}{lw}$ **57.** $r = \dfrac{Rw}{(2F + w)}$ **59.** $m = \dfrac{y - b}{x}$ **61.** $r = \dfrac{I}{Pt}$ **63.** $b_1 = \dfrac{2A - b_2 h}{h}$ **65.** $h = \dfrac{V}{\pi r^2}$

Section 7.8

1. 18 **3.** $\dfrac{2}{5}$ **5.** $\dfrac{3}{8}, \dfrac{3}{4}$ **7.** $\dfrac{1}{3}, 4$ **9.** 25 mi/hr **11.** 3mi/hr **13.** 55 miles/hr and 40 mi/hour

15. 140 mi/hr **17.** 15 hr **19.** 2 hr 24 min **21.** $\dfrac{84}{19} = 4\dfrac{8}{19}$ hours **23.** $2\dfrac{6}{7}$ hr **25.** $7\dfrac{1}{2}$ hr **27.** $440

29. 1 hour and 24 minutes **31.** 21 when $y = 6$ **33.** $k = 16 ; v = \dfrac{1}{4}$ **35.** 30 **37.** $s = 16t^2$ **39.** $x = \dfrac{r^2}{s^2} ; \dfrac{36}{25}$

Review Exercises 7.10

1. $\dfrac{2}{3}$ **3.** 2 **5.** $-\dfrac{1}{2}, \dfrac{1}{3}$ **7.** 0 **9.** $\dfrac{1}{11}$ **11.** 1 **13.** $\dfrac{9}{28}$ **15.** $\dfrac{1}{2}$ **17.** $\dfrac{3}{4p^2}$

19. $\dfrac{2x}{3y}$ **21.** -1 **23.** $\dfrac{x + 2}{2}$ **25.** $\dfrac{x(x + 9)}{x - 9}$ **27.** $\dfrac{3a - 4b}{3a + 4b}$ **29.** $\dfrac{4p + 3q}{p + 2}$ **31.** $\dfrac{6xy}{5}$ **33.** $\dfrac{15x^2 + 10x}{8x + 4}$

35. $\dfrac{8x^2 - 14x + 3}{6x^2 + 13x + 5}$ **37.** $\dfrac{5x}{14}$ **39.** $\dfrac{3x + 3}{10x + 14}$ **41.** $\dfrac{3}{2}$ **43.** $\dfrac{y^2 - y - 2}{y - 5}$ **45.** $x^2 - 3x + 2$

47. $\dfrac{(x + 2)^2 (x + 3)}{(x - 4)^3}$ **49.** 1 **51.** $\dfrac{(p + 5)^2}{(p - 7)^2}$ **53.** xy **55.** $x - 4$ **57.** $(x - 1)^2 (2x - 1)$

59. $12x^3 ; \dfrac{2x^2 + 2x}{12x^3}, \dfrac{9x - 3}{12x^3}$ **61.** $2(x + 1)^2 ; \dfrac{6x}{2(x + 1)^2}, \dfrac{5x + 5}{2(x + 1)^2}$ **63.** $(x - 2)(x - 3)(x + 3); \dfrac{2x^2 - 4x}{(x - 2)(x - 3)(x + 3)}, \dfrac{3x^2 + 10x + 3}{(x - 2)(x - 3)(x + 3)}$

65. $\dfrac{9}{x}$ **67.** $\dfrac{2x - 5}{4x}$ **69.** $\dfrac{-a}{a - 3}\left(or\ \dfrac{a}{3 - a}\right)$ **71.** $\dfrac{3}{p - 3}$ **73.** $\dfrac{y}{(x - y)^2}$ **75.** $-\dfrac{x}{x^2 + x + 1}$ **77.** $\dfrac{9x + 2}{x(x - 1)(x + 2)}$ **79.** $\dfrac{yz}{2x^2}$

81. $-\dfrac{x^2 y^2}{(x + y)^2}$ **83.** -1 **85.** -7 **87.** 7 **89.** 6 **91.** $\dfrac{xz}{z - x}$ **93.** $\dfrac{3b^2 - a^2}{a + b}$ **95.** $\dfrac{32}{36}$ **97.** $\dfrac{3}{5}, \dfrac{6}{5}$

99. 110 miles per hour **101.** 25 miles per hour **103.** 12 hours **105.** 10 hours **107.** 1250 tons

109. 288 π cubic centimeters **111.** becomes 16 times

Self Test 7.11

1. $\dfrac{1}{2}, -2$ **3.** -9 **5.** (a) $\dfrac{3x}{4y}$ (b) $\dfrac{3yz}{4x}$ (c) $\dfrac{4a^2}{5b}$ (d) Already in lowest term (e) $3(x + y)$

7. $\dfrac{2}{9}$ **9.** $\dfrac{x + 1}{x - 3}$ **11.** $\dfrac{x - 2}{x + 2}$ **13.** LCD $= 24x^3$ **15.** $15(2x - 1)$ **17.** $\dfrac{31}{20a}$ **19.** $\dfrac{4x^2 - 4}{x^4}$

21. $\dfrac{6x - 6}{(3x - 5)(3x + 5)}$ **23.** $\dfrac{4x^2 + 5x + 28}{(x + 4)^2 (x - 4)}$ **25.** $\dfrac{2x - 1}{x + 5}$ **27.** $\dfrac{(x + 1)(x + 3)}{x + 9}$ **29.** $-3, 1$ are extraneous solutions

31. -4 and 2 are extraneous solutions **33.** $-5, 3$ **35.** $\dfrac{6}{5}, \dfrac{1}{2}$ **37.** 2 miles / hr **39.** 3 hr

CHAPTER 8

SECTION 8.1

1. 2   **3.** 9   **5.** $\frac{1}{5}$ **7.** 0   **9.** Non-real   **11.** 2   **13.** -2 **15.** 3, -3

17. Non-real   **19.** 3, -3 **21.** $\frac{2}{5}$ **23.** 6   **25.** 12   **27.** -4 **29.** $\frac{1}{3}$ **31.** $\frac{2}{3}$

33. 5   **35.** Non-real   **37.** Rational   **39.** Irrational   **41.** Non-real   **43.** Rational   **45.** Rational

47. 1.732   **49.** 2.351   **51.** 6.286   **53.** 13 inches   **55.** 8.062 cm   **57.** 75.9374 ft ; 75.937 ft   **59.** 8.66 ft

SECTION 8.2

1. $\sqrt{28}$ **3.** $\sqrt{40}$ **5.** $\sqrt[4]{18}$ **7.** $\sqrt[3]{-875}$ **9.** $\sqrt[5]{63}$ **11.** $\sqrt{13x^3}$ or $x\sqrt{13x}$ **13.** $\sqrt[3]{xy^2}$

15. 20   **17.** 20   **19.** $6x^2y^2$ **21.** $5xy\sqrt[3]{6x}$ **23.** $4uv\sqrt[4]{6v}$ **25.** $\frac{1}{2}\sqrt{\frac{7}{5}}$ **27.** $\frac{\sqrt[3]{25}}{2}$

29. $|x|$ **31.** $\sqrt[5]{\frac{p^2q}{r^3}}$ **33.** $4\sqrt{3}$ **35.** $8\sqrt{2}$ **37.** $3\sqrt{6}$ **39.** $2\sqrt{30}$ **41.** $6\sqrt[3]{5}$

43. $2\sqrt[4]{15}$ **45.** $-2\sqrt[5]{9}$ **47.** $-5\sqrt[3]{25}$ **49.** $5\sqrt[3]{25}$ **51.** $4p^2\sqrt{2p}$ **53.** $ab^2\sqrt{b}$ **55.** $ab\sqrt[3]{a^2b}$

57. $\frac{20\sqrt{5}}{9}$ **59.** $-\frac{6}{5}$ **61.** $\frac{1}{2x\sqrt[4]{xy^2}}$ **63.** x^3 **65.** $y^5\sqrt{y}$ **67.** $2a^3$ **69.** $xy^3\sqrt{x}$

71. $4x^3y^2\sqrt{2y}$ **73.** x^6y^2 **75.** $\frac{y}{\sqrt{3}}$ **77.** $\frac{35a^3b\sqrt{b}}{12}$

SECTION 8.3

1. $-\sqrt{2}$ **3.** $3\sqrt{7}$ **5.** $3\sqrt{3}$ **7.** $3\sqrt[3]{4}$ **9.** $-4\sqrt[4]{2}$ **11.** $2\sqrt[3]{5}$ **13.** $-7\sqrt[4]{6}$

15. $6\sqrt[5]{3}$ **17.** $\frac{3}{40}\sqrt{15}$ **19.** $\frac{23}{18}\sqrt[4]{11}$ **21.** $-\frac{1}{12}\sqrt[3]{4}$ **23.** 0   **25.** $\sqrt{15}$ **27.** $2\sqrt{6}$

29. $5-\sqrt{30}$ **31.** $a-\sqrt{ab}$ **33.** $10\sqrt{2}-\sqrt{10a}$ **35.** $72-40\sqrt{6}$ **37.** 104   **39.** 7   **41.** -19

43. $9x-25y$ **45.** $9x-y$ **47.** $9x+25y+30\sqrt{xy}$ **49.** $4x-12\sqrt{xy}+9y$ **51.** $15a-22b\sqrt{a}+8b^2$

53. $q-25p^3$ **55.** $x-\sqrt{xy}-6y$

SECTION 8.4

1. $\frac{3\sqrt{2}}{2}$ **3.** $\frac{4\sqrt{5}}{5}$ **5.** $\frac{2\sqrt{6}}{3}$ **7.** $\frac{\sqrt{2}}{4}$ **9.** $\frac{3\sqrt{2}}{2}$ **11.** $\frac{1}{5}\sqrt{5}$ **13.** $\frac{2}{3}\sqrt{3}$

15. $\frac{2}{3}\sqrt{3}$ **17.** $\frac{2\sqrt[3]{100}}{5}$ **19.** $\frac{1}{2}\sqrt[3]{25}$ **21.** $\frac{2}{5}\sqrt[3]{10}$ **23.** $\sqrt[4]{8}$ **25.** $\frac{5\sqrt[4]{4}}{4}$ **27.** $\frac{\sqrt[4]{12}}{4}$

29. $\frac{3\sqrt{10}}{10}$ **31.** 3   **33.** $\frac{4\sqrt{7}}{7}$ **35.** $\frac{2\sqrt{30}}{3}$ **37.** $\frac{\sqrt{3}}{5}$ **39.** $\frac{\sqrt{30}}{10}$ **41.** $\frac{1}{3}\sqrt{6}$

43. $\frac{2\sqrt{x}}{x}$ **45.** $\frac{x\sqrt{6xy}}{2y}$ **47.** $\frac{2\sqrt{b}}{ab}$ **49.** $ab\sqrt{2}$ **51.** $\frac{5}{6z}$ **53.** $\frac{2z}{3x}$ **55.** $4+3\sqrt{2}$

57. $2\sqrt{5}+3\sqrt{3}$ **59.** $-2\sqrt{3}+7\sqrt{7}$ **61.** $2(\sqrt{3}+\sqrt{2})$ **63.** $\frac{3(\sqrt{5}-1)}{4}$ **65.** $\frac{1}{5}(9-2\sqrt{14})$ **67.** $2-\sqrt{3}$

69. $\frac{x+2\sqrt{xy}+y}{x-y}$ **71.** -5 **73.** 7   **75.** $\frac{x-5\sqrt{x}+4}{2(x-1)}$ **77.** $\frac{14-9\sqrt{2}}{17}$ **79.** $\frac{a+b-2\sqrt{ab}}{a-b}$

Section 8.5

1. $\sqrt{16}$, 4   3. $\sqrt{36}$, 6   5. $\sqrt[3]{8}$, 2   7. $-\sqrt[3]{8}$, -2 9. $\sqrt[3]{-8}$, -2 11. $\sqrt{4^5}$, 32   13. $\dfrac{1}{\sqrt[3]{27^2}}$, $\dfrac{1}{9}$

15. $\sqrt{121^3}$, 1,331   17. $\sqrt[4]{81^3}$, 27   19. $2x^{1/3}$ 21. $\dfrac{y^{1/3}}{2x^{2/3}}$ 23. $2x$ 25. $\dfrac{y}{2x}$ 27. $\dfrac{a^3}{b^5}$

29. $\dfrac{2y^2}{x}$ 31. $\dfrac{2p}{3}$ 33. $x^{1/2}\,y^{1/2}$ 35. $\dfrac{y^{5/4}}{2}$ 37. $\dfrac{1}{4}x^2$ 39. $\dfrac{5}{6}x$ 41. $\dfrac{1}{x^2}$

43. xy^2 45. x^2y^3 47. $\dfrac{2}{3}y\sqrt[5]{x}$ 49. 1

Section 8.6

1. 9   3. 16   5. 144   7. 16   9. 3   11. $\dfrac{1}{7}$ 13. 5   15. No solution

17. 16   19. 81   21. 24   23. $\dfrac{1}{2}$ 25. 2   27. $-\dfrac{2}{5}$ 29. No solution   31. 16

33. 3   35. 3, 1   37. 3, 4   39. 2   41. 21   43. 1, 1   45. 2   47. 0

49. 4   51. 1   53. 6   55. 3   57. 1   59. 2   61. No solution   63. 2

65. 2, 10   67. 5   69. 0, 4   71. 1, 2

Review Exercises 8.8

1. 5   3. Not a real number   5. 9   7. Irrational   9. Non-real   11. Rational

13. (a) 12, -12 (b) $\dfrac{9}{4}$, $-\dfrac{9}{4}$ 15. $\sqrt{40}$ cm   17. 6.71 ft   19. $\sqrt{30}$ 21. -4 23. xy

25. $3rs\sqrt[3]{r^2s^2}$ 27. -2 29. $\dfrac{1}{2xy^2}$ 31. $3a\sqrt{2b}$ 33. $\dfrac{b}{2}$ 35. $5\sqrt{3}-9\sqrt{2}$

37. 5   39. $x^2-2x\sqrt{2y}+2y$ 41. $x^2+2y+2x\sqrt{2y}$ 43. $2x+(\sqrt{7}-2\sqrt{3})\sqrt{x}-\sqrt{21}$ 45. $\dfrac{7\sqrt{6}}{6}$

47. $\dfrac{3\sqrt{x}}{4}$ 49. $\dfrac{5\sqrt[3]{2}}{2}$ 51. $\dfrac{15-5\sqrt{5}}{4}$ 53. $\dfrac{8+2\sqrt{3}+4\sqrt{5}+\sqrt{15}}{13}$ 55. $4-\sqrt{15}$

57. $\dfrac{2a+b+3\sqrt{ab}}{a-b}$ 59. $\dfrac{\sqrt{5}}{2p}$ 61. $\dfrac{a\sqrt{3}-3\sqrt{a}}{a-3}$ 63. 5   65. -3 67. 125   69. $2x^{2/3}$

71. $\dfrac{a^3}{8b^{\frac{3}{2}}}$ 73. 6   75. 6 ; 3 is extraneous root   77. 3   79. 3, 8   81. 28.278 in^2

Self Test 8.9

1. 13   3. -7 5. $3x\sqrt{3}$ 7. $\dfrac{5}{9}$ 9. $-2\sqrt[5]{4}$ 11. $8x^2y^3\sqrt[4]{3x^3y}$ 13. $2\sqrt{3}$

15. $\sqrt{3p}+25\sqrt{3}$ 17. -7 19. $y\sqrt{6}+7\sqrt{y}\left(\sqrt{3}-\sqrt{2}\right)-49$ 21. $\dfrac{\sqrt{2}\left(3+\sqrt{5}\right)}{4}$ or $\dfrac{\sqrt{2}\left(3+\sqrt{5}\right)}{4}$

23. $-\dfrac{21+11\sqrt{6}}{19}$ 25. $\dfrac{25x+9y+30\sqrt{xy}}{25x-9y}$ 27. 4 [Extraneous] , no solution   29. 4, and -3 is extraneous

CHAPTER 9

SECTION 9.1

1. ± 5 **3.** ± 9 **5.** $\pm 7\sqrt{2}$ **7.** $\pm 2\sqrt{11}$ **9.** ± 3 **11.** $\pm\sqrt{5}$ **13.** ± 2 **15.** $\pm 3\sqrt{3}$

17. $\pm\sqrt{5}$ **19.** $\pm\sqrt{3}$ **21.** $1, -\dfrac{1}{3}$ **23.** $\dfrac{-5\pm 2\sqrt{2}}{2}$ **25.** $\dfrac{-6}{5}, \dfrac{4}{5}$ **27.** $\dfrac{3}{7}, -\dfrac{1}{7}$ **29.** $\dfrac{7\pm\sqrt{7}}{6}$ **31.** $\dfrac{1\pm 2\sqrt{2}}{2}$

33. $-\dfrac{1}{4}, \dfrac{3}{4}$ **35.** $\dfrac{-7\pm 2\sqrt{3}}{2}$ **37.** $0, 3$ **39.** $0, 1$ **41.** $\dfrac{3\pm 3\sqrt{2}}{5}$ or $\dfrac{3\left(1\pm\sqrt{2}\right)}{5}$ **43.** $\dfrac{3\pm\sqrt{6}}{5}$ **45.** No real solution

47. No real solution   **49.** No real solution   **51.** No real solution   **53.** No real solution

55. No real solution   **57.** No real solution   **59.** $\dfrac{11}{10}, \dfrac{-9}{10}$ **61.** $\dfrac{1\pm 3\sqrt{5}}{3}$ **63.** $\dfrac{4\pm 3\sqrt{2}}{6}$

65. $2\pm 2\sqrt{3}$ or $2\left(1\pm\sqrt{3}\right)$ **67.** $\dfrac{4\pm\sqrt{3}}{6}$ **69.** $\dfrac{13}{75}, \dfrac{-7}{75}$ **71.** $\dfrac{-25}{28}, \dfrac{-17}{28}$ **73.** $\dfrac{-3\pm 2\sqrt{2}}{6}$ **75.** $\dfrac{-1}{8}, \dfrac{-5}{8}$

SECTION 9.2

1. 4 **3.** $\dfrac{49}{4}$ **5.** 9 **7.** $\dfrac{1}{4}$ **9.** 1 **11.** 9 **13.** 16 **15.** 36 **17.** $\dfrac{1}{64}$ **19.** $\dfrac{9}{4}$ **21.** 49 **23.** $\dfrac{9}{64}$

25. $(x+4)^2 - 7$ **27.** $\left(x-\dfrac{7}{2}\right)^2 - \dfrac{29}{4}$ **29.** $\left(y+\dfrac{1}{2}\right)^2 - \dfrac{41}{4}$ **31.** $\left(z-\dfrac{3}{2}\right)^2 + \dfrac{19}{4}$ **33.** $3\left[\left(x-\dfrac{1}{3}\right)^2 + \dfrac{26}{9}\right]$

35. $4\left[\left(x-\dfrac{3}{8}\right)^2 + \dfrac{247}{64}\right]$ **37.** $4\left[\left(x+\dfrac{3}{4}\right)^2 - \dfrac{17}{16}\right]$ **39.** $9\left[\left(x-\dfrac{4}{3}\right)^2 - 1\right]$ **41.** $4\left[\left(u-\dfrac{3}{8}\right)^2 - \dfrac{41}{64}\right]$ **43.** $2\left[\left(u-\dfrac{3}{2}\right)^2 - \dfrac{3}{4}\right]$

45. $-2\pm\sqrt{2}$ **47.** $-\dfrac{1}{2}\pm\dfrac{\sqrt{41}}{2}$ **49.** $\dfrac{3}{2}\pm\dfrac{3\sqrt{5}}{2}$ **51.** $\dfrac{1}{2}\pm\dfrac{1}{2}\sqrt{5}$ **53.** $0, -5$ **55.** $-\dfrac{7}{2}\pm\dfrac{\sqrt{77}}{2}$

57. $-2, -4$ **59.** $\dfrac{5}{2}\pm\dfrac{\sqrt{37}}{2}$ **61.** $\dfrac{7}{4}\pm\dfrac{\sqrt{57}}{4}$ **63.** $1, -\dfrac{1}{3}$ **65.** $\dfrac{2}{5}\pm\dfrac{\sqrt{19}}{5}$ **67.** $\dfrac{3}{8}\pm\dfrac{\sqrt{41}}{8}$

69. $\dfrac{-3}{2}\pm\dfrac{\sqrt{65}}{2}$ **71.** $\dfrac{-19}{6}\pm\dfrac{\sqrt{85}}{6}$ **73.** $0, -\dfrac{7}{3}$ **75.** $\dfrac{-3\pm\sqrt{201}}{4}$ **77.** $-2, 4$ **79.** $-1, -5$

SECTION 9.3

1. $1, 2$ **3.** $-1, -5$ **5.** $1, \dfrac{1}{2}$ **7.** $-1, -\dfrac{1}{5}$ **9.** 1 **11.** $-\dfrac{2}{3}$ **13.** $-\dfrac{5}{2}\pm\dfrac{\sqrt{41}}{2}$

15. $\dfrac{7}{2}\pm\dfrac{\sqrt{41}}{2}$ **17.** $\dfrac{-5}{2}\pm\dfrac{\sqrt{129}}{6}$ **19.** $\dfrac{-7}{10}\pm\dfrac{\sqrt{89}}{10}$ **21.** $\dfrac{5\pm\sqrt{181}}{6}$ **23.** $\dfrac{3}{2}$ **25.** $\dfrac{3\pm\sqrt{3}}{3}$ **27.** $1, \dfrac{5}{3}$ **29.** $-\dfrac{1}{2}, \dfrac{4}{3}$

31. $\dfrac{5}{3}, \dfrac{5}{3}$ **33.** $-1\pm\dfrac{1}{3}\sqrt{10}$ **35.** $14, 16$ **37.** $3, 5$ **39.** 6 **41.** **(i)** 50 ft   **(ii)** 2.5 seconds

43. 120 **45.** 15 **47.** $9, \sqrt{19}$ **49.** 8 seconds

SECTION 9.4

1. Vertex is $(0, 0)$ **3.** Vertex is $(0, 0)$ **5.** Vertex is $(-1, 0)$ **7.** Vertex is $(2, 0)$ **9.** Vertex is $(1, 3)$

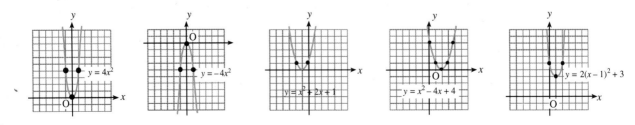

11. Vertex is (−2, 8)   **13.** Vertex is (−1 , 3)   **15.** Vertex is (−2/3,−1/3)

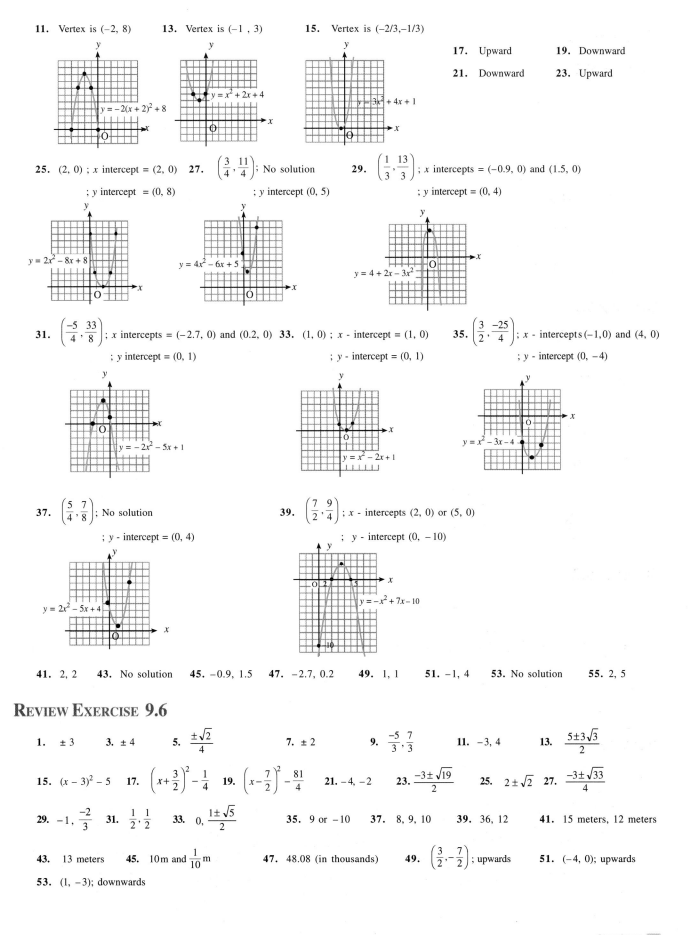

17. Upward   **19.** Downward

21. Downward   **23.** Upward

25. (2, 0) ; x intercept = (2, 0)   **27.** $\left(\dfrac{3}{4},\dfrac{11}{4}\right)$; No solution   **29.** $\left(\dfrac{1}{3},\dfrac{13}{3}\right)$; x intercepts = (−0.9, 0) and (1.5, 0)

; y intercept = (0, 8)   ; y intercept (0, 5)   ; y intercept = (0, 4)

31. $\left(\dfrac{-5}{4},\dfrac{33}{8}\right)$; x intercepts = (−2.7, 0) and (0.2, 0) **33.** (1, 0) ; x - intercept = (1, 0)   **35.** $\left(\dfrac{3}{2},\dfrac{-25}{4}\right)$; x - intercepts (−1,0) and (4, 0)

; y intercept = (0, 1)   ; y - intercept = (0, 1)   ; y - intercept (0, −4)

37. $\left(\dfrac{5}{4},\dfrac{7}{8}\right)$; No solution   **39.** $\left(\dfrac{7}{2},\dfrac{9}{4}\right)$; x - intercepts (2, 0) or (5, 0)

; y - intercept = (0, 4)   ; y - intercept (0, −10)

41. 2, 2   **43.** No solution   **45.** −0.9, 1.5   **47.** −2.7, 0.2   **49.** 1, 1   **51.** −1, 4   **53.** No solution   **55.** 2, 5

REVIEW EXERCISE 9.6

1. ± 3   **3.** ± 4   **5.** $\dfrac{\pm\sqrt{2}}{4}$ **7.** ± 2   **9.** $\dfrac{-5}{3},\dfrac{7}{3}$ **11.** −3, 4   **13.** $\dfrac{5\pm3\sqrt{3}}{2}$

15. $(x-3)^2-5$ **17.** $\left(x+\dfrac{3}{2}\right)^2-\dfrac{1}{4}$ **19.** $\left(x-\dfrac{7}{2}\right)^2-\dfrac{81}{4}$ **21.** −4, −2   **23.** $\dfrac{-3\pm\sqrt{19}}{2}$ **25.** $2\pm\sqrt{2}$ **27.** $\dfrac{-3\pm\sqrt{33}}{4}$

29. −1, $\dfrac{-2}{3}$ **31.** $\dfrac{1}{2},\dfrac{1}{2}$ **33.** 0, $\dfrac{1\pm\sqrt{5}}{2}$ **35.** 9 or −10   **37.** 8, 9, 10   **39.** 36, 12   **41.** 15 meters, 12 meters

43. 13 meters   **45.** 10m and $\dfrac{1}{10}$ m   **47.** 48.08 (in thousands)   **49.** $\left(\dfrac{3}{2},-\dfrac{7}{2}\right)$; upwards   **51.** (−4, 0); upwards

53. (1, −3); downwards

SELF TEST 9.7

1. $t = \dfrac{-6}{5}, \dfrac{8}{5}$

3. $\left(x + \dfrac{7}{2}\right)^2 - \dfrac{61}{4}$

5. $\left(x - \dfrac{11}{2}\right)^2 - \dfrac{89}{4}$

7. $\dfrac{3 \pm \sqrt{37}}{2}$

9. No real solution

11. $\dfrac{1}{2}, 1$

13. $-2, \dfrac{7}{2}$

15. $\dfrac{1 \pm \sqrt{41}}{4}$

17. No real solution

19. $\dfrac{1 \pm \sqrt{13}}{2}$

21. $\dfrac{2}{5}$ or $\dfrac{5}{2}$

23. $20

25.

$y = x^2 + 3$

27.

$y = x^2 + 6x + 4$

29.

$y = -9 - 6x - x^2$

31. i) No real solution; parabola does not intersect x-axis

ii) Two real solutions; parabola intersects x- axis in two points.

iii) Only two real solutions ; parabola meets x-axis in just two points.

APPENDIX

Appendix B

Use of Calculator (TI-83/Plus)

Some General Remarks

1. Press **MODE**

    a. First line: **Normal**   **Sci**   **Eng**

    Highlight to set the calculations in the desired form : normal, scientific notation, or engineering notation.

    b. Second line: **Float**   **0 1 2 3 4 5 6 7 8 9**

    Highlight the number of places of decimals to which the calculations are desired to be rounded.

    c. Fourth line: Always select **Func;** unless told to do otherwise.

2. If the display is too light or too dark, adjust the contrast by pressing   2nd and △ or 2nd and ▽.

3. Expressions are entered from left to right horizontally in the same way as you will write them in a single line format.

4. Use ^ for exponentiation.

Examples

*   To enter the expression $4^3\left(5+\left(7^2 - \sqrt{2}\right)\right)$, we use the following key strokes:

    4   ^   3   (5   +   (7 x^2 −   2nd x^2 2   )   )

*   To enter the expression $\dfrac{3^2 + 7^5 \cdot 6^4}{-3 + 5 \cdot 4}$

    press the following sequence of keys:

    (3   ^   2   +   7   ^   5   ×   6   ^   4   )   ÷

    ((-)   3   +   5   ×   4   )

    Note   Sometimes an expression inside the brackets will be used to show what the screen looks like.

CHAPTER 1 Real Number System

SECTION 1.1 FRACTIONS

Set Mode to **Float**.

Example 1   Check if 3 and 5 are factors of 20?

A number is a factor of 20 if the quotient of 20 and the number is an integer.

- To check if 3 is a factor of 20, press

  [2] [0] [÷] [3]   [ENTER]   Answer = 6.666666667

  which is not an integer. Therefore, 3 is not a factor of 20.

- To check if 5 is a factor of 20, press

  [2] [0] [÷] [5]   [ENTER]   Answer = 4

  which is an integer. This shows that 5 is a factor of 20.

Example 2   Check if 13 and 21 are prime numbers?

(i) 13:   Use the method in Example 1 above, to see that 1 and 13 are the only factors of 13.

Check that $\dfrac{13}{2}, \dfrac{13}{3}, \dfrac{13}{4}, \dfrac{13}{5}, \dfrac{13}{6}, \dfrac{13}{7}$ are not integers

Hence 13 is prime.

(ii) 21:   Check if 21 has a positive factor different from 1 and 21. For this, press:

[2] [1] [÷] [2]   [ENTER]   Answer = 10.5

Thus, 2 is not a factor of 21.   Now try 3 for a factor.

[2] [1] [÷] [3]   [ENTER]   Answer = 7

This shows that 3 is a factor of 21. Therefore, 21 is not prime.

Following examples should be used to check the answers only.

Example 3   Write the fraction $\dfrac{14}{21}$ in lowest terms

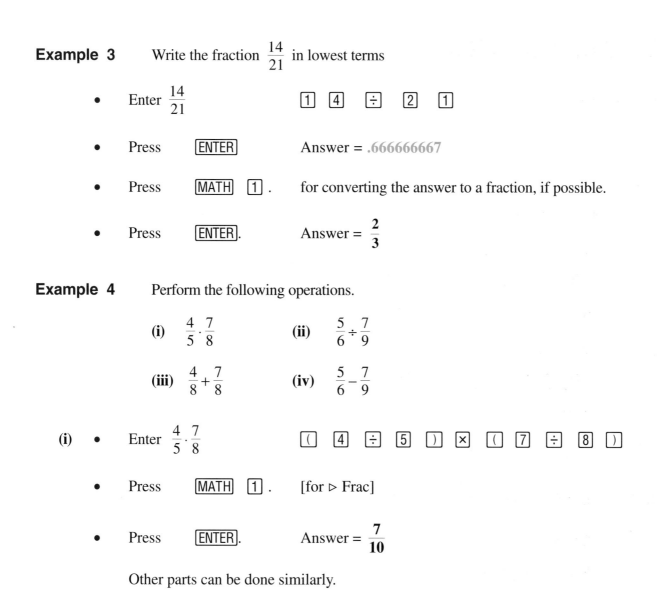

- Enter $\dfrac{14}{21}$ 1 4 ÷ 2 1

- Press   ENTER   Answer = .666666667

- Press   MATH 1 .   for converting the answer to a fraction, if possible.

- Press   ENTER.   Answer = $\dfrac{2}{3}$

Example 4   Perform the following operations.

       (i) $\dfrac{4}{5} \cdot \dfrac{7}{8}$ **(ii)** $\dfrac{5}{6} \div \dfrac{7}{9}$

       (iii) $\dfrac{4}{8} + \dfrac{7}{8}$ **(iv)** $\dfrac{5}{6} - \dfrac{7}{9}$

(i)
- Enter $\dfrac{4}{5} \cdot \dfrac{7}{8}$ (4 ÷ 5) × (7 ÷ 8)

- Press   MATH 1 .   [for ▷ Frac]

- Press   ENTER.   Answer = $\dfrac{7}{10}$

Other parts can be done similarly.

SECTION 1.2 ORDER OF OPERATIONS

Example 1   Evaluate $(3 + 5 \times 6) \div \left[12 - \dfrac{6 - 2 \cdot 2}{3^2 - 7} \right]$.

- Enter the expression. Keystrokes:

    (3 + 5 × 6) ÷ (1 2 − (

    6 − 2 × 2) ÷ (3 x^2 − 7))

- Press   ENTER   Answer = 3

> **Note** Observe that we entered *parentheses* even where brackets are shown in the expression. While using the calculator, parentheses are used for grouping.

Example 2   Which of the following are true ?

   (i) $12 \div 2 > 5$ **(ii)** $8 + 5 \times 2 \le 15$

(i)   Enter the keystrokes:

-   [1] [2] [÷] [2] [2nd] [MATH] [3] [5]
-   Press   [ENTER].   Answer = 1: True

(ii)   Enter the keystrokes:

-   [8] [+] [5] [×] [2] [2nd] [MATH] [6] [1] [5]
-   Press   [ENTER].   Answer = 0: False

   In verification of *statements* **1 → True** and **0 → False.**

SECTION 1.3   EVALUATING EXPRESSIONS

To enter x press [X,T,Θ,n]   [Remember that we are in **Func** mode.]

To enter any alphabet, we press [ALPHA] and the key over which the desired alphabet is printed in green color.

Example 1   Enter the expressions:

   (i) $(4x + 7)\left\{5x^2 + 6x + \dfrac{4}{x}\right\}$ **(ii)** $\dfrac{4A^2 + 7B^2}{3A - 4B}$

   (i)   Enter the keystrokes:

   [(] [4] [X,T,Θ,n] [+] [7] [)] [(] [5] [X,T,Θ,n] [x^2] [+] [6]

   [X,T,Θ,n]   [+]   [4] [÷] [X,T,Θ,n] [)]

   (ii)   Enter the keystrokes:

   [(] [4] [ALPHA] [MATH] [x^2] [+] [7] [ALPHA] [MATRX] [x^2]

   [)] [÷] [(] [3] [ALPHA] [MATH] [–] [4] [ALPHA]   [MATRX] [)]

Example 2   Evaluate the following:

   (i) $(4x + 7)\left\{5x^2 + 6x + \dfrac{4}{x}\right\}$, at $x = 4$ and $x = -6$.

   (ii) $\dfrac{4A^2 + 7B^2}{3A - 4B}$, at $A = 5$ and $B = 3$.

(i) **Method 1:**

Enter the following

- 4 $\boxed{\text{STO}\triangleright}$ $\boxed{\text{X,T,}\Theta,n}$

- Enter the expression $(4x + 7)\left\{5x^2 + 6x + \dfrac{4}{x}\right\}$.

  [Refer to the preceding example.]

- Press $\boxed{\text{ENTER}}$.

- Press $\boxed{\text{(-)}}$ $\boxed{6}$ $\boxed{\text{STO}\triangleright}$ $\boxed{\text{X,T,}\Theta,n}$

- Press $\boxed{\text{ENTER}}$.

- Press $\boxed{\text{2nd}}$ $\boxed{\text{ENTER}}$ repeatedly until the expression $(4x + 7)\left\{5x^2 + 6x + \dfrac{4}{x}\right\}$ shows up on the screen.

- Press $\boxed{\text{ENTER}}$.   Answer $= -2436.666667$

Notes

1) Pressing $\boxed{\text{2nd}}$ $\boxed{\text{ENTER}}$ repeatedly recalls last few commands entered in the calculator.

2) To see whether the second answer is a fraction or not, press $\boxed{\text{MATH}}$ $\boxed{1}$ for $\triangleright$ **Frac.** Press $\boxed{\text{ENTER}}$ Answer $= -.7310/3$ shows that the answer is indeed a fraction.

Mothod 2:

- Press $\boxed{\text{Y=}}$.

  There are ten function slots Y_1, Y_2, ... Y_9, Y_0.

- Enter the expression $(4x + 7)\left\{5x^2 + 6x + \dfrac{4}{x}\right\}$ in, $Y_1 =$, say

- Press $\boxed{\text{2nd}}$ $\boxed{\text{MODE}}$ to leave the **Function** editor.

- Press $\boxed{\text{VARS}}$ $\boxed{\triangleright}$ $\boxed{\text{ENTER}}$ $\boxed{1}$

  $Y_1($ is printed on the Home Screen.

- Continue to type 4) next to $Y_1($.   [Screen display looks like $Y_1(4)$]

- Press $\boxed{\text{ENTER}}$.   Answer $= 2415$

- Press $\boxed{\text{2nd}}$ $\boxed{\text{ENTER}}$.

- Edit 4 to -6. [Screen display looks like $Y_1(-6)$.]

- Press $\boxed{\text{ENTER}}$.   Answer $= -2436.666667$

  Press $\boxed{\text{MATH}}$ $\boxed{1}$ $\boxed{\triangleright}$ Answer $= -7310/3$ [See note above]

(ii) •   Store 5 in A: 5 STO▷ ALPHA MATH

     •   Press   ENTER .

     •   Store 3 in B.

     •   Press   ENTER .

     •   Enter the expression $\dfrac{4A^2+7B^2}{3A-4B}$. (See the preceding example).

     •   Press   ENTER .   Answer = 54.33333333

     •   Use ▷ **Frac**   Answer = 163/3

SECTION 1.4   CLASSIFICATION OF NUMBERS

Example 1   Which of the numbers $\dfrac{\sqrt{16}-1}{5}$ and $\sqrt{2}$ is rational?

$\dfrac{\sqrt{16}-1}{5}$:

     •   Enter $\dfrac{\sqrt{16}-1}{5}$.

        KEYSTROKES: (2nd x^2 1   6   )   −   1   )   ÷   5

     •   Press   ENTER .   Answer = .6

     •   Press   MATH 1 ENTER .   Answer = 3/5

        This shows that $\dfrac{\sqrt{16}-1}{5}$ is a rational number.

$\sqrt{2}$:

     •   Enter $\sqrt{2}$.

     •   Press   ENTER .   Answer = 1.414213562

     •   Press   ▷ **Frac**   Answer = 1.414213562

        This does not convert the answer into a fraction. Therefore, $\sqrt{2}$ may not be a rational number. In fact, it is not.

Example 2   Find $\left| \dfrac{2^2 - 13}{4 \cdot 5 + 7} \right|$

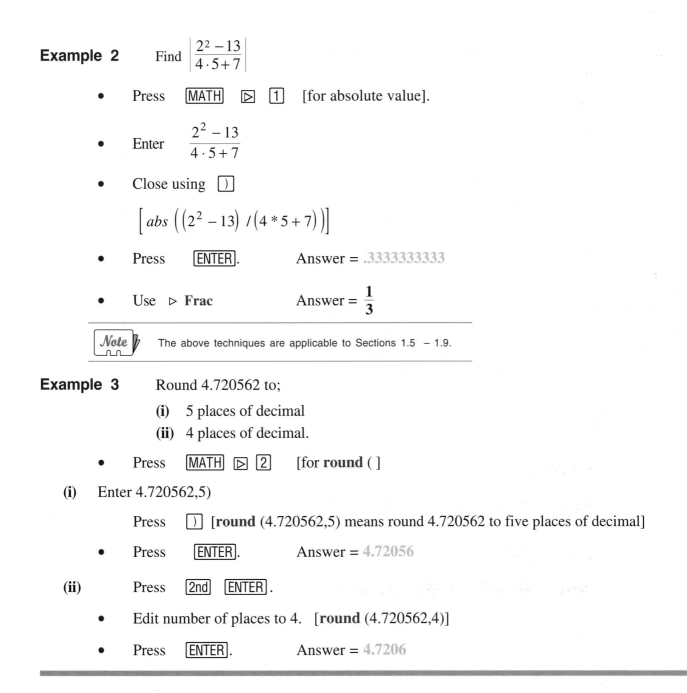

- Press $\boxed{\text{MATH}}$ $\boxed{\triangleright}$ $\boxed{1}$ [for absolute value].

- Enter $\dfrac{2^2 - 13}{4 \cdot 5 + 7}$

- Close using $\boxed{)}$

$$\left[abs\left(\left(2^2 - 13\right) / \left(4 * 5 + 7\right) \right) \right]$$

- Press $\boxed{\text{ENTER}}$.   Answer = .3333333333

- Use   ▷ **Frac**   Answer = $\dfrac{1}{3}$

> *Note*   The above techniques are applicable to Sections 1.5 – 1.9.

Example 3   Round 4.720562 to;

   (i)   5 places of decimal

   (ii) 4 places of decimal.

- Press $\boxed{\text{MATH}}$ $\boxed{\triangleright}$ $\boxed{2}$ [for **round** ( ]

(i)   Enter 4.720562,5)

   Press $\boxed{)}$ [**round** (4.720562,5) means round 4.720562 to five places of decimal]

- Press $\boxed{\text{ENTER}}$.   Answer = 4.72056

(ii)   Press $\boxed{\text{2nd}}$ $\boxed{\text{ENTER}}$.

- Edit number of places to 4.   [**round** (4.720562,4)]

- Press $\boxed{\text{ENTER}}$.   Answer = 4.7206

CHAPTER 2 Solutions of Equations and Inequalities in One Variable

SECTIONS 2.2 – 2.3   SOLVING EQUATIONS

Example 1   Solve the equation

$$3(6x - 2) + 4(3 - 4x) = 2(1 - x)$$

and check your answer using the calculator.

Solution of the above equation is –1. [Refer to Section 2.2, Example 6]

- Store –1 in x.

  KEYSTROKES: $\boxed{(\text{-})}$ $\boxed{1}$ $\boxed{\text{STO}\triangleright}$ $\boxed{\text{X,T,}\Theta,n}$

- Enter the equation $3(6x - 2) + 4(3 - 4x) = 2(1 - x)$.

- Press $\boxed{\text{ENTER}}$. Answer = **1: True**

📝 *Note*   Recall that: Answer 1 means **true**, 0 means **false**.

Example 2   Solve the following equation and check your solution

$$\frac{2}{3}x + 2 = x - \frac{x-1}{2} + \frac{5}{3}$$

- Solve the equation using the methods of Sections 2.2 and 2.3. Solution is $x = 1$.

- Store 1 in x: 1 $\boxed{1}$ $\boxed{\text{STO}\triangleright}$ $\boxed{\text{X,T,}\Theta,n}$

- Enter the equation $\frac{2}{3}x + 2 = x - \frac{x-1}{2} + \frac{5}{3}$.

- Press $\boxed{\text{ENTER}}$ Answer = **1: True**

Example 3   Solve the equation

$$\frac{2}{3}x + 2 = x - \frac{x-1}{2} + \frac{5}{3} .$$

     using calculator and check your solution too.

- Convert $\frac{2}{3}x + 2 = x - \frac{x-1}{2} + \frac{5}{3}$ into $\frac{2}{3}x + 2 - \left(x - \frac{x-1}{2} + \frac{5}{3}\right) = 0$.

  [Transfer everything to one side.]

- Press $\boxed{\text{Y=}}$.

- Enter $\frac{2}{3}x + 2 - \left(x - \frac{x-1}{2} + \frac{5}{3}\right)$ in one of the function slots, say Y_1.

- Press $\boxed{\text{2nd}}$ $\boxed{\text{MODE}}$ to go to the HOME screen.

- Press $\boxed{\text{CLEAR}}$ or move the cursor to a new line.

- Press $\boxed{\text{MATH}}$ $\boxed{0}$

- Press $\boxed{\triangle}$

- Enter Y_1 next to equation : 0   [Recall Y_1 is entered by VARS ▷ ENTER 1

- Press   ENTER

- Enter a guess next to $X =$.

- Enter 0 for guess.

- With cursor still blinking on the $X =$ line

- Press   ALPHA ENTER   Answer = 1

1) *Check:*

   - On a new line enter Y_1.

   - Type 1) next to $Y_1<$.   [Screen: $Y_1(1)$]

   - Press ENTER.   Answer = 0

Notes

1. Remember $Y_1(1)$ is the value of Y_1 at $x = 1$. Therefore, $Y_1(1) = 0$ means 1 is a solution of the equation $Y_1 = 0$.

2. Notice the difference in checking by using the *equation* in terms of true or false in Examples 1 and 2 above. In example 3 above, we *did not* use the equation $\frac{2}{3}x + 2 = \frac{x-1}{2} + \frac{5}{3}$. In fact, we used the expression $\frac{2}{3}x + 2 - \left(x - \frac{x-1}{2} + \frac{5}{3}\right)$, which defines this equation when equated to 0.

3. Later on we will give additional methods to solve equations using TI-83 / 83-PLUS.

SECTION 2.8 SOLUTIONS OF LINEAR INEQUALITIES

Example 1   Which of the following satisfy the inequality $\frac{3}{4}x - 4 < \frac{4}{5}x + 1$?

x : 0, –2, –100, –150, 25

- Enter $\frac{3}{4}x - 4 < \frac{4}{5}x + 1$ [< is entered by 2nd MATH 5].

- Store 0 in x.

- Use 2nd ENTER to get the inequality on the next line.

- Press ENTER   Answer = 1: True

Thus, $x = 0$ satisfies the inequality.

- Store –100 in x.

- Use 2nd ENTER repeatedly to get the inequality on the next line.

- Press ENTER.   Answer = 0: False

Thus, $x = -100$ does not satisfy the inequality.
Similarly, check for $x = -2, -150$ and 25.

Example 2   Solve the inequality

$$\frac{3}{4}x - 4 < \frac{4}{5}x + 1 \text{ using the calculator.}$$

- Solve the equation:

$$\frac{3}{4}x - 4 = \frac{4}{5}x + 1$$

  [Use the method of sections 2.2 – 2.3, example 3 in this appendix]

  Answer $= -100$

- Enter the inequality:

$$\frac{3}{4}x - 4 < \frac{4}{5}x + 1$$

- Select a number different from -100, and store in x. Suppose you store 0 in x.

- Use [2nd] [ENTER] repeatedly until the inequality shows up on the next line.

- Press [ENTER].   Answer $= 1: \text{True}$

Thus $x = 0$ satisfies the inequality. This means that between $x < -100$ and $x > -100$ the solution of the inequality is that which *contains 0*. Therefore, $x > -100$ is the solution.

Note The calculator returns 0 when we store -200 in x. Answer 0 means false. Thus between $x > -100$ and $x < -100$, the solution of the given inequality is that which *does not contain* -200. Hence $x > -100$ is the solution. Recall you can use any *test point*.

CHAPTER 3   Linear Equations In Two Variables

SECTION 3.1 LINEAR EQUATIONS IN TWO VARIABLES

Example 1   Which of $(1, -3)$ and $(2, 4)$ is a solution of $2P - Q = 5$?

Use the method of Sections 2.2 – 2.3, Example 1.

- Store 1 in P .

  KEYSTROKES: [1] [STO▷] [ALPHA] [8]

- Store -3 in Q.

- Enter the equation $2P - Q = 5$.

  [2] [ALPHA] [8] [−] [ALPHA] [9] [2nd] [MATH] [1] [5]

- Press [ENTER].   Answer $= 1$

This means **True.** Therefore $(1, -3)$ is a solution of $2P - Q = 5$.

Next

- Store 2 in P.

- Store 4 in Q.

- Use [2nd] [ENTER] repeatedly to bring $2P - Q = 5$ on the next line.

- Press [ENTER].   Answer = 0

This means **False.** Therefore, $(2, 4)$ is not a solution of $2P - Q = 5$.

Preparation for graphing

For graphing we should have a suitable screen (viewing window) to graph. This is done by setting the window. Press [WINDOW].

Format: You will always need to set the **Window Format** as **RectGC.** Other choices are optional. Unless stated otherwise, we shall select, **CoordOn, GridOff, AxesOn and LabelOff.**

WINDOW: Xmin defines the *left end* of the screen, Xmax defines the *right end* of the screen; Ymin defines the *lower end* of the screen; and Ymax defines the *upper end* of the screen. Together they form the viewing rectangle or viewing screen. Xscl and Yscl should be set appropriately to see the hash marks on the two axes.

Built in Window Settings

- Press [ZOOM].

    In this menu ZDecimal and Zstandard are built-in Window Settings. You may like to select these and view their defining parameters.

Zsquare

Setting Xmin = Ymin = Xmax = Ymax should be supposed to define a square view screen, but actually it does not do that. Thus, for example, when you select ZStandard [Xmin = Ymin = -10, Xmax = Ymax = Ymax = 10], and if you draw a circle, it will not look like a circle. ZDecimal is an example of a Square screen. Sometimes, it may be desirable to have a square screen bigger than Zdecimal for viewing actual shape. For this, select Xmin and Xmax with desired scales and press [ZOOM] [ZSQUARE]. Ymin and Ymax will be automatically so set that the resulting view screen is square.

We will use the following window settings:

i.   Xmin = - 9.4,   Xmax = 9.4,   Xscl = 1
       Ymin = - 12.4, Ymax = 12.4,   Yscl = 1

This window will be referred as **Friendly Window I**

ii.   Xmin = − 9.4,   Xmax = 9.4,   Xscl = 1

           Ymin = − 6.2,   Ymax = 6.2,   Yscl = 1

                        This window will be referred as **Friendly Window II**

iii.   Xmin = − 4.7,   Xmax = 4.7,   Xscl = 1

           Ymin = − 6.2,   Ymax = 6.2,   Yscl = 1

                        This window will be referred as **Friendly Window III**

You may set these windows by pressing WINDOW and changing the values to the desired values. Set any of these windows or the **ZDecimal** Window, and press GRAPH . You are in Graph-Screen. Now if you press various arrow keys, and you will notice a cursor moving on the screen. Coordinates of its position are shown at the bottom of the screen. As the cursor moves, you will notice that the coordinates jump by a convenient unit fraction. Compare this to **ZStandard** Window.

A Note About Clearing Graphs

CLEAR *does not* clear graphs. It clears text on the Home Screen only. TI-83/83 plus constructs graphs using essentially three menus.

1.   STAT-PLOT: This menu helps construct statistical plots Option 4 on the menu turns off all *Stat Plots*. Since we shall not discuss Stat Plots you are advised to select PlotsOff on this menu.

           KEYSTROKES: 2nd Y= 4 ENTER

2.   Graph using Y=   This menu constructs graphs using the functions stored in **Y=**. Graphs of only active functions are plotted. A function is active or not according as ' = ' sign next to Y, where the function is stored, is highlighted or not. To activate or deactive a function, move the cursor on '=' and press ENTER .

           To deactivate all functions, press

           KEYSTROKES: VARS ▷ 4 2 ENTER

           To clear a function, press Y= , move the cursor to the function to be cleared, and press CLEAR.

3.   Draw   This menu also constructs graphs. All graphs drawn using this menu can be cleared by using **ClrDraw** in **DRAW** menu.

           KEYSTROKES: 2nd PRGM 1 ENTER

Example 2   Plot the point (–2, 5).

-    Set **Window** to **ZStandard.**

     KEYSTROKES: ZOOM 6

-    Press   2nd MODE

- Press CLEAR.

- Press 2nd PRGM

- Select **POINTS** menu using ▷.

- Press 1 [for **Pt – On** ( ].

- Type the points so that your screen has **Pt - On (–2, 5).**

- Press ENTER.

You see (–2, 5) is plotted on the screen.

In the last example, the calculator plotted the point (–2, 5) for us. How about if we want to plot this point ourselves directly on the Graph Screen?

Example 3   Plot the point (–2, 5) on a coordinate plane.

- Clear Graph Screen. [2nd PRGM 1 ENTER]

- Set Friendly Window II.

- Press GRAPH.

- Press 2nd PRGM ▷ 1 .   [for **Pt-On** ( ]

  [You are brought back to Graph Screen, with $x = 0$ and $y = 0$ at the bottom line, and the cursor blinking at the origin.]

- Use ◁ until $x = -2$ appears in the bottom line.

- Use △ until $y = 5$ appears in the bottom line. Now cursor is at (–2, 5).

- Press ENTER , (–2, 5) is plotted.

To plot additional points, move the cursor to the desired location and press ENTER.

Section 3.2 Graphing Linear Equations

Example 1   Graph the equation $x = 4$.

- Clear Graph Screen.

- Set Window to ZDecimal [ZOOM 4]   (See Note # 1 above.)

- Press 2nd PRGM 4   [for **vertical**; notice $x = 4$ is a vertical line.]

  [Graph screen appears with $x = 0$, $y = 0$ in the bottom line, and a blinking cursor at the origin.]

- Use ▷ until $x = 4$ in the bottom line.

- Press ENTER

The moving vertical line is now located at $x = 4$.

Alternatively, after setting the window, you may quit. Now press [2nd] [PRGM] [4]. **Vertical** appears on the Home Screen. Type 4, and press [ENTER]. The line $x = 4$ is graphed on the Graph Screen.

Horizontal line may be graphed by selecting **Horizontal** from **DRAW** menu as above. Alternatively, we may use the method described below.

Example 2   Graph the equation $2x + 3y = 6$.

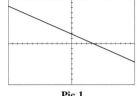
Pic 1

- Rewrite the equation as $y = \frac{1}{3}(6 - 2x)$ by solving for y.

- Set Window to ZStandard.

- Press [Y=].

- Enter $\frac{1}{3}(6 - 2x)$ in one of the slots, say Y_1.
  [This function becomes active.]

- Press [GRAPH]. The line appears as shown.

Example 3   Graph the equation $2x + 3y = 6$, and find its x-intercept and y-intercept.
  You have drawn the graph in Example 2 above. We continue from where we left in example 2.

- Press [TRACE].
  [Coordinates appear at the bottom, and a cursor blinks on the line.]

- Use [◁] and [▷] only to move the cursor along the line and explore the coordinates of various points on the line.

As you move along the curve, you find that x-intercept is not found exactly as the cursor never sits on x-axis. *Try Friendly Window III or ZDecimal window.* This shows the necessity of setting a suitable window.

1. Any equation of the form $y = f(x)$ can be graphed using DRAW menu [[2nd] [PRGM] [6] (for **DrawF**)]. But graphs drawn in this manner cannot be explored by using [TRACE].

2. The equation of a vertical line cannot be written in the form $y = ...$ So, [TRACE] cannot be used for the graph of a vertical line.

SECTION 3.4   LINE JOINING TWO POINTS

Example 1   Draw the line joining $(-2, 5)$ and $(3, 4)$.

If you are interested in the extended line, the best method is to find its equation and graph as explained above in Section 3, example 2. In case you are interested only in the line segment joining $(-2, 5)$ and $(3, 4)$, proceed as follows:

Appendix B

- Set a suitable Window.

- Clear Graph Screen.

- Quit and clear Home Screen

- Press [2nd] [PRGM] [2]   [for **Line** ( ].

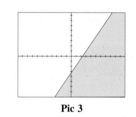

Pic 2

- Type (–2, 5, 3, 4).

  [Screen looks like : **Line** (–2, 5, 3, 4)].

- Press [ENTER].   (There appears the desired line segment.)

> *Note* You can also draw line segment using **Line** while still on the Graph Screen.
> Recall how points were plotted in two different ways.

SECTION 3.5   GRAPHING LINEAR INEQUALITIES IN TWO VARIABLES

Example 1   Graph the linear inequality $2x - y > 3$.

Method 1:

- Clear Graph Screen.

- Set Window to ZStandard.

- (Use algebra to rewrite $2x - y > 3$ as $y < 2x - 3$.)

- Press [2nd] [MODE].

- Press [2nd] [PRGM] [7]   [For **Shade** ( ].

Pic 3

- Type –20, $2x - 3$).

  [Screen looks like **Shade** (–20, $2x - 3$)].

- Press [ENTER].

Shaded portion is the graphical solution of the inequality.

> *Note* A syntax for **Shade** is Shade ($f_1(x)$, $f_2(x)$, Xmin, Xmax where $f_1(x)$ is the lower function $f_2(x)$ is the upper
> function, Xmin is the least x-value, and Xmax is the greatest x-value. In the above example, since $y < 2x - 3$,
> $2x - 3$ was selected as an upper function. Lower function should be selected as $y = k$ where $k < $ Ymin. For
> more details on the syntax for shade refer to the manual.

Method 2:

- Clear Graph Screen.

- Enter $2x - 3$ as $Y1$.

- Use [◁] to move the cursor to the icon on the left of $Y1 = $.

- Press [ENTER] repeatedly until the icon ▙ appears.

- Press [GRAPH] to get the shaded region for the solution in Pic 3.

Example 2   Graph the inequality $x + 4y \geq 5$.

Method 1:

- Rewrite $x + 4y \geq 5$ as $y \geq \dfrac{5-x}{4}$.

- Clear Graph Screen.

- Set Window to ZStandard.

- Press [2nd] [PRGM] [7]   [For **Shade ( )**].

- Type $\dfrac{5-x}{4}$, 20).

  Screen looks like **Shade** $\left(\dfrac{5-x}{4}, 20\right)$.

- Press [ENTER].

Shaded area is the solution of the inequality.

Note   Observe that **−20 < Ymin** and **20 > Ymax**.

Method 2:

- Clear Graph Screen.

- Enter $\dfrac{5-x}{4}$ as $Y1$.

- Use [◁] to move the cursor to the icon on the left of $Y1 =$

- Press [ENTER] repeatedly until you see the ▜ .

- Press [GRAPH] to obtain the shaded region that is the solution of the inequality.

SECTION 3.6 FUNCTIONS

Example 1 For the function $f(x) = 3x^2 + 4x - 1$ find $f(-3)$.

- Use any of the methods explained in Section 1.3, Example 2(i).

  Answer = **14**

Example 2 Find the domain and range of $f(x) = \dfrac{2}{2-x}$.

Method 1: We know that the rational expression $\dfrac{2}{2-x}$ is not defined when the denominator is $2 - x = 0$. Solve $2 - x = 0$ and determine domain. Use the domain to determine the range. [Use of calculator will be justified if there was a complicated expression in place of $2 - x$].

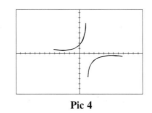

Pic 4

Method 2:
- Clear Graph Screen.

- Set Window to **Friendly Window I**.

- Press ⬚MODE⬚ and select **DOT.**

- Press ⬚Y=⬚ and enter the expression $\dfrac{2}{2-x}$ in one of the function slots, say Y_1.

- Press ⬚GRAPH⬚.

Observe that the *graph appears in dots and not connected lines.* Also observe that the graph exists on the left of $x = 2$ and on the right of $x = 2$, and the two pieces are not connected at $x = 2$.

- Press ⬚TRACE⬚

- Continue to press ⬚◁⬚ or ⬚▷⬚ to explore the graph on the right or left of outside the viewing window.

It is found that the graph exists at all points x except $x = 2$. Therefore, domain of $f(x) = \dfrac{2}{2-x}$ is $\{x \mid x \neq 2\}$, i.e., all real numbers except 2.

Again the graph never touches or crosses the x-axis. Range of $f(x)$ is $\{x \mid x \neq 0\}$, i.e., all nonzero real numbers.

Note 🗒 You are advised to go over Method #2 using ZStandard window [⬚ZOOM⬚ ⬚6⬚] and observe the difference as you trace.

CHAPTER 4 Systems of Linear Equations and Inequalities

SECTION 4.1 SOLVING SYSTEMS OF LINEAR EQUATIONS

Example 1   Show graphically that the system of linear equations: $2x + 3y = 6$
is inconsistent. $4x + 6y = 24$

• Write $2x + 3y = 6$ as $y = \dfrac{6 - 2x}{3}$.   [Solve for y.]

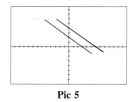

Pic 5

• Write $4x + 6y = 24$ as $y = \dfrac{24 - 4x}{6}$.

• Set Window to ZStandard.

• Clear the Graph Screen.

• Press Y=.

• Enter $\dfrac{6 - 2x}{3}$ for Y_1.

• Enter $\dfrac{24 - 4x}{6}$ for Y_2.

• Enter GRAPH.

The graph of two linear equations is a pair of distinct parallel lines. The two lines never meet. Therefore, the given system of linear equations is inconsistent.

Example 2   Show graphically that the system of linear equations: $2x + y = 1$ is independent.
                                                                              $x - 2y = 7$

• Use the steps in Example 1 above. Graph of the two linear equations of this system is a pair of intersecting lines. Therefore, the system is linearly independent.

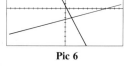

Pic 6

Example 3   Show graphically that the system of linear equations: $3x - 2y = 5$
is dependent. $6x = 4y + 10$

• Use the steps in Example 1 above.
Graph is a single line. The two lines are coincident. Therefore, the system is linearly dependent.

In Example 2 above, we saw that the system $2x + y = 1$, $x - 2y = 7$ of linear equations is independent. In the following example we demonstrate how to solve this system.

Appendix B

Example 4   Solve the system of linear equations: $2x + y = 1$, $x - 2y = 7$

Method 1:

- Set Window to ZDecimal.

- Clear Graph Screen by deactivating active function in equation editor ($\boxed{Y=}$), deactivating active plots (END $\boxed{Y=}$), and clearing with Draw menu.

- Rewrite $2x + y = 1$ as $y = 1 - 2x$ and $x - 2y = 7$ as $y = \dfrac{x - 7}{2}$.

- Press $\boxed{Y=}$.

- Enter $Y_1 = 1 - 2x$ and $Y_2 = \dfrac{x - 7}{2}$ in the $Y =$ menu.

- Press Graph.
  Two intersecting lines appear.

- Press $\boxed{TRACE}$ use $\boxed{\triangleleft}$ and $\boxed{\triangleright}$ to move the cursor to the point of intersection.

Coordinates of this point appear as $x = 1.8$ and $y = -2.6$. This is the solution. You may like to verify this solution.

 *Note* ▷ Sometimes the cursor may not sit exactly on the point of intersection since cursor jumps and does not move continuously. In that case ZBox $[\boxed{ZOOM} \ \boxed{1}]$ can be used to get a better approximation. Refer to the manual for TI-83-PLUS to learn how to use Zbox.

Method 2:   Follow all the steps of the above example starting from clearing the Graph Screen to entering the expressions in Y_1 and Y_2.

- Press $\boxed{2nd}$ $\boxed{TRACE}$ $\boxed{5}$ [for **intersect**].

- Cursor is on the first line. Prompt : *First Curve?*
  Select it by pressing $\boxed{ENTER}$.

- Cursor jumps to the second line. Prompt : *Second Curve?*
  Select it by pressing $\boxed{ENTER}$.

- Press $\boxed{ENTER}$ when prompted for *Guess*.
  Cursor moves to the point of intersection with coordinates of the point displayed at the bottom as $x = 1.8$ and $y = -2.6$. Therefore the solution of the system is $x = 1.8$, $y = -2.6$.

Notes ▷
1. In Method #2 even when you select ZStandard, you get the answer as x = 1.8 and y = −26. This is not so if you use ZStandard Window with Method #1.

2. Do the above example using ZStandard Window and Method #1. Observe the difference.

SECTION 4.4 SYSTEMS OF LINEAR INEQUALITIES

Although **Shade** can be used to graph the solution of a system of linear inequalities, we will prefer the following method of shading (setting the icon for shading in the $\boxed{Y=}$ menu) because of its distinct advantages as explained in Note # 3 following Example 1 in section 3.5. However, a general syntax for **Shade** is **Shade** (lowerfunc, upper func [, xleft, xright, pattern, patres]). The parameters inside [ ] are optional.

Example 1   Graph the solution of the linear system:

$$x + y \le 2$$
$$2x - y > 3$$

- Rewrite $x + y \le 2$ as $y \le 2 - x$ and $3x - y > 3$ as $y < 2x - 3$.

  Observe both are upper functions.
  Shade $<$ *cannot be used.*

- Set the Window to ZDecimal.

- Enter $2 - x$ as Y_1.

- Select shading icon ▙ for Y_1.

- Enter $2x - 3$ as Y_2.

- Select the shading icon ▙ for Y_2.

- Set the window to ZDecimal [$\boxed{ZOOM}$ $\boxed{4}$]

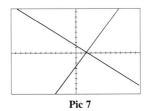

Pic 7

The common shaded region is the graph of the solution which can be explored by using the four navigation arrows ($\boxed{\triangleright}$, $\boxed{\triangleleft}$, $\boxed{\triangle}$, $\boxed{\triangledown}$)

Example 2   Graph the solution of the linear system:

$$x + y \le 2$$
$$2x - y < 3$$

- Rewrite $x + y \le 2$ as $y \le 2 - x$ and $2x - y < 3$ as $y > 2x - 3$.

- Clear Graph Screen.

- Enter $2 - x$ as Y_1.

- Select the shading icon ▙ for Y_1.

- Enter $2x - 3$ as Y_2.

- Select shading icon ▜ for Y_2.

- Set the Window to ZDecimal.

  [If the window is alread set to ZDecimal, press GRAPH .]

Note | This method has a limitation. Vertical lines or equations of the form ax = b cannot be entered as Y_1 =

CHAPTER 5   Exponents and Polynomials

SECTION 5.7   SCIENTIFIC NOTATION

Example 1   Write 95.37 and .000000678 in scientific notation

- Press **Mode**.

- Select **Sci** on the top line.

- Press 2nd QUIT .

- Enter 95.37

- Press ENTER .   Answer = 9.537E1 → 9.537×10^1

- Enter .000000678

- Press ENTER .   Answer = 6.78E1 → 6.78×10^{-7}

CHAPTER 7   Rational Expressions

Rational expressions can be entered in the normal way by making adequate use of parentheses.
For example,

- $t + \dfrac{t}{1 - \dfrac{t+1}{t}}$ will be entered as $t + (t \div (1 - (t + 1) \div t))$

- $\dfrac{4x}{x^2 + 2x - 3} - \dfrac{5x}{x^2 + 5x + 6}$ is entered as $(4x) \div (x^2 + 2x - 3) - (5x) \div (x^2 + 5x + 6)$

Rational expressions are evaluated as in Section 1.3, Example 2.

Rational functions can be graphed as explained in example 2, section 3.6. If domain of a rational function leaves out a few real numbers, then you must always choose **Dot** mode for its graph.

Dot mode can be selected either as explained in example 2, section 3.6, or by using the following procedure.

- In the [Y=] menu move the cursor to the icon on the left of $Y_1 =$

- Press [ENTER] repeatedly until one icon with three dots, namely ∵ , shows up.

The advantage of this procedure is that every function in [Y=] can be assigned its own graphing style.

CHAPTER 8   Roots and Radicals

SECTION 8.1 FINDING ROOTS

Press [MODE] . The second line from below is

Real   a + bi   r e ^ θ i

The calculator cannot find the square root of a negative number when **Real** is selected. To work with numbers that are complex (not real) select **a + bi**.

For examples below select **Real** and quit the menu. First we show how to enter expressions that contain radicals.

- Enter $\sqrt[5]{2}$

  Keystrokes: [5] [MATH] [5] [2]

- Enter $\left(-\sqrt[3]{-9}\right)^3$

  Keystrokes: [(] [(-)] [MATH] [4] [(-)] [9] [)] [)] [^] [3]

  ([^] [3] at the end can also be replaced by [MATH] [3])

- Enter $\left(\sqrt{8x^2+5}\right)^2$

  Keystrokes: [(] [2nd] [x^2] [8] [X,T,Θ,n] [x^2] [+] [5] [)] [)] [x^2]

- Enter $\dfrac{\sqrt{4}}{27}$

  Keystrokes: [2nd] [x^2] [4] [÷] [2] [7] [)]

Example 1   Find the value of

      i. $\sqrt[3]{-64}$ ii. $\sqrt[5]{\dfrac{32}{243}}$

   i.   Enter the keystrokes:

      MATH | 4 | (-) | 6 | 4 |) | ENTER

                                 Answer : -4

   ii.   Enter the keystrokes:

      5 | MATH | 5 | (| 3 | 2 | ÷ | 2 | 4 | 3 |)

      ENTER

                           Answer = .6666666667

      MATH | 1   [For ▷ Frac]

      ENTER   Answer = $\dfrac{2}{3}$

Example 2   Show that $\sqrt{\dfrac{4}{49}}$ is a rational number.

- 2nd | x^2 | 4 | ÷ | 4 | 9 |)   ENTER

                           Answer = .2857142857

- MATH | 1   [For ▷ Frac]

- ENTER   Answer = $\dfrac{2}{7}$

   This shows that $\sqrt{\dfrac{4}{49}}$ is rational.

Example 3   Show that $\sqrt{18}$ is an irrational number.

- 2nd | x^2 | 1 | 8 | ENTER

                           Answer = 4.242640687

- MATH | 1   ENTER

                           Answer = 4.242640687

Answer does not convert into a fraction. Possibly, $\sqrt{18}$ is an irrational number.

Example 4   Show that $\sqrt{-25}$ is non-real.

- 2nd | x^2 | (-) | 2 | 5 |) | ENTER

If you have set MODE to real, the calculator returns error, otherwise it returns $5i$.

In any case, it means that $\sqrt{-25}$ is not real.

SECTION 8.2 RADICALS

Show that $\sqrt{x^2} = \left|x\right|$:

- Enter $\sqrt{x^2}$ in Y_1.

- Enter 2nd WINDOW.   [For TBLSET]

- Enter TblMin = any number, say –10

  Δ Tbl = 1(say).

  Indpnt = Auto, **Depend** = Auto

  Press   2nd GRAPH   [For Table]

X	Y1	Y2
– 10	10	10
– 9	9	9
– 8	8	8
– 7	7	7
– 6	6	6
– 5	5	5
– 4	4	4
X = –10		

Pic 8

Three columns appear on the screen, one with values of x differing by 1, second with values of $Y_1 = \sqrt{x^2}$ for the corresponding values of x, and third with values of $Y_2 = |x|$.

- Move the cursor in the x-column. Browse through this column using △ and ▽ , observe the values in the $Y_1 = \sqrt{x^2}$ and $Y_2 = |x|$ columns. You find that $\sqrt{x^2} = |x|$ for all values of x.

- Alternatively, press ZOOM 6.

  This sets Window to ZStandard and shows the graphs. You see only one graph (which is V-shaped). This is because the two functions are essentially the same.

SECTION 8.6 EQUATIONS WITH RADICALS

Equations can be solved graphically, by using **zero** or by using **Solver** (MATH 0).

Extraneous roots *cannot* be determined with the calculator.

Example 1   Solve the equation $x - \sqrt{x-2} = 4$.

Method 1:

- Press MATH 0 △ .

- Enter $x - \sqrt{x-2} - 4$ to the right of eqn : 0 = .

- Press ENTER

- Enter a suitable guess at $x = $.

Appendix B

- Press ALPHA ENTER .

- Answer: $x = 6$

Method 2:

With the same settings as above:

- Press 2nd TRACE 2 .   [for **root**]
  [Graph pops up with some prompts.]

- Use ▷ and ◁ to move the cursor on the graph, if necessary.

- Select *lower bound* by pressing ENTER on the left of the point of intersection of the curve with x-axis.

- Move the cursor to the right of the point of intersection of the curve with the x-axis, and select *upper bound* by pressing ENTER .

- With the cursor either at the upperbound or anywhere between the lower and upper bounds press ENTER to accept a *guess*.   Answer = 6

Method 3:

- Clear Graph Screen.

- Set a suitable window, say ZStandard.

- Enter $Y_1 = x - \sqrt{x-2}$.

- Enter $Y_2 = 4$.

- Press 2nd TRACE 5 [for **intersect**].
  [Graphs pop up with some prompts]

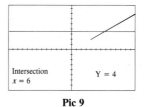

Pic 9

- Press ENTER to accept *first curve*.

- Press ENTER to accept *second curve*.

- Press ENTER to accept *guess*.

- Therefore, solution is $x = $ **6**.

CHAPTER 9 Complex Numbers and Quadratic Equations

SECTION 9.3 QUADRATIC FORMULA

To solve a quadratic equation $Ax^2 + Bx + C = 0$ by quadratic formula, we make the following preparation.

- Enter $B^2 - 4AC$ in Y_8.

- Enter $\dfrac{-B - \sqrt{Y_8}}{2A}$ in Y_9.

  KEYSTROKES:

- Enter $\dfrac{-B + \sqrt{Y_8}}{2A}$ in Y_0.

  Deactivate these functions.

  Recall that in order to deactivate an individual function, you move the cursor to the "=" sign and hit [ENTER].

Example 1   Find the nature of the roots of the equations:

        i. $2x^2 + 3x - 7 = 0$

        ii. $x^2 + 3x + 5 = 0$

        iii. $2x^2 + 12x + 18 = 0$

i. Here $A = 2$, $B = 3$ and $C = -7$.

- Store 2 in A.
- Store 3 in B.
- Store -7 in C.
- Press [2nd] [VARS] [▷] [1] [8].

  (to bring Y_8 on the next line).

- Press [ENTER] .   Answer = 65

  Since $Y_8 = B^2 - 4AC = 65 > 0$, the roots are real and distinct.

ii. •   Store 1 in A, 3 in B, and 5 in C.

       •   Press [2nd] [VARS] [▷] [1] [8] [ENTER].

                                 Answer = -11

Appendix B

Since $B^2 - 4AC = -11 < 0$, the roots are complex numbers.

iii. • Store 2 in A, 12 in B, and 18 in C.

   • Press [2nd] [VARS] [▷] [1] [8] [ENTER].

   Answer = 0

Since $B^2 - 4AC = 0$, the roots are real and equal.

Example 2   Solve $5x - 2x^2 = 2$

Method 1: (with Quadratic Formula)

   • Rewrite $5x - 2x^2 = 2$ as $2x^2 - 5x + 2 = 0$.

   • Store 2 in A, -5 in B, and 2 in C.

   • Press [2nd] [VARS] [▷] [1] [9] [ENTER].

   Answer = $.5 = \dfrac{1}{2}$

   • Press [2nd] [VARS] [▷] [1] [0] [ENTER].

   Answer = **2**

   Solutions are $x = \dfrac{1}{2}$ and $x = 2$.

Notes 1. To verify the solutions, evaluate $2x^2 - 5x + 2$ at $x = \dfrac{1}{2}$ and $x = 2$ by the methods explained in Section 1.3, Example (2(ii)).

2. You may like to find the value of $B^2 - 4AC$ by evaluating Y_8 to first see if the solutions are real. If the solutions are complex numbers, evaluation of Y_9 and Y_0 with show error. (why?)

Method 2: (without Quadratic Formula)

   • Rewrite $5x - 2x^2 = 2$ as $2x^2 - 5x + 2 = 0$.

   • Clear Graph Screen.

   • Set a window, say ZStandard.

   • Use **TRACE** to explore approximate values of the x-intercepts.

   • Press [2nd] [MODE] to quit the graph screen.

   • Press [MATH] [0] for **solver**.

   • Press [▷].

   • Enter $2x^2 - 5x + 2$ after **eqn : 0 =**

- Press ENTER .

- Enter a guess (determined by you earlier).

- Press ALPHA ENTER .

- Repeat this process for the second root.

SECTION 9.4 SOLVING QUADRATIC EQUATIONS GRAPHICALLY

Example 1   Determine graphically if the equation $x^2 + 3x + 5 = 0$ has real roots.

- Clear Graph Screen.

- Set Window to ZStandard.

- Enter $x^2 + 3x + 5$ in Y_1.

- Press GRAPH .

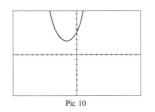

Pic 10

Points of intersection of the graph of $y = x^2 + 3x + 5$ with x-axis correspond to real solutions of the equation. There are no such points in this case. Hence $x^2 + 3x + 5 = 0$ has no real solutions.

Example 2   Solve $5x - 2x^2 = 2$ graphically.

Method 1:

- Rewrite the equation as $2x^2 - 5x + 2 = 0$.

- Clear Graph Screen.

- Set window to ZStandard.

- Enter $2x^2 - 5x + 2$ in y_1.

- Press 2nd TRACE 2   [for **root**].

- Press ENTER .

There are two points of intersection of the graph with x-axis. To determine a solution:

- Move the cursor to the left of a point of intersection and accept it as a lower bound by pressing ENTER .

- Move the cursor to the right of the point of intersection, and accept it as an upper bound by pressing ENTER .

Answer : root = .5

- Press [ENTER] [for **guess**]. Answer = 2

- Repeat the process for the second part.

Method 2:

- Clear Graph Screen.

- Set Window to ZStandard.

- Enter $5x - 2x^2$ in Y_1.

- Enter 2 in Y_2.

- Press [2nd] [TRACE] [5] for [**intersect**].

  [Graph screen pops up.]

There are two points of intersection of $y = 5x - 2x^2$ and $y = 2$

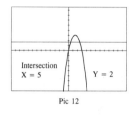

Pic 12

- Press [ENTER] to accept *first curve*.

- Press [ENTER] to accept *second curve*.

- Move the cursor near a point corresponding to which the solution is to be determined and press [ENTER] for *guess*.

(The screen shows smaller of the two solutions.)

Answer : $x = .5$, $y = 2$

Therefore a solution is $x = .5$

Repeat Steps #5 onward for the other solution.

Answer: $x = 2$, $y = 2$

Another solution is $x = 2$.

INDEX

Index